Tunnelling '85

Tunnelling '85

Proceedings of the fourth international symposium, organized by the Institution of Mining and Metallurgy, with the cooperation of the British Tunnelling Society and the Transport and Road Research Laboratory, Department of Transport, held in Brighton, England, from 10 to 15 March, 1985

Edited by M. J. Jones

THE INSTITUTION OF MINING AND METALLURGY

Published at the office of
The Institution of Mining and Metallurgy
44 Portland Place London W1 England
© The Institution of Mining and Metallurgy 1985

ISSN 0143-3911

ISBN 0 900488 83 2

Printed in England by Stephen Austin/Hertford

Foreword

'Tunnelling '85' is the fourth in the series of international symposia organized by the Institution of Mining and Metallurgy in cooperation with the British Tunnelling Society and the Transport and Road Research Laboratory, Department of Transport. The three-year cycle established after the first symposium – 'Tunnelling '76' – has proved successful and the next event in the series will be 'Tunnelling '88'.

Each symposium has reinforced the original objectives of providing an international forum for senior mining, civil, municipal and foundation engineers and geologists to present and discuss the very latest developments in tunnelling. Informal discussions provide an opportunity for information and opinions, often not suitable for publication, to be exchanged. Until such time as information technology is sufficiently advanced for this type of interchange to take place via VDUs, conferences such as 'Tunnelling '85' provide a vital and valuable service to the community.

The conference was jointly opened by Philip Gray, President of the Institution of Mining and Metallurgy, and John Derrington, President of the Institution of Civil Engineers. This was followed by the Nineteenth Sir Julius Wernher Memorial Lecture, 'From theory to practice in rock engineering', by Professor E. T. Brown, which is reprinted in this volume.

A total of 34 papers was presented from almost half as many different countries spread throughout Europe, North and South America and the Far East. The five days of the symposium were split into 13 technical sessions, which covered major projects, concreting, geotechnical studies, machine tunnelling, drill and blast, shield tunnelling, grouting and, finally, general topics. The technical review of the event was undertaken with clarity, humour, skill and charm by Myles O'Reilly, who has been a valued member of the Organizing Committee since 'Tunnelling '76'.

Members of an organizing committee rarely obtain adequate recognition for all the hard work that they undertake. I wish to record my debt to my colleagues for their important part in making 'Tunnelling '85' such a successful event: in particular, the three sub-committee chairmen – Geoff Pearse, Tom King and again Myles O'Reilly – have been towers of strength. Those committee members and international experts who chaired the various technical sessions played a vital role, which was recognized by the delegates.

This volume of proceedings will complement those of the previous symposia. These reference works continue to be important landmarks in chronicling advances in international tunnelling technology.

Peter Phillips
Chairman, Organizing Committee
July, 1985

Organizing Committee

Contents

From theory to practice in rock engineering*

E. T. Brown

Sir Julius Wernher is a well-known figure at the Royal School of Mines. He was a member of the committee established by the Board of Education in 1904 to enquire into the working of the Royal College of Science and the Royal School of Mines. The *Final report* of that committee[1] led to the formation in 1907 of the Imperial College of Science and Technology, on whose Governing Body Wernher served until his death in 1912. Wernher and his business partner, Alfred Beit, gave generously to the new institution, and the present Royal School of Mines building owes its existence largely to their munificence. Bronze busts of Wernher and Beit gaze out on the world from suitably elevated positions on either side of the main entrance to the RSM, and a large portrait of Sir Julius hangs in one of the College's committee rooms in which some of us are sentenced to spend much of our time. No doubt, when next we meet, Sir Julius' gaze will be much less benign than it usually is because of the folly that I am about to perpetrate in his name!

The subject that I have chosen is not new. Discussion of the relations between theory, abstract science and engineering practice is as old as the theories and sciences themselves. Indeed, the subject was chosen by one of Imperial College's great figures, Sir Lyon Playfair, in a lecture presented in 1851 on the opening of the Government School of Mines and of Science Applied to the Arts, the antecedent of the Royal School of Mines.[2] It was also the essential theme of at least one of the previous lectures in this series—that given in 1979 by Sir Alan Muir Wood.[3] I find that much of what I wish to say about the relevance of theoretical concepts to the development of modern rock engineering practice echoes Sir Alan's views, but I hope that, some six years on, the message will bear repetition. As befits a lecture of the Institution of Mining and Metallurgy, many of the examples that I shall introduce deal with underground metalliferous mining—an area that is not often referred to in discussions of this type.

Theory and engineering practice

The *Oxford English Dictionary* defines theory as, among other things, 'a scheme or system of ideas or statements held as an explanation or account of a group of facts or phenomena' or 'a statement of what are held to be the general laws, principles or causes of something known or observed'. The development and application of theory are an intellectual process. To apply theory in engineering practice, methods of analysis are required. In this sense analysis consists of resolving a problem into its simple elements, representing the problem by tractable equations and solving the equations.[4] For present purposes the concept of theory will be extended to include analysis defined in this way.

*The Nineteenth Sir Julius Wernher Memorial Lecture of the Institution of Mining and Metallurgy was delivered by E. T. Brown, Professor of Rock Mechanics, Royal School of Mines, Imperial College of Science and Technology, London, on 11 March, 1985, on the occasion of the 'Tunnelling '85' symposium. The lecture was first published in *Trans. Instn Min. Metall.* (*Sect. A: Min. industry*), **94**, 1985, A67–83.

The title of this lecture is adapted from that chosen by Bjerrum *et al.*[5] for their edited collection of the writings of Karl Terzaghi. After several years in professional practice Terzaghi was disturbed by his inability to predict the behaviour of soil structures and in 1916 began the research that was to lead to the discovery of the basic principles of modern soil engineering, the principle of effective stress and the mechanics of the process of consolidation.[6] Although Terzaghi discovered the underlying principles of his subject and wrote the definitive theoretical treatise on it,[7] he was also its most distinguished practitioner.

In the 45th James Forrest Lecture of the Institution of Civil Engineers, given in London in 1939, Terzaghi[8] eloquently discussed the need for a theoretical insight into the mechanics of the behaviour of soils in order to account for occurrences that might otherwise be ascribed to an 'act of God' or the 'allegedly lawless behaviour of the soil'. He endorsed the views of the first James Forrest Lecturer, Dr. W. Anderson,[9] who, in 1893, wrote: 'The competent and successful engineer will still show himself as the man who in his work is careful to make theory and practice walk side by side, the one ever aiding and guiding the other, neither asserting undue supremacy'.

In a more recent discussion of the role of the analytical method in soil mechanics Gibson[4] concluded: 'The analytical method draws attention to broad trends and helps to distinguish between which factors are of primary significance and which are of secondary importance. It is neither a dispensable supplement to engineering intuition nor merely a procedure for quantifying results. It is able to "speak for itself" and on occasion does so in characteristic ways'. It is this view of the role of theory (taken to be interchangeable with Gibson's analytical method) in engineering practice that is advanced in this lecture.

Theory in rock engineering

In rock engineering, as in most branches of civil and mining engineering, practice has usually preceded the development of the relevant theory. Mines and other underground excavations were made successfully in rock before elasto-plastic methods of stress analysis and rock–support interaction theory were developed, spectacular cathedrals and other stone structures were built before the advent of the relevant theories of structural mechanics, and sub-aqueous tunnels were built before the principle of effective stress was discovered. The retrospective development of these theories has, however, provided a rational means of interpreting and extrapolating experience, and a basis for advancing the subject by a process other than the often very expensive one of trial and error. Although the theories of rock mechanics are perhaps less well developed than those of soil mechanics, and could well remain so, it will be my aim to show how necessary and useful they now are in the design of large underground excavations in rock. I shall try to show that it is now possible to take the important step from theory to practice in some areas of rock engineering.

Of course, there are bad and inappropriate theories, just as there are good and relevant theories. Indeed, it has been said, not entirely facetiously, that a good theory is one that works in practice. A given piece of theory may be the wrong one for a particular problem, or it may be applied inexpertly with unrealistic boundary conditions or material properties being used. It is probably for this reason that the usefulness of rock mechanics was not always, and may still not have been, accepted in some parts of the mining industry as readily as it could have been. Because of the variability of the mechanical properties of rock masses, the generally statically indeterminate nature of the problems considered and the range of possible modes of rock mass response to be modelled the correct selection and use of theoretical models in rock engineering are not always a straightforward matter.

The words of Anderson,[9] also quoted by Terzaghi,[8] are again relevant here. 'There is a tendency among the young and inexperienced to put blind faith in formulae forgetting that most of them are based on premises which are not accurately reproduced in practice, and which, in any case, are frequently unable to take into account collateral disturbances which only observation and experience can foresee and common sense provide against'.

Dangerous though the attitudes described by Anderson are, they are less dangerous, in my view, than the attitudes of those few engineers who avoid the use of all formulae or the application of the principles of mechanics in solving practical problems. This attitude, which I have known some to proclaim in a manner that suggests that it provides proof of their virility, is not one that I believe to be compatible with the status and obligations of a professional engineer. It is often said by such people that such subjects as applied mechanics, fluid mechanics and rock mechanics are 'too mathematical' for the 'ordinary' civil or mining engineer or, more sadly, for many engineering students. Almost all of the *mathematics* that I have ever used to make rock engineering calculations (algebra, coordinate geometry, trigonometry, calculus) I learnt as a schoolboy by the age of 15; a small amount, notably vector and matrix algebra and the solution of simple differential equations, I learnt as a 17- and 18-year old engineering undergraduate. My appreciation of the *mechanics* of the practical problems to which I apply this elementary knowledge of mathematics did not develop, however, until much later and, of necessity, is still developing.

Analysis in underground excavation design

Fig. 1 shows a widely accepted idealization of the way in which rock mechanics is used in the design of civil and mining engineering projects. Theory, based on the principles of mechanics, is used in the design analysis stage, in the design of monitoring programs, in the interpretation of monitoring results and in retrospective analysis and re-design. Most of these analyses are concerned with the stresses and displacements induced around an excavation, with its stability or with the provision of support or reinforcement. The examples of the application of theory given here will be all of this type. Theories associated with the geometrical and mechanical properties of rock masses, excavation processes and their effects or the flow of heat and water through rock masses will not be considered.

The theories and analyses used to study the stability of underground excavations in rock are of three general types.

Continuum models use the two classic theories of elasticity and plasticity to calculate the stresses and displacements induced in the initially stressed rock following excavation. They assume that displacements are continuous everywhere within the rock mass and necessarily involve idealization and simplification of its geometrical and mechanical

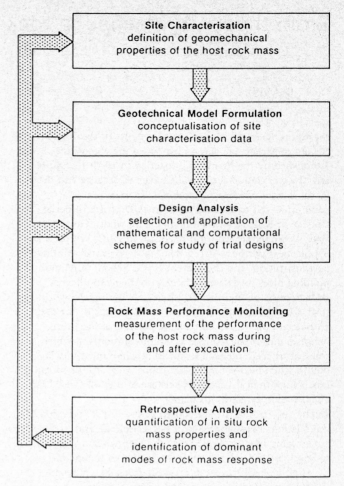

Fig. 1 Components of a generalized rock mechanics programme

properties. For simple excavation shapes and boundary conditions closed-form and pseudo closed-form solutions may be obtained to problems in elasticity[10,11,12] and, more rarely, plasticity.[13] For more complex excavation shapes and boundary conditions numerical methods, notably the finite-element method[14] and the boundary-element method,[15] must be used. The boundary-element method is especially suitable for modelling unbounded problems in elasticity. The finite-element method has advantages in modelling non-linear material behaviour, sequential excavation and post-yield displacements.[16] For some applications hybrid computational schemes that combine finite and boundary elements[16] or boundary elements and discrete elements[17] provide the best approach.

Discontinuum models treat the rock mass as an assembly of discrete blocks, thereby recognizing the essentially discontinuous nature of rock masses and the fact that displacements may be not continuous within them—in particular, around the periphery of an excavation. Solutions to inter-block forces and block displacements may be obtained by use of dynamic or static relaxation techniques.[18,19,20] Although these methods have not yet been used with notable success in design analyses, they have been very useful in developing an improved understanding of aspects of discontinuous rock mass behaviour (e.g. the mechanics of arching, as discussed by Voegele and co-workers[19]) and, as noted above, have recently been incorporated into hybrid computational schemes,[17] which have great potential for practical applications.

Limiting equilibrium methods are used in making calculations of a quite different type from those which are made by use of continuum numerical models. They generally involve considerations of only the equilibrium of forces and a limiting shear strength criterion and do not lead to estimates of displacements within the rock mass. The simplest form of limiting equilibrium calculation is used to determine a factor of safety against sliding of a potentially unstable block[21] or mass[22] of rock. Slightly more complex statically indeterminate problems may be solved by use of simplified equilibrium models to assess the stability of assemblies of rock plates or blocks. Such solutions have been obtained for roofs and hanging-walls in bedded or blocky strata.[23]

It is important to recognize that these three approaches are used to make different kinds of calculations under different circumstances. Not only must the analysis and the problem be matched correctly if a useful result is to be obtained but suitable boundary conditions and material properties must be used. The primary requirement is for a sound assessment of the basic mechanics of the problem that is being considered. For example, the most sophisticated boundary-element or elasto-plastic finite-element analysis would be of no use in analysing the stability of the shallow tunnel in jointed rock shown in Fig. 2. In this case the progressive failure of the tunnel was associated with the action of gravity on a small number of individual blocks isolated by joints, bedding planes and the tunnel periphery.[24] Continuum methods of stress analysis do not address such problems.

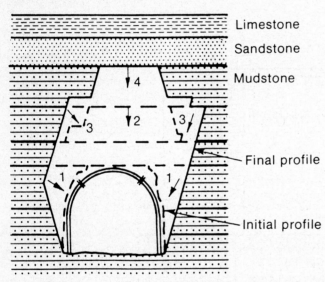

Fig. 2 Progressive collapse of part of Kielder experimental tunnel excavated in blocky mudstone. After Ward[24]

The development of efficient computer codes to solve problems in rock engineering by use of either continuum or discontinuum models of the types outlined above requires a high order of knowledge of engineering mechanics, numerical methods, computer programming and, in some instances, mathematics. It is not reasonable to expect that every practising civil and mining engineer will possess the knowledge and skill that are necessary to develop other than the simplest programs. This task is rightly one for the specialist. It is, however, reasonable to expect that the civil or mining engineer should be able to formulate the problem correctly in mechanical terms, communicate his requirements to the computing or analytical specialist, understand the capabilities of the analytical tools and computer programs available, determine reasonable boundary conditions for his problem, understand and interpret the results and, above all, decide whether or not the results make engineering sense.

Before any of the methods of calculation with which we are at present concerned can be used in practice it is necessary that the pre-excavation or *in-situ* stresses in the rock mass be either measured or estimated. The inability to measure or estimate satisfactorily the *in-situ* state of stress in many circumstances provides one of the major impediments to the utility of theoretical models in underground excavation design. The small borehole overcoring techniques used in the most successful stress measurement methods[25] are difficult to use in highly fractured, weak and anisotropic rocks.[26] It is also found that in fractured, faulted, folded, altered and heterogeneous rock masses the *in-situ* stresses may vary dramatically over a given site.

From a compilation of stress measurement data obtained from sites throughout the world (Fig. 3) Hoek and Brown[21]

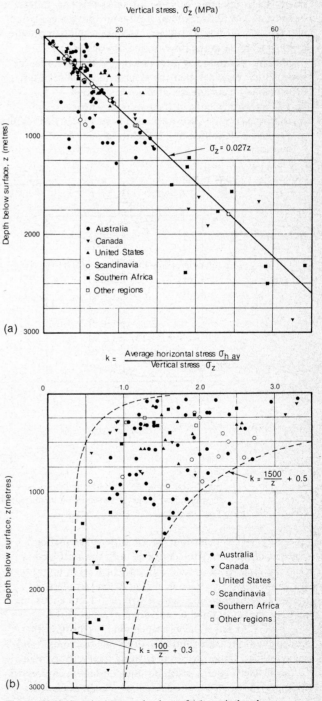

Fig. 3 Variations in measured values of (*a*) vertical and (*b*) average horizontal *in-situ* stress with depth below surface. After Hoek and Brown[21]

showed that, in many cases, the vertical *in-situ* stress can be estimated from the weight of the superincumbent strata. The ratio of the horizontal to vertical *in-situ* stress can vary between wide limits, however, especially at depths of less than 1 km, and so is extremely difficult to predict. Hoek and Brown based their conclusions on the average horizontal stress measured at each test site. It is now known that quite large differences can exist between the maximum and minimum horizontal stresses at a given location.[27] This can add considerably to the difficulty of predicting *in-situ* stress fields.

Applications of elastic theory

Although more complex constitutive models may be used, calculations made by use of the theory of elasticity generally assume that the rock behaves as a homogeneous, isotropic, linear elastic material. In some instances this may represent a realistic model of rock mass behaviour, but generally it will not. Nevertheless, an elastic solution can often provide a valuable guide to the distribution of stresses and displacements around an excavation, and the potential for rock failure, provided that the assumption of continuum behaviour remains a reasonable approximation.

A general knowledge of the nature of elastic stress distributions can be used to explain occurrences that might otherwise be attributed to Terzaghi's 'acts of God' or

distributed uniformly across the loaded surfaces of individual blocks. Elastic theory shows clearly that non-uniform or partial boundary loads tend to induce tensile stresses in a direction normal to that of the applied load[30,31,32] (Fig. 4). Thus, tensile failure may be produced by non-uniformly applied loads that are much lower than those which correspond to the crushing strength of the rock under a uniformly applied load. Such failures under induced tension have been found to occur commonly in compression tests on block-jointed plaster models.[32] A line load represents a limiting case of non-uniform load application (Fig. 4(a)). In this case elastic stress analysis[31] gives the horizontal tensile stress at the mid-height of the block as

$$\sigma_t = -0.62 \frac{F_t}{dt} \qquad (1)$$

Assume that crushing under a uniformly applied compressive load, F_c, will occur when

$$\sigma_c = \frac{F_c}{dt} \qquad (2)$$

If, as for most rocks, $\sigma_c/|\sigma_t|$ equals 10 to 20, F_t/F_c equals about $\frac{1}{6}$ to $\frac{1}{12}$, which indicates that the line loaded block will

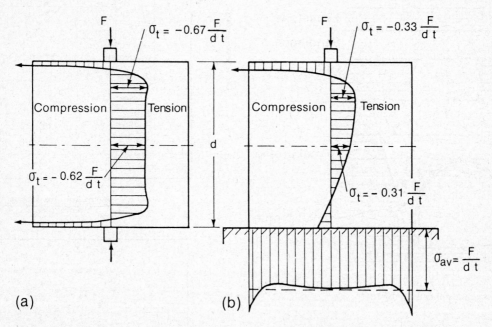

Fig. 4 Distributions of horizontal elastic stresses across vertical centre line and of vertical reactive stresses in two cases of non-uniform loading of rectangular blocks. After Davies and Stagg[31]

'allegedly lawless behaviour' of the rock. A fascinating example of this arises in connexion with the axial load-carrying capacity of a stone column. It has been found that the working stresses in stone compression members in medieval cathedral construction were limited to about one-tenth of the unconfined compressive strength of the rock.[28,29] This sets a theoretical column height limit that accords with the sizes found in surviving structures[29] and suggests that, rather than representing a reasonably high factor of safety against crushing, the one-tenth compressive strength rule provides a realistic limit design guideline.

It is inevitable that, because of slight mismatches in adjoining block surfaces and eccentricities in the applied loads, column loads in stone structures will not be

fail when the total applied load is only a small fraction of that which produces compressive failure in uniform compression. This provides some rationale for the limitation on the compressive strengths of stone columns observed in practice.

Plane strain and three-dimensional solutions
Most elastic solutions that are used in underground excavation design are plane strain solutions. In plane strain the increments of strain that occur when the excavation is made are restricted to the plane of the cross-section and are independent of location along the excavation axis. For homogeneous, isotropic materials the stresses induced around an excavation in the plane of the cross-section in

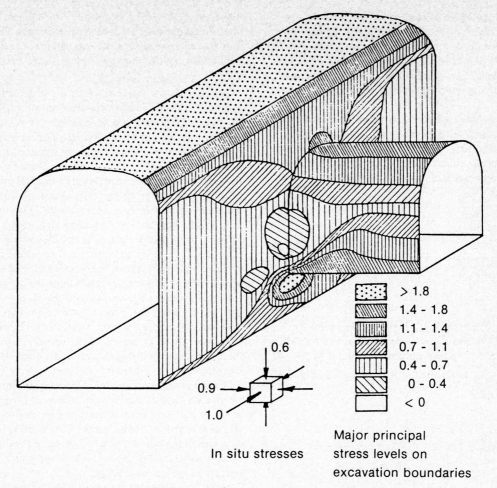

░░	> 1.8
▨	1.4 - 1.8
▥	1.1 - 1.4
▧	0.7 - 1.1
▤	0.4 - 0.7
▨	0 - 0.4
☐	< 0

0.6

0.9 →

1.0 →

In situ stresses

Major principal stress levels on excavation boundaries

Fig. 5 Distribution of major principal stresses on boundaries of two intersecting underground excavations. After Hoek and Brown[21]

plane strain are independent of the elastic constants of the material, but, of course, the displacements are not. For uniform excavation cross-sections, other than those with extreme axial ratios, the plane strain boundary stresses usually approximate the correct three-dimensional stresses to within less than ten, and sometimes five, per cent at locations removed by at least two excavation 'diameters' from intersections, excavation ends or changes of cross-section.[33] Thus, plane strain solutions often provide more widely applicable results than might be expected. Accordingly, the need to carry out fully three-dimensional stress analyses arises only rarely.

Fig. 5 shows the results of a three-dimensional elastic stress analysis carried out by use of the boundary integral equation code developed by Watson.[34] The results clearly show the influence of an intersection on the elastic stresses calculated on the excavation boundaries. The large open stopes that are now being used to mine massive orebodies can provide other cases in which truly three-dimensional analyses are required. Fig. 6 shows an example of five adjacent stopes that form part of a much larger mining block in the 1100 orebody at Mount Isa mine, Australia.[35,36] The axial ratios and the irregular and variable shapes and spacings of these large stopes require that a complete three-dimensional analysis be carried out to enable the boundary and pillar stresses to be determined satisfactorily. At the mid-height of this group of stopes the major and minor principal *in-situ* stresses are in the xz plane with σ_1 and σ_3 rotated clockwise by 25° from the x and z axes, respectively. The intermediate principal *in-situ* stress acts in the direction of the y axis. The three-dimensional stress analysis carried out by Watson and

Cowling[36] gave lower maximum stress concentrations than those which were calculated by use of plane strain approximations. The effect of the group of openings on the stress field was found to be more localized in three-dimensional than in two-dimensional solutions.

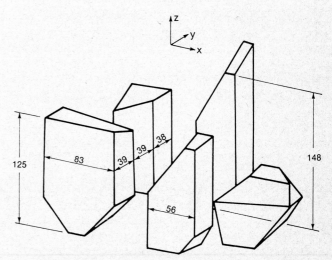

Fig. 6 Group of five open stopes in 1100 orebody, Mount Isa mine, analysed by three-dimensional boundary-element method (dimensions in metres). After Watson and Cowling[36]

The following examples illustrate the effective use of plane strain solutions for homogeneous, isotropic, linear elastic media to provide an appreciation of the manner in which stresses are redistributed following excavation and, in some cases, to make detailed design calculations.

Zone of influence of an excavation

The zone of influence of an excavation is that domain in which the excavation disturbs the pre-excavation stress field by a predetermined amount. It differentiates the far-field from the near-field of an opening and provides a valuable tool for use in laying out complexes of underground excavations.

Consider the simple case of a circular excavation of radius a, made in a medium initially subjected to a hydrostatic stress field of magnitude, p (Fig. 7(a)). At any point in the rock mass at radius r from the axis of the excavation the normal radial and tangential stresses are given by

$$\sigma_{rr} = p\left(1 - \frac{a^2}{r^2}\right) \qquad (3)$$

$$\sigma_{\theta\theta} = p\left(1 + \frac{a^2}{r^2}\right) \qquad (4)$$

In this case the shear stress, $\tau_{r\theta}$, is everywhere zero. By putting $\sigma_{rr} = 0.95p$ and $\sigma_{\theta\theta} = 1.05p$ in equations 3 and 4, respectively, the '5% zone of influence' is found to be defined by $r = \sqrt{20}a$. This result is illustrated in Fig. 7(b).

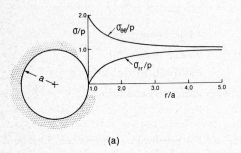

(a)

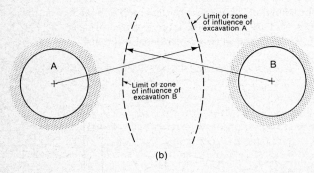

(b)

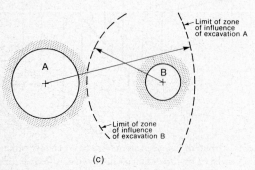

(c)

Fig. 7 (a) Axi-symmetric stress distribution around circular opening in hydrostatic stress field; (b) circular openings of same diameter in hydrostatic stress field, effectively isolated by virtue of their locations outside each other's 5% zone of influence; (c) circular openings of different diameters in hydrostatic stress field (zone of influence of excavation A includes excavation B, but converse does not apply). After Brady and Brown[37]

Thus, parallel circular excavations of the same size may be considered not to interact mechanically with each other, and may be designed as separate excavations in the virgin stress field if their centre lines are separated by not less than $(\sqrt{20} + 1)a$, approximately $5.5a$.

Fig. 7(c) shows a case in which the larger diameter opening (A) has a smaller diameter opening (B) within its 5% zone of influence. Since excavation A is outside the zone of influence of excavation B, a fair estimate of the boundary stresses around it may be obtained by considering it as a single opening. For excavation B the field stresses are those which arise from the presence of excavation A. They may be estimated from equations 3 and 4 by use of the value of r at the centre of excavation B. The stress field is now anisotropic, and the boundary stresses for excavation B must be calculated by use of the well-known Kirsch equations[38] from which equations 3 and 4 are derived.

Eissa[39] has shown that, in the more general case, the size of the zone of influence depends more on the axial ratio of the cross-section and the nature of the in-situ stress field than on the exact shape of the excavation. Fig. 8 shows the zone outside which the field stresses depart from their in-situ values by less than 5% of the vertical in-situ stress, p, for three excavation shapes with axial ratios of 2:1 with in-situ stresses of $p = 1.0$ vertically and $kp = 0.5$ horizontally. These diagrams were prepared from stress contours obtained by use of the boundary-element method. The zones of influence may be described by ellipses of width, W_i, and height, H_i. Note, however, that these circumscribing ellipses give conservative results in that they enclose substantial regions in which the stress field is perturbed by less than $0.05p$.

Bray[40] has shown that, for an elliptical excavation, the zone in which the stresses depart from the maximum in-situ stress (p or kp) by more than c per cent may be approximated by an ellipse with axes equal to the greater of each of the following sets of values

$$W_i = H\sqrt{Aa|q(q+2) - k(3+2q)|} \qquad (5)$$
or
$$W_i = H\sqrt{a\{A(k+q^2) + kq^2\}} \qquad (6)$$
and
$$H_i = H\sqrt{Aa|k(1+2q) - q(3q+2)|} \qquad (7)$$
or
$$H_i = H\sqrt{a\{A(k+q^2) + 1\}} \qquad (8)$$

where W and H are the width and height of the elliptical excavation, $q = W/H$, $A = 100/2c$, k is the ratio of horizontal to vertical in-situ stress and

$$a = \begin{cases} 1 \text{ if } k < 1 \\ \dfrac{1}{k} \text{ if } k > 1 \end{cases}$$

The zone of influence concept may be of use in locating mine haulage, access and service openings with respect to productive openings. In the case shown in Fig. 9 a zone of influence could be calculated for an ellipse inscribed in the stope cross-section for any given stage of the up-dip advance of mining. The stope is likely to be outside the zone of influence of each of the access drives and so the boundary stresses at each stage of mining may be calculated without reference to the existence of the smaller excavations. The access drives will not, however, always be outside the zone of influence of the stope. Reasonable estimates of the access opening boundary stresses may be

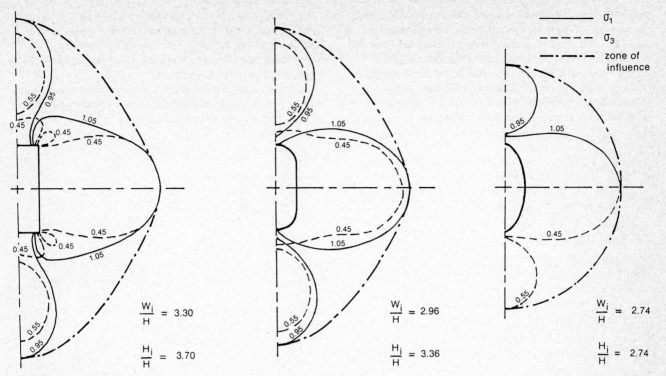

Fig. 8   Five per cent zones of influence of rectangular, ovaloidal and elliptical openings with width/height ratios of 0.5 in biaxial stress field of $p = 1.0$ vertically and $kp = 0.5$ horizontally. After Eissa[39]

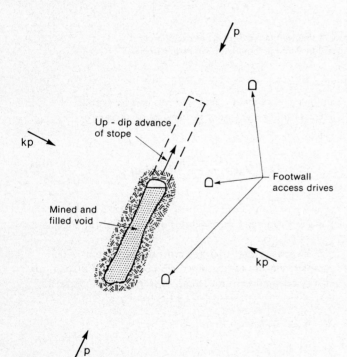

Fig. 9   Example of semi-coupling between cut and fill stope and smaller access openings. After Brady and Brown[37]

obtained from the local stresses due to the pseudo-elliptical stope and the boundary stress concentrations due to the shapes of the access drives themselves. The local stresses at the access drive locations will tend to increase as stoping progresses up-dip, except at high values of k, in which case the central access drive could fall in a stress shadow produced by the stope. Generally, it would be preferable to excavate the drives before stoping is too far advanced and while the zone of influence of the stope remains small. If necessary, the drives could be reinforced in anticipation of the increased stresses to be imposed on them as mining advances up-dip.

Longwall mining in hard rock

The classic example of longwall mining in hard rock is provided by the deep-level gold mines of South Africa, where longwall methods are used to mine narrow, flat-dipping orebodies of large areal extent. The near-field rock is strong quartzite, which contains relatively few natural discontinuities other than bedding planes. Mining usually takes place at considerable depth, where the *in-situ* stresses are high and, except in the highest stress environments, can be measured satisfactorily. As is well known, a major problem in mining under these conditions is rockbursting associated with stress-induced fracturing or slip on geological features.[41,42]

The theory of elasticity has been used with outstanding success to develop an understanding of the causes of rockbursts in longwall mining in hard rock and to develop mining strategies to limit the incidence and effects of rockbursts and other ramifications of overstressing.[11,41-45] A longwall stope is represented as a narrow slot in an initially stressed and usually homogeneous, isotropic, linear

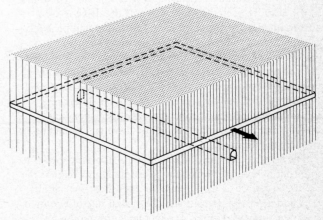

Fig. 10   Footwall drive being developed in conjunction with advancing longwall stope

elastic medium. The stresses and displacements induced by the creation of a new excavation, or by the extension of a longwall stope, may be calculated most conveniently by use of one of the forms of the boundary-element method.[11,15] Closed-form solutions may be obtained for some simple problem configurations.[11] The two following examples illustrate the application of the theory of elasticity in the design of mine layouts under these conditions.

done most effectively by controlling the volume convergence in the mined-out area. Cook et al.[41] showed that this end can be achieved by using a layout that incorporates permanent stabilizing pillars that are able to support the overburden stresses.

If a large area of a flat-lying, narrow, tabular orebody is mined to a height H, the difference between the quantity of energy released per unit length of stope by extraction of a

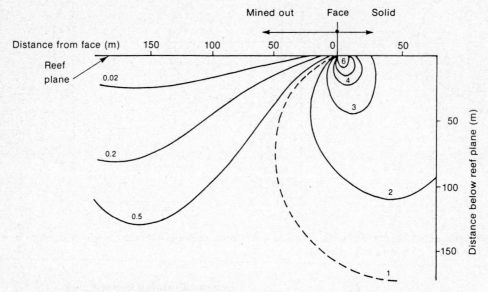

Fig. 11 Contours of major principal stress in vicinity of longwall face expressed as multiples of vertical *in-situ* stress (mining depth, 2000 m; stoping width, 1 m; horizontal/vertical *in-situ* stress ratio, 0.5). After Wagner[44]

The protection of service openings is an important aspect of mine design in high stress conditions. The provision of this protection requires the use of sound mechanical reasoning during the design stage.[43,44] Suppose that a drive is to be excavated in the footwall below the advancing longwall face illustrated in Fig. 10. As is shown in the longitudinal section in Fig. 11, a high stress concentration occurs ahead of, and above and below, the advancing face. If, as in this example, full closure of the mined-out void does not occur, the stresses immediately above and below the mined-out area will be less than the *in-situ* vertical stress. Even if total convergence of the hanging- and footwalls of the stope does occur, the induced stress will not exceed the *in-situ* vertical stress, provided that the stoping width is constant.

The major principal stress distribution shown in Fig. 11 points to a significant conclusion concerning the scheduling of the advance of the footwall drive. If the drive is advanced ahead of the stope face, excavation will probably take place in a zone of high stress concentration and each section of the completed drive will be subject to very high stresses as the face passes over it. If, on the other hand, operational requirements permit the drive to be developed behind the longwall face, excavation can be always in a relatively low stress environment, with corresponding improvement in the condition of the drive and reduction in support requirements.

The second example concerns the use of elastic theory to point the way to the use of partial extraction to combat the rockburst hazard. There is a well-established correlation between rockburst damage and the spatial rate of energy release associated with a given increment of mining.[41,42] Thus, the overall strategy for minimizing the rockburst hazard is to minimize the energy release rate. This can be

single panel of span L and that released by partial extraction in panels of span l spaced on centres of S (Fig. 12(a)) is

$$\delta W_r = p\,L[H + \frac{(1-v)\,S\,p}{\pi G}\ln(\cos a)] \qquad (9)$$

where p is the vertical *in-situ* stress, v and G are the Poisson's ratio and the modulus of rigidity of the rock, and $a = \pi l/2S$.

For spans greater than the critical (that span at which complete closure of the mined void occurs at mid-span) the energy released per unit length of stope by total extraction is

$$W_r = L\,H\,p \qquad (10)$$

Dividing equation 9 by equation 10 and substituting the expression for the critical span[41]

$$L_0 = \frac{GH}{(1-v)p} \qquad (11)$$

lead to the result

$$\frac{\delta W_r}{W_r} = 1 + \frac{S}{\pi L_0}\ln(\cos a) \qquad (12)$$

Fig. 12(b) shows a plot of $\delta W_r/W_r$ against extraction ratio, l/S, for varying values of S/L_0. Note that, even at quite high extraction ratios, major reductions in energy change are achieved by use of partial extraction. It is also found that partial extraction layouts lead to considerable

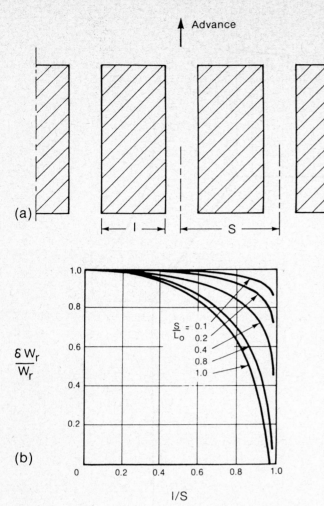

Fig. 12 (a) Mining plan and (b) normalized reduction in released energy for partial extraction of flat-lying, narrow, tabular orebody. After Salamon[11]

reductions in stress concentrations around the stope face.[42] The stress concentration remains virtually constant once the panel length reaches two or three times the stope span, l.

Several of the deepest South African gold mines have introduced versions of partial extraction with impressive results in terms of reduced seismicity.[45] There is the obvious disadvantage of sterilizing ore in permanent pillars, but there appear to be cases in which the advantages of the scheme outweigh this disadvantage. The essential point of present concern is that analytical work with the use of elastic theory carried out in the early 1960s pointed the way to this radical development in deep-level mining practice.

Poatina underground power station

The Poatina underground power station in Tasmania, Australia, provides an excellent example of the early and innovative use of elastic stress analysis to solve a difficult design problem. Details of this example are taken from the definitive paper by Endersbee and Hofto[46] and the more recent summary by Sharp and co-workers.[47] The power station cavern, which was completed in 1965, has a maximum excavated span of 13.7 m and is located at a depth of 160 m. The cavern is excavated in horizontally bedded, dense, fine-grained mudstones. The roof is located within a thinly bedded highly fossiliferous calcareous mudstone with an *in-situ* compressive strength at the natural water content (1.5%) of 35–40 MPa. *In-situ* stresses in the cavern area were measured as 8.3 MPa vertically, 16.6 MPa horizontally normal to the cavern axis and 12.4 MPa horizontally parallel to the cavern axis.

The behaviour of exploratory excavations and of a one-sixth scale trial excavation indicated that a conventional arched roof would be unstable, tending to break to a flat crown. Accordingly, a trapezoidal roof profile was selected with the haunches inclined at 35° to the vertical—an angle equivalent to the angle of friction on the horizontal bedding planes (Fig. 13). Because this design represented a significant departure from the profiles then normally used, detailed elastic stress analyses of the excavation were carried out. At the time when these studies were made photoelasticity was the most suitable technique available. The stress analysis was undertaken by G. Worotnicki at the photoelastic laboratory of the Snowy Mountains Hydro-Electric Authority, Australia.

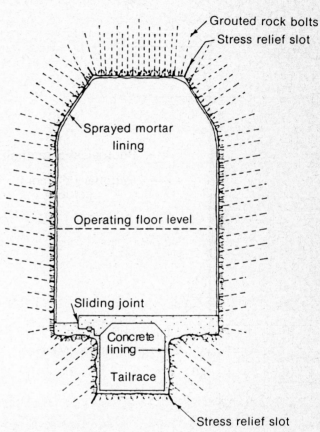

Fig. 13 Final design cross-section, Poatina underground power station. After Endersbee and Hofto[46]

Fig. 14 shows the distribution of final boundary stresses determined by Worotnicki for an excavation profile that excludes the tail race shown in Fig. 13. These stresses were scaled from a diagram presented by Endersbee and Hofto.[46] Fig. 14 also shows the boundary stresses determined by Watson[48] by use of a boundary-element program for plane elastostatics incorporating Hermitian cubic boundary elements.[49] Only seven boundary elements were used in the analysis of the half-section shown in Fig. 14. Except in the immediate vicinity of sharp corners, no significant difference in the calculated boundary stress resulted when the number of elements was increased from seven to 14. In the boundary-element solution singularities occur at the sharp corners. Some curvature existed at these corners in the photoelastic model, and so finite boundary stresses were determined. Notwithstanding this difference between the two models, the two sets of results are remarkably similar. The greatest proportional difference in the results occurs, understandably, in the tensile zone on the side walls where maximum tensile stresses of 0.9 and 2.3 MPa were calculated by use of photoelasticity and boundary elements,

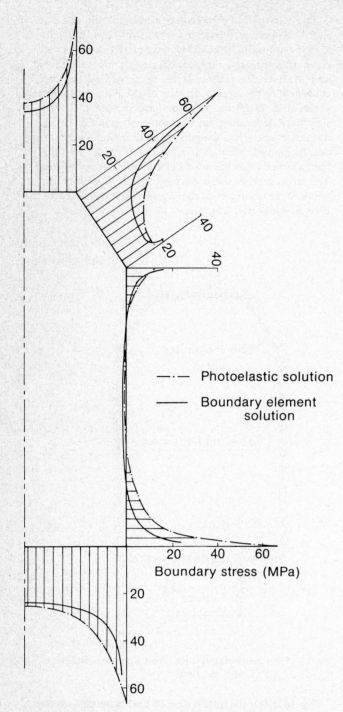

Fig. 14 Elastic boundary stresses (MPa) for final Poatina cavern excavation determined by photoelasticity[46] and boundary-element method[48]

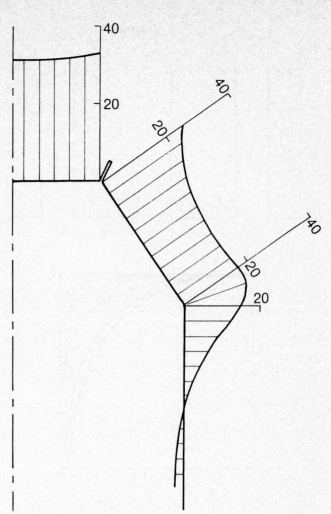

Fig. 15 Elastic boundary stresses (MPa) in Poatina cavern roof at completion of excavation, with stress-relief slots introduced during first stage of excavation. After Endersbee and Hofto[46]

respectively. Watson's program has been shown to give quite accurate results for problems of this type with the numbers of elements used in the present study.[49] Therefore, the results are considered to provide testimony to the great skill and care with which Worotnicki carried out this difficult photoelastic stress analysis some 25 years ago.

The elastic stress analysis showed that the boundary stresses would exceed the *in-situ* uniaxial compressive strength of the mudstone over the entire roof span, at the corners and over much of the floor. Slip on horizontal bedding planes in the roof and haunches was also predicted. The influence of the induced tensile stresses calculated in the side walls could be resisted by the pattern of grouted rockbolts 4.3 m long shown in Fig. 13.

To limit the boundary stresses to safe values a destressing

system was used in the roof and floor areas. Destressing of the roof was achieved by cutting a slot at the haunch–roof junction (see Fig. 13) when only the roof section had been excavated. A controlled amount of destressing was permitted to occur so that the boundary compressive stresses were limited to predetermined acceptable values. Further photoelastic stress analyses were carried out to study the effect of the stress-relief slots. Fig. 15 shows boundary stress distributions calculated at the completion of excavation, when 0.9-m deep slots were drilled and grouted during the first stage of excavation. The high stress concentrations induced at the top of the slot were of no cause for concern because there was no free boundary available into which displacement could occur. The analysis gave the important practical result that the boundary stresses in the roof and corners could be reduced to acceptable levels by the introduction of the stress-relief slots.

It was determined that a slot closure of 2–3 mm was required to produce the required reduction in boundary stresses. The slots were made by a series of 48-mm diameter diamond drill holes spaced with approximately 6-mm thick pillars of rock left between them. These pillars could be expected to crush at some predetermined stress level. To control the closure a 'brake' in the form of a wooden dowel was inserted into every second hole. The progress of the operation was monitored by stress measurements made with flatjacks installed in the roof. As closure progressed the dowels crushed with increasing

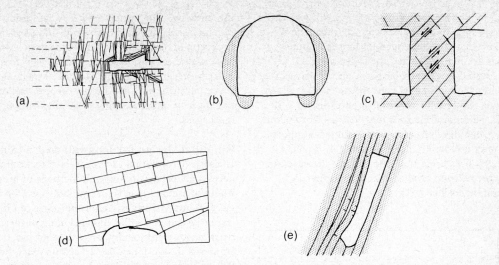

Fig. 16   Some types of inelastic response of rock masses around underground excavations: (a) shear and tensile fracture (after Joughin and Jager[50]); (b) formation of plastic yield zones; (c) slip on discontinuities; (d) translation and rotation of discrete blocks (after Voegele and co-workers[19]); (e) bending and cracking of rock beams or plates (after Beer and co-workers[52])

resistance. At the required closure and boundary stress level the open holes were packed with quick-setting mortar.

The successful construction of the Poatina power station cavern and the development of an innovative destressing technique owed much to the informed use of elastic stress analysis. Given the limited state of knowledge of rock mechanics, and the limited range of analytical tools available at the time, this project stands as a remarkable example of the knowledge, skill, daring and ingenuity of the engineers associated with its design and construction.

Inelastic behaviour

Fig. 16 illustrates some of the types of inelastic rock mass response that can develop around underground excavations in rock. These include shear and tensile fracture of rock material,[50] the development of zones of plastic deformation,[3,13] slip on discontinuities,[21,51] translation, rotation and local fracture of interacting rock blocks[19,24] and bending of individual beams or plates of rock.[52] The development and application of analytical or numerical models in these cases are much more difficult than when elastic rock mass behaviour is assumed. The problems generally involve non-linearities, so the solutions are stress-path dependent and the principle òf superposition may not

be used. Furthermore, a number of imprecisely defined material properties may be required for use in the analyses. Despite these difficulties, the use of an analysis that correctly models the mechanics of rock mass response can be of great value in developing an understanding of the problem and in devising an engineering solution, even though the numerical results may not always accurately predict field performance. This will be illustrated by way of three examples.

Rock–support interaction diagrams

Stresses and displacements in the rock surrounding tunnels and in the lining or support elements depend not only on the rock mass properties and the *in-situ* stresses but on the type and stiffness of the lining or support and the timing of its installation. The interdependence of these various factors is commonly represented by rock mass response lines and support reaction lines on rock–support interaction diagrams.

Detailed accounts of the features and methods of calculation of these diagrams have been given elsewhere[3,13,21,24,37] and will not be repeated here. The essential concepts can be appreciated from the simple example given in Fig. 17. A circular tunnel is to be excavated in a homogeneous, isotropic, initially elastic rock

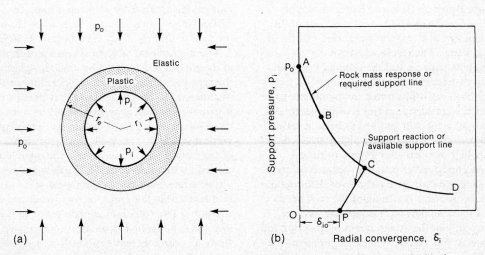

Fig. 17   (a) Formation of plastic zone around circular excavation in hydrostatic stress field and (b) rock–support interaction diagram

mass subjected to a hydrostatic *in-situ* stress field, p_0. As the pre-existing rock support is removed during excavation displacements occur in the rock surrounding the tunnel, and the stresses are redistributed. The radial support pressure, p_i, required at a particular point on the excavation boundary to limit the local radial convergence to δ_i is given by the rock mass response or required support line. In the illustrated case yielding of the rock mass occurs from point B and a plastic zone develops around the tunnel. Support is installed at P after a radial wall displacement of δ_{i0} has occurred. Stress builds up in the support with displacement along the support reaction or available support line PC until equilibrium is reached at C.

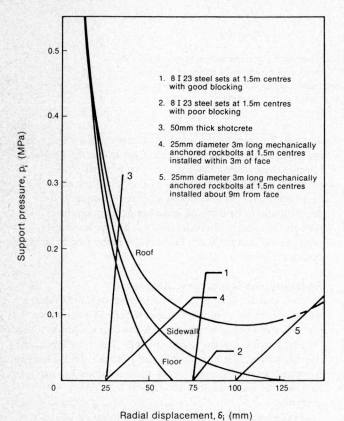

Fig. 18   Rock–support interaction analysis for 10.7-m diameter tunnel in fair-quality gneiss in hydrostatic stress field of $p_0 = 3.3$ MPa. After Hoek and Brown[21]

Fig. 18 shows a numerical example, details of which were given by Hoek and Brown.[21] Different required support lines were obtained for the roof, side wall and floor of the circular tunnel, and available support lines were calculated for five support systems. The results illustrate the importance of support stiffness and the timing of support installation. Support 1 (steel sets) may be acceptable, but the effect of poor blocking is illustrated by the performance of support 2, which is unable to control roof displacements. Support 3 (shotcrete) is too stiff and/or has been installed too early, and so becomes unnecessarily highly stressed. Support 4 (rockbolts), installed after 25 mm of tunnel deformation has occurred, gives a close to optimal solution, but the same system installed after 100 mm of deformation (support 5) permits excessive loosening of the rock mass.

Calculations of rock–support interaction diagrams are made only infrequently in the design stages of underground construction projects. For non-axisymmetric problems the calculations are not easily performed and, in all cases, the relevant rock mass properties are difficult to estimate. For these reasons, the curves are often determined by measurement during construction and used to guide the provision of secondary or tertiary support. Such curves have played an important part in the development of the New Austrian Tunnelling Method, which, as has been argued elsewhere,[53] is a successful approach to tunnelling based on an understanding of ground–support interaction mechanics.

Rib pillar design for longwall coal mining

Inelastic deformation of the strata surrounding the seam necessarily occurs in longwall methods of mining coal. Zones of yielded material commonly develop around the face, around roadways and at the edges of pillars. Mine layout design and pillar dimensioning in these cases have been based, traditionally, on precedent practice and empirical design formulae. In recent years, however, Wilson[54,55,56] has developed a rational approach to these design problems, using a limited number of sound mechanical and theoretical concepts.

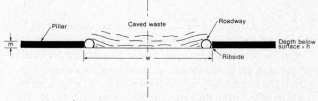

Fig. 19   Cross-section through mined-out longwall coal face

Wilson first developed a model of the distribution of vertical stress in the cross-section of a longwall extraction (Fig. 19) removed from the influence of the face. This analysis is based on a stress balance or vertical equilibrium method in which the total vertical force applied over a large plan area must remain equal to that arising from the overburden, even after part of the seam has been removed. It is assumed that, compared with the total vertical force to be redistributed, the vertical forces transmitted by the roadway supports are small and may be ignored. No account is taken of the redistribution of the horizontal components of *in-situ* stress.

Fig. 20 shows Wilson's approximations to the vertical stress distributions acting at cross-sections such as that shown in Fig. 19. The distribution of vertical stress in the caved waste is based on an assumption, derived from field observations made in British coal fields, that the stress reaches the overburden stress at a distance of $0.3h$ from the ribside. Thus, there are two cases to be considered—those for $w > 0.6h$ (Fig. 20(a)) and for $w < 0.6h$ (Fig. 20(b)).

The distribution of vertical stress within the yielded zone at the ribside is calculated by an elasto-plastic analysis of the type introduced in rock–support interaction calculations.[13] This produces a non-linear stress distribution, which is approximated by a triangular distribution (Fig. 20(c)). Wilson has given equations for the vertical stress, σ_{zz}, the peak abutment stress, σ_y, the width of the ribside yield zone, x_b, and the total vertical force carried by the yield zone, A_b. Results are presented for two sets of strata conditions—for a weak seam between a strong roof and strong floor and for roof, seam and floor of similar strengths. The equations contain terms in the vertical *in-situ* stress, p, the *in-situ* uniaxial compressive strength of the strata, C_o, the constant b in the principal stress form of the Coulomb shear strength equation, $\sigma_1 = C_o + b\,\sigma_3$, and $p^\star = p_i + 0.1$ MPa, where p_i is the support pressure. The

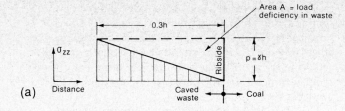

(a)

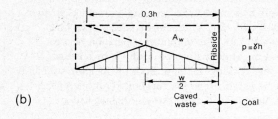

(b)

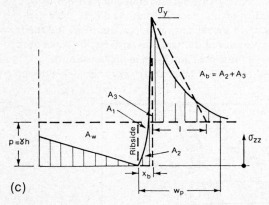

(c)

Fig. 20   Idealized distribution of vertical stress, σ_{zz}, in caved waste for face length of (a) $w > 0.6h$, and (b) $w < 0.6h$; (c) vertical stress distribution across ribside. After Wilson[54,55,56]

stress in the zone beyond the peak stress is assumed to decay asymptotically towards the overburden stress according to the equation

$$(\sigma_{zz} - p) = (\sigma_y - p) \exp\left(\frac{x_b - x}{C}\right) \tag{13}$$

where C is a constant having the units of distance. By equating areas under the curves in Fig. 20(c) so as to maintain a vertical stress balance the value of C is calculated as

$$C = \frac{A_w + p\,x_b - A_b}{\sigma_y - p} \tag{14}$$

where A_w is the 'load deficiency' associated with each ribside as shown in Fig. 20(a) and (b). When the exponential vertical stress decay curve is replaced by a triangular distribution of base width l the vertical stress balance requires that

$$\tfrac{1}{2}l(\sigma_y - p) = C(\sigma_y - p)$$

i.e. $\tag{15}$

$$l = 2C$$

The required width of a long protection pillar, or rib pillar, between two parallel longwall panels may be

determined by use of the zone of influence concept. This may be taken to require that the roadway on one side of the pillar will not be influenced by the stress concentration arising from the extraction on the other side of the pillar. If the zone of stress increase is taken to be defined by the triangular base width, l, and the yield zone width, x_b, is added at either extremity to ensure that the roadway is located in a low stress area at the edge of the yield zone, it follows that the required minimum pillar width is

$$w_p = 2(C + x_b) \tag{16}$$

Wilson[54,55,56] has shown that, in a number of cases, pillar sizes calculated by use of equation 16 agree well with those given by empirical rules developed on the basis of precedent practice. His method, however, has the great advantage that, because it is rationally based, it is capable of extrapolation to mining depths beyond those for which

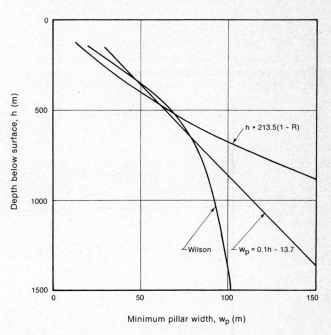

Fig. 21   Minimum pillar width required between longwall faces 217 m wide in Canadian coal mine determined by three methods. After Wilson[54,55,56]

experience has been gained in a particular mining field. Fig. 21 shows the results obtained in a case in which mining had been at depths of from 100 to 700 m and mining to a depth of 1400 m was planned. Although all methods give similar results for $h = 300$–600 m, the design formula used on this Canadian coal field, $h(\text{ft}) = 7000(1 - R)$, where R is the areal extraction ratio, and the traditional United Kingdom rule, $w_p = 0.1h + 15$ yd, both give pillar widths greatly in excess of those predicted by Wilson for the increased mining depths.

Experience elsewhere suggests that Wilson's values are probably more realistic.

Behaviour of crown pillars between cut and fill stopes at Mount Isa mine

At the Mount Isa mine, Australia, silver–lead–zinc mineralization occurs as distinct concordant beds within the Urquhart Shale—a sequence of well-bedded dolomitic and pyritic shales and siltstones. The bedding strikes north–south and dips at 65° to the west. The most important geological structures in the Urquhart Shale are bedding-plane breaks, fractures striking north–south and dipping at about 60° to the east, two sets of orthogonal extension fractures orientated normal to the bedding, and conjugate shear fractures. Bedding-plane breaks are frequently planar, smooth, graphite-coated and slickensided and can have continuities of up to several hundred metres. The major principal *in-situ* stress is perpendicular to the bedding. The other two principal *in-situ* stresses have similar magnitudes and act in the plane of the bedding. The measured vertical component of *in-situ* stress is equal to the weight of the overlying rock.

The silver–lead–zinc orebodies are disposed in an *en échelon* pattern downdip and along strike. The Racecourse orebodies to the east or footwall side are narrow and are mined mainly by a mechanized cut and fill method, known locally as MICAF. The widths of MICAF stopes vary between 3 and 11 m. The minimum separation between stopes is 3–4 m. Mining advance up-dip is by a breast stoping or 'flat-backing' method. Both the hanging-wall and crowns (or backs) of stopes are rockbolted routinely, and pre-placed, untensioned cable dowels are installed as required.[51]

The stability of the crown pillars is of major concern in this type of mining. A justifiable mining objective is to recover as much ore as possible from the pillars. Men and machines work in the advancing stopes, however, and their safety must be ensured. Potential hazards in the stopes are rock falls from the crown and buckling failures in the hanging- and footwalls[52] (Fig. 16(e)). For the 11–9 level and

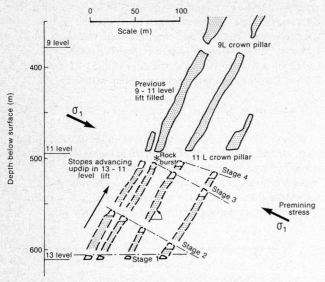

Fig. 22   Cross-section through Racecourse orebodies at 6570N, Mount Isa mine, Australia, showing mining sequence in 13–11 level lift that led to formation of 11 level crown pillar. After Lee[57]

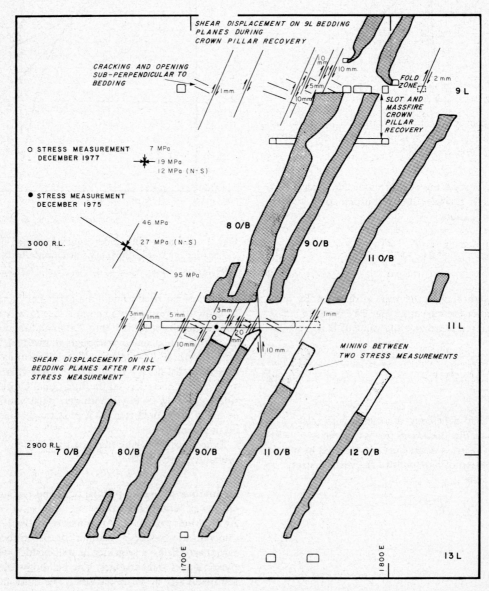

Fig. 23   Cross-section at 6650N, looking north, showing results of two stress measurements and shear displacements on bedding planes. After Lee and Bridges[51]

13–11 level lifts the stopes were advanced up-dip in a sequence that ensured that all stope backs were kept in a line perpendicular to bedding (Fig. 22). This method was adopted to ensure that the major principal stress would always act normally to bedding and so eliminate the possibility of crown instability being induced by slip on the bedding planes.

At stage 3 of the 13–11 level lift (Fig. 22) very high stresses developed in the stope backs. This produced spalling of intact rock, rock falls, audible rock noise and rockbursts in the 11 level crown pillar above 7 and 8 orebodies. A series of stress measurements made at various locations on 11 level showed that the induced stresses were very high. At 6650N (Fig. 23) a major principal stress of 95 MPa was measured perpendicular to the bedding.

Because of the bad ground conditions in the crowns of the leading hanging-wall stopes mining in these stopes ceased, and further mining was undertaken in the footwall orebodies, which were 'lagging' behind under the mining strategy that was being used. It was noted that, where this was done, shear displacement occurred on a few bedding planes in the crown pillars of the hanging-wall orebodies and ground conditions improved. Fig. 23 shows the shear displacements measured in such a case at 6650N between December, 1975, when the high stresses previously referred to were measured on 11 level, and December, 1977, when much lower stresses were measured.

The mechanical explanation of this destressing phenomenon is that, by advancing the footwall stopes, the principal stress directions in the crown pillar became inclined to the bedding planes. Because of the very low shear strengths of the bedding planes slip could occur readily, the relative displacement being footwall side down. The angle of friction on the bedding planes was 10° and their dilatation angles were less than 2°. As the stopes were progressively mined to and through 11 level non-dilatant shear displacement on bedding planes continued, but tensile cracking sub-perpendicular to the bedding began to occur. Slip on the bedding planes was a strain-softening process, which decreased the stiffness of the whole crown pillar. This produced a regional redistribution of stress away from the crown pillar to the north and south abutments of the stopes where high stresses could still be sustained.

Although these mechanisms were satisfactorily modelled by a finite-element analysis that incorporated suitable yield mechanisms,[58] such sophisticated analyses are not required to develop an appreciation of the fundamental mechanics of the problem. The keys to an understanding of why slip occurred on the bedding planes and ground conditions improved with a modified extraction schedule are (1) a general appreciation of the directions that would be taken by the principal stress trajectories in the crown pillar at the different stages of mining and the implications for slip on bedding planes; (2) a recognition of the low frictional resistance likely to be generated on smooth, continuous, graphite coated and slickensided bedding planes; and (3) an understanding of the role played by rock mass stiffness in governing induced stress magnitudes.

Conclusions

The application of theory based on the principles of mechanics is an important component of modern rock engineering practice. In limited numbers of cases numerical results obtained on the assumption of homogeneous, isotropic, linear elastic rock mass behaviour may be directly applicable in design. More generally, rock masses will not be homogeneous, isotropic and linearly elastic materials. In these cases the results of elastic stress analyses can be of value in providing qualitative indications of likely areas of stress concentration or destressing, zones of influence of individual excavations and interactions between multiple excavations. The models that are available for the analysis of problems that involve the several possible types of non-linear inelastic behaviour may not always produce reliable numerical results. They can, however, serve to elucidate the mechanics of the problem and to identify those factors which are likely to exert a primary influence on rock mass response. They can also provide explanations for field observations that may be inexplicable without recourse to the concepts of mechanics and a knowledge of the stress–strain behaviour of rock masses and their constituent parts. The ability to understand and apply theory in this sense is an essential part of the armoury of the professional engineer concerned with underground excavations in rock.

Acknowledgement

I should like to thank the following colleagues and friends who generously provided me with information and/or material for presentation or otherwise assisted in the preparation of this lecture: Dr. A. R. Atkins (Chamber of Mines of South Africa), Associate Professor H. F. Bock (James Cook University of North Queensland, Australia), Professor L. A. Endersbee (Monash University, Australia), Dr. E. Hoek (Golder Associates (Western Canada) Ltd.), F. J. Leahy and M. F. Lee (Mount Isa Mines Ltd., Australia), Dr. H. Wagner (Chamber of Mines of South Africa), Dr. J. W. Bray, A. M. Clark, W. Harman, B. H. Holt, Miss M. J. Knox, Dr. J. O. Watson and L. D. Wilson (Imperial College).

References
1.   Great Britain, Board of Education. *Final report of the Departmental Committee on the Royal College of Science (including the Royal School of Mines)* (London: HMSO, 1906). (*Cd.* 2956)
2.   Playfair L. The study of abstract science essential to the progress of industry. *Rec. R. Sch. Mines*, **1**, pt 1 1852, 23–49.
3.   Muir Wood A. M. Ground behaviour and support for mining and tunnelling. *Trans. Instn Min. Metall.* (*Sect A: Min. industry*), **88**, 1979, A23–34.
4.   Gibson R. E. Fourteenth Rankine Lecture: The analytical method in soil mechanics. *Géotechnique*, **24**, 1974, 114–40.
5.   Bjerrum L. *et al.* eds. *From theory to practice in soil mechanics: selections from the writings of Karl Terzaghi* (New York: John Wiley, 1960), 425 p.
6.   Casagrande A. Karl Terzaghi – his life and achievements. Reference 5, 3–21.
7.   Terzaghi K. *Theoretical soil mechanics* (New York: John Wiley, 1943), 510 p.
8.   Terzaghi K. Soil mechanics – a new chapter in engineering science. *J. Instn civ. Engrs*, **12**, 1939, 106–41.
9.   Anderson W. The interdependence of abstract science and engineering. *Min. Proc. Instn civ. Engrs*, **114**, pt 4 1892–93, 255–83.
10.   Savin G. N. *Stress concentrations around holes* (London: Pergamon, 1960), 430 p.
11.   Salamon M. D. G. Rock mechanics of underground excavations. In *Advances in rock mechanics, volume 1, part B: proceedings 3rd congress International Society for Rock Mechanics, Denver, 1974* (Washington D.C.: National Academy of Sciences, 1974), 951–1099.
12.   Jaeger J. C. and Cook N. G. W. *Fundamentals of rock mechanics, 3rd edn* (London: Chapman and Hall, 1979), 593 p.
13.   Brown E. T. *et al.* Characteristic line calculations for rock tunnels. *J. geotech. Engng, Am. Soc. civ. Engrs*, **109**, 1983, 15–39.
14.   Zienkiewicz O. C. *The finite element method, 3rd edn* (London, etc: McGraw-Hill, 1977), 787 p.
15.   Crouch S. L. and Starfield A. M. *Boundary element methods in solid mechanics* (London: George Allen and Unwin, 1983), 322 p.
16.   Meek J. L. and Beer G. A review of analysis techniques for the determination of stresses around and performance of excavations in hard rock. In *Design and performance of underground excavations: ISRM symposium, Cambridge, 1984* Brown E. T. and

Hudson J. A. eds (London: British Geotechnical Society, 1984), 1–10.

17. Lorig L. J. and Brady B. G. H. A hybrid computational scheme for excavation and support design in jointed rock media. Reference 16, 105–12.

18. Cundall P. A. A computer model for simulating progressive large scale movements in blocky rock systems. In *Rock fracture: proceedings of the international symposium on rock mechanics, Nancy, 1971, pap.* 2-8.

19. Voegele M. Fairhurst C. and Cundall P. Analysis of tunnel support loads using a large displacement, distinct block model. In *Rockstore 77: Storage in excavated rock caverns: proceedings of the first international symposium, Stockholm, 1977* Bergman M. ed. (Oxford, etc.: Pergamon, 1978), vol. 2, 247–52.

20. Stewart I. J. and Brown E. T. A static relaxation method for the analysis of excavations in discontinuous rock. Reference 16, 149–55.

21. Hoek E. and Brown E. T. *Underground excavations in rock* (London: IMM, 1980), 527 p.

22. Hoek E. Progressive caving induced by mining an inclined orebody. *Trans. Instn Min. Metall. (Sect. A: Min. industry)*, **83**, 1974, A133–9.

23. Beer G. and Meek J. L. Design curves for roofs and hanging-walls in bedded rock based on 'voussoir' beam and plate solutions. *Trans. Instn Min. Metall. (Sect. A: Min. industry)*, **91**, 1982, A18–22.

24. Ward W. H. Eighteenth Rankine Lecture: Ground supports for tunnels in weak rocks. *Géotechnique*, **28**, 1978, 133–70.

25. Worotnicki G. and Walton R. J. Triaxial 'hollow inclusion' gauges for determination of rock stresses in situ. In *Investigation of stress in rock: advances in stress measurement: ISRM symposium, Sydney, 1976* (Sydney: The Institution of Engineers, Australia, 1976), supplement, 1–8. (*Natn. Conf. Publ.* no. 76/4)

26. Gonano L. P. and Sharp J. C. Critical evaluation of rock behaviour for in-situ stress determination using overcoring methods. In *Proceedings fifth international congress on rock mechanics, Melbourne, 1983* (Rotterdam: Balkema, 1983), vol. 1, A241–50.

27. Pine R. J. and Batchelor A. S. Downward migration of shearing in jointed rock during hydraulic injections. *Int. J. Rock Mech. Min. Sci.*, **21**, 1984, 249–63.

28. Villarceau Y. L'établissement des arches de pont. *C.r. Acad. Sci., Mémoires présentés par divers savants*, **12**, 1854, 503.

29. Heyman J. The stone skeleton. *Int. J. Solids Structures*, **2**, 1966, 249–79.

30. Goodier J. N. Compression of rectangular blocks, and the bending of beams by non-linear distributions of bending forces. *Trans. Am. Soc. mech. Engrs, Appl. Mech.*, **54**, 1932, 173–80.

31. Davies J. D. and Stagg K. G. Splitting tests on rock specimens. In *Proceedings second congress International Society for Rock Mechanics, Belgrade, 1970* (Belgrade: Jaroslav Cerni Institute for Development of Water Resources, 1970), vol. 2, 343–9.

32. Brown E. T. and Hudson J. A. Progressive collapse of simple block-jointed systems. *Aust. Geomech. J.*, **G2**, 1972, 49–54.

33. Hocking G. Stresses around tunnel intersections. In *Computer methods in tunnel design* (London: Institution of Civil Engineers, 1978), 41–60.

34. Watson J. O. Advanced implementation of the boundary element method for two- and three-dimensional elastostatics. In *Developments in boundary element methods – 1* Banerjee P. K. and Butterfield R. eds (Barking, Essex: Applied Science Publishers, 1979), 31–63.

35. Alexander L. A. and Fabjanczyk M. W. Extraction design using open stopes for pillar recovery in the 1100 ore body at Mount Isa. In *Design and operation of caving and sublevel stoping mines* Stewart D. R. ed. (New York: AIME, 1981), 437–58.

36. Watson J. O. and Cowling R. Application of three-dimensional boundary element method to modelling of large mining excavations at depth. Paper presented at 5th international conference on numerical methods in geomechanics, Nagoya, 1985.

37. Brady B. H. G. and Brown E. T. *Rock mechanics for underground mining* (London: George Allen and Unwin, 1985), 523 p.

38. Kirsch G. Die Theorie der Elastizität und die Bedürfnisse der Festigkeitslehre. *Z. Ver. dt. Ing.*, **42**, 1898, 797–807.

39. Eissa E. S. A. Stress analysis of underground excavations in isotropic and stratified rock using the boundary element method. Ph.D. thesis, University of London, 1980.

40. Bray J. W. Personal communication, 1984.

41. Cook N. G. W. *et al.* Rock mechanics applied to the study of rockbursts. *J. S. Afr. Inst. Min. Metall.*, **66**, 1965–66, 435–528.

42. Salamon M. D. G. Rockburst hazard and the fight for its alleviation in South African gold mines. In *Rockbursts: prediction and control* (London: IMM, 1983), 11–36.

43. Cook N. G. W. The siting of mine tunnels and other factors affecting their layout and design. *Pap. Discuss. Ass. Mine Mgrs S. Afr. 1972–73*, 1975, 199–215.

44. Wagner H. Protection of service excavations. In *Rock mechanics in mining practice* Budavari S. ed. (Johannesburg: South African Institute of Mining and Metallurgy, 1983), 201–20.

45. Salamon M. D. G. and Wagner H. Role of stabilizing pillars in the alleviation of rock burst hazard in deep mines. In *Proceedings fourth congress of the International Society for Rock Mechanics, Montreux, 1979* (Rotterdam: Balkema and Swiss Society for Soil and Rock Mechanics, 1979), vol. 2, 561–6.

46. Endersbee L. A. and Hofto E. O. Civil engineering design and studies in rock mechanics for the Poatina underground power station, Tasmania. *J. Instn Engrs Aust.*, **35**, 1963, 187–206.

47. Sharp J. C. Endersbee L. A. and Mellors T. W. Design and observed performance of permanent cavern excavations in weak, bedded strata. Reference 16, 493–507.

48. Watson J. O. Personal communication, 1984.

49. Watson J. O. Hermitian cubic boundary elements for plane elastostatics. In *Innovative numerical analysis for the engineering sciences, proceedings 2nd international symposium, Montreal, 1980* Shaw R. *et al.* eds (Charlottesville: University Press of Virginia, 1980), 403–12.

50. Joughin N. C. and Jager A. J. Fracture of rock at stope faces in South African gold mines. Reference 42, 53–66.

51. Lee M. F. and Bridges M. C. Rock mechanics of crown pillars between cut-and-fill stopes at Mount Isa Mine. In *Application of rock mechanics to cut and fill mining* Stephansson O. and Jones M. J. eds (London: IMM, 1981), 316–29.

52. Beer G. Meek J. L. and Cowling R. Prediction of the behaviour of shale hangingwalls in deep underground excavations. Reference 26, vol. 2, D45–51.

53. Brown E. T. Putting the NATM into perspective. *Tunnels Tunnell.*, **13**, no. 10 1981, 13–17.

54. Wilson A. H. Stress and stability in coal ribsides and pillars. In *Proceedings 1st conference on ground control in mining, West Virginia University, Morgantown, 1981* Peng S. S. ed., 1–12.

55. Wilson A. H. Pillar stability in longwall mining. In *State-of-the-art of ground control in longwall mining and mining subsidence* Chugh Y. P. and Karmis M. eds (New York: AIME, 1982), 85–95.

56. Wilson A. H. The stability of underground workings in the soft rocks of the Coal Measures. *Int. J. Min. Engng*, **1**, 1983, 91–187.

57. Lee M. F. A review of stope performance and ground behaviour associated with the MICAF mining method, Mount Isa Mines, Australia. M.Eng.Sc. thesis, James Cook University of North Queensland, 1981.

58. Lawrence W. J. C. and Bock H. F. Numerical modelling of the yielding 11-level crown pillar at Mount Isa. *Aust. geomechs News*, no. 5, 1982, 9–16.

Vote of thanks

Dr. P H. Phillips said that it gave him great pleasure to propose the vote of thanks to Professor Brown for not only having enthralled his audience but also for having added to the reputation of the Sir Julius Wernher Memorial Lectures. He need have no fear that the spirit of Sir Julius would disrupt his calm progress at the Royal School of Mines—an institution that they both held in high regard. The Sir Julius Wernher Memorial Lecture was a very important event for the Institution of Mining and Metallurgy, and it was a reflexion of the high esteem of the Institution's Council for the Tunnelling conferences that each had started with a lecture in that series. By tradition the vote of thanks was given by a senior member of the Institution and the speaker was asked if he had any preference for an appropriate person. Professor Brown had paid him a great compliment and honour in asking through the Secretary of the Institution whether or not he could undertake that task and had been concerned that his role as Chairman of the Organizing Committee of Tunnelling '85 would exclude him. A benefit of the position of Chairman, however, was that at times one could not only make but break the rules—and those present thus became party to an undisguised and unapologetic misuse of power.

Ted Brown had concluded in his own efficient, incisive and succinct way each of the last three Tunnelling conferences. Very few delegates appreciated how difficult a task that really was, in that it involved not only reading the papers but also attending each presentation and discussion session and then producing a final technical—and often humourous—text under extreme pressure. His own debt to Professor Brown for his contribution to the success of past Tunnelling conferences was so great that it would have been very difficult for him to have been prevented from proposing the vote of thanks.

They had been privileged to hear a lecture from an academic expert who had 'both feet on the ground', which made him a rather unusual animal. Progress in any scientific discipline was of value to engineers only if the applications were logical, practical and cost-effective. Too often, mathematical theories had been based on the analysis of homogeneous material that produced a solution to three or four places of decimals. The design or constructional engineer then added a 'safety' factor of such magnitude to take account of his own experiences that it rendered the degree of sophistication of the original calculation practically worthless. Thus, a great deal of effort was wasted, but, more importantly, the gulf between the academic and the practical engineer widened, with a vital loss of confidence. Professor Brown had never fallen into that all too frequent trap, and for that alone they owed him a debt of gratitude. Those were the factors that would truly take rock mechanics from theory to practice.

His own professional career had been associated with rock mechanics to a greater or lesser extent right from the start. In the 1950s, as a young undergraduate at Sheffield University, he had met first Charles Fairhurst and then Ivor Hawkes, both of whom had carried out research projects for their doctorates that were incredible in both size and importance. Later, the creation of commercial organizations specializing solely in the applications of rock mechanics had brought him into contact with such people as Glossop, Skempton, Potts, Cook, Hoek, Salamon, Roxborough, Farmer and, of course, Ted Brown. As some were aware, he had been fortunate enough to have a very special relationship with one of those outstanding people, the late Ivor Hawkes. Some 20 years earlier he had been asked to give the first course of postgraduate lectures in rock mechanics held in the United Kingdom, and it had seemed natural for him to ask Hawkes to assist in the laboratory sections of those courses. In 1979 he had travelled to New Hampshire to see Hawkes, who was then terminally ill, and in his home had compiled a *curriculum vitae* detailing all his work in the field of rock mechanics. As a result, the U.S. National Committee for Rock Mechanics had produced for Hawkes a special award for outstanding and continuous contribution to rock mechanics. The official citation stated: 'Seldom has there been an individual who has created so much for our profession. The Committee feel that our award is all too small a token of our appreciation for the many ways in which your work has benefited all of rock mechanics.'

His vote of thanks had been rather long, complex and personal in nature, yet to couple someone with Ivor Hawkes was the greatest compliment that he could pay: there was today no one to whom the citation from the U.S. National Committee for Rock Mechanics applied more than it did to Ted Brown, and he invited those present to join him in thanking Professor Brown for his lecture.

Session 1 – Major projects

Co-Chairmen: V. W. Shtenko and G. E. Pearse

First mined hydrocarbon storage in Great Britain

J. G. Trotter
D. M. Thompson
T. J. M. Paterson
Geostore (South Killingholme), Ltd., Whitby, North Yorkshire, England

Synopsis
Accurate exploration and site investigation are vital to every tunnelling project: when the tunnels are then to be used for the storage of liquid gases under pressure the geological, hydrological and geomechanical interpretations assume an even greater importance. The methods by which these parameters were revealed and assessed at South Killingholme, South Humberside, England, are described. The concept of 'keyhole' mining, whereby large galleries were developed from small-diameter drilled shafts, is discussed. The equipment and methods that were employed in the construction of the galleries are described and some of the difficulties that were encountered, together with the remedies that were applied, are explained.

The two 120 000-m^3 underground storage caverns that are being constructed at South Killingholme, South Humberside, are the first mined caverns for hydrocarbon storage in the United Kingdom. Much use is made in the United Kingdom of caverns solution-mined or 'washed' in salt deposits, but this is a completely different storage technique.

In mid-1979 Calor Gas, Ltd., asked Geostore, Ltd., a British company with close ties with Geostock of Paris, to carry out preliminary studies on the feasibility of constructing underground caverns for seasonal storage of LPG. Calor required very large-capacity storage near a deep-water port to be used as an import terminal. An increasing annual demand for LPG, coupled with a reduction in traditional supplies from United Kingdom refineries, had led to the need for the new terminal.

Although Geostore looked at a number of possible locations, South Humberside was always the favourite. There already existed excellent deep-water facilities, and the presence of two large oil refineries had provided a ready made oil-related infrastructure. Planners, Port Authorities, Water Authorities, Fire Departments and many other groups, both public and private, were all accustomed to dealing with the special requirements of handling and storing large quantities of crude oil and oil products. The geographical location of the area was also important, being well connected by both road and rail links to the major LPG marketing centres.

From preliminary feasibility studies the Northern Province of the Upper Cretaceous Chalk, present throughout the area, was soon identified as a potentially excellent host rock for unlined LPG storage caverns. Although there was no history of tunnelling or mining in this particular rock, there did exist a large body of information about the chalk. The top part of the succession is a large groundwater reservoir and the vast number of boreholes that had been drilled and logged made it relatively easy to forecast the disposition of the chalk and to estimate the thickness of the various beds within the series. Calor wished to store both butane and propane, but it was required that the two caverns should be interchangeable to respond to future market trends. It was necessary, therefore, to seek a suitable rock structure at sufficient depth to ensure that the static head of groundwater would be sufficient to prevent leakage of propane, which has the higher vapour pressure. Both caverns were planned for this depth.

The chalk in the area of interest is extremely consistent, and appears to be almost completely undisturbed. The only feature that could negate the feasibility of construction of the caverns was the Kirmington Fjord – a very deep glacial valley eroded into the chalk that passed almost directly beneath the Immingham dock complex. Calor joined forces with Conoco and sought to develop the storage complex on Conoco-owned land northwest of Immingham, which was clear of the influence of the Kirmington Fjord.

Calor's decision to have its new storage scheme built underground must have been difficult. Many mined LPG caverns exist in the U.S.A., Scandinavia and France, but the technology had never been used in the United Kingdom. Although the principles are well understood, there existed, as has been noted, no previous United Kingdom experience on which important planning decisions could be based. The Health and Safety Executive, which plays an important role in any new 'major hazard' development, had to develop a precedent-setting scheme, as did the Anglian Water Authority, in whose aquifer the storage caverns were to be built. Calor's determination to make available the technical details of the project to all interested parties has resulted in excellent working relationships.

The several advantages of the use of underground storage are (1) that it is much safer than any other method for large volumes of LPG; (2) in comparison with state of the art designs for refrigerated storage tanks on surface, where three containment barriers are used, considerable cost savings result; (3) as the stored product is safely out of the way, deep underground, the facility can be constructed much closer to existing plants; and (4) the final surface area that is occupied is very small and compact.

Site selection and exploration programme

The preliminary feasibility study outlined in the previous section showed that the Conoco site at Marsh Lane, South Killingholme, appeared to offer excellent rock and favourable containment properties. It was then necessary to prove the feasibility of the site by exploratory drilling, core testing and hydrological assessment.

A contract was let to Boldon Drilling, Ltd., to drill five holes spaced out over the land that was available for development. Each hole was drilled from the surface to a predetermined depth below rock head by use of bentonite mud. A surface casing was then set and cemented. The holes were then cored at 114 mm for the remainder of their depth. The first hole was drilled completely through the chalk and into the underlying Carstone aquifer, which was found to be slightly artesian. The remaining holes were bottomed in the Lower Chalk (Ferriby). The cores were logged on site by a resident geologist and a photographic record was made. Both the Upper (Burnham) and Middle (Welton) Chalk have many flint bands, and these, predictably, prevented full recovery of the softer chalk cores. Even so, the recovery was high, and *RQD* often approached 100%.

As the holes were drilled, permeability tests were conducted on each 10-m interval by use of a single packer. Testing was done by the Lugeon method. Initially, a mechanical packer was used, but it was soon realized that this tool did not provide a sufficiently tight seal to yield satisfactory results in the very low-permeability rock encountered. The inflatable packer that was then used gave excellent results.

The five holes correlated well with one another, which indicated a predictable stratigraphy and well-defined zones of

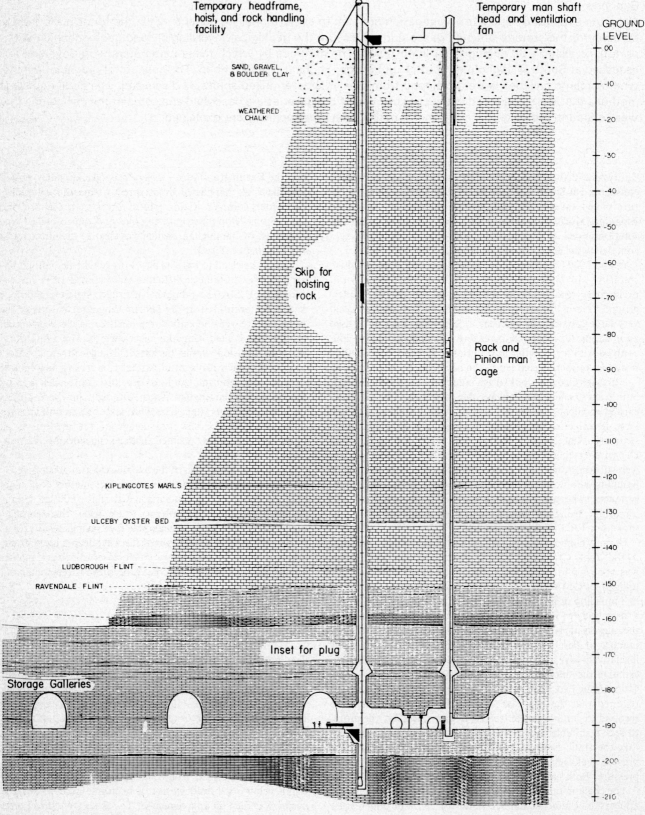

Fig. 1 Location of cavern on geological section

4

high and low permeability. High permeability was identified with cores that exhibited a concentration of joints. The permeability of such zones was of the order of one Darcy. Conversely, much of the chalk – in particular, the lower part of the Middle and Lower Chalk – had very low permeability (~0.1 mD – about the same as good concrete).

As coring proceeded, fresh samples of core were selected for laboratory testing. It is known that the mechanical strength of chalk increases markedly as the chalk dries out: for this reason cores for testing were selected as soon after recovery as was practicable. The fresh cores were encapsulated in wax, and tested at Newcastle University under the supervision of Dr. E. K. S. Passaris. Tests were carried out for unconfined and confined compressive strength, perpendicular and parallel to the bedding, triaxial shear strength, sonic velocity, porosity, nitrogen permeability and chemical composition.

Special tests on some samples included those on the dry rock for the comparison of properties with the saturated samples, compatibility tests with propane and butane, analyses of clay samples and stylolite material and electron-microscope examination of the chalk.

To assist in the final correlation, a suite of logs was run in each hole, including gamma-ray, linear density, caliper multi-channel sonic, focused electric and bed resolution density. On completion, each hole was fitted with a gravel pack and screen opposite specific horizons at which formation water pressures were to be observed before, during and after cavern mining. In addition, a second gravel pack was installed at the foot of each surface casing to provide a means of following accurately changes in the water-table.

Cavern geology

At South Killingholme the Upper Cretaceous chalk extends from some 20 to 215 m below ground level. The storage galleries are located near the base of the Welton Chalk, the sumps extending some 3 m into the Ferriby Chalk. Two prominent marker beds are exposed – the Grasby Marl in the bottom bench of the galleries and the Plenus Marl (Black Band) at the top of the Ferriby Chalk in the sumps (Fig. 1).

As exposed in the cavern, the Welton Chalk is massive and undisturbed with a dip of 1.2° NE. There is no evidence of any folding. Sub-vertical displacements of up to 300 mm occur on rare, minor faults. Many horizontal stylolitic partings contain marl, but the sawtooth profile of the partings gives mechanical interlock. The only significant horizontal discontinuity in the galleries is the Grasby Marl, which comprises up to 15 mm of

Fig. 2   Flint and marl bands at cavern horizon

montmorillonite clay. This is believed to originate from volcanic ash.

In engineering terms the chalk at cavern level is largely un-jointed. Minor sub-vertical joints exist, but these are generally healed with secondary calcite. Obvious sub-vertical joints are present at a spacing of several metres.

Flints occur at cavern level – generally in discrete bands. The flints in the bands are generally not continuous, though, locally, they may appear so because of the agglomeration of adjacent flints. The concentration of flints in each band varies considerably. The size range of flints varies markedly between the bands. Individual flints attain a rare maximum of 300-mm width and 200-mm thickness. Occasional random flints, often burrow-fill type, occur outside the flint bands. The density of flints on a volume basis in the chalk in the top heading is estimated at 0.1% and in the bottom bench at 0.2% (Fig. 2).

Where it is visible in the sumps and sump heading the top of the Ferriby Chalk is much more jointed with many minor marl bands. The unconfined compressive strength of the chalk at cavern level is in the range 30–60 MPa. The seismic velocity measured *in situ* and on core samples is about 4000 m/s. Logging of discontinuities in the chalk at cavern level suggests that the *RQD* figures from site investigation borehole cores give an underestimate of rock quality *in situ*. This may have been due to damage caused by flints or breakage of core during handling, despite the relatively large diameter of the cores.

Geotechnical and hydrological studies leading to cavern design

The success of an underground storage project depends on the satisfactory fulfilment of two main criteria. It must be possible to carry out large-scale excavation economically and, in particular, to avoid expensive cavern lining and support. It is also necessary that the hydrological environment be suitable for the proper containment of the product that is to be stored.

Given that propane was to be stored, and that the vapour pressure at ambient temperatures is in the region of 8 bar, a preliminary assessment for proper storage depth can be made. To counter the leakage of product from the cavern the ground-water pressure surrounding the cavern would have to exceed 8 bar by a 'shape factor' of, say, 2 bar plus a safety factor of, say, another 2 bar. The 'shape factor' is complex and its detailed consideration is beyond the scope of this paper. In terms of water head, the above results in 80 m plus 20 m plus 20 m, giving a required theoretical head of 120 m. The cavern must then be constructed at least 120 m below the permanent water-table. At South Killingholme the rock at this depth contains many flint bands and would not be conducive to economic mining methods.

Looking down the geological succession, a very 'wet' band is encountered at about 150 m, followed by more flint bands and marl bands, but at about 180 m there exists 10 m of chalk relatively low in flints and of very low permeability. This area was chosen for preliminary study. If butane alone was to be stored, the theoretical depth for containment could be reduced to about 50 m because of its lower vapour pressure.

The cavern cross-section was fixed next. At this stage it was imagined that roadheaders would be used to mine the caverns. A decision had also been made to use two 2-m diameter shafts for access, and this, in turn, limited the size of the equipment that could be taken underground. It was found that a 5-m height was the maximum practical reach for roadheaders and that two passes of the machine to give a final cavern height of 10 m would produce the most economical cavern cross-section. In the meantime, geotechnical studies had shown that a span of about 10 m would be acceptable.

A tentative cavern layout was also made to define the pillar width and the configuration of the major intersections, account also being taken of the area of the available site and the quantity of LPG to be stored. It is worth noting that in a site of 260 m by 140 m it has been possible to provide 120 000 m³ of storage. Finite-element modelling was then used to study the stress magnitude and distribution around the openings, and at the major intersections. The various FEM calculations made are beyond the scope of this paper but, in general, the following parameters were introduced and studied: the effect of changing the horizontal to vertical *in-situ* stress ratio; the effect of introducing horizontal discontinuities (bedding planes); the effect of introducing vertical discontinuities (vertical joints); the stress distribution at major intersections; and the effect of changing water pressure and gas (internal) pressure.

The four types of analyses that were used were simple two-dimensional elastic and elastoplastic analyses, three-dimensional elastic analysis of a major intersection and three-dimensional elastoplastic analysis of a major intersection.

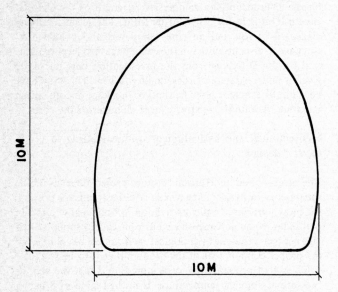

Fig. 3   Selected profile of storage gallery (cross-section, 85 m²)

For ease of construction the cross-section shown in Fig. 3 was chosen for the cavern. Later, the smaller cross-section used for the access roadways around the station area was checked by a two-dimensional analysis. The effect of the Grasby Marl in the side wall of the main gallery was also checked and found to be satisfactory. During construction, various parts of the cavern were instrumented to establish that the geotechnical behaviour of the rock followed that which had been foreseen in the analytical work: no discrepancies were found.

The hydrological assessment is rather more complex and difficult to describe. Given that the cavern is of suitable depth to provide the required hydrostatic head, and that the cavern is to be constructed in a zone of very low permeability, the following question has to be answered: 'Will there be sufficient replenishment water flowing toward the cavern to ensure that no part of the surrounding rock will become desaturated as seepage water flows into the cavern?' If it were found that desaturation could occur, it would be necessary to supply artificially the replenishment water. This could have been done by means of a water gallery constructed above the cavern with a 'fan' of boreholes to distribute water into the strata.

The exploratory work had indicated that there existed a 'wet zone' at about 150 m that was capable of supplying all the required water. Between the wet zone and the gallery there existed a number of marl bands that would impede the downward flow of water, and the chalk rock itself was of very low permeability. Initial excavation revealed very few joints or fissures to provide natural flow paths. It was then necessary to

determine if the joints seen would be capable of providing flow paths through the marl layers.

As soon as possible a series of experiments underground was set up to determine if desaturation could occur. The experiments consisted in drilling a number of boreholes from the cavern into specific strata. By use of a deadweight tester to achieve very precise readings the changes in water pressure in these holes, plus the relevant piezometric head in two of the surface boreholes, were monitored carefully as the underground excavation was enlarged. From the information gained and from very detailed logging of the jointing pattern of the rock it was possible to prove that adequate natural replenishment water could make its way to the caverns. No artificial replenishment was therefore required, which led to a considerable saving in cost.

South Killingholme is ideal as a cavern site in that there is a sufficient but modest inflow of water into the cavern. The cost of pumping will be minimal, but there is no danger of drawdown of the water-table.

Geotechnical and hydrological measurements during the subsequent construction of the cavern have served to confirm the criteria for the stability of the cavern and its ability to contain the stored product.

Design and construction of access shafts and operating boreholes

Shafts
Two 2-m diameter shafts provide access to each cavern during construction. Thereafter, they are sealed by concrete plugs and play no part in the operational life of the storage. Access for the equipment for the operation of each cavern is provided by nine boreholes.

Geostore conducted a study to evaluate the merits of drilled shafts. Drilling of shafts is not yet widely practised in Europe, whereas in North America many hundreds of shafts have been constructed by this method. In the United Kingdom only five drilled shafts onshore had preceded the four shafts that have since been built at Killingholme. All of the earlier shafts had been drilled by the Pigott Titan rig.

When the present shafts were planned the Titan rig was capable of drilling at 2.44-m maximum diameter, which permitted a finished lining of 2.00 m. Despite their small diameter, the concept of drilled shafts was attractive for this project. The principal factors are compared below for both drilled and conventionally sunk mined shafts.

Cost
At a cost of less than £1 500 000 for each pair of shafts construction economics favoured drilled shafts. Although the chalk at South Killingholme has a generally very low permeability, it contains three distinct zones that are highly water-bearing. These are almost inconsequential to the shaft driller, but they represent serious obstacles in an orthodox sinking and would necessitate special and costly methods.

Table 1

Shaft no.	1	2	3	4
	Duration of operation			
Drilling,* weeks	5	3	6†	6†
Lining, days	6	5	5	4
Cementing, days	4	3	3	5

*Excludes foreshaft.
†Duration influenced by extraneous factors.

Duration of construction
The contract for the four South Killingholme shafts was completed in less than nine months. It was felt that this performance would be hard to match by orthodox sinking. Details of the duration of each shaft drilling are shown in Table 1.

Safety and working conditions
Shaft-sinking carries inherent hazards. In shaft drilling no man is exposed to these hazards, nor yet to the hostile environment that is so typical of shaft work. Perhaps this should be rated as the major factor in this comparison!

Handling of large mining machines through shafts
There is no doubt that had these shafts been sunk conventionally, a diameter greater than 2 m would have been selected. Nevertheless, it was discovered that most of the mining machines that were suitable for use at South Killingholme could be dismantled into components that were small enough to pass through the hoisting compartment of one of the shafts. The space available within the shaft was represented by a rectangle of cross-section 1 m × 1.5 m.

Ventilation
The small-diameter drilled shafts represent a very high resistance element within the mine ventilation circuit. The further obstruction of the rock skip in one shaft and the man cage in the other serve to exacerbate this condition.

Drilling of shafts
The shafts have an internal diameter of 2 m and were drilled by the Thyssen–Pigott Consortium with the Titan drilling rig (Figs. 12 and 15). Although the caverns were to be mined consecutively, a decision was taken to award a single contract for the construction of all four shafts to serve both caverns: this represented a significant saving on the costs of mobilization.

At South Killingholme the cavern site is located close to the bank of the River Humber. The chalk rock head is at a depth of about 25 m and it is overlain by boulder clay and soft estuarine silt. The water-table is within a few metres of the surface. A piled reinforced concrete slab was provided as the foundation for the Titan rig. Before the foundation slab was constructed an oversize surface casing was installed to rock head to support the overburden. The hole for this casing was drilled by a crane-mounted auger.

The Titan drilling rig used the principle of reverse circulation. Drilling mud charged with cuttings was pumped up the 300-mm diameter flanged drill string to the mud plant and clean mud returned to the open hole. Initially, bentonite was used, but it was replaced later by polymer muds. Drilling commenced with the use of a flat plate bit fitted with Hughes toothed roller cutters. These were replaced by disc cutters, which produced good penetration and were less vulnerable to damage by the flints (Fig. 14). Penetration rates of the order of 10 m/day were achieved consistently. The mud was cleaned at surface by an array of shaker screens, hydrocyclones and, latterly, a centrifuge. Mud circulation rates of up to 12 m³/min were required by this method.

Design and installation of shaft lining
The shaft lining consists of a steel casing 20 mm thick at surface and increasing by 5-mm steps to 40-mm thickness at the shaft bottom (Fig. 12). The lining was designed to withstand full hydrostatic pressure, but not geostatic forces. At the horizons of the shaft sealing plug and of the main inset, sections of bolted steel tubbing were incorporated (Fig. 13). The annulus had an average thickness of about 200 mm, but no effort was made to centralize the lining in the drilled hole.

The lining was fabricated into cylinders 12 m in length and pre-furnished as described elsewhere. On completion of the drilled hole the first cylinder, which incorporated the shaft bottom end plate, was lowered by the Titan rig into the drilled hole, which was kept full of drilling mud. Successive 12-m lining sections were welded at surface on to those already in the shaft. A combination of the self-weight of the lining and water that was added caused the lining to sink under controlled buoyancy. The drilling mud was displaced progressively at surface as the lining was 'floated' into the drilled hole. Since the clearance between the casing and the shaft wall was very small the accuracy and straightness of the drilled hole to receive the lining was of paramount importance.

The drilled hole was surveyed at one-third, two-thirds and full depth by oilfield methods. Of the four shafts at South Killingholme, the worst deviation was 400 mm between the top and bottom shaft circles.

The remaining drilling mud in the annulus was displaced by cement grout. Six grout injection pipes were led down the annulus to the bottom. The injection of cement was divided into three or four distinct 'lifts' to limit uplift and stresses on the lining. Each lift was allowed an initial 'set' before the next cement was pumped. The grout injection pipes were withdrawn in stages and recovered at surface.

The first of these shafts suffered a setback. A breach of the tubbing occurred at the horizon of the shaft plug and water flowed down the annulus from the aquifers above to flood the shaft. There is evidence that the annulus was not completely filled with cement and that a water path or paths filled with soft material existed. The shaft was recovered by cement grout injections through the steel casing from within the shaft. This secondary grouting was carried out below each of the major aquifers above cavern level.

To ensure that no possibility of flooding of the cavern remained the annulus grout was removed and a key was cut into sound chalk at the top ring of the plug tubbing. The excavation so formed was then filled with a grouted aggregate concrete to ensure that the annulus was sealed completely. It was then felt that an absolute barrier had been constructed around the shaft annulus to cut off any water paths linked to aquifers above. As a precautionary measure this procedure of secondary grouting and concrete seal ring was repeated in the other three shafts.

Shaft furnishings
An interesting feature of the drilled shafts at South Killingholme was the concept of pre-furnishing the steel lining cylinders in the fabrication shop (Fig. 4). Thus, for the rock-hoisting shaft the supporting buntons, skip guides and service pipes were built into each 12-m lining section. When handed over by the shaft driller the only work that was necessary to make that shaft ready for use was the fitting of fish plates to

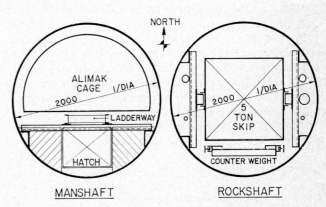

Fig. 4 Cross-section of both shafts showing furnishings

7

the skip guides and victaulic pipe joints to compressed-air, water and pumping columns. For the man-hoisting shaft the Alimak rack and its supporting steelwork were installed in the fabrication shop and the shaft was instantly ready for use as soon as the cage was fitted and commissioned. Since shaft drilling and cavern mining were let as separate contracts, the client, Calor Gas, Ltd., agreed in advance to purchase the Alimak man-hoist so that the rack could be installed as part of the shaft drilling contract. To pre-furnish a shaft in the manner described requires great care and forethought in design, fabrication, checking and installation.

Hoisting equipment

The concept of constructing large caverns from very small shafts has become known as 'keyhole mining'. In North America such storage caverns have been developed from a single small-diameter shaft and a borehole. Geostore considered that the drilling of two shafts per cavern, each fitted out with an independent means of hoisting men, was necessary. Accordingly, the specification required the cavern mining contractor to design and install a rock skip to run on the shaft guides already installed in the rock shaft. The selected contractor, Fairclough Civil Engineering, Ltd., purchased a redundant hoist and headframe from a West Yorkshire colliery – a single-drum hoist of about 350 hp and adapted by Fairclough to operate a 5.5-t capacity skip and counterweight. At an hourly winding rate of 25 skips this small shaft was developed into a highly efficient hoisting system. A small man cage was mounted on top of the skip.

Meanwhile, the second shaft was fitted out with a double-deck Alimak rack and pinion man cage with capacity for 12 men. It is worth noting that the support structure for the rack is fabricated in the form of a ladder. Resting platforms were built in at intervals of 6 m. Although there was no intention to use this vertical ladder as a means of egress, other than in dire emergency, it does provide a means of reaching the cage should a breakdown develop in mid-shaft.

Drilling of operating boreholes

Each cavern is served by nine operating boreholes – three to accommodate submersible pumps to deliver liquid gas from cavern to surface, two to accommodate submersible water pumps to dispose of the very small inflow in the cavern, two holes to accommodate instrumentation and control functions (liquid and vapour interfaces are monitored and controlled), a single-vent borehole to discharge gas vapour if excessive pressure were to develop in the cavern and, finally, one borehole to serve as a filling line for LPG from ships or refinery into the cavern. These boreholes vary in diameter from 6 to 20 in. All the borehole casings were examined for metal defects in the stockyard, and all site welds were tested by ultrasonic methods.

The cased boreholes were 'logged' for deviation and cement bond. This latter test gives confidence that neither groundwater will flow into the cavern down the borehole annulus nor gas escape via the same path.

The boreholes are arranged in two groups of four. Each group penetrates the cavern through the roof of a 10-m deep sub-shaft that serves as a sump. For operational reasons the filling line borehole enters the cavern in a smaller separate chamber. All 18 boreholes were drilled under a single contract by the Boldon Division of Foraky, Ltd. The contractor used a National rig and conventional oilfield methods. Water rather than mud was used as drilling fluid.

Cavern excavation

Breakout and pit bottom development

The first operation was to connect the two shafts by a small

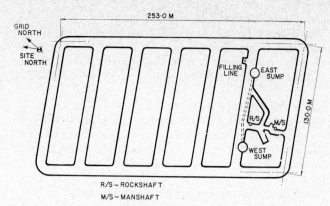

Fig. 5   Plan of Riverside cavern

R/S ~ ROCKSHAFT
M/S ~ MANSHAFT

heading to allow two means of egress. A heading 1.5 m × 2 m was started by hand excavation and completed by carefully controlled blasting, an erection chamber just south of the rock shaft then being excavated by blasting. The first Titan roadheader was then lowered and built in less than six days, being used to enlarge the heading to the man shaft, to excavate the first half of the geotechnical bay and to start the access heading to the top bench of gallery B. The second roadheader was then built in the erection chamber. The roadheaders completed pit bottom excavation between galleries B and A, the geotechnical bay and the access heading to gallery B (Fig. 5).

Muck hoisting was carried out, initially, by a two-deck working cage with tubs and then by the rockskip, which operated at reduced speed without the counterweight. After installation of the skip loading flask and the counterweight the rockskip was fully commissioned.

Roadheader excavation

The original plan was to carry out all excavation with two roadheaders, the top heading being completed before excavation of the bottom bench, with all haulage of spoil underground by conveyor. During pit bottom development and the initial drivage of gallery B top heading it became obvious that the roadheaders were excavating at a fraction of the planned rate. Despite changes to the picks, cutting heads and chassis, no significant improvement in the roadheader excavation rate was achieved. It was decided to introduce drill and blast techniques for the bulk of the excavation of the galleries. The two roadheaders were then used to excavate the full top heading in

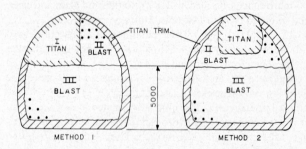

Fig. 6   Cross-section of storage gallery showing sequence of mining

galleries B, E and F, a half top heading (left or right) in galleries 1, 4 and A and a central crown heading in galleries C, D and G. Roadheader progress was markedly better in the drivage of the symmetrical crown heading than in that of the asymmetrical half top heading (Fig. 6). The roadheaders were also used to trim the remainder of the top heading after it had been excavated by blasting and to trim the bottom bench excavation after blasting. The combination of roadheader and drill and blast excavation allowed the faster rate of progress achievable

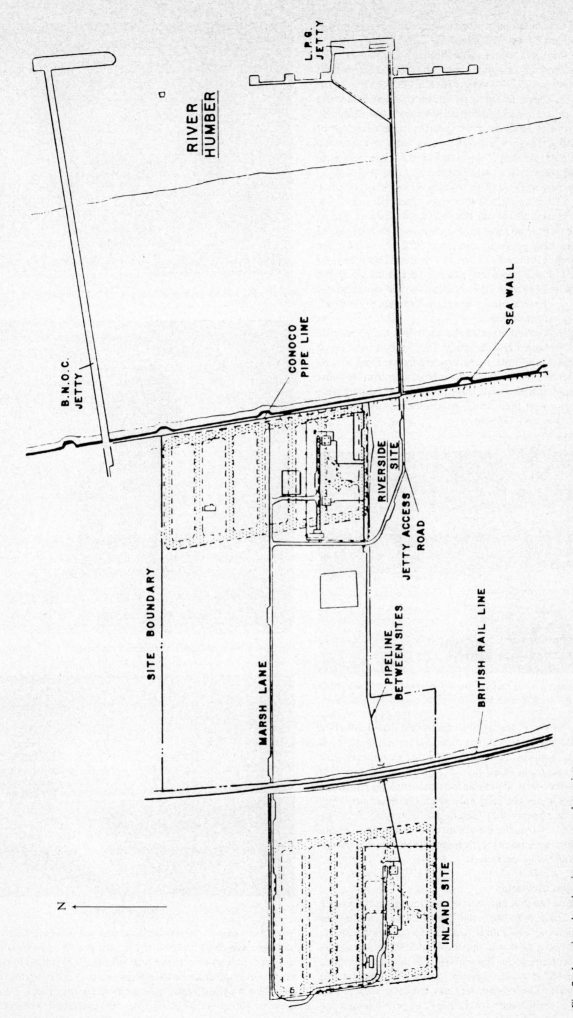

Fig. 7 Location plan showing caverns and new jetty

9

by blasting to be combined with the very good gallery profile that was achieved by the roadheader.

Peak performance from the roadheader was about 49 m of advance per week in the crown heading of 18-m² cross-section. The roadheaders were the Thyssen Titan E 205, a version of the 46-t E 169 fitted with raised turret and extended boom to give a 5-m vertical cutting height. These machines were originally supplied with flat-faced drum-type cutting heads designed for potash mining. These heads proved unsuitable and were replaced by a more pointed conical head. Parrot-nose picks were tried before point attack picks became standard (Fig. 10).

The poor performance of the roadheaders is believed to be due to two factors. First, the density of flints, particularly in the bottom bench, was higher than had been expected. Flints, particularly large flints, shattered the tungsten carbide tips of the picks, making the cutting action inefficient. Because the diameter of the Titan cutting head was greater than the spacing of flint beds, it was impossible to cut a horizontal slot in the chalk above and below the flint beds that would have allowed the flints to be broken out by leverage of the boom. Instead, all the flints had to be cut.

The second problem was that the chalk had a high specific energy and contained few discontinuities, such as bedding or jointing, that would have aided roadheader excavation. The spoil produced ranged from small 'cobble' size down to dust. It was obvious at a very early stage that the roadheaders were operating at or near their limits. As a result downtime on the roadheaders was considerable.

Fig. 9 Rock shaft bottom showing muck bin and backacter

Fig. 10 Titan roadheader working on top bench

Fig. 8 Cavern surface layout during construction: rock shaft headframe and surface conveyor

With the benefit of hindsight it can be said that the Welton Chalk at cavern level was not 'roadheader country'. It is possible that the heavy-duty roadheaders that are now available or under development would cut the chalk efficiently, provided that it was flint-free. It was unfortunate that the Northern Province Chalk has not been worked previously at any depth in Europe. It appears that present-day laboratory tests are inadequate to predict the cuttability of a stratum the *in-situ* geotechnical properties of which are not known from previous mining or tunnelling operations.

Drill and blast excavation
The changeover to drill and blast excavation raised three main problems. First, even with the most accurate drilling of perimeter holes, it was unlikely that the specification requirement of nil underbreak and maximum of 200-mm overbreak could be met consistently. The problem was solved by using the roadheaders to trim the blasted profile, which had the incidental advantage of removing any loosened rock left by blasting. The roadheader proved to be a superb scaling tool.

Fig. 11 Tamrock drill rig working in lower bench

Second, it had to be established that the blasting had not damaged the chalk beyond the cavern profile, which would have caused long-term stability problems. Comparison of rock properties in cores at the cavern perimeter and 1 m beyond the perimeter confirmed that no blast damage was caused. Third, the vibration caused by blasting near the shafts had to be strictly controlled to prevent damage to the seal rings at plug level in the shafts. To this end, vibrographs were installed in both shafts at seal ring level and maximum values of peak particle velocity were specified. It proved possible to carry out blasting in both galleries *A* and *B* very close to the two shafts by using shorter rounds and reducing the cross-sectional area of the working face.

Drilling for blasting was carried out by a single Tamrock three-boom hydraulic drill jumbo with charging basket (Fig. 11). The Tamrock used was in operation about two weeks after its arrival from Finland. This jumbo drilled 45-mm diameter holes to a depth of 4.5 m in about 90 s, giving a pull of more than 4 m. Controlled blasting was used throughout with perimeter holes at 600-mm centres. Perimeter holes were charged with spaced sticks of 80% tunnel gelignite fitted to plastic tubing.

Mucking and plant

The contractor changed from conveyor to dumper haulage before the switch to excavation by blasting. Up to nine 3.5-t capacity Benford dumpers were used. These were readily available and of such a size that they could be lowered down the rock shaft easily. Two Cat 911 wheeled loaders with 1-m³ buckets were used to load the dumpers. All diesel plant was fitted with catalytic exhaust cleaners or wet 'scrubbers'.

The roadheaders loaded dumpers via a bridge conveyor. The multiple faces available for blasting allowed efficient usage of the jumbo, loaders and dumpers with little waiting time. Dumpers discharged muck from top heading level in gallery *B* into a muck bin excavated at bottom bench level. A static backacter arm fitted to the side wall loaded muck from the muck bin into the flask (Fig. 9).

Fig. 12   Pigott Titan rig showing downhole assembly and shaft lining

Fig. 14   Titan rig cutting head showing disc cutters

Fig. 13   Pigott Titan rig during installation of shaft casing (tubbing section)

Fig. 15   Boldon drilling rig at work on service boreholes and Titan rig drilling shaft

Production holes were charged with ICI NE 1669 slurry explosive capsules. Magnadet millisecond detonators were used throughout. No 'cut' was required because part of the top heading had already been excavated by roadheader to form a free face. The half top heading round comprised some 12 perimeter and 21 production holes with a total charge of 135 kg and a powder factor of 1.7 kg/m³. The bench round comprised 30 perimeter and 45 production holes with a total charge of 254 kg, and a powder factor of 1.3 kg/m³. The powder factor was high because the chalk did not fragment easily. Good fragmentation was essential because an underground crusher had not been installed and large lumps of chalk would have blocked the flask or skip.

Hoisting system and surface muck disposal

The skip was loaded at pit bottom by a flask that discharged into the top of the skip via a vertical guillotine door. In turn, the skip discharged at surface into a hopper loading a chain conveyor, which loaded a belt conveyor some 100 m long (Fig. 8). Muck was spread from the end of the belt conveyor by bulldozer and scraper on to a tipping area adjacent to the cavern site.

Probe drilling

The cavern lies below three major water-bearing zones in the chalk and above the basal Carstone aquifer. It was possible that fissures existed in the chalk that connected the cavern with one of these zones. Two probe holes ahead of the faces were drilled to prove any such fissures. A minimum cover of one heading width had to be maintained at all times. Probe holes were drilled through mechanical packer standpipes. Longhole drilling by Diamec drills proved unsuccessful because of damage to the rotary drill string by flints in the chalk. Rotary percussive drilling by airleg drills was then used up to a maximum length of some 25 m. In the Riverside cavern no significant water-bearing fissures were found (any such fissures would have been cement grouted before the face was advanced).

Operational experience of small shaft mining

The jumbo, which was designed for portal access to a tunnel, required a considerable amount of burning and welding to reduce the components to a size that was sufficiently small to go down the shaft. The maximum size of tyred wheel that will pass down the shaft is a major restraint on the size of wheeled plant – not only for initial access but also for replacement or repair of tyres.

The quantity of air that can be passed up or down a 2-m diameter shaft that is partially blocked by the buntons and rockskip, or Alimak cage, is limited. At South Killingholme some 25 m^3/s of air was forced by a pair of 100-kW fans down the man shaft and two of the 20-in diameter boreholes. The rock shaft and the remainder of the operating boreholes were upcast. This quantity was more than adequate for machine excavation with conveyor haulage, but some problems with 'layering' of diesel and blasting fumes were experienced.

Rock support

From the site investigation it was not expected that systematic rock support would be required in the cavern. Limited rock support in the form of resin dowels 1.5 and 3 m long was provided in the junction noses at gallery intersections. Resin dowels, mesh and shotcrete were installed in the sumps and sump heading up to 1 m above the Plenus Marl because of the blocky, marly nature of the chalk at this level. A feature of the South Killingholme cavern is that it has been possible to excavate 1.3 km of 10-m horseshoe galleries without significant rock support.

At the time of writing mining of the first (propane) cavern is complete and preparations for commissioning are in hand. The excavation of the second (butane) cavern will commence shortly. It is hoped that the success of the first cavern at South Killingholme will focus attention on the potential of this type of storage and will herald the construction of further projects in this country.

Twenty years' experience of constructing oil cavern storage at Porvoo works, Finland

S. Johansson
Neste Oy, Espoo, Finland

Synopsis

At the Porvoo works of Neste Oy, Finland's national oil company, underground oil storage caverns of a total capacity of 5 200 000 m³ are in operation. The first caverns were constructed in 1965–67 and the most recent in 1980–82. The total volume of crude oil storage is about 3 300 000 m³ and that of petroleum products, ranging from butane to heavy fuel oil, is some 1 900 000 m³.

The 35 individual caverns are divided into 22 separate plants. The caverns were constructed under ten separate contract phases by private contracting companies under the supervision of Neste Oy.

The strength and intact nature of the Precambrian migmatite rock (a mixture of granite and gneiss) have meant that construction methods based on drilling and blasting have been the most economical. Cavern cross-sections range from 341 to 580 m² and the shapes of the profiles differ widely. The size of the access tunnels has ranged from 17 to 50 m², depending on the need for transportation of blasted rock.

The reinforcement methods that have been used most commonly are bolting and shotcrete lining. A new bolt type to carry heavy loads has also been developed. The need for grouting has been limited.

Two main types of contract have been used – one on the turnkey principle and the other a so-called divided contract. In both cases all design work, construction supervision, purchase of operating equipment, etc., has been carried out by Neste.

In the company's experience a rock cavern of 150 000 m³ or more has been cheaper to build than steel tanks under all market conditions. For LPG the corresponding cavern volume is considerably smaller. Operation and maintenance costs have also been very low in comparison with those for surface steel tanks. Although some operational problems have occurred, including even a fire in one crude oil cavern, it can be stated that all installations are working completely satisfactorily. No serious drawdown of groundwater has occurred and there are no signs of any environmental pollution.

Finland must import all her fossil fuels. Energy imports are particularly high because the climate is cold and many Finnish industries are energy-intensive. Consumption of oil products amounted to 10 400 000 t in 1983 – equivalent to 36% of the country's primary energy consumption.

Neste Oy was established in 1948 to ensure Finland's supplies of oil products. The company has no oil production of its own, and all crude is purchased under long-term contracts. In 1983 the main sources of crude supply were the U.S.S.R., Saudi Arabia, Iran, Great Britain and Norway.

The generally severe winter conditions freeze sea lanes and hinder the shipment of crude with VLCC-type tankers. These tankers can navigate the Baltic Sea for about eight months of the year. Climate is therefore one reason why the company must store relatively large amounts of crude oil (3 000 000–4 000 000 t) for winter use: it is stored in unlined rock caverns excavated into bedrock in the refinery areas.

The crude oil cavern at the Naantali refinery has a capacity of about 250 000 m³; all other caverns are located at the Porvoo refinery. The crude oil storage caverns at Porvoo have a combined capacity of about 3 300 000 m³, divided between 14 separate plants. In addition, the Porvoo refinery has eight caverns for the storage of oil products with a combined capacity of some 1 900 000 m³. Details of the individual cavern plants are presented in Table 1.

The caverns are in intensive use and form an essential part of the operational space for the 200 000 bbl per day refinery. The refinery also operates a surface steel tank farm with more than 100 tanks with a combined capacity of 1 600 000 m³.

Table 1 Construction phases, effective oil storage volume of individual caverns, and product stored

Construction phase	Total volume, m³	Cavern code	Effective volume, m³	Product stored
I	209 000	U-1	65 000	Crude oil
		U-2	74 000	Crude oil
		U-3	70 000	Crude oil
II	375 000	U-4	145 000	Crude oil
		U-5–U-6	230 000	Crude oil
III	675 000	U-7	150 000	Crude oil
		U-8	170 000	Crude oil
		U-9	173 000	Crude oil
		U-10	182 000	Crude oil
IV	506 000	U-11	306 000	Light fuel oil
		U-12	200 000	Heavy fuel oil
V	495 000	U-13	495 000	Crude oil
VI	550 000	U-14	550 000	Crude oil
VII	1 042 000	U-15	580 000	Crude oil
		U-16	462 000	Crude oil
VIII	422 000	U-17	211 000	Light fuel oil
		U-18	211 000	Heavy fuel oil
IX	116 000	U-19	116 000	Butane
X	845 000	U-20	215 000	Heavy fuel oil
		U-21	315 000	Light fuel oil
		U-22	315 000	Light fuel oil

The company has itself designed all cavern facilities and supervised their construction, acting as the main contractor.

Porvoo works

The Porvoo works are located in the rural district of Porvoo, about 50 km east of Helsinki on the southern coast of the Baltic Sea (Fig. 1). The foundations for the first refinery were laid in 1963, and the refinery went on stream in 1965. In 1975 an

Fig. 1   Location of Neste Oy Porvoo works

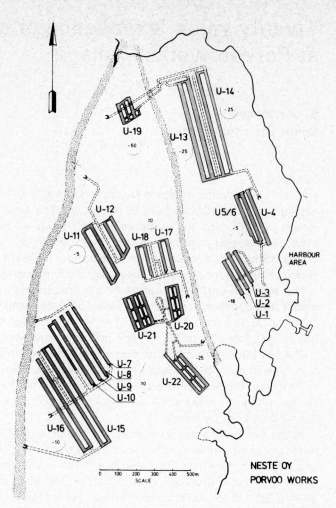

Fig. 2   Principal layout of caverns in rock body between major discontinuities

additional unit was brought into use and current combined annual refining capacity is 12 000 000 t.

Geology
The coastal area is characterized by a rather broken coastline, narrow bays cutting inland from the open sea. The variations in the topography are primarily dependent on variations in the bedrock topography and, hence, bedrock outcrops dominate surface features. The absolute elevation of the natural ground surface varies between ±0 m (Baltic Sea level) and more than +40 m.

The Precambrian rock crust of the area is a typical and central part of the Baltic or Fennoscandian Shield, which is the broadest shield area on the European Continent. The bedrock of the Porvoo works area belongs to a later part of the so-called Sveco-Karelidic orogeny, the folding of which took place about 1800 m.y. ago. A characteristic feature is an abundance of mixed rocks, with two or more components of different character. Mica schists and gneisses are common rock types: because of migmatization they are commonly micro-folded. Microcline granite is another very common rock type. The granite is generally coarse-grained, even resembling pegmatite. Dykes and thin layers of amphibolitic composition, together with meta-diabase dykes, are also present.

The general strike of the gneissic rocks on the Porvoo site is 50–70° (ENE–WSW) and the dips are mostly very steep (75–85°) or vertical.

The body of rock utilized for cavern construction is located between three major tectonic disturbance zones: the first is located under the open sea to the east, the second divides the body into two halves and the third, popularly known as 'Grand Canyon', occurs to the west (Fig. 2). A number of second- and

third-order shear zones and strongly fractured zones also occur in this rock body.

The joint system of the gneissic granite rock consists of three well-defined joint sets, one set corresponding to the strike and dip of the gneiss. The second has an orientation almost perpendicular to the first. Horizontal and/or gently inclined joints form the third distinct set of joints, and this type of jointing has a tendency to decrease with depth.

One characteristic of the rock mass is the frequent occurrence of slickensides (strongly chloritized, polished and striated joint surfaces). These tectonic movement surfaces have caused considerable overbreaks in the excavation profiles, and have also necessitated additional reinforcements. A summary of the mechanical characteristics of rocks is presented in Table 2. The mechanical strength values of the intact rock specimens can be considered good to excellent for the construction of caverns with large profiles.

Table 2   Mechanical properties of rock core samples

Density	
Gneiss	27.1–28.9 kN/m³
Granite and pegmatite	25.9–26.8 kN/m³
Uniaxial compressive strength	
Gneiss	120–280 MPa
Granite and pegmatite	40–140 MPa
Indirect tensile strength	
Gneiss	9–20 MPa
Granite and pegmatite	4–12 MPa
Porosity	0.05–0.5%
Young's modulus	19–103 GPa
Sound velocity	>5100 m/s

In-situ state of stress measurements indicate that a relatively 'weak' compressive stress field exists in the area. The measured values have been in the range 5–15 MPa.

The groundwater level follows in a regular manner the variations in the topography. Variations in the groundwater level surrounding the caverns are checked at regular intervals, through some 40 observation wells, most of which have been in operation since 1971.

Details of the geology of the Porvoo site have been given, for example, by Simonen,[21] Ignatius and co-workers[8] and Johansson.[11]

Site investigations

The general procedures for geological surveys for oil storage caverns in Finland have been discussed by several authors.[9, 12, 13] The main engineering geological site investigation methods have concerned the location of major discontinuity zones based on interpretation of aerial photographs and field control, bedrock outcrop mapping and diamond core drillings. Percussion drilling with penetration–time measurements and the sampling of drill cuttings have compensated for the lack of seismic refraction soundings.

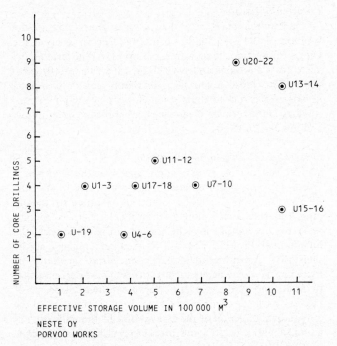

Fig. 3 Core drilling in relation to effective volume of caverns

A total of 41 core drilling holes, with a total length of 3157 linear metres, has been made in the different site investigation phases. The number of drill-holes in relation to storage volume is presented in Fig. 3. In certain cases drill-hole data from a previous site investigation phase have also served a later construction phase. The abundance of outcrops and previous knowledge of rock mass conditions have, of course, also influenced the need for drilling.

All drilling work has been carried out by outside geotechnical consulting and drilling companies. The costs of site investigation work have in all cases been less than 1% of the total investment cost, the average figure being 0.25%, which agrees fairly well with published data.[4, 25]

Cavern history

According to Fagerholm,[2] the first unlined oil storage in rock in Finland was completed in early 1964. About 18 months later construction of the three first crude oil storage caverns at the Porvoo works was begun and in October, 1966, the construction of seven additional crude oil units was started. During 1971–72 three additional caverns were completed. Crude oil cavern U-14 was completed by September, 1975.

Work on the largest cavern project to be executed under one single contract was started in early 1974 and caverns U-15 and U-16 (in excess of 1 000 000 m³ of total effective volume) were ready for oil fill in late 1975. Product caverns U-17 and U-18 were completed on New Year's Eve, 1975. The sole, to date, cavern for LPG (butane) (capacity, >100 000 m³) was completed in May, 1976.

Between May, 1976, and February, 1980, no cavern construction took place. In March, 1980, construction of the tenth separate cavern phase was initiated, cavern U-20 being ready for oil fill in October, 1981, U-21 in late December of the same year and U-22 in September, 1982. Caverns U-20 and U-21 were in full operation while work was being completed on U-22.

The actual effective volumes of individual caverns and total effective volumes excavated in the same construction phase are presented in Table 1. Further details on cavern history were given by Kilpinen[14] and Johansson.[10]

Storage principles

The well-known Scandinavian method of storing oil in unlined rock caverns below the natural groundwater level is based on four main factors: (1) it must be insoluble in water; (2) it must be lighter than water; (3) the bedrock should be suited to the construction of caverns with large profiles, sufficiently homogeneous and near the surface; and (4) the caverns must be excavated well below the groundwater-table.

The exploitation of the difference in specific gravity between the oil stored and water and the excavation of the caverns below the groundwater-table together ensure that the hydrostatic pressure of the groundwater that surrounds the rock cavern is greater than that of the stored oil and so the latter cannot penetrate the rock. Depending on the action of the layer of water – the so-called 'water bed' – at the bottom of the storage, the following main types of facilities can be distinguished: storage with a fixed water bed, storage with a fluctuating water bed and storage with a dry bottom.

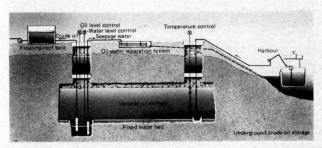

Fig. 4 Crude oil storage on fixed water bed

All the rock caverns that are owned by Neste operate on the fixed water bed principle (Fig. 4). Crude oil is stored both in unpressurized and pressurized caverns. None of the pressurized caverns has any water curtain system above the caverns, but an overpressure of up to 2.5 bar is permitted.

The liquefied butane cavern operates according to the pressurized cavern principle. Its vault level is located 60 m below the Baltic Sea level. Different types of distillates are stored in unpressurized caverns.

All crude oil caverns are operated by submersible pumps, suspended from pipes located in the shafts that lead from the cavern to the surface. Distillate caverns U-11 and U-12 and butane cavern U-19 are also operated in a similar way. Discharge pumping rates vary from 150 to 2000 m³/h. Filling rates of the crude oil caverns are related to the pump capacity of the tanker, i.e. up to 12 000 m³/h, and those for the product caverns are geared to pumping rates from the process day tanks.

Caverns U-17 and U-18 and U-20, U-21 and U-22 are operated via a dry pump room located at the bottom level of the caverns and separated from them (Fig. 5). Discharge rates vary between 1000 and 6000 m³/h, the pumps being conventional transfer pumps.

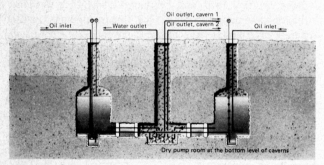

Fig. 5   Oil storage operation via dry pump room

Leakage water pumps all have a capacity of 15 m³/h, which has proved to be more than satisfactory. Moreover, the standard design includes several parallel pumps. All leakage waters are treated in the refinery waste water treatment plant before discharge into the open sea.

The caverns have complete instrumentation for the control of pressure, surface levels and temperatures and for checking of the operation of the equipment. Caverns are normally

Fig. 6   Remote control centre for operation of 22 caverns and more than 100 steel tanks

provided with double or even triple instrumentation. All caverns are remote controlled and operated from the control centre (Fig. 6), which is located in the vicinity of the process units, i.e. several hundred metres from the actual cavern locations.

Design aspects

The basic aim of any underground excavation design should be to utilize the rock itself as the principal structural material, as little disturbance as possible being created during the excavation and as little as possible being added by way of concrete

and steel support. This observation of Hoek and Brown[5] is basic to oil storage design in Finland.

Rock mass data requirements
Evaluation of the geological and hydrogeological conditions in a potential cavern construction area is required at an early stage in the design process. Studies of rock mass characteristics are usually carried out on the basis of information from outcrop mapping, logging of cores from exploratory drilling and water pressure tests.

It is normal in the planning and design of caverns to have the following stages. (1) A location is selected that from a stability point of view shows the optimal engineering geological conditions in the area. Major discontinuity and crushed zones should be avoided. (2) The longitudinal direction of the caverns and the length of each are orientated to give minimal overbreak and need for reinforcement. (3) The openings, including both caverns and tunnels, are shaped to take into account the mechanical properties of the rock, the jointing of the rock mass and the *in-situ* stress conditions. According to Kähönen,[16] stress conditions can vary over short distances. (4) The depth of the caverns is determined on the basis of the level of the groundwater and hydraulic conductivity tests in boreholes.

Location of cavern
Of maximum importance in the site investigation phase is the location of the right place, position and depth level, as the choice of location, if such freedom exists, will determine the geological conditions under which the caverns are to be excavated. The most favourable conditions generally include homogeneous rock material, with few or no major discontinuities in the form of shear zones, insignificant water inflow and low *in-situ* stress.

Orientation of longitudinal direction
The detailed joint pattern is of importance when the longitudinal direction of the cavern is determined. In the evaluation of the joint sets not only should the number of sets, their strikes and dips be considered but, more particularly, the character of joint surfaces. If a storage is to be located in a gneissic rock, the longitudinal direction is always planned perpendicular to the schistosity. According to Maijala,[18] the strike facilitates the loosening of rock when the schistosity is almost perpendicular to the advance of the excavation because the tensile strength of the rock in the direction of the throw is at its minimum. If the longitudinal direction of the excavation cuts the schistosity at a small angle (< 20–30°), overbreaks may occur readily and the stability is less good.

If only *one* dominant fracture set occurs, the longitudinal direction is normally also chosen perpendicular to this. For *two* dominant joint directions the situation is more complicated.

Shaping and dimensioning
In the design of rock caverns it is important to remember that the rock mass is a discontinuous material, and the ability to withstand tensile stresses is low. A basic design concept is to aim at evenly distributed compressive stresses along the whole periphery of the cavern: this is best obtained by giving the caverns a simple form with an arched roof.[20]

The thickness of the columns that separate adjacent caverns is dependent on rock mass quality and prevailing stress. Under normal rock mass conditions and with properly orientated caverns the thickness should be equal to or greater than the height of the cavern. In Neste's case column widths have varied from 25 to 50 m (Fig. 7).

Stability problems underground become more apparent with increasing excavation span: as a result of the influence of the broken zone after blasting, it is pronounced when spans exceed

20 m. In general, excavation spans at Neste's site have varied between 12 and 16 m. It has been found to be preferable to meet the need for increased volumes by extending the cavern length. The largest spans so far in Finland have a width of 32 m, these caverns being civil defence shelters, which are normally used as ice-hockey halls.[6, 24]

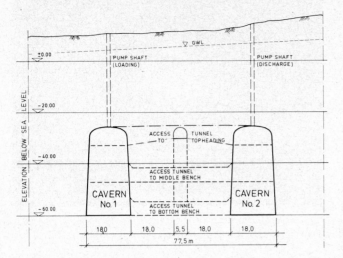

Fig. 7 Example of width of column between adjacent caverns and location of adits to different excavation levels

The height of Neste's caverns has generally been 30 m. Vertical bench height is limited in the design to 15 m – otherwise, deviations in drilling accuracy become too large (>2%).

Dimensioning based on detailed static calculations is usually not carried out because of the problems of inserting realistic parameters when the material is as complicated as a large rock mass of several million cubic metres. Dimensioning is thus to a great extent based on experience. Dimensioning of required reinforcements is generally carried out in connexion with actual excavation operations, following guidelines discussed, among others, by Bergman and Bjurström[22, 27] and also as recommended in Finnish rock construction handbooks.[28, 29]

Technical considerations

The underground storage of crude oil lays special demands on the design of caverns for three main reasons – the presence of sludge on the bottom of the caverns, crude oil contains volatile gases and the risk of emulsions.

The storage of other products may be hampered by one but not all of these problems – for example, some heavy fuel oils have a tendency to form emulsions.

Although the risk of fire is much smaller in an underground storage, the potential ignition sources (spontaneous combustion, static electricity, lightning and sparks from falling blocks) require a proper design.

One of the main tasks is therefore to design a layout and cavern profile that suit the characteristics of the rock mass as well as the excavation methods and operational requirements.

Excavation methods

The strength and intact nature of the migmatite rock at the Porvoo site has meant that excavation procedures based on drilling and blasting have proved to be the most economical. In addition, the need to excavate a large underground space at minimal cost and in a short time makes this method advantageous.

Cavern design has also favoured the use of heavy mobile tunnelling and open-pit drilling equipment and the use of large-capacity loading and transportation machinery, which reduces construction time considerably.

Objectives

There are several clearly distinguishable excavation objectives in a storage project, the most important of which are the open-cut, the access and branch tunnels, equipment and piping tunnels, vertical shafts to the surface and the caverns themselves. Different working techniques are required for the different objectives.

Open-cut

Open-cut excavation is carried out by use of conventional open-pit drilling equipment, going into the rock until the point at which tunnelling can start. Tunnelling is normally begun when solid rock above the crown is equal to the width of the tunnel (without reinforcements). All walls are blasted by smooth blasting methods to avoid overbreak and to minimize costs for reinforcements (Fig. 8).

Fig. 8 Open-cut and two-way traffic access tunnel ($A = 50$ m²) to storage caverns U-20, U-21 and U-22. Height of tunnel portal ~7 m (Note small water leakage from inclined joint and in left wall)

Access and branch tunnels

The main access tunnel for the transportation of equipment, materials and personnel, as well as for that of broken rock from the actual cavern space, normally has an inclination of 1:7. Depending on the size of the project and the pressure of the timetable, the main access tunnel is excavated either for one- or two-way traffic. At the Porvoo site access and branch tunnels for one-way traffic have ranged in size from 17 to 30.5 m². The corresponding sizes for two-way traffic have been 36 and 50 m².

Increased tunnel size has depended mainly on developments in equipment and the relative cheapness of an increase in size (Fig. 9). In some instances the company has also permitted the contractor to modify the tunnel shape to provide better space for ventilation ducts, pipes, cables, etc. Concrete paved access tunnels have also been introduced to increase driving speeds and to save tyre wear. High driving speeds are also achieved by making the tunnels straight and by minimizing the number of bends. Passing points in one-way tunnels are generally constructed at locations where branch tunnels lead towards actual cavern space.

17

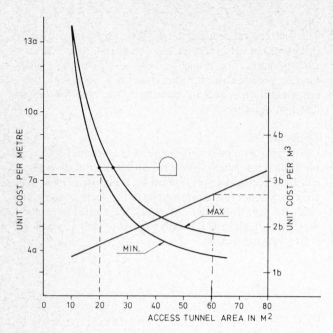

Fig. 9   Unit cost of access tunnel in relation to size

Fig. 11   Installation of pressure plug in pipe tunnel

Equipment and piping tunnels

In caverns that are operated through a dry pump room (Fig. 10), in particular, equipment and piping tunnels are required. Pressure plugs (Fig. 11), generally designed to withstand an internal pressure of 10 bar and an external pressure of 20 bar,

Fig. 10   Underground dry pump located at bottom level of caverns and between them (roof systematically bolted and shotcreted)

are normally located in these tunnels. The exact location of the rock groove for the plugs is determined after the completion of excavation works in accordance with actual rock conditions. Naturally, the tightness requirements of such plugs are extremely high, which means that the most homogeneous and impermeable rock conditions are sought. In fact, grouting of rock surrounding plugs both in tunnels and in shafts has been quite reasonable, a cement consumption of 1–2 t per plug having generally been experienced.

Vertical shafts

Vertical shafts that lead to the surface have been constructed in three main ways – by longhole drilling with drill and blast, the up-hole method by drill and blast and by raise boring.
Experience has shown that shafts with a length of up to 40 m

and of a size larger than 3 m × 5 m can be excavated by the longhole drilling method, in which the entire shaft length is drilled from the surface. Blasting is carried out in short rounds.

The up-hole excavation method has been used in shafts that exceed 40 m in depth. In this case a 150-mm diameter hole is drilled from the surface through the arch of the cavern, a wire rope is sunk into the hole and a drill platform is attached to it from below. A pilot drift, generally 2 m × 3 m in size, is excavated up to the surface by use of short rounds. After completion of the pilot drift the final contour of the shaft is excavated by smooth blasting methods from the surface towards the cavern arch.

The raise-boring method (Fig. 12) has, to date, been used only in three instrument shafts with diameters of 1500 and 2400 mm and depths of 43–45 m. The advantages of the raise-boring method arise from the minimal overbreak, the significant reduction in reinforcement and the low consumption of concrete in plugs. No disturbance of the main excavation process occurs. The only disadvantage at present is that of high costs.

Fig. 12   Reaming up of 2400-mm diameter shaft started

Cavern excavation

The excavation methods that are used in the different construction phases have depended mainly on the type of oil storage (crude or product), time of construction, design in terms of size, shape and volume, availability of contractor's equipment and personnel, developments in drill performance and use of improved types of explosives.

The excavation of large cavern profiles can be divided into two phases – tunnelling of the top heading and benching of the lower parts of the cavern. The top headings at the Porvoo site have been drilled with hand-held drills with pusher-legs and mechanized rubber-tyred drilling jumbos (both pneumatic and hydraulic). The subsequent benches have, for the most part, been drilled either inclined outwards (10:1) or vertically with the use of various types of mechanized crawler rigs. This has been made possible by the low arch/span ratio (average 0.16), which leaves enough space for a crawler rig feed boom to be placed at the contour of the profile. In one case the arch/span ratio was about 0.36 and, subsequently, the first bench was drilled horizontally and lifted. The bottom bench, with a height of 15 m, could then be drilled vertically. This excavation method is common in Sweden.[1]

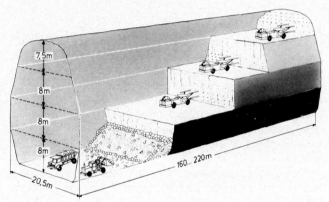

Fig. 13   Excavation principle of cavern U-20, U-21 and U-22 (all drilling with hydraulic drill jumbos and all benches horizontal)

In the last cavern project (U-20, U-21 and U-22) all benches were drilled horizontally by the same electric-hydraulic drill jumbos as were used in the top-heading excavation (Fig. 13; pilot tunnels in top headings and adits to different excavation levels are not shown).

Until the early 1970s top headings were blasted by V- and cylinder cuts, but, more recently, the pilot drift method with

consequent slashing has been employed (Fig. 14). Vertical benching corresponds closely to normal open-pit excavation, whereas horizontal benching may be considered a modified form of tunnelling.

The use of explosives to remove rock requires controlled blasting to minimize damage to the remaining rock wall. It is insufficient to have a low charge density in the contour holes only – at least the next row of holes from the contour holes towards the centre must also have a reduced charge density to prevent the occurrence of an extensive zone of damage.

The normal methods that are used in controlled blasting are smooth blasting and presplitting. The main visible result in both cases is the drill-hole 'halves'. The zone of damage can, in this case, be limited to 0.3–0.5 m.

Smooth blasting, in which the contour charges are initiated last in the round, has been applied in top headings (Fig. 14) and in horizontal benching. Presplitting, in which the contour charges are initiated before the rest of the charges in the round, has been applied in vertical benching (Fig. 15).

Various recommendations on blasting [3,17,23,26] have formed the basis for design considerations. In Neste's experience the additional cost for contour blasting has been fully justified.

A general view of completed cavern excavation is given in Fig. 16. Experience has shown that the method of vertical benching has been the more economical, horizontal benching having tended to create a greater need for reinforcement (Table 3). Average weekly achievements in drilling and blasting in the more recent projects are presented in Tables 4 and 5. The application of these rates in the preparation of the overall time schedule is realistic.

The equipment that is needed to load and remove broken rock is generally selected by the excavation contractor on the basis of required capacities and transport distances. The loading of broken rock has largely been by use of rubber-tyred front loaders (CAT 977 and CAT 988). The working capacity of one such loader is well in excess of 100 m^3 of rock per hour with a bucket of 4- to 5-m^3 capacity. The transportation of broken rock has generally been handled with off-highway dump trucks. A daily transportation capacity of 2000–4000 m^3 can normally be achieved in the benching stages.

In the main, dump trucks of the Kockums KL 420 and KL 440 series have been utilized, these having a payload of 20–30 t. A truck fleet of six to ten trucks has normally been required, which means that during the busiest period a loaded truck passes the access tunnel portal every 2–3 min.

Rock support and reinforcement

In Finland almost all rock support measures in underground civil engineering works have traditionally been based on careful blasting, rockbolting, shotcreting and, to a lesser extent, grouting. The philosophy that is applied to normal reinforcement is that the rock mass itself is a construction material and able to support itself. Careful blasting is therefore one important support measure, as no rock can be so good that it could not be shattered by careless drilling and blasting. An old axiom is that the excavation result cannot be better than the drilling.

Rockbolting

Rockbolting is one of the most common and widespread rock reinforcement methods in underground oil storage construction, being simple, efficient, reliable and economical. Most of Neste's experience with rockbolting is with the use of fully grouted untensioned bolts and, to a lesser extent, with mechanical point anchor type untensioned or tensioned grouted bolts. In cavern project U-20, U-21 and U-22 a special type of bolt

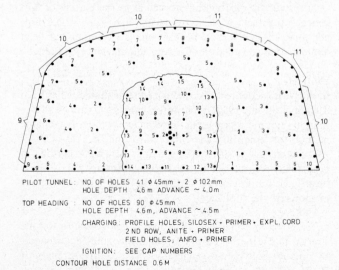

PILOT TUNNEL: NO. OF HOLES   41 ⌀45mm + 2 ⌀102mm
                HOLE DEPTH   4.6 m ADVANCE ~ 4.0m

TOP HEADING: NO. OF HOLES   90 ⌀45mm
                HOLE DEPTH   4.6m, ADVANCE ~ 4.5m

        CHARGING: PROFILE HOLES; SILOSEX + PRIMER + EXPL. CORD
                   2ND ROW, ANITE + PRIMER
                   FIELD HOLES; ANFO + PRIMER

        IGNITION: SEE CAP NUMBERS

    CONTOUR HOLE DISTANCE   0.6 M

Fig. 14   Example of drilling and charging pattern in excavation of top heading with pilot tunnel and slashing

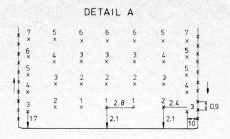

DETAIL A

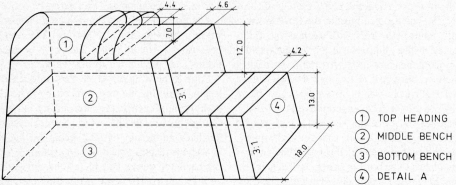

Fig. 15 Excavation principle of cavern U-15–U-16 and example of drilling and ignition pattern in presplitting of bottom bench excavation

① TOP HEADING
② MIDDLE BENCH
③ BOTTOM BENCH
④ DETAIL A

Fig. 16 General view of product cavern U-22 after completion of excavation works (height of cavern 31.5 m)

was developed by the company's engineering staff to carry loads up to 36 t (Fig. 17). This bolt type is covered by European and U.S. patents.

In the late 1960s the main type of bolt in use was the untensioned or tensioned point anchor rockbolt (it was extensively used in cavern projects U-11 and U-12). Tensioning was made with hand tools and capacities were limited. More recently, the fully grouted untensioned (slack) bolt, which is activated in the event of rock mass deformation has become increasingly popular. Where it has been necessary to prevent loosening of key blocks, or where a risk of immediate collapse has been evident, however, wedge bolts have been used.

Bolt lengths for permanent reinforcement depend on the size of the excavation. Bolt lengths in the arch part of the caverns have ranged, typically, from 2.4 to 4.0 m – that is, 0.15–0.30 times the width of the span. In walls the corresponding lengths have varied from 2.4 to 6.0 m (0.10–0.20 times the height of the cavern).

The steel type has been A 400 H ($f_y = 400$ N/mm^2) and the diameter of re-bars 20, 22 and 25 mm. There have been two schools of thought regarding bolt installations – to install the bolts close to the face after each round or to wait until the face has progressed 20–30 m, provided that no immediate need for bolting has occurred. Lately, the latter method has been chosen, as it is more easily fitted into the excavation process.

Systematic roofbolting has been carried out with a bolt density of 1 bolt/4 m^2, unless actual rock conditions have required a denser spacing or a combination of bolts and shotcrete lining. A summary of bolting performed in cavern projects U-11 to U-22 is presented in Table 3. The average number of bolts has been 1100 bolts/100 000 m^3 of cavern space.

In systematic roofbolting, as well as in the bolting of 8-m benches, the weekly rate has been 650–750 bolts ($L = 3200$ mm) per crew. In high vertical benches only spot-bolting has been done, special so-called sky-lift type equipment being used.

Shotcrete

In the Nordic countries sprayed concrete or shotcrete has been used since the late 1950s to reinforce tunnels and caverns. More than 30 years of experience has shown that shotcrete is a reliable method for temporary and final reinforcement.

Shotcrete has not been used systematically but according to need. In this respect the Finnish and Swedish design philosophies regarding oil storage caverns differ. In Sweden it is obligatory to shotcrete the roof part.

Shotcrete can be considered to be high-class concrete; it differs from normal concrete in its slightly higher tensile strength and in the more rapid development of the final strength. In Finland shotcrete has, generally, a compressive strength of 30–70 MN/m^2, a tensile strength of 1.5–3.0 MN/m^2 and an adhesion strength of 2–5 MN/m^2.[29]

Table 3 Summary of rock reinforcements in cavern projects U-11–U-22

Cavern no.	Volume, m³	Profile, m²	Bolts (no.) Roof + Wall		Per m³	Shotcrete, m² Roofs 40 mm + 60 mm		Walls 40 mm + 60 mm	
U-11	306 000	458	1900	7500	0.031	1500	—	3700	1000
U-12	200 000	458	2500	2600	0.025	1400	600	1700	—
U-13	495 000	442	2500	2700	0.010	1150		850	
U-14	550 000	524	3300		0.006	9500		950	
U-15, U-16	1 042 000	471	6000		0.006	24 500		1600	
U-17, U-18	422 000	580	2800	3500	0.015	6000	1750	13 700	1300
U-19	116 000	458	650		0.006	500		—	
U-20, U-21, U-22	845 000	566	6750	4600	0.013	6100	15 400	400	4100

Table 4 Average weekly (5 days, 3 shifts) achievements in drilling and blasting in cavern project U-15–U-16

Drilling of top heading with pneumatic jumbo (twin-boom), area 105 m²; $H = 7$ m	4000 linear m
Drilling of vertical bench with pneumatic crawler (twin-boom), area 205 m², $H = 13$ m	2800 linear m
Blasting of access tunnel, 50 m²	2000 m³
Blasting of top heading	6400 m³
Blasting of vertical bench	16 000 m³

Table 5 Average weekly (5 days, 3 shifts) achievements in drilling and blasting in cavern project U-20, U-21 and U-22

Drilling of top heading with hydraulic jumbo (three booms), area 99 m², $H = 7.5$ m	8100 linear m
Drilling of horizontal bench with hydraulic jumbo (three booms), area 164 m², $H = 8$ m	7600 linear m
Blasting of access tunnel, 50 m²	2800 m³
Blasting of top heading	8200 m³
Blasting of horizontal bench	12 800 m³

The dry-mix method is that which is most commonly applied and this method has been used in the Porvoo works area. The shotcrete lining has been applied in layers 20–30 mm thick and 'watertight' shotcrete has to have a minimum thickness of 60 mm. Wire mesh reinforcement has also been used to a limited extent. The average weekly performance of 60-mm shotcrete application work without mesh reinforcement has been 1200 m².

The major advantages of shotcrete have been its flexibility and applicability, even in difficult places. Shotcrete also follows the rock wall contour in a smooth manner (Fig. 18). In comparing bolting and shotcreting as an integrated part of the cavern excavation process it can be said that the latter has a tendency to cause a greater slowdown of the excavation process than bolting. Shotcreting also requires separate crews, whereas spot-bolting can be done by the drilling crew.

It has been calculated[19] that an immediate reinforcement of a tunnel by bolting reduces the excavation performance by about 20% (the corresponding figure for shotcreting is 80%). In the event that these works are required in the benching stage of two parallel caverns that are being excavated simultaneously the excavation effect will fall by 20–30%.

It is therefore of importance that the design of a cavern be such that the negative impact caused by immediate reinforcements can be minimized.

Time-schedules

In planning the total time-schedule for a cavern project special attention is focused on ensuring that all parts are designed in such way that none of them will form a bottleneck and, also, so that the separate work phases can be synchronized with applicable capacities. A shortened time-schedule, where excavation, civil works, instrumentation and installation works overlap, requires detailed planning for each phase. Special attention should also be given in preparing the overall schedule to the fact that certain pumps and piping material have extremely long delivery times.

An example of a master schedule for a 1 000 000-m³ crude oil storage is presented in Fig. 19. The corresponding actual cumulative progress curves for this project are shown in Fig. 20. Electrical installations and insulation works during 1976 are related to pipes from the caverns to the process day-tanks and, hence, are indirectly connected to the project.

Table 6 presents scheduled and actual construction times for all projects at the Porvoo site. In some cases it has been possible to use parts of an already constructed open-cut or access tunnel in the execution of a later project. The main access tunnel of caverns U-15, U-16 and U-20, U-21 and U-22 was partly constructed prior to the start of actual main contract works, valuable time thereby being saved. The time spent on these works is *not* included in Table 6.

It seems, however, reasonable to state that in a normal case the entire construction time for a 500 000-m³ effective volume project – the construction time from start of open-cut excavation to oil fill – will be around two years. The time that is required for pre-engineering, site investigation, cost estimates, contract specifications and tendering is approximately one year.

Contract forms

Two main types of contract have been used in the company's cavern projects: one involves the turnkey principle and the other the so-called divided contract, in which rock removal and civil works are undertaken by one contractor and the rest of the technical construction and installation works are carried out by other specialized contractors.

In a single case the company used the so-called target agreement contract, which is a form of payment on a cost-plus basis, with a bonus for early completion and a penalty for delay not caused by factors beyond the control of the contractor.

The excavation contract normally includes an estimated amount of different types of reinforcement work, which is included in the contract sum and also the time-schedule. If the actual amount of reinforcement is smaller than was estimated, the contractor compensates the client, and vice versa, in accordance with the unit price list. The contractor may also be entitled to additional time, provided that he can prove that unforeseen difficulties lie on the so-called 'critical path' of the project. It

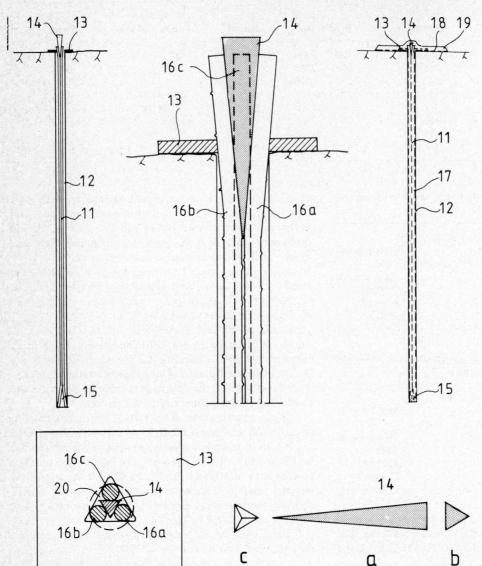

SF 64224
US 444529
EP 0064362

11 BOLT ELEMENT
12 BOLT HOLE ∅ 45 mm
13 COVER PLATE
14 TRIANGULAR WEDGE
15 BOTTOM WEDGE
16 RIBBED STEEL BAR A 400 H OR A 600 H
   $f_v = 400$ N/mm^2 OR $f_v = 600$ N/mm^2
17 MORTAR (SAND/CEMENT)
18 MESH # 50 mm OR # 100
19 SHOTCRETE LAYER
20 TRIANGULAR HOLE IN PLATE

Fig. 17 Patented bolt type for loads up to 36 t

should be noted that many decisions can be made directly at the site by the construction supervision team, which facilitates good collaboration with the contracting company. Claims and disputes are very rare in cavern construction projects.

All contracting companies have been independent private enterprises. The excavation works have been done by Elovuori Oy, Y.I.T. and the joint venture Elovuori Oy-Vesto Oy.

Storage costs

Based on the cost control system of 16 different major items, a division of total costs into six main groups was carried out; the results are presented in Table 7 in the form of minimum, average and maximum costs.[11] The major part of all costs is related to excavation works. For details of other cost factors,

Fig. 18 Shotcrete and bolted portion of cavern wall owing to over-break in vertical profile caused by slickensided joints

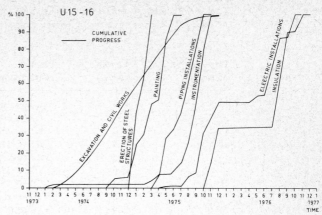

Fig. 20 Cumulative progress curves for separate construction phases

investment costs for all completed projects are presented in Fig. 22. The increase in cavern volume leads to increased costs, generally, only in regard to excavation works. This, on the

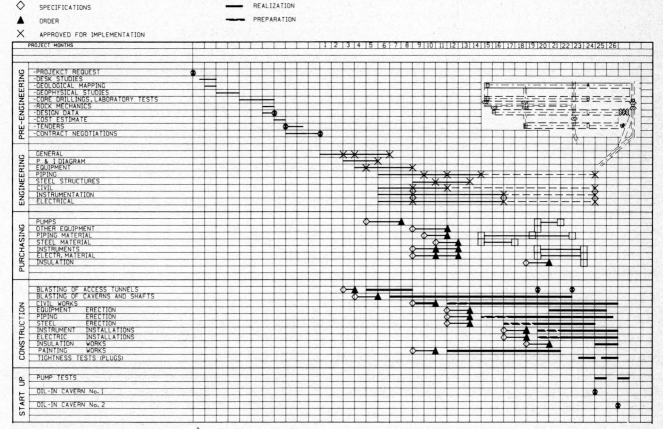

Fig. 19 Master schedule for 1 000 000-m³ crude oil cavern project

etc., the interested reader is referred to the recent article by Johansson.[11]

The costs for excavation and reinforcements are, of course, affected primarily by the rock mass quality and the type and amount of reinforcement that is required. Another major cost factor is the shape and size of the actual caverns, which should be as favourable to mining as possible.

In terms of excavation costs, a case study of a 200 000-m³ cavern was carried out on the basis of a standard design and cavern profiles and prices experienced by the company (Fig. 21). From the above point of view the most economic profile would be that used in the excavation of the crude oil caverns with a height of 35 m.

Obtained excavation costs expressed as a percentage of total

other hand, indicates that the total costs per cubic metre of effective volume will decrease as the size of the cavern project increases.

It should also be noted that, according to Koivisto,[15] relative excavation costs for oil storage caverns during the 1970s decreased by more than 50% in comparison with the 1965 level – mainly as a result of developments in drilling equipment, explosives and blasting techniques.

In cavern projects U-1–U-10 temporary support and safety bolting was the contractor's responsibility, and a certain, but not precisely specified, amount was included in the lump sum contract price. Only permanent support ordered by the owner was paid for according to the unit price list. From construction phase V (U-13) onwards the payment for any type of support

Table 6 Planned and actual construction times for underground oil storage caverns

Construction phase	Cavern code	Planned construction time	Actual construction time	Delayed/shortened (−) (+) days
I	U-1	1.3.66–10.8.67	12.1.66–10.8.67	±0
	U-2	1.3.66–5.8.67	12.1.66–1.8.67	+4
	U-3	1.3.66–25.8.67	12.1.66–15.9.67	−21
II	U-4	3.7.66–25.9.68	24.10.66–1.10.68	−5
	U-5	5.12.66–25.9.68	24.10.66–5.10.68	−10
	U-6	1.3.66–25.9.68	24.10.66–5.10.68	−10
III	U-7	5.10.66–15.9.68	5.10.66–10.8.68	+35
	U-8	5.10.66–10.9.68	5.10.66–1.9.68	+9
	U-9	5.10.66–15.10.68	5.10.66–15.11.68	−31
	U-10	1.8.66–25.10.68	5.10.66–15.11.68	−21
IV	U-11	1.3.70–30.5.72	10.3.70–15.8.72	−75
	U-12	1.3.70–31.12.71	10.3.70–31.12.71	±0
V	U-13	15.11.70–31.12.72	10.11.70–30.10.72	+60
VI	U-14	1.10.73–31.8.75	10.11.73–1.9.75	±0
VII	U-15	15.1.74–31.12.75	15.1.74–15.12.75	+16
	U-16	15.1.74–30.9.75	15.1.74–30.9.75	±0
VIII	U-17	10.3.74–30.11.75	10.3.74–31.12.75	−31
	U-18	10.3.74–30.11.75	10.3.74–31.12.75	−31
IX	U-19	20.1.75–2.5.76	20.1.75–2.5.76	±0
X	U-20	3.3.80–15.10.81	3.3.80–18.10.81	−3
	U-21	3.3.80–15.12.81	3.3.80–28.12.81	−14
	U-22	15.12.80–15.8.82	8.12.80–17.9.82	−32

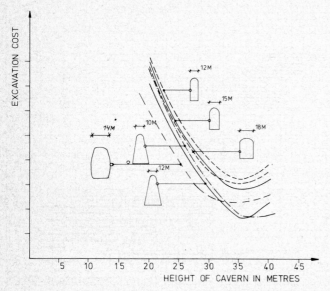

Fig. 21 Excavation costs in relation to cavern profiles in a 200 000-m³ case study. Design, J. Pulkkinen

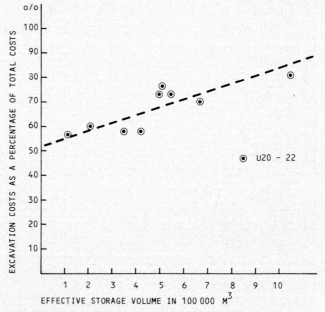

Fig. 22 Excavation costs as percentage of total investment costs at Porvoo works

Table 7 Division of total costs for oil storage cavern construction

Item	Percentage of total cost		
	Minimum	Average	Maximum
Administration, design, construction supervision	1.5	4.0	8.0
Excavation works	48.0	66.0	81.0
Reinforcing	4.0	5.0	8.5
Concrete structures	4.0	9.0	18.0
Mechanical equipment, piping, steel structures	5.5	9.0	14.0
Electric installations, instruments, insulations	2.5	6.0	9.0

or reinforcement became the owner's responsibility – it is, after all, the owner's rock, not the contractor's. The overall responsibility for the safety of the work naturally remained with the contractor.

A detailed cost control system was also established at that time to ensure good statistical knowledge of reinforcements. The cost relation between cavern volume and reinforcement costs, expressed as a percentage of excavation costs, is presented in Fig. 23. Reinforcement costs have, in general, varied between 5 and 10% of the excavation costs. In cavern project U-17–U-18 the costs reached a level of 15%, mainly because of the need for heavy reinforcement of an overthrust crushed rock zone that had not been 'located' in the site investigation.

In presenting absolute cost figures it is difficult to equate

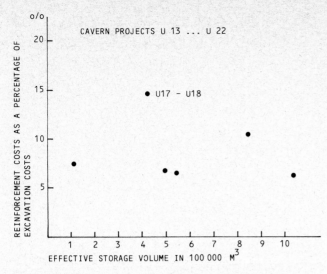

Fig. 23   Reinforcement costs in relation to cavern volume

costs from different years, owing to inflation, and in other than domestic currencies, owing to fluctuations in exchange rates. The unit cost figures for caverns U-13–U-22 (Table 8) are all inflated to be current at 31 December, 1983, by use of the official building cost index in Finland as well as Neste's own index (established in 1948) as a basis for calculations. The unit costs have varied to a very small extent in regard to crude oil and distillate caverns. The costs for cavern U-19, used to store liquefied butane, must also be considered very favourable in comparison with costs for corresponding spheres.

Table 8   Unit cost per m³ of effective cavern volume in Finnish Marks, £ Sterling and $ U.S. for caverns U-13–U-22 at constant 1983 prices

Cavern code	Construction time	Unit cost per m³		
		FIM	GBP	USD
U-13	1970–72	115	14	20
U-14	1973–75	100	12.5	17
U-15, U-16	1974–75	105	13	18
U-17, U-18	1974–75	115	14	20
U-19	1975–76	200	25	35
U-20–U-22	1980–82	100	12.5	17

£1.00 = Finnish Marks 8.00; $ U.S. 1.00 = 5.8 FM.

In calculating the costs that are presented in Table 8 those for land acquisition are excluded, as well as those for pipelines outside the actual cavern area. Control centre building costs and those for the waste water treatment plant are also excluded, as these form a part of the refinery unit. A cost comparison between steel tanks (30 000 m³) and underground caverns constructed at the same time indicates that the caverns have been about 50% cheaper to construct.

It should, however, be clearly understood that the above cost figures are specific to the Porvoo works and are not, as such, universally applicable.

Operational experience

Long-term operational experience has indicated that a rock storage alternative offers several advantages over above ground steel tanks. In a rock cavern there are, however, certain problems that are not of the same magnitude in steel tanks: these are related to service and repair of underground pumps and instruments, corrosion phenomena and sludge formation. As a result of increased experience in operation, these problems have been overcome and today the storage facilities are functioning satisfactorily and reliably.

The operation and maintenance costs of underground caverns have, according to Ignatius,[7] been approximately one-sixth of the corresponding figures for steel tanks.

Summary

In comparing underground excavated oil storage caverns with conventional steel tanks above ground, especially when large storage volumes are involved, a number of factors favour the construction of rock caverns. In summary form such factors are: investment costs are smaller than those for steel tanks; the risk of fires and explosions is small, and insurance premiums can be reduced greatly; the rock cavern plant is almost invisible, and valuable land can be utilized for other construction purposes; in unloading tankers, high pumping capacities can be used, thereby decreasing expensive harbour time for tankers; crude oil can be stored under pressure, so reducing evaporation losses; maintenance and repair costs are low and the design lifetime of a cavern is exceptionally long, i.e. 30–50 years; the use of conventional transfer pumps in a dry pump room system is feasible when high discharge capacities are needed; the need for operational personnel is small; and the excavated rock can often find an economical secondary use.

References
1. Bergman S. G. A. and Stille H. Rockburst problems in a 2.6 million m³ underground crude oil storage in granite. In *Proceedings fifth congress International Society for Rock Mechanics, Melbourne, 1983* (Rotterdam: Balkema, 1983), vol. 1, 301–9.
2. Fagerholm G. Oil in rock caverns – a future storing method? *Tekniskt Forum* no. 18, 1964, 655–8. (Swedish text)
3. Gustafsson R. *Swedish blasting technique* (Gothenburg: SPI, 1973), 323 p.
4. Helfrich H. K. ed. Optimal site investigations. *BeFo (Swedish Rock Mechanics Research Foundation) Rep.* no. 18: 2-79, 1979, 226 p. (Swedish text)
5. Hoek E. and Brown E. T. *Underground excavations in rock* (London: IMM, 1980), 527 p.
6. Holopainen P. and Oksanen J. The use of an underground bomb shelter as ice-hockey rinks. In *Subsurface Space, volume 1, proceedings of international symposium (Rockstore '80), Stockholm, 1980* Bergman M. ed. (Oxford: Pergamon, 1980), vol. 1, 137–40.
7. Ignatius Y. Underground storage of oil and gas products. Reference 6, 53–7.
8. Ignatius Y. Johansson S. and Ravaska P. Underground oil cavern project U20-U22, Neste Oy Porvoo Works. In *Rock mechanics: caverns and pressure shafts, ISRM symposium, Aachen 1982* Wittke W. ed. (Rotterdam: Balkema, 1982), vol. 2, 923–34.
9. Johansson S. Geological surveys for underground oil storage facilities. *Underground Space*, **5**, 1980-81, 36–9.
10. Johansson S. Neste Oy's underground oil storage. *Oil Gas J.*, **79**, Nov. 1981, 277–86.
11. Johansson S. Costs of mined oil caverns at Neste Oy's Porvoo Works in Finland. *Underground Space*, **8**, no. 5-6 1984, 372–80.
12. Johansson S. and Lahtinen R. Oil storage in rock caverns in Finland. In *Tunnelling '76* Jones M. J. ed. (London: IMM, 1976), 41–58.
13. Kalla J. On bedrock investigations of construction sites. *Tehostaja* no. 8, 1964, 3–7. (Finnish text with English summary)
14. Kilpinen M. Underground oil storage in Finland. In *The technology and potential of tunnelling, volume 1* (Johannesburg: Tuncon, 1970), 59–64; *Tamrock News*, no. 4, 1970, 5–7, 18.
15. Koivisto H. Construction of oil storages in rock. In *Fifty years of Finnish civil engineering* (Helsinki: RIL, Association of Finnish Civil Engineers, 1984), 28–33. (Finnish text)
16. Kähönen Y. The Hanasaari deep storage: A, design and implementation. *Paper XIII A, Finnish rock mechanics seminar, Helsinki, 1983*, 13 p. (Finnish text)
17. Langefors U. and Kihlström B. *The modern technique of rock blasting, 2nd edn* (New York, etc.: Wiley, 1967), 405 p.
18. Maijala P. V. ed. The effect of the structural and mechanical properties of rock masses on the kind of excavation. *Mining and Metallurgical Soc. Finland, Work Committee Rep.* no. 17, 1980, 80 p.
19. Sallinen P. On the coordination of reinforcement and grouting works with the excavation process in a rock cavern project. *Finnish Rock Mechanics Workshop – INSKO* no. 122, Pap. XI, 1976, 15 p. (Finnish text)

20. Selmer-Olsen R. and Brock E. General design procedure for underground openings in Norway. In *Norwegian hard rock tunneling, publication no. 1, Norwegian Soil and Rock Engineering Association* (Trondheim: Tapir Publishers, 1982), 11–18.

21. Simonen A. The Precambrian in Finland. *Bull. geol. Surv. Finland* 304, 1980, 58 p.

22. Stephansson O. ed. *Rock bolting: theory and application in mining and underground construction, proceedings of the international symposium, Abisko, 1983* (Rotterdam: Balkema, 1983), 630 p.

23. Svanholm B. O. Persson P. A. and Larsson B. Smooth blasting for reliable underground openings. In *Rockstore 77; storage in excavated rock caverns, proceedings of the first international symposium, Stockholm, 1977* Bergman M. ed. (Oxford, etc.: Pergamon, 1977), vol. 3, 573–9.

24. Särkkä P. S. Planning and construction of the bedrock shelter of Hervanta. Reference 8, vol. 1, 443–50.

25. Wills L. S. and Ridgen W. J. Cavern storage: a client's viewpoint. Reference 23, vol. 1, 125–30.

26. Vuolio R. *Design and execution of blasting* (Helsinki: SMK, 1980), 188 p. (Finnish text)

27. BeFo, Swedish Rock Mechanics Research Foundation. *Rock-bolting* (Stockholm: BeFo, 1974), 87 p. (Swedish text)

28. RIL, Association of Finnish Civil Engineers. *Soil and rock construction handbook* (Helsinki: RIL, 1976), 520 p. (Finnish text) (*RIL* 98)

29. VMY, The Mining and Metallurgical Society of Finland. Handbook of mining and excavation techniques. *VMY Publ.* no. B 29, Helsinki, 1982, 801 p. (Finnish text)

Underground pumped hydro-storage project for The Netherlands

K. B. Braat
AVECO Infrastructure Consultants, Rotterdam, The Netherlands
H. P. S. van Lohuizen
Department of Civil Engineering, Delft University of Technology, Delft, The Netherlands
J. F. de Haan
Haskoning, Royal Dutch Consulting Engineers and Architects, Nijmegen, The Netherlands

Synopsis
In a country with only few hills and no mountains, serious consideration is being given to a large-scale underground project with a substantial element of rock tunnelling. The project will be located in The Netherlands and involves the construction of an underground pumped hydro storage (UPHS) power station for large-scale storage of electrical energy.

In principle similar to conventional pumped hydro-storage schemes, the UPHS method of energy storage involves the use of a large underground water reservoir at approximately 1200 m below ground level. The well-known, surface-level lower reservoir of conventional pumped storage schemes is thus replaced by an underground version that consists of an extensive system of water tunnels. Based on the required storage capacity, a maximum tunnel length of 150 km may be built in rock formations, and tunnels will also be used to house the underground machine halls for hydroelectric equipment.

The outline of the 1200–2000 MW project is given, together with a review of the results that have been achieved to date of several preliminary investigations that deal with geology, shafts, caverns, tunnels and total layout. Particular attention is paid to alternative methods that are under consideration for the construction of the lower reservoir.

Principal elements of UPHS

The method of energy storage that is used most widely is that based on pumped storage, high-head pumped storage being predominant, and is therefore applied in power stations, which are usually located in mountainous regions. Storage of electricity is obtained by pumping water from one (lower) reservoir to another (upper) reservoir via pump turbines. Both reservoirs are above ground and of the artificial-lake type.

In the application of underground pumped hydro storage (UPHS) the lower reservoir is transformed into a subsurface system at great depth (Fig. 1). Reservoir space is created in the form of underground openings, which can take any shape and cross-section. The main criterion for the selection of a particular form of reservoir space is construction cost, lower reservoir costs representing the largest item of expenditure for the whole scheme.

The upper reservoir will not differ from conventional pumped storage reservoirs, but with UPHS there is the distinct advantage that siting is not restricted to mountainous areas as a result of the lack of a need for natural height differences. This aspect is a major feature of UPHS, adding numerous possibilities for the implementation of pumped storage power stations in regions and countries in which conventional sites have all been utilized fully.

The hydroelectric machines that are available for UPHS are the same as those which are already in use at many conventional schemes, i.e. reversible pump turbines or a combined arrangement of multistage pumps with separate Pelton turbines. For the depths envisaged in The Netherlands the former group will result in a double-drop UPHS layout, whereas the latter group of machines leads to a single-drop layout (Fig. 2). In a double-drop UPHS 50% of the machines will be installed at each of the two levels.

At present the power station sizes that are under examination are 1200 and 2000 MW, with associated storage capacities of 12 and 20 GWh, respectively. In volume terms the capacities of 12 and 20 GWh are equivalent to approximately 4 500 000 and 7 000 000 m^3 of water, respectively. Throughout the UPHS this water will follow a lined hydraulic circuit that will be designed to keep pumped storage water and natural groundwater separate.

Project status

The Dutch electricity supply system has always operated without any form of electricity storage – this has been possible as a result of effective load-prediction methods and the wide use of fuel oil and natural gas as energy sources for medium- and fast-response power stations. As a result of Government policy a shift in energy sources for electricity generation in The Netherlands is planned, so more slow-response, base-load (coal and nuclear) power stations are to be expected, as well as the introduction of highly intermittent power from renewable energy sources, such as wind. This shift in energy sources will not only increase the need for fast-response power stations, such as UPHS, to maintain grid performance but will also point towards extensive storage requirements to meet, for example, load-insensitive output from large-scale wind farms.[1]

In view of these developments the UPHS concept was introduced several years ago[2] by the OPAC group (OPAC is the Dutch term for UPHS), formed by the university and two companies represented by the authors of this paper. The plan was accepted by the Dutch Ministry of Economic Affairs[3] and the Dutch equivalent of the Central Electricity Generating Board, an important contributory factor to its acceptance being the relatively limited claim on ground-level space in such an overcrowded country as The Netherlands.

27

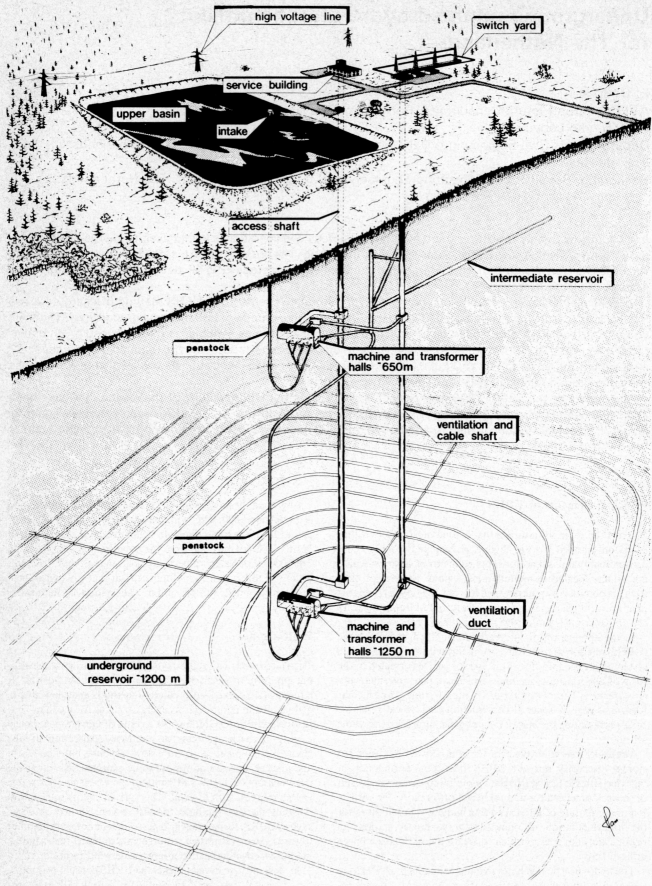

Fig. 1 Artist's impression of double-drop UPHS

The project was and is still based on the application of state of the art techniques. An extensive review of the proposed UPHS methods[4] has resulted in positive initial indications that the project is technically feasible. Examination of existing geological data has led to a preliminary selection of potential sites, which will be re-evaluated in future studies. Part of these studies will consist of field investigations at one of the selected sites. After these investigations a preliminary design for the UPHS and an assessment of its environmental impact will be prepared. The results of this work are required to enable a

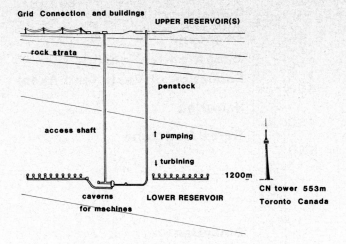

Fig. 2   Vertical arrangement of single-drop UPHS

financial feasibility study to be carried out to allow the Dutch authorities to decide in 1985 on the actual implementation of this new type of power station. The final design will then precede the actual construction period, commencing at the end of this decade.

Engineering geology

In The Netherlands most of the land consists of unconsolidated strata at ground level. These Quaternary and Tertiary strata are mostly water-bearing and decrease in thickness from the north-west to the southeast across the country. The underlying Mesozoic and Palaeozoic strata form outcrops only in the southern and eastern extremities of the country. For UPHS siting a two-phase selection process was adopted.
(1) Determination of those areas in the country in which water-bearing overburden is less than or equal to 600 m in thickness: this limit was chosen as the maximum depth for large-diameter shaft construction with the use of present-day methods.
(2) Evaluation of underlying rock characteristics in those areas

Fig. 3   Possible UPHS (OPAC) sites in The Netherlands

that fulfilled the overburden depth criterion, followed by a further selection of potential sites, primarily based on the existence of suitable rock between depths of 1000 and 1500 m, rock of sufficient strength and rock mass quality, the maximum possible uniformity of geological conditions for an underground plan area of 5–15 km^2, a minimum thickness of rock formation at the required depth of 150 m and little or no chance of water ingress during construction.

A number of parameters could not be assessed properly in this first part of the site selection process owing to the lack of relevant data. These parameters included fault patterns and the magnitude and direction of *in-situ* stresses, and deep ground-water quality. For the initial selection, however, sufficient data could be used to establish three main regions for the siting of the UPHS – the southwestern, southeastern and mid-eastern part of The Netherlands (Fig. 3).

Of these regions, the southeastern part (in the province of South Limburg) is the most favourable (it also has the most reliable information base). Specific UPHS field investigations are therefore being carried out there in an attempt to supply missing geotechnical information. These investigations involve seismic mapping of an area of approximately 90 km^2 in two stages, followed by a borehole drilled at a suitable point. The host rock for the placement of the lower level of the UPHS may either be limestone of the Dinantian Formation of the Lower Carboniferous or sandstone of the Famenian Formation of Devonian age. For the intermediate level of the UPHS, when applicable, Dinantian limestone or Namurian slates (Upper Carboniferous) would be appropriate.

For varied reasons preference is being given to the use of the Dinantian limestone as the main formation for the lower level of the UPHS. The average uniaxial rock strength is likely to be at least 100 MPa, the rock mass quality is expected to be between fair and good, formation thickness will, on average, be of the order of 700 m, with a uniform dip of 10–15°N, and water inflow will not be very marked owing to the dense material and the medium jointing intensity that is expected. Moreover, the excavated limestone will enjoy a commercial value for its various uses.

Prior to the final design phase detailed seismic mapping and a reasonable number of boreholes will serve to ensure the availability of a high level of reliable data. It would be desirable to construct a small-diameter exploration shaft with trial excavations to confirm the main design criteria. During UPHS construction close and continuous observation of the rock formations by engineering geologists in cooperation with tunnel engineers will be necessary to design the support of tunnels and caverns.

Underground UPHS works

The UPHS power station is characterized by three sets of underground structure – shafts, caverns and tunnels. Shafts are required, essentially, for the vertical transport of various items and can be subdivided by function into wet and dry shafts. The caverns are used to house all hydroelectric machinery and associated equipment, and are interconnected by a system of access tunnels leading to the shafts. Most of the tunnels, however, are not for access but for water storage at the intermediate and lower level of the power station.

Underground layout

Two main alternatives are available for the vertical arrangement of the UPHS – single- and double-drop, each with associated types of pump turbines. Under present Dutch conditions no clear preference is apparent in regard to electricity generation. In geological terms a clear preference arises for a single-drop UPHS if it is found that at a particular site the rock strata at the intermediate level are not suitable for the housing of the underground structures at that level.

In terms of overall project costs the double-drop arrangement is favoured in that the total expenditure would be lower – mainly because of the higher investment that would be required for the multistage pumps and the Pelton turbines in a single-drop scheme.

The horizontal arrangement of the UPHS is not strictly regulated, provided that the hydraulic circuit is maintained. Hence, there is a fairly basic departure from the traditional design approach in hydroelectric and transportation engineering in the design of a UPHS. Unlike conventional pumped storage power stations, only one surface-level reservoir is in use with a UPHS, so the problem of linking two surface-level reservoirs, often through adverse geological conditions, should not arise. The same reasoning holds for the comparison of UPHS with road and rail transportation tunnels, which are routed more or less inflexibly through varying geology between the connexion points to surface transportation systems. The design of the UPHS layout can therefore be more effective than that of most traditional underground schemes in that the best geological conditions may be sought and exploited and, thereby, unfavourable conditions are effectively avoided. Thus, in the given project area orientation the depth, cross-section and plan of the underground UPHS structures can be optimized.

Shafts

A minimum number of four shafts is expected for normal UPHS operation. Two wet shafts will function as penstocks of approximately 6-m diameter (the double arrangement is chosen to take account of maintenance requirements, to guarantee full operational reliability and for phased construction and possible subdivision of the surface-level reservoir. One dry shaft (approximately 8-m diameter) will serve for access of personnel and equipment and as the intake for fresh ventilation air. One dry shaft (6–7 m in diameter) will serve for exhaust ventilation and electric power cabling, but it will also be equipped with access facilities.

The shafts will be constructed in two stages – the first in water-bearing overburden and the second in sound rock. For overburden construction a choice is possible between the ground freezing method and the Honingmann–de Vooys drilling method. Ground freezing allows for diameters of up to 10 m, but it is relatively slow owing to the length of the initial freezing period. The second method is faster, pre-drilling with bentonite being used in combination with the sinking of a precast shaft lining. The maximum diameter with this method is limited, however, to 5–6 m. Both methods are used for conventional deep mines, as in the Ruhr area of Germany, where shafts have been sunk through 600 m of overburden to total depths of a maximum of approximately 1400 m.

Caverns

In the region that is currently being examined for UPHS siting the overburden thickness varies from 100 to 400 m (Fig. 4). The selection of the shaft construction method in overburden will be made not in the feasibility phase but during the final design, when more certainty will exist in regard to the allowable construction period and UPHS phasing requirements.

At each UPHS level six different functions for caverns can be distinguished for the housing of various types of plant and equipment: (1) main machine hall for the pump turbines; (2) transformer hall; (3) valve hall for high-pressure ball valves; (4) valve hall for low-pressure butterfly valves; (5) circuit-breaker hall; and (6) drainage gallery for dewatering conduits and pump turbine casings.

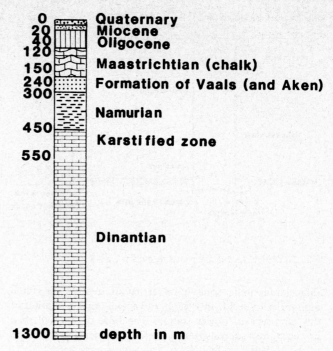

Fig. 4   Typical borehole profile in South Limburg region

Each cavern will be spaced from the other caverns by a distance that will avoid stress concentrations reaching too high a level. At the lowest depths that have been considered the vertical stress in the rock will be of the order of 30–35 MPa, excluding residual tectonic stresses. Total stress concentration as a result of the group and individual influence of caverns will necessitate proper design tolerances, the greatest effort being required for the main machine hall cavern. This hall will house a number of separate pump turbine units and may take either or both of two forms (Fig. 5) – the traditional horseshoe shape

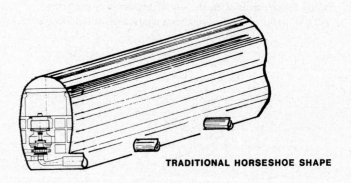

TRADITIONAL HORSESHOE SHAPE

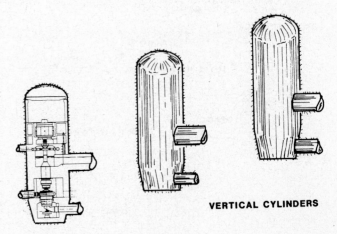

VERTICAL CYLINDERS

Fig. 5   Cavern forms for machine halls

30

that is used for hydroelectric power stations, its dimensions ranging from 20 to 40 m in height and from 10 to 25 m in width for a UPHS, and a vertical, cylindrical shape for each separate pump turbine unit, diameters ranging from 10 to 20 m and heights from 20 to 65 m.

Depending on the type of pump turbine, the unit size and the geological conditions, a choice will be made between the two forms, the cylindrical solution being preferable from a rock mechanics point of view.

Cavern lining for all halls will be the same. After excavation and initial shotcreting the rock will be allowed to redistribute the stresses in a process of controlled relaxation, supported by rockbolts and, possibly, rock anchors. Final shotcreting will complete the lining prior to the next phase in preparing each hall for UPHS operation. For the main machine hall cavern in Dinantian limestone a total concrete lining thickness of 20–25 cm may result. Rockbolts approximately 6 m long and 25 mm in diameter in a grid pattern of 2.0–2.5 m may then be used for the cavern roof and walls in combination with 20-m rock anchors in the roof and haunches of the cavern.

Tunnels

Dry access tunnels form a small part of UPHS tunnelling. Mostly used for access and ventilation, such tunnels will be built mainly in the vicinity of the halls. As only short sections are involved, these tunnels will be constructed in the same fashion as the caverns, i.e. by drill and blast methods followed by a lining method as described above.

With regard to water tunnels, a distinction can be made between water storage tunnels and water conduits to connect various UPHS sections hydraulically. The relatively high cost of underground water storage space demands that the extent of this part of the works be minimized. Energy storage is accomplished by means of potential energy – water mass × height differences between reservoirs is proportional to stored energy. By maximizing the height difference a minimal water mass or storage volume is obtained, which results in the lowest cost for underground water storage. Stress is therefore placed on increasing the depth of the lowest level of the UPHS as much as possible. The depth limit is governed by rock mechanics constraints and will therefore vary at each different UPHS site. In general terms depths of 1000–1300 m are considered realistic for Dutch geological conditions. The main underground water storage system could well be constructed at a depth of 1200–1300 m in the South Limburg region.

The intermediate-level storage reservoir will be much smaller than the main reservoir, but similar in construction. It serves as a buffer for taking up the differences in water flow between the intermediate- and lower-level power houses, where synchronous operation of pump turbine units at each level is called for.

The various water conduits form the last group of UPHS tunnel types and function as horizontal collection and distribution systems from penstocks via machine halls to underground reservoirs and back. As these and other water-bearing tunnels all contribute to the hydraulic friction loss during UPHS operation, the concrete surface finish has to be completed to a high standard of smoothness.

Lower reservoir construction

The two power station sizes that are under consideration are of 1200 and 2000 MW. For simplicity only the larger size will be examined here, a storage capacity of 20 GWh or approximately 7 000 000 m³ of stored water being involved.

Lower-reservoir storage space for the Dutch UPHS was originally proposed in the form of a system of tunnels – in contrast with the UPHS that is planned in the U.S.A.,[5] for

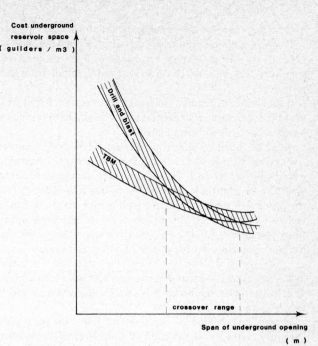

Fig. 6   Cost trends for reservoir space construction

which large caverns in hard rock were proposed. Since the original Dutch proposal stronger rock has been found to exist in The Netherlands than had been predicted, so the cavern option has, in fact, become feasible. One of the results of the 1984 review was a preliminary indication that tunnel and cavern storage space would cost roughly the same. Apparently, the crossover range shown in Fig. 6 was applicable to the selected tunnel-boring machine diameter (8 m) and standard cavern dimensions (20 m high × 12 m wide). No significant departure from these findings is expected in future studies, so other factors will determine the preference for the actual form of storage space.

One of these factors will be the plan area occupied underground by each option. The major influence of height difference between the upper and lower reservoirs is clear from Fig. 7, from which will also be clear that a tunnelled reservoir calls

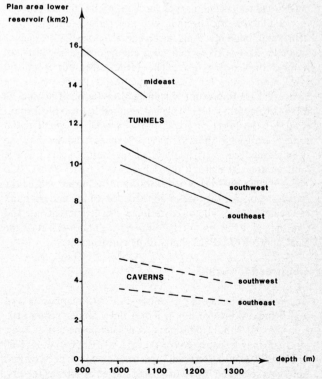

Fig. 7   Plan area required for lower reservoir options (2000 MW; 20 GWh)

31

for a larger plan area than a reservoir that is formed by caverns. The tunnel solution would require a total tunnel length of 140-150 km, which may be compared with the total tunnel length of 163 km for the London underground transport system.

If the existence of major faults in the reservoir rock prohibits the full development of a tunnel system, the alternative solution based on caverns will be adopted.

A further point of difference between TBM-driven tunnels and caverns is the intrinsically higher rate of progress attainable with the former method. Typical figures for limestone working would be 10-15 m/day, whereas 1-2 m/day could be expected for caverns. A uniform rock formation with few or no faults and an acceptable rock convergence behaviour is a prerequisite for a high level of TBM efficiency. On the other hand, the circular excavation profile of the TBM is advantageous from a rock stress distribution viewpoint and the minimal disturbance that is created in the virgin rock by smooth boring. The drill and blast method that is used for the caverns is much less favourable in this respect.

Phased construction of the reservoir may also be a contributory factor to the selection of tunnels or caverns, early completion of part of the works allowing direct usage for UPHS operation and thereby providing early revenue.

The various factors that will influence the ultimate choice of reservoir option have been identified, but quantification will have to be carried out in the later stages of project design when more geological information is available and the UPHS planning requirements are known.

Reservoir lining details will follow those of the other hydraulic structures. A tentative design of 8-m diameter tunnels indicates that rockbolt usage may vary between two and ten bolts per linear metre at 4-m length and 22-mm diameter depending on rock mass quality. Shotcrete application may vary from nil to a layer thickness of 25 cm prior to the high-finish layer of final concrete. In principle, the tunnels will be watertight and points of groundwater inflow will need to be grouted during construction. A form of permanent drainage will also be installed to keep the two types of water separate at all times.

During construction the high temperatures at these working depths will necessitate proper ventilation as well as cooling of the ventilation air. Together with the transportation of rock debris and lining materials, a considerable logistics problem is created when work is carried out simultaneously at a significant number of working faces. The vertical transportation and ventilation routes are through the shafts, from which the horizontal transportation distances below ground should be minimized continuously. This has resulted in the typical spiral shape of the lower reservoir tunnel system in which radial tunnels are used to shorten the access routes from the shafts to the working faces. Vertical shaft transportation capacity will be laid out for 700-800 t/h of rock debris for each shaft, skip hoists being used. The vertical transportation rate will be the critical factor for the rate of construction of the underground reservoir. The overall power station construction schedule and phasing requirements will therefore have a major effect on the final number of UPHS shafts to be constructed.

Construction period

As has been pointed out previously, construction phasing is of major importance for construction time. Under normal circumstances, without phasing, a construction period of some ten years may be expected for the largest UPHS version (2000 MW and 20 GWh). Reservoir construction will then be carried out by six to eight TBM, work being started as soon as the first shafts reach final level. The construction period will be extended by one or two years if, for example, a three-phase schedule is adopted.

During and after construction the possibility always exists for alteration of the final reservoir capacity (equal to tunnel length) in view of changes in UPHS operating philosophy. This translates simply into reducing or extending the tunnel length that is eventually required. The high degree of flexibility and adaptability of the UPHS system to customers' requirements, even very late in the construction programme, is therefore apparent.

Next project stages

The present stage of development of the UPHS project involves the completion of a preparation period prior to the carrying out of an elaborate preliminary design, which will be required to establish UPHS financial and economic feasibility. In preparation for the preliminary design a process of field investigation at one particular site will be completed, together with the collection of information for an environmental impact analysis. During this preparatory work a parallel study will be conducted to establish the power station size that may be necessary for the Dutch electricity generating system. Both studies will provide essential data for the preliminary design in the next study phase.

After the completion of the preliminary design a financial cost–benefit analysis and a multi-criteria analysis will form the basis for a comparison with other energy storage options (low-head pumped storage and compressed-air storage). When UPHS is selected for implementation, a programme of detailed field investigations will be executed prior to the final design stage. Construction activities could begin in 1988 to produce the first of its kind in the next generation of pumped storage power stations.

References
1. Halberg N. and van Lohuizen H. P. S. Feasibility of an underground pumped hydro storage in the Netherlands. Paper presented to AIAA/EPRI international conference on underground pumped hydro and compressed air energy storage, San Francisco, California, September 1982.
2. Ondergrondse Pomp Accumalatie Centrale (OPAC) in Nederland – Vooronderzoek (UPHS pilot study). Delft University of Technology, Haskoning Royal Dutch Consulting Engineers and Architects, Royal Volker Stevin, Rotterdam, 1980.
3. Windenergie en Opslag (Government paper on wind energy and storage). The Hague, Tweede Kamer der Staten-Generaal zitting 1981–1982. *Pap.* no. 17500.
4. OPAC Inventarisatie gegevens (Report for NEOM (Dutch Ministry of Economic Affairs)), Sittard, June 1984.
5. Preliminary design study of underground pumped hydro and compressed-air energy storage in hard rock. *EPRI Rep.* EM-1589, project 1081-1, DOE/ET 5047-1, Palo Alto, California, May 1981.

Discussion

Dr. P. H. Phillips* said that one of the advantages of the 'Tunnelling' series of conferences was that senior engineers could discuss not only their successes but also their problems, which were often much more interesting and valuable.

In regard to safety aspects, he asked Johansson to elaborate on the initial procedures, measures taken to contain the problem and changes, if any, in operational methods.

Frank Rowbottom† asked Johansson to give details of the relative cost of comparable steel tank storage and rock cavern storage. Details of the land areas required on the surface for the two methods of storage and a comparison of operating costs for tanks versus cavern facilities would be welcomed.

M. C. Knights‡ asked Braat and co-workers to explain in further detail the method of lining the shafts – in particular, the formation of the blockwork skin.

Authors' replies

S. Johansson In reply to Dr. P. H. Phillips, a detailed discussion of the impact of explosions in underground crude oil storage caverns has been given by Shaw and co-workers.§ In Neste's case the damage caused by a detonation and/or a fire in crude cavern U-1 corresponded to the design criteria used, and the cavern was repaired and is today in normal operation. A fire in an underground cavern will last only a short time, owing to lack of oxygen, but that is not so with an above-ground steel tank (Fig. 1).

Fig. 1

In reply to Frank Rowbottom, cavern and steel tank costs were discussed in an earlier paper.** The costs of the caverns have been about 50% of those of the steel tanks. Operating and maintenance costs have been approximately one-sixth of the corresponding figure for steel tanks. Neste has constructed product caverns directly below the steel tank farm and additional land has therefore not been required for the caverns. A steel tank farm for 5 000 000 m³ of oil storage would require about 300 hectares of land.

K. B. Braat, Professor H. P. S. van Lohuizen and J. F. de Haan The shafts in water-bearing overburden strata are principally of a different lining solution than is the case in firm and impervious rock. To ensure shaft watertightness and settlement adaptability (laterally) in overburden a multiple-layer lining is adopted, consisting of an outer skin of blockwork, an infill of bitumen and inner skin of welded steel lining plus a reinforced concrete annulus. The blockwork is built up in 10-m lifts from rebates in the (frozen) ground to form a slightly compressible outer ring, which also contains the bitumen. Compressibility is achieved by using concrete blocks with wood-packing in between. The blockwork is of secondary importance in the lining structure since the inner lining (steel plus reinforced concrete) is the main load-bearing element.

*Phillips and Sons, Cookham, Berkshire, England.
†Department of Minerals and Energy, Port Moresby, Papua New Guinea.
§Shaw D. E. Plooster M. N. and Ellison R. D. Explosion impacts in underground oil storage facilities. In *Subsurface space* Bergman M. ed. (Oxford, etc: Pergamon, 1980), vol. 1, 385–92.
Johansson S. Costs of mined oil caverns at Neste Oy's Porvoo Works in Finland. *Underground Space*, **8, no. 5-6 1984, 372–80.

Session 2 – Major projects

Co-Chairmen: F. Von Mandach and T. A. Talbott

Design and construction of the S. Domingos–Morgavel tunnel, Portugal

F. de Mello Mendes
F. R. da Silva Amado
Hidroprojecto, Lisbon, Portugal

Synopsis
The S. Domingos–Morgavel tunnel (total length, 13 km; cross-sectional area, 7 m²) is a component of the water-supply scheme for the Sines, Portugal, industrial complex. Its construction, started at the end of 1976, is now (1984) being completed. The slow rate of advance and the consequential cost increase were the result not only of the geology of the region, which is characterized by very heterogeneous intensely folded slate and greywacke formations with frequent crush zones, but also of the inadequacy of some of the methods of excavation and support that were utilized in this type of ground.

Excavation methods included, mainly, TBM and boom-type machines, together with drill and blast techniques. Immediate support was provided by systems that ranged from steel arches and bolting to shotcrete. The advantages and disadvantages of these various methods, in relation to the rate of excavation, and the selection and installation of support and lining, are discussed, rates of advance being given. In addition, the need to modify contractual arrangements during the course of the project, owner–contractor relations being made more flexible, is emphasized and discussed.

On 13 August, 1984, excavation of the S. Domingos–Morgavel tunnel was completed. Lining of the last excavated stretch is being carried out, and it is expected that the work will be concluded and able to come into service at the end of 1984.

The tunnel, with a length of about 13 km and a minimum effective cross-section of 6.5 m², forms part of the water-supply

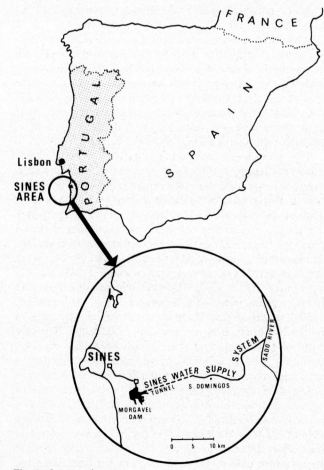

Fig. 1   Layout plan

system to the industrial complex of Sines in Portugal (Fig. 1). It was designed as a gravity conduit for a flow of 12 m³/s, its average gradient being about 1 mm/m.

Excavation of the tunnel was started on 29 November, 1976, and its construction had originally been estimated to take about two years, with completion at the end of 1978. Unfortunately, this time limit has been nearly quadrupled, which has led to a whole series of inconveniences and losses, the estimated cost having more than tripled. The causes of these differences between reality and prediction are numerous, ranging from geological factors - difficult ground in which no analogous work had been undertaken - to the inapplicability of several of the technologies envisaged for specific geotechnical situations. More important, however, were the bureaucratic obstacles that had to be overcome to enable the situations that kept occurring to be accepted as real situations, and the lack of contractual flexibility that prevented process changes when such changes proved to be appropriate.

A great deal was, however, achieved during the construction of the tunnel in regard to the attainment of a more suitable system for collaboration between client, project designer, consultants and contractors. It is perhaps this last aspect of the work rather than the importance of the S. Domingos–Morgavel tunnel and a description of its design characteristics and construction details that justifies the presentation of this paper.

Geological environment

The S. Domingos–Morgavel tunnel passes through formations that comprise alternating slates and greywackes, which Oliveira and co-workers[1] attributed to the Namurian, regarding them as integrated in the Carboniferous Basin of the Iberian Peninsula, which covers a vast zone in the south of Portugal. These formations are intensely folded and there are frequent occurrences of crush zones, with an abundance of faults and also acid and basic veins; metamorphism is not, however, very apparent.

As has been described by Mello Mendes and co-workers,[2] geomorphologically, the region may be regarded as of subdued relief, with maximum altitudes of about 200 m. Cover over the

37

tunnel varies, for most of its length, between 40 and 120 m. On a regional scale the geostructural aspects are apparently simple. On the scale of the work, however, they proved to be very complex, great importance being assumed by the above-mentioned faults, veins and folds; moreover, the frequent changes in attitude of the formations and their intense compartmentation introduced complementary factors of a disturbing kind. The predominance, generally speaking, of the slates over the greywackes emphasizes the importance of the foliation of the former, and this plays a decisive part in defining the compartmentation in general of the rock mass and in penetration of weathering.

Surface topography and, additionally, photogeology do not conceal the existence of zones of poor resistance, these being easy to explain by the occurrence of the faults and their associations with the previously mentioned crush zones. Hydrogeological aspects are conditioned, on the one hand, by the major compartments created by the impermeable argillaceous material of the faults and crush zones and, on the other, by the occurrence of zones of highly fractured veins of quartz, which act as major seepage pathways.

Geotechnical characterization of rock mass

For the preliminary study, and for the various design stages of the tunnel, a relatively large number of geological and geotechnical investigations were carried out.[3] Moreover, the information acquired on the rock mass during the first stages of execution of the work enabled Ojima[4] to prepare a geotechnical classification of the ground traversed by the tunnel, and that classification was later successfully applied during the construction of its final stretches.

As regards the geological studies,[3] during the preliminary study stage on the tunnel not only was use made of all available regional information and surface investigations but also, with regard to the zone covered by the selected layout for the tunnel, a survey was plotted on a scale of 1 : 10 000 that made it possible to draft a rough geological profile – to be made more precise subsequently with the use of data obtained from drilling and geophysical prospecting studies. Later, during the execution stage of the work, a topographical survey of a strip 100 m wide was carried out along the course of the tunnel at a scale of 1 : 1000 to provide a more convenient detailed interpretation of the region traversed. That interpretation also included photogeological data on the basis of air photo strips that had been taken for the general survey of the region.[5]

In the preliminary design stage of the tunnel a summary seismic refraction survey[2,3] showed that, for the zone concerned, the rock mass displayed considerable variation in wave propagation velocity (from <1600 to >4000 m/s), which indicated the occurrence of formations of very different mechanical strengths. At a later stage, during the construction of the tunnel and after the first TBM blockage, that geophysical information was confirmed by further seismic refraction measurements and by geoelectrical prospecting, the latter covering the whole length of the tunnel and allowing the preparation of resistivity profiles and lines of iso-resistivity. These latter investigations showed, in effect, a marked irregularity in the characteristics of the ground and, owing to the significant resistivity contrasts, that certain zones were to be expected in which the advance of the work would be difficult.

This geotechnical information on the rock mass was not, in fact, in disagreement with the data that had in the meantime been obtained from mechanical drilling – the marked irregularity in test core recoveries pointed to the frequent occurrence of zones of very bad ground quality, alternating with others the mechanical characteristics of which were clearly superior. In six drillings, totalling 266 m, along the profile of the tunnel and

beyond its elevation the distribution of the average recoveries of test cores, calculated for successive lengths of 2 m, showed that in 50% of such lengths the recovery was less than 60%, i.e. that more than 40% of the rock material was lost during drilling.[2] Furthermore, it was only possible to obtain samples for laboratory mechanical tests in the zones of better-quality rock, which yielded the highest recovery rates.

The mechanical tests, the significance of which in relation to the rock mass as a whole was thus of little relevance, provided moduli of deformability of between 0.6×10^3 and 55×10^3 MPa and uniaxial compressive strengths of between 1.8 and 50 MPa. In laboratory samples the propagation velocities of longitudinal ultrasonic waves varied between 1000 and 5000 m/s, and in several cases velocities parallel to the foliation were noted to have a value that was twice that of the corresponding velocities perpendicular to the foliation.

It was very significant that during the mechanical drilling it proved impracticable to take integral samples by the method developed by LNEC and reported by Rocha and Barroso[6] owing to the instability of the walls of the boreholes. In addition, in the zones of poorer-quality rock mass, in which the real diameters of the boreholes were clearly greater than the nominal, *in-situ* deformability tests with use of the dilatometer, also developed by LNEC and described by Rocha *et al.*,[7] could not be carried out. The dilatometric moduli obtained therefore did not include values that related to the zones of poor-quality rock, but they displayed a practically lognormal distribution despite having corresponded to different orientations in relation to the foliation. This distribution showed that the mean for the moduli of deformability considered (greater than 71% of all such moduli) gave a value of only 2.15×10^3 MPa and that the median (geometric mean) of the moduli was only 1.16×10^3 MPa. As was mentioned elsewhere,[2] these latter facts point to the poor characteristics of the rock mass.

The heterogeneity of the rock mass varied greatly from point to point – not only because of the lithological heterogeneity but also because of the different states of weathering.

When these aspects are combined with the very important variations in attitude of the foliation, the foldings and crush zones, the occurrence of numerous faults, acid and basic veins and the very different compartmentation conditions of the ground (mainly dependent on the lithology), it is easy to accept the enormous variations in rock mass quality that were encountered and the many major differences in ground behaviour during the excavation of the tunnel.

This geotechnical aspect was also demonstrated clearly during the execution of the work by the convergence measurements that were systematically carried out for safety control and to obtain data for the rational selection of the primary support and calculation of the definitive lining of the tunnel. The marks for measuring convergences, taken along cords laid out in the form of a cross or triangle, were installed in sections 25 m apart (less whenever there were observed to be changes in the characteristics of the rock mass or major deformations in the contour of the tunnel). The measurements were made with a convergence meter with a telescopic rod, developed by LNEC, equipped with a deflectometer of hundredths of a millimetre, which ensures a precision of 0.05 mm. The data from this observation were systematically stored and computer-processed for the detection of any situations regarded as abnormal and the periodic presentation of the behaviour observed in graphical form. Among the various types of behaviour it was possible to distinguish (Fig. 2) a clear tendency towards stabilization (*a*), a similar tendency only after the application or reinforcement of the primary support (*b*) and an unequivocal tendency to rupture of the rock mass, which could be prevented only by the application of the final lining (*c*). Abnormal behaviour of the rock mass that justified special

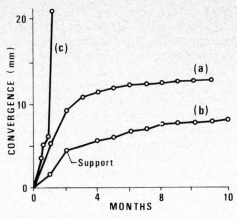

Fig. 2 Typical convergences

attention was defined as a rate of convergence of more than 1 mm/month one month after the installation of the measurement marks.

It should be noted that because of the difficulties of working at the tunnel face with any of the mechanized methods of excavation that were being used, it was not possible to set up marks for measuring convergences at less than three diameters' distance from the face of the tunnel; this meant that the time–convergence curves obtained seldom showed clearly the effect of the distance from the face and represented only the influence of the time factor.

The detailed geological survey of a large number of zones of the tunnel enabled the convergences that were ascertained to be correlated with the fracturing of the mass and its degree of weathering. This weathering, both from viewpoints of intensity and the mineralogical composition of the material in the altered zones, was of great importance in the mechanical behaviour of the rock mass.

In relation to the intensity of alteration it was shown that for the rock mass in question the *slake durability test*, with some adaptations in respect of the test envisaged by the ISRM[8] (owing to the need to make use of samples constituted by more or less tabular elements), permitted a quantitative definition of three degrees of weathering (A_1, A_2 and A_3) of the rock material, for which the losses in the first cycle of the test were, respectively, $<3\%$, between 3 and 24% and $>24\%$. In qualitative terms A_1 corresponds to practically sound rock material, difficult to fracture with a geologist's hammer, A_2 to average altered material, easy to separate with a hammer along the planes of foliation, and A_3 to the altered material, generally argillaceous and easy to crumble with one's fingers.

The presence of clayey material, which owes its origin to the alteration of the rock mass, was very important – in particular, owing to its effect on the sensitivity to water of the rock material. In the argillaceous material, whenever expansive components, such as montmorillonite or unstable chlorites were detected by means of X-ray diffractometry, there were found to be expansions of the rock mass with the development of occasional significant pressures. In laboratory tests with an Instron 1195 press, in a constant deformation regime normal to the foliation, some samples of schistose rock, after being soaked in water for 48 h, developed expansion pressures that varied between 1 and 2 MPa.[2]

The aptitude shown by the schistose rock material to weather by exfoliation when exposed to water or to humid air was also investigated by means of a technique suggested by Rodrigues,[9] saturated samples being subjected to thermic shocks of 700°C for 15 min: the samples exfoliated intensely, some of them tripling their apparent dimension perpendicular to the schistosity.

Determination of the aptitude for degradation (weathering) of the rock material when exposed to humid air was tested by

attack by hydrogen peroxide, followed by sieving and weighing of the resultant fine fraction, to obtain the respective percentage amount: this technique, though in some cases apparently promising, was, however, abandoned owing to the frequent occurrence of pyrite finely disseminated in the rock matrix, which was an obstacle to interpretation of the results.[2]

The very marked tendency for separation of the rock material along the planes of foliation made it extremely difficult to collect drill samples for systematic laboratory tests on the strength and deformability of the various lithological types. Such data as were obtained were virtually confined to those referred to previously and, as has been explained, must be regarded as corresponding only to unaltered samples of rock types the schistosity of which is not pronounced. The ease of separation of the rock material along the planes of foliation also hindered the execution of laboratory tests that involved alternate humidification and drying to ascertain the effects that similar conditions seemed to have on convergence measurements.

Finally, during the construction of the tunnel an effort was made to characterize the rock mass by means of the operational parameters (speed of advance, longitudinal pressure, torque) of the TBM that were being used, but the results were not very convincing – possibly because of the absence of any proper standardization of the conditions for determination of those parameters. Nonetheless, there was an apparent correlation between the values of such operational parameters, the support required after excavation, the data obtained in the geophysical investigation and, in particular, the local geological and geotechnical characteristics of the rock mass.

Geotechnical classification of rock mass

In the light of the geotechnical characteristics of the rock mass, already referred to, and the methodology developed by Ojima,[4] it was possible to establish a geotechnical classification applicable to the rock mass to be traversed by the S. Domingos–Morgavel tunnel.[10] As classification parameters the degree of alteration, the degree of fracturing, the sensitivity to water and the number of fracture sets were used. By analysing the importance of all or some of these parameters, in the order in which they are mentioned, it was possible to divide the rock mass into zones that correspond to three distinct classes (I, II and III) and two intermediate classes (I–II and II–III).

The degree of alteration was quantified by means of the slake durability test, the materials that showed losses of up to 24% being termed W_1 and those which gave greater losses W_2. The W_2 materials were then put to correspond with class III rock mass (that of the worst quality). For the zones with W_1 material the degree of fracturing was analysed, J_1, J_2 and J_3 corresponding to spacings between fractures that were >0.25 m, between 0.25 and 0.10 m and <0.10 m. Zones of W_1 material and J_1 fracturing were allocated to class I (the best of the rock mass) without further analysis.

For zones with W_1 material and J_3 fracturing it was considered to be necessary to ascertain the sensitivity to water by observing the presence or absence of clayey materials – detectable by their soapiness or slippery nature after immersion in water. The degrees s (sensitive) and i (insensitive) were thus defined. Zones with W_1 material and J_3 fracturing were then, according to their respective sensitivity, assigned to the intermediate class II–III (s) or class II (i).

Finally, zones with W_1 material and J_2 fracturing required not only determination of their sensitivity to water but also that of the number of fracture sets; for this parameter n_1 corresponded to a single well-defined set (apart from eventual sparse fractures) and n_2 to two or more sets (also ignoring eventual sparse fractures). Zones with W_1 material, J_2 fracturing and sensitive (*s*) to water were thus, according to whether the number of fracture sets was n_2 or n_1, attributed to class II or intermediate class I–II; zones with the same material and fracturing, but insensitive (*i*) to water, were then, depending on the number of fracture sets of n_2 or n_1, allocated to intermediate class I–II or class I.

It is noteworthy that defined relationships were found between the fracture spacing of the rock mass, expansion of the contour of the tunnel (known from the convergence measurements) and the characteristics of the instabilities in that contour, on the one hand, and the rock mass classes established, on the other. For instance, for class III there is a corresponding infra-centimetric spacing, for intermediate class II–III a centimetric spacing, for class II a centimetric or decimetric spacing, for intermediate class I–II a decimetric spacing and for class I a decimetric or supra-decimetric spacing. As regards the displacements of the contour of the tunnel, classes II and II–III show them as centimetric, class II as between centimetric and millimetric and classes I–II and I as millimetric. Finally, with regard to the instabilities of the rock contour, classes III and II–III show them as generalized and immediate, classes II and I–II as generalized but delayed and class I as only occasional and delayed in relation to the excavation.

In general terms, in the tunnel as a whole, it can be stated that the zones that were geomechanically good (class I), intermediate (classes I–II and II) and poor (classes II–III and III) occurred, respectively, to the extent of 40, 40 and 20%.

Excavation and support of tunnel

Initially, excavation of the approximately 13-km tunnel (Fig. 3) was planned with two excavation faces, with entrances in the flanks of the slopes – one on the upstream side (S. Domingos) and the other on the downstream side (Morgavel). In spite of the various unfavourable geotechnical indications that were already available, a too optimistic view was taken of the possibility of using TBM and it was agreed that those machines should be used.

With the TBM a circular section of 3.40-m diameter would be obtained; this, after lining with a thickness of 0.25 m, would give an effective circular tunnel section of 2.90-m diameter. For the general gradient of the tunnel, of about 1 in 1000, it would thus be possible to ensure the maximum water flow envisaged (12 m³/s) in free flow, occupying about 80% of the available height of the section. For removal of the debris it was expected to use 4.5-m³ Granby wagons and battery locomotives. Ventilation was to be of the blowing type, ensured by helicoidal fans inserted in a flexible duct with a diameter of 0.65 m.

To line the tunnel it was planned to use, according to the classes of rock mass to be traversed, ordinary shotcrete, shotcrete over bolted steel mesh, shotcrete over steel mesh and UNP120 steel arches, more or less separate from one another, shotcrete over steel plates and UNP160 steel arches, also more or less separate from one another, and *in-situ* cast concrete. The final sill components, precast, were to be installed as excavation progressed.

It soon became necessary, however, to consider modifications and alternatives. A serious blockage of the tunnelling machine that had just begun the excavation of the tunnel from the Morgavel side showed that, in reality, the geotechnical characteristics of the rock mass – its heterogeneity – meant that the excavation sometimes presented difficulties far greater than those which had been expected. The alternation of hard and fairly brittle layers of greywackes with slate layers that were sometimes very plastic, with contacts between both that were oblique in relation to the axis of the tunnel, the intense folding of the slates, frequently accompanied by crush zones, and the occurrence of numerous veins of quartz, highly fractured, and some faults were the principal reasons for these difficulties.

It was then decided, for excavation of the more difficult rock mass zones, to use boom-type machines, with tungsten carbide picks. These units were selected mainly for the more heterogeneous or softer zones that were less suited to the use of the TBM.

Since the boom-type machines, on caterpillar tracks, are not very convenient for use for circular sections it was decided to use them to excavate horseshoe sections, of 9.1 and 6.8 m², respectively, according to whether or not it was necessary to bring the TBM through those sections after they had been lined. For the lining the types and variants were maintained as had been planned, but with the substitution of the U-section circular arches by sliding horseshoe arches with TH 21/58G sections, these also being spaced as appropriate. With these horseshoe tunnel sections the precast sills were abandoned and replaced by *in-situ* cast concrete pre-sill and sill.

For the rock mass zones of poorer quality, to be protected later with the stronger type of lining, it was also planned to carry out the previous driving in of iron rods or steel beams (forepoling), as well as the possibility of the pre-consolidation of the rock mass by cement grouting. The highly plastic characteristics of the rock mass, in the less resistant argillaceous zones, proved, nevertheless, to be an obstacle to efficient treatment by means of grouting, so in such zones the pre-establishment of the driven in rods or steel beams remained the only acceptable method of controlling the ground during excavation.

The types of lining described were initially envisaged as final, although they might act as immediate or provisional support. The behaviour of the rock mass during the course of time, detected by the systematic convergence measurements, showed, however, that over most of the distance that was being excavated the ground, although in many cases no short-term safety problems were posed, remained unstable in spite of the application of virtually all the types of support, with the exception of *in-situ* cast concrete. It was therefore decided, contrary to what had initially been planned, to line the whole tunnel with *in-situ* cast concrete, regardless of the immediate or provisional support already applied.

These main changes in the constructional conception and methodology meant that the original plans for the excavation of the tunnel had to be modified. Accordingly, between the distances to the origin (S. Domingos entrance) 0.636 and 0.824 km (Fig. 3) – a zone in which there was a thin cover of about 6 m – the tunnel was constructed by cut and cover excavation with concreting of an inverted U-section of 11.6 m². From the excavation that had been done for the construction of this sector, two new work faces were created – one upstream with an enlarged horseshoe section, by use of a boom-type machine, advancing towards the circular section work face that was being excavated by TBM from S. Domingos, and another work face downstream, also with a boom-type machine but with a reduced horseshoe section, since there the cover was not very thick and it was expected, mainly from the geophysical investigation data, that over a considerable distance the ground would exhibit extremely heterogeneous characteristics, with various zones of very bad quality. In the meantime the counter-face that was being excavated from the Morgavel side was also started with a boom-type machine in an enlarged horseshoe section, moving to a TBM-excavated circular section only after an advance of about 350 m when the cover was sufficient for it to be assumed that this latter machine would be able to work under proper conditions. After about 1550 m of excavation, however, and after very serious blockages, the TBM was withdrawn and replaced by a boom-type machine.

The qualities of ground encountered and all the changes that have been mentioned meant that excavation of the tunnel was falling far behind the original schedule. Accordingly, as early

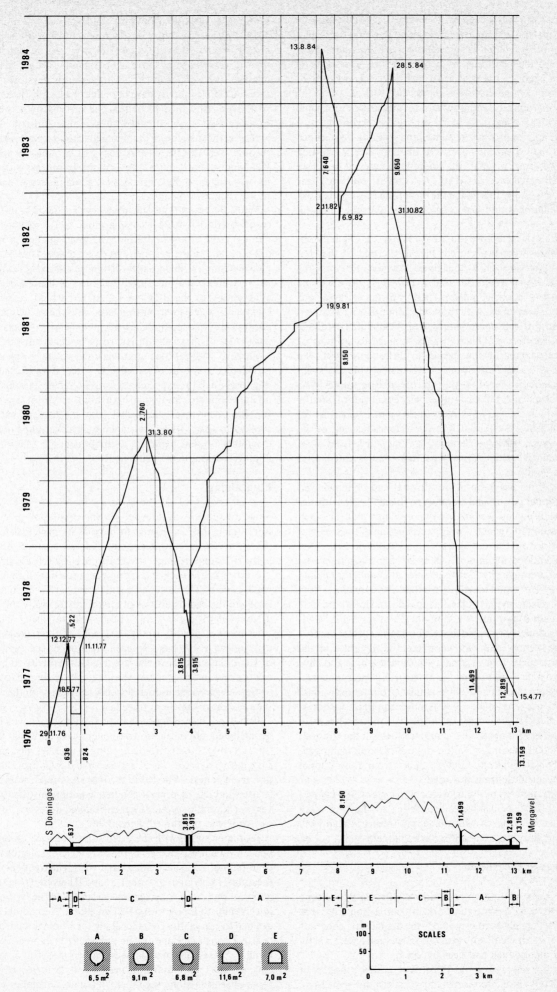

Fig. 3   Profile along tunnel and progress of excavation

as 1977, at 3.815 and 3.915 km, two vertical shafts 36 m deep were opened – the first for extraction and the second for service and entry of machines. These shafts were intended, after connexion of their bottoms, to create two further work faces that would enable, in part at least, lost time to be recovered. The location of these shafts was established with regard to the surface topographical conditions and the qualities of rock mass expected in the zones still to be excavated; according to a criterion that later proved not to be valid, these were assumed to depend mainly on the cover. On the new face, advancing upstream, use was made of the boom-type machine removed from the Morgavel face, and on the new downstream work face one TBM was set up: this had in the meantime finished its work from S. Domingos and was taken out through the open-cut stretch.

The two work faces upstream of the shafts, on which boom-type machines were being used, met at the end of the first quarter of 1980 (Fig. 3). At that time, however, the two work faces on the downstream side that were being constructed by TBM were very much behindhand, mainly owing to the various blockages that occurred with those machines that necessitated lengthy and difficult operations to free them and re-establish conditions for boring. This state of affairs led to the start of a further vertical shaft being opened, in the last quarter of 1980 – this time with a depth of 80 m – to create new work faces and a consequent reduction of the time to complete the tunnel. This shaft was bored at 8.150 km – practically equidistant from the points at which the two work faces of the tunnel were (Fig. 3); for reasons that were unrelated to the technical aspects of the work, however, when in September, 1982, new faces were started from the bottom of this shaft, its location seemed, after all, not to be the best.

In view of the disappointing results that had been achieved with the tunnel-boring and boom-type machines, the former were not allowed and the latter were considered inadvisable in the competition for tenders for the construction of the stretches of the tunnel from this last shaft. These sectors were executed by the conventional method of drilling and blasting, preference being given to support by shotcrete, as far as possible according to the New Austrian Tunnelling Method. The quality of the ground, however – in particular, its rapid degradation with time – made it necessary to make additional use of forepoling and, along many zones, of steel arches and sometimes steel support plates. The section used was the inverted U, regarded as the most convenient as it gave greater width at the base and thus facilitated debris handling and the movement of personnel and accessory services. For drilling, apart from conventional equipment, use was made of a jumbo, equipped with two hydraulic drifters; the lengths of the blasts varied between 1.0 and 2.5 m, according to the characteristics of the ground; perimeter holes, according to the smooth blasting technique, were used. To remove the debris, apart from conventional equipment, a shuttle-train was used.

These two stretches of tunnel were completed on 28 May and 13 August, 1984, respectively, connecting to the face from Morgavel and linking up with the length from upstream, the latter terminating the excavation of the tunnel.

Efficiencies in excavation

Generally speaking, and, in fact, fully confirmed by the time that was taken to execute the work in comparison with that which had originally been estimated, the actual efficiencies of the various equipment and excavation methods were vastly inferior to those which had been expected.

In regard to the use of the TBM, with which it had been assumed that rates of 2 m/24 h in the worst ground, 4 m/24 h–12.5 m/24 h in medium-quality ground and 25 m/24 h in the best-quality ground would be achieved, it was possible to achieve on average 3 m/calendar day. Only in 1981, when it had already been decided to create new work faces, did the TBM then in service, in an advance of about 1800 m, achieve an average speed of 7.4 m/day. Although it is possible that such unusual efficiency may have been due to a locally better-quality rock mass, it is more likely that the real reason is the greater experience of the personnel who were operating the TBM. In any case, the difficulties that these machines have in excavating through very heterogeneous zones of ground, in which the behaviour of hard greywackes is in sharp contrast with the very low resistance of the plastic slates, made their use inadvisable in the rock mass concerned.

With the boom-type machines it was expected, initially, to reach speeds of 4 m/24 h in bad ground, 5–6 m/24 h in average-quality ground and 9 m/24 h in good-quality ground. In practice, and in the best periods, average speeds were only 1.6 m/calendar day. The smaller differences, with these machines, between the actual and predicted rates indicate their greater adaptability to the rock mass to be excavated, in which the biggest difficulties were encountered with the occurrence of the hardest greywacke zones, when there were problems of high wear rates of picks and in regard to mechanical sturdiness.

Finally, with drilling and blasting, average speeds of 3 m/calendar day were obtained – the forecast was 5 m/calendar day. Although the expected rate was not achieved, there seems no doubt that this traditional excavation process was preferable for the rock mass concerned: the mechanical excavation processes, apart from requiring more highly skilled operators, inevitably present higher cost components in relation to the immobilization of the equipment.

Final lining

Since the tunnel was intended for the circulation of water the final lining was considered to have as its principal functions those of resistance, protection of the steel components placed in the first support stage, smoothing of the internal surface and protection of the rock mass from alteration due to contact with water and air. This latter aspect assumed particular importance owing to the characteristics of alterability (already referred to) of some of the constituents of the rock mass, such characteristics being clearly shown by the results of the slake durability test; moreover, as has also been mentioned, the expansibility of some clays also gave rise to the high sensitivity to humidity of the excavated rock mass. The greater or lesser predominance of the functions mentioned depends, however, on the zones of the rock mass that were traversed.

Initially, it was assumed that the final lining, in which would be included all the steel components constituting the first support stage, might differ according to whether the zone of the rock mass traversed was of good or bad quality (cases of crush or altered zones). Whereas in the first situation it was expected to use shotcrete or precast concrete components that were not very thick, in the second it was considered necessary to cast *in-situ* concrete, reinforced if required.

In a later stage, with the excavation works at an advanced phase, when it was necessary to study general solutions for the final lining, it was recognized that the great frequency, along the tunnel excavated, of types I, II and III ground (Fig. 4) made it uneconomical to consider any variations in the type of lining or thickness of lining within the same type. Accordingly, it was decided to cast *in-situ* concrete along the whole tunnel, and also to use a constant value for its minimum thickness. Except in localized cases of enlarged sections, created for operational reasons, that minimum thickness was 0.25 m for any of the types of section along the tunnel (circular, normal or enlarged horseshoe and inverted U) (Fig. 5).

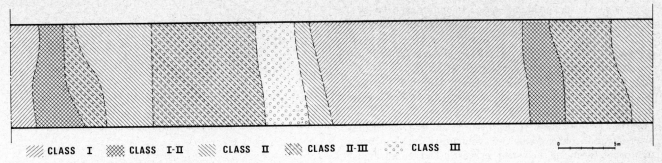

Fig. 4   Typical variation in quality of rock mass

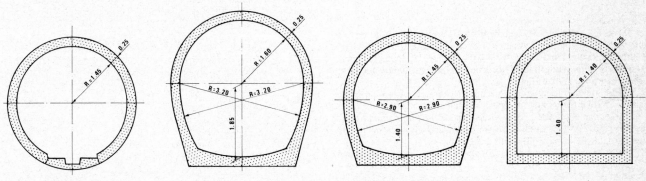

Fig. 5   Final lining sections

The application of ordinary cast concrete was, however, in principle related to those ground zones which showed themselves to be stabilized, i.e. those zones in which, before concreting and owing, or not, to the application of first-phase support, the measurements taken showed rates of convergence that were less than 1 mm/month one month after excavation. When that situation occurred it meant that no significant loads were being exerted on the lining, which would be allocated only the functions of protection and smoothing referred to above.

For those zones which were not stabilized the possibility was kept open of the use of reinforced concrete, but calculations of the respective sections, apart from being complex, proved inconclusive. The complexity was due to the difficulty of simulating not only the heterogeneities of the rock mass and the expansibility of some of the constituents of the rock material but also to the irregular excavation profiles, the variety of steel components left from the first support phase and the need to consider the time factor. Nevertheless, the importance, from the economic point of view, of the choice between 'reinforcing' or 'not reinforcing' led to concreting of some of those zones, initially without reinforcement; these constituted the experimental stretches on which intensified measurements of convergences were made on marks placed on the actual surface of the concrete or on the rock through windows left open in the lining. As such experimental stretches were found to behave well, it was decided not to reinforce the lining of such initially unstable zones.

In certain unstable zones it was found that partial concreting in some places proved to be extremely beneficial. Examples of such cases were the concreting of some sills, which led to substantial reductions in the horizontal convergences measured, and concreting of the lower parts of the lateral zones, which slowed down significantly the tendency towards curvature observed in some steel arches. A similar effect to that of the concreting of the sill was achieved in the first-phase support by steel bracing of the feet of the arches.

Administrative aspects

The difficulties of a geotechnical nature presented by the rock mass, in regard to which there was insufficient experience in excavating analogous works, explain part of the delay and increased cost over those predicted for the construction of the S. Domingos–Morgavel tunnel, but they cannot, of course, justify all of them. It is therefore necessary to look for the other causes so that the same mistakes can be avoided in similar works.

It is important to consider, first and foremost, that in this case the client was a State entity that, constricted by a wide variety of regulations, was unable to adapt official procedures to the flexible conditions that must be accepted in the design and construction of a tunnel. In the specific case of the S. Domingos–Morgavel tunnel, of an appreciable length and passing through ground that was geologically monotonous on a regional scale but very heterogeneous on the scale of the undertaking, the geological and geotechnical site investigations could never have sufficed to allow definition in advance, metre by metre, of the best methods for excavation, support and final lining of the work. Such work methods would be established as work progressed.

This procedure, however, was, initially, not considered. On the basis of the originally perceived project the contract was awarded after competitive bidding in which the criterion for the selection of the contractor was mainly based on price aspects and operational efficiencies that it might be possible to attain with the equipment that at the time was technologically most advanced. The eventual need for a rapid alteration in processes whenever the methods envisaged proved to be unsuitable for the rock mass involved was, unfortunately, not contemplated, and this may well have been the main source of the arduous work conditions that were encountered during the major part of the construction work on the tunnel.

Once the contractual conditions had been established between client and contractor they could not easily be modified, even though the client was becoming increasingly aware that there were good reasons for modifications and, at the same time, reasons were being given by the project designer and by consultants and were evident from the course of the works. Only in about mid-1980, after a very difficult stage of the works, was it possible to envisage solutions that were likely to change the work processes and speed up the performance of the tunnel. The bureaucratic obstacles to effecting such solutions were, however, very great and caused an additional delay of at least a year and a half, apart from weakening the feasibility of the proposed solutions.

As from 1981, however, it was finally possible for the client to begin to benefit, on an increasingly effective and efficient scale, from cooperation between his own technicians and those of the designer, consultants and contractors. If the best use was not made of that cooperation, at least the way for its achievement had been defined. If this result could be reached only when it was no longer possible to avoid most of the drawbacks that occurred during the works, at least it had the advantage of constituting a very positive development for use in future undertakings.

References

1. Oliveira J. T. Horn M. and Paproth E. Preliminary note on the stratigraphy of the Baixo Alentejo Flysch Group, Carboniferous of southern Portugal and on the palaeogeographic development, compared to corresponding units in Northwest Germany. *Comunções Servs geol. Port.,* **65,** 1979, 151–68.

2. Mello Mendes F. *et al.* Geotechnical characterization of weak Carboniferous formations of South Portugal. In *Weak rock: soft, fractured and weathered rock, proceedings of the international symposium, Tokyo, 1981* Akai K. Hayashi M. and Nishimatsu Y. eds (Rotterdam: Balkema, 1981), vol. 2, 915–20.

3. Mello Mendes F. O túnel S. Domingos–Morgavel e a geotecnia. *Geotecnia* no. 37, 1983, 103–17.

4. Ojima L. M. Classificação geotécnica do maciço atravessado pelo túnel do adutor Sado–Morgavel. *Geotecnia* no. 31, 1981, 47–69.

5. Horta da Silva J. A. Gomes Teixeira J. A. and Saraiva A. L. A. Túnel S. Domingos–Morgavel: Contribuição para o estudo geológico-geotécnico. Unpublished G.A.S. report D.S.L. 32/78, 1978.

6. Rocha M. and Barroso M. Some applications of the new integral sampling method in rock masses. In *Rock fracture, symposium of the International Society for Rock Mechanics, Nancy, 1971,* pap. 1-21, 12 p.

7. Rocha M. *et al.* Characterization of the deformability of rock masses by dilatometer tests. In *Proceedings 2nd conference of International Society for Rock Mechanics, Belgrade, 1970,* vol. 1, pap. 2-32, 8 p.

8. International Society for Rock Mechanics, Commission on Standardization. Suggested methods for determining water content, porosity, density, absorption and related properties and swelling and slake-durability index properties. *Int. J. Rock Mech. Min. Sci.,* **16,** 1979, 141–56.

9. Rodrigues J. D. Alterabilidade de rochas em problemas de geologia de engenharia. Aplicação a casos portugueses. Research Officer thesis presented to LNEC, Lisbon, 1975.

10. Mello Mendes F. and Ojima L. M. Geotechnical rock mass classifications applicable to tunnel design and construction. In *Proceedings 4th international congress, International Association of Engineering Geology, India, 1982* (Rotterdam: Balkema, 1982), vol. 5, 183–6.

The Tumbler Ridge branch line tunnel, northeastern British Columbia, Canada

R. D. Hendry
F. E. Kimball
V. W. Shtenko
BC Rail, Vancouver, British Columbia, Canada

Synopsis
In 1983 British Columbia Railway successfully completed 16 km of tunnel – the first tunnels through the Canadian Rocky Mountains in 100 years – for a new 130-km branch line crossing the Rockies to link the coal-field of northeastern British Columbia with a new west coast port. The lapsed time from exploration to the first coal train over the line was 36 months. The branch line, the construction of which is fully described, including the tunnels, was completed on time and within the budget.

General background

In the autumn of 1983 the British Columbia Railway completed a 130-km branch line to provide a means of moving the high-grade metallurgical coal from the immense fields in north-eastern British Columbia to market. This $455 000 000 branch line is the connecting link in and part of a $2 500 000 000 project known as the Northeast Coal Project – one of the largest projects ever undertaken in Canada. Approximately 13 000 man-years of direct construction labour was involved. Included are the development of two new coal mines with a combined yearly production capability of 8 000 000 ton (one mine is the largest in Canada and there is a prospect of several more mines in the future), a new town for 10 000 people, two new highways 110 km long, a major new 168-km 230 000-V power line, a new deep-sea terminal, the upgrading of some 853 km of existing railway line and the new 130-km branch line. Projects of this magnitude have been undertaken in other times and places, but we are not aware of any that was completed in 36 months. More than $25 000 000 was spent each week during the construction phase.

Route

The route that was chosen for the new branch line (Fig. 1) resulted from a series of comparative studies of several alternative routes in terms of capital cost, long-term operating and maintenance cost, terrain traversed, length of route, construction obstacles and time required for construction. The outcome of these studies pointed to the route that connected the coalfields with a small BC Rail junction at Anzac. The main obstacles along this route were two ridges of the Rocky Mountains, which called for tunnels – one, the Table tunnel, at 9 km, and the other, the Wolverine tunnel, at 6 km. In addition, there are two short tunnels at km 80 and 86, totalling approximately 660 m, bridges across the valleys of three large rivers and ten smaller rivers and creeks, ledges cut along the sides of mountains and the traversing of ancient lake bottoms filled with thixotropic saturated silty clays. An all-inclusive budget of $455 000 000 was developed for the 130-km branch line, including electrification. Of this $455 000 000 branch line budget, the tunnels accounted for approximately $200 000 000.

The tunnels are located in a very remote and inaccessible part of British Columbia. All the initial exploration work, including the drilling, had to be supported by helicopter. Crews pioneering the roads into the future camp sites and clearing the portals were transported every day by helicopter. Transport between headings throughout tunnel construction was by helicopter stationed at Sukunka Camp. Unfortunately, two helicopters and two men were lost as a result of accidents. One other fatality occurred during the construction of the branch line as a result of a landslide at a bridge construction site.

Detailed route study

The detailed geological investigation, preliminary design and contractor-type cost estimate for the two long tunnels was undertaken by the tunnel consultants in September, 1980. The scope of the work included (a) geological exploration of the selected tunnel alignment, including mapping, drilling and geophysical surveys; (b) topographic surveys of the portal areas; (c) an evaluation of the geology along the proposed tunnel alignments; (d) selection of specific tunnel alignment, profiles and portal location; (e) an assessment of tunnelling conditions as influenced by the rock types and geological formations; (f) tunnel design, including support, drainage and permanent ventilation; (g) construction infrastructure, i.e. camps, shops and storage areas, waste rock and drainage water disposal, aggregate sources and contract packages; and (h) a definitive, contractor-type cost estimate.

As the field work proceeded the emphasis was concentrated on portal location, surface and subsurface conditions and the geological profile of tunnel alignment. The geological profiles developed are shown in Figs. 2 and 3. These field studies were completed in November, 1980, followed by the final report and cost estimates in April, 1981.

Portal sites

In British Columbia the interface between the surface cover and bedrock is almost always troublesome. Usually, the bedrock surface is badly weathered and fissured, silty clays filling the cracks; the overburden can be either pervious glacial or alluvial soils or some combination of the two, covering ancient screes, and in at least two places soft, easily eroded shales. These conditions, often accompanied by critical groundwater flows, severely hindered the excavation and were encountered to varying degrees at all eight portal locations.

In the spring of 1982 groundwater and surface runoff continued to cause erosion, landslides and drainage problems.

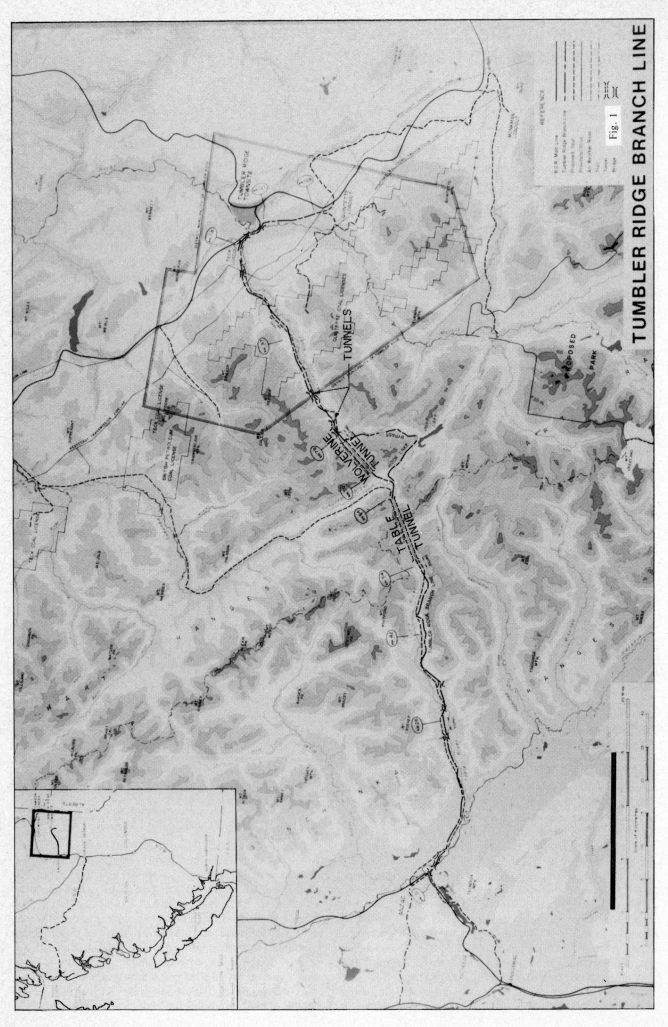

TUMBLER RIDGE BRANCH LINE

Fig. 1

46

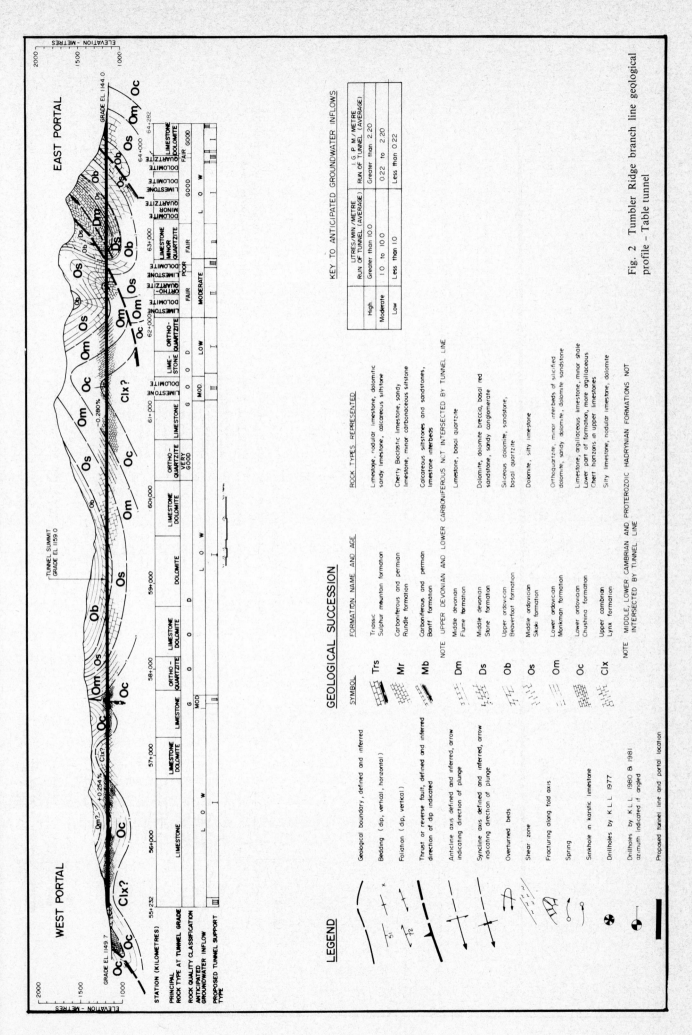

Fig. 2 Tumbler Ridge branch line geological profile – Table tunnel

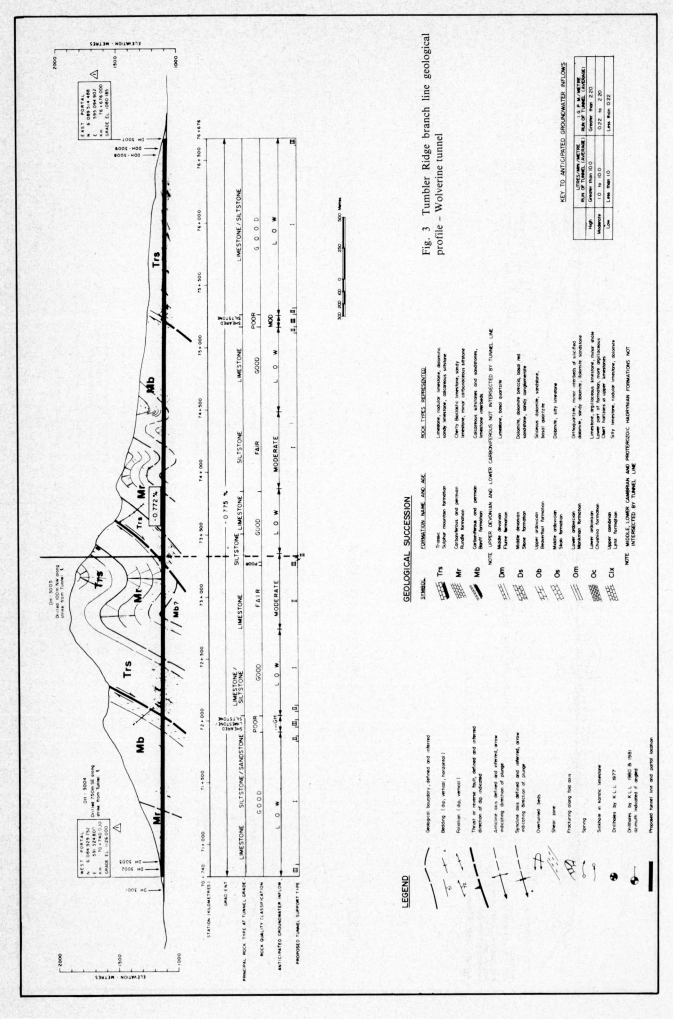

Fig. 3 Tumbler Ridge branch line geological
profile – Wolverine tunnel

The extremely fine silts and clays would not settle out and some ended up in the creeks and rivers. This eventually brought the project into conflict with environmentalists, who viewed the whole project with some indignation. The runoff, combined with dirty water from the tunnels, continued to give problems until the job was completed, even though the contaminated water was passed through extensive settling basins. In the summer of 1982 proper drainage ditches were established and the cut surfaces were seeded, which improved the situation markedly.

The portals were excavated from October, 1981, to February, 1982, in severe winter weather, which was a blessing in disguise: although snow storms, wind, ice and darkness hindered the work, the frost in the ground actually improved the excavation of the saturated silty clays. The excavation of the portals proved to be more difficult than had been expected.

Tunnel location and geological conditions

For the tunnels themselves it was important to identify potential problem spots – specifically, the extent of fault zones, possible groundwater conditions and type of support that would be required. In practice, the rock formations and location were much the same as had been forecast in the field study report, except that a large fault zone that had been predicted around 72 + 000 in the Wolverine tunnel did not materialize. It was suggested later that it was not a fault but a very tight fold that bottomed above the tunnel; the ground in that area proved to be very good. Other faults predicted for 73 + 300 and 75 + 150 also were not evident in the tunnel. The quality of the ground throughout the Wolverine tunnel was considerably better than had been predicted. In fact, it was estimated that the Wolverine tunnel unit cost (cost per metre) would be significantly greater than the Table tunnel costs, because of the rock conditions, and the bids confirmed this. This resulted in the revival of a scheme known as the Hook Lake bypass.

When the decision was made to locate the rail line along the Table River Valley the construction of the Table tunnel was committed since there was no other way of traversing between the Upper Table Valley and the Sukunka and still maintain the ruling gradient of 1.5%. This was not so for the Wolverine

tunnel as there was an alternative overland route (Hook Lake bypass), which would proceed east along the Sukunka Valley to Hook Lake, then northwest into the Upper Wolverine Valley (Fig. 1). This route had been considered previously and had been rejected on the basis of avalanche conditions, very rugged topography and the additional 12-km length that was involved with the route.

Drilling and exploration work in 1980 had indicated that the rock conditions for the Wolverine tunnel were not expected to be as good as those for the Table tunnel. A further examination of the Hook Lake bypass route on the ground confirmed that the route would be difficult and expensive, but that it was a viable alternative. This was important at the time in that if the tenders for the Wolverine tunnel were unreasonable owing to the predicted poorer ground, the company would have the option of following the Hook Lake bypass route. This option did not materialize as tenders and projected cost to completion for both tunnels were within reasonable budgetary limits.

In fact, as has been noted, the rock in the Wolverine tunnel was better than that in the Table tunnel. Unfortunately, underground rock mechanics studies can be made only after the excavation of the tunnel, serving their most useful purpose in determining the kind and amount of support required and the tunnel lining that should be installed to secure the rock against short- and long-term failure.

Succession of events

The field investigations were concluded in November, 1980, the final report and cost estimate being submitted in April, 1981. The results of these investigations and subsequent analyses are represented in Figs. 2 and 3, showing the geological profiles of the Table and Wolverine tunnels and highlighting such features as principal rock type, rock quality classification, expected groundwater flow, fault zones and proposed type of tunnel support.

The design and contract documents for construction of the tunnels were developed and prepared, based on the results of the field exploration programme, which included drilling, seismic surveys, petrographic analysis, permeability analysis and geological mapping. Tenders were received on 25 September, 1981, from seven contractors to drive the Table and

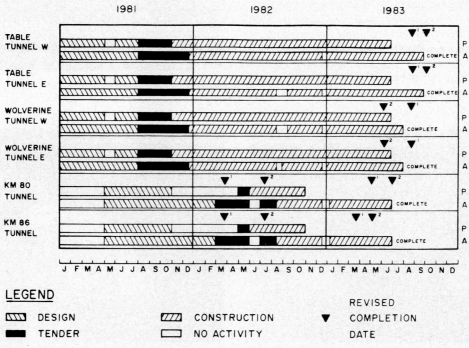

Fig. 4   Design and construction schedule

49

Wolverine tunnels. Four contracts were awarded on 9 December, 1981, for construction to proceed from four headings. All bidders were pre-qualified in June, 1981, followed by a site visit and briefing, all prior to the preparation of bids.

The specifications allowed for bids based on the use of tunnel-boring machines as well as the drill and blast method, but only one bid for one heading was submitted that proposed to use a TBM, and it was much higher than the other bids.

Some of the items in the specifications that were peculiar to the main tunnels were as follow: the tenderers were pre-qualified; 100% performance and labour and material payment bonds were required; provision was made for tenderers to offer credits for multi-contract awards; provision was made for generous front-end mobilization costs, and the holdback was limited to $1 500 000; a differing site conditions clause was included; provision was made for bonus payments for achieving stipulated milestone dates; and as an incentive to the contractors and to provide the owner with some control over the tunnel completion date, provision was made to delete up to 500 m from one heading contract and award it to the opposite heading.

Fig. 4 shows the scheduled and actual design and construction schedule for the tunnels, which were completed well within the limitations imposed by the design schedule. The tunnels were also completed within the constraints of the budget.

Contracts for the excavation of portal overburden and portal preparation were awarded and work was begun by mid-1981 and concluded in the winter of 1982. Three camps, to be occupied by the tunnel contractors, were also installed during the summer and autumn of 1981. These camps were provided to the contractor with a capacity of 50% of the expected manpower needed to drive the tunnels, it being the tunnel contractors' responsibility to expand the camps to satisfy their total requirements. The three camps were located as close to the tunnel work as topography and soil conditions would allow. The camps were constructed before the tunnel contracts were tendered. This provided for the tunnel contractors to mobilize immediately following the award of contracts.

Camps for Table and Wolverine tunnels

Three camps were constructed for the crews working on the long tunnels and one for the crews working on the two short tunnels. Sukunka, the largest camp (a 375-man camp), served the two adjacent (Wolverine west and Table east) headings; it was located centrally between the two headings, which were about 6 km apart. The camps at the other two headings started out as 168-man camps, but at the peak period the capacity was increased to accommodate a further 20 people. Not all of these

people were contractors' men working in the tunnels; 15 or 20 BC Rail employees, some of whom were working on other jobs, were also living in these camps.

The kitchens, dining halls and half of the sleeping accommodation were constructed by BCR prior to contract award and were completed by the contractor after the contract was awarded.

Chronology of tunnel construction

The contracts were awarded on 9 December, 1981, and the contractors commenced mobilization by purchasing and fabricating equipment to start driving of the tunnel by 1 April, 1982. All headings were to be driven by conventional methods

Fig. 6   Table east drill jumbo, 1 March, 1982

Fig. 7   Table east portal cut showing sliding floor in place, 25 March, 1982

Fig. 5   Table east portal areas, 28 February, 1982

Fig. 8   Table east portal, 1 May, 1982

Fig. 9 Table east ice in portal area, 10 December, 1982

Fig. 10 Table east solution cavern at km 62 + 964, 4 February, 1983

Fig. 11 Table east solution cavern at km 62 + 964, 4 February, 1983 (note clay-infilled fracture in sediments)

Fig. 12 Wolverine west portal: jumbo at face preparing for first round, 18 May, 1982

Fig. 13 Wolverine west: aerial view, May, 1982

of drilling and blasting by use of hydraulic drill jumbos with six drills mounted on each jumbo, and with each drill jumbo operating on a sliding floor. Mucking was to be carried out by Conway and Hagglund loaders, the muck being transported by rail-mounted cars.

Tunnel excavation was begun on 16 March, 1982, at Wolverine east portal, on 5 April at Table west and east, and on 27 May at Wolverine west. The most difficult problem proved to be the portal excavations and the preparation of the portal face to an acceptable standard for tunnelling. The tunnels were completed thus: the Table west heading (total contract 4204 m) 'holed through' on 21 August, 1983, and the contractor was fully demobilized by October, 1983; the Table east heading

Fig. 14   Wolverine west Conway mucker moving to face, May, 1982

Fig. 15   Wolverine west and Sukunka camp (upper right), 9 October, 1982

Fig.16   98-car unit coal train, Tumbler Ridge branch line

(total contract 4844 m) 'holed through' on 21 August, 1983, and the contractor was fully demobilized by October, 1983; the Wolverine west heading (total contract 2533.5 m) 'holed through' on 28 May, 1983, and the contractor was fully demobilized by August, 1983; and the Wolverine east heading (total contract 3378.8 m) 'holed through' on 28 May, 1983, and the contractor was fully demobilized by August, 1983.

Figs. 5–15 show aspects of the work and Fig. 16 is a photograph of the 98-car train on the Tumbler Ridge branch line.

Geological investigations and surveys of the two sites for the km 80 and 86 tunnels (269 and 366 m in length, respectively), completed in 1981, included the excavation of several trenches, seismic infraction surveys, drilling and geological mapping at the proposed tunnel sites. Tunnel support types were selected

and the possible distribution of support along the tunnel was determined. The design parameters were also prepared for cut slopes in rock and overburden at the portals. The drawings and specifications for the contract documents were prepared with use of the data obtained from the field programme, and finalized by February, 1982. Construction was begun in September, 1982, the excavation being concluded in December, 1982, and the tunnel completed in July, 1983. (Fig. 4 gives an overview of the planned (P) and actual (A) schedule, covering the design, tendering and construction of the tunnels.)

The Wolverine east heading crew started to drill the first round on 16 March, 1982, about two weeks ahead of the schedule. They were able to do this because they started the drive with a seven-boom rubber-tyred jumbo and rubber-tyred front-end loader. The tunnel was advanced 151 m in about 10 weeks working, first, a single shift and then on a two shift per day schedule. During this ten-week period the contractor assembled his permanent equipment, the first round with this equipment being taken on 29 May, 1982.

Tunnel design

The tunnels are a standard 'D' section 5.5 m wide and 8.07 m high. Typical cross-sections are shown in Fig. 17, which shows the details of the proposed support (types I, II and III).

The rock quality in all headings was considerably better than had been expected with the singular exception of a quartzite zone between 61 + 700 and 62 + 050 in Table tunnel. The prediction for this section was good-quality rock requiring type I support, whereas it was characterized by rather severe rock-bursting – explosive separations of slabs, weighing a few grammes to many kilogrammes, from walls and ceilings of the tunnel. The bursting was severe immediately after each round and diminished to zero activity after a week or two. The type III support that was used in approximately 40% of this section required the installation of 140 steel sets.

Excluding the portals, the only other place where type III support was used was an 8-m section near 62 + 964 in Table tunnel, where eight sets were installed at the site of a large solution cavern; here the rock around the cavity was badly fissured and its stability questionable. Ten sets were installed at each portal to support the weathered and shattered rock around the opening; five of the portals also have a poured concrete collar.

The original design required a minimum support of type I throughout the tunnel, but this was reduced to the extent that only about 60% was supported.

Excavation methods and equipment

The drill and blast method was used to excavate all the tunnels. The long tunnels were driven full face; all the headings used 4-m steel with button bits at the start of the drive but, later, two were changed to 5-m steel. In the long tunnels all contractors used the six-boom, double-deck rail-mounted hydraulic jumbos and sliding floors; three headings used Conway mucking machines with side-dump cars and diesel locomotives, and the fourth heading used Hagglund mucking and tramming equipment with diesel locomotives.

The headings that used the short steel (4-m steel) achieved an average advance of about 3.5 m per round and at times five rounds in 24 h were possible, and the headings on which 5-m steel was employed were averaging 4.4 m per round and at times achieved four rounds per day. The record advance for one 24-h period was 18.4 m and for one week (seven days) the record was 116.1 m. The 4- and 5-m steels both have their advocates, but there is no doubt that improved performance was achieved on the two headings that changed from 4- to 5-m steel. A point to

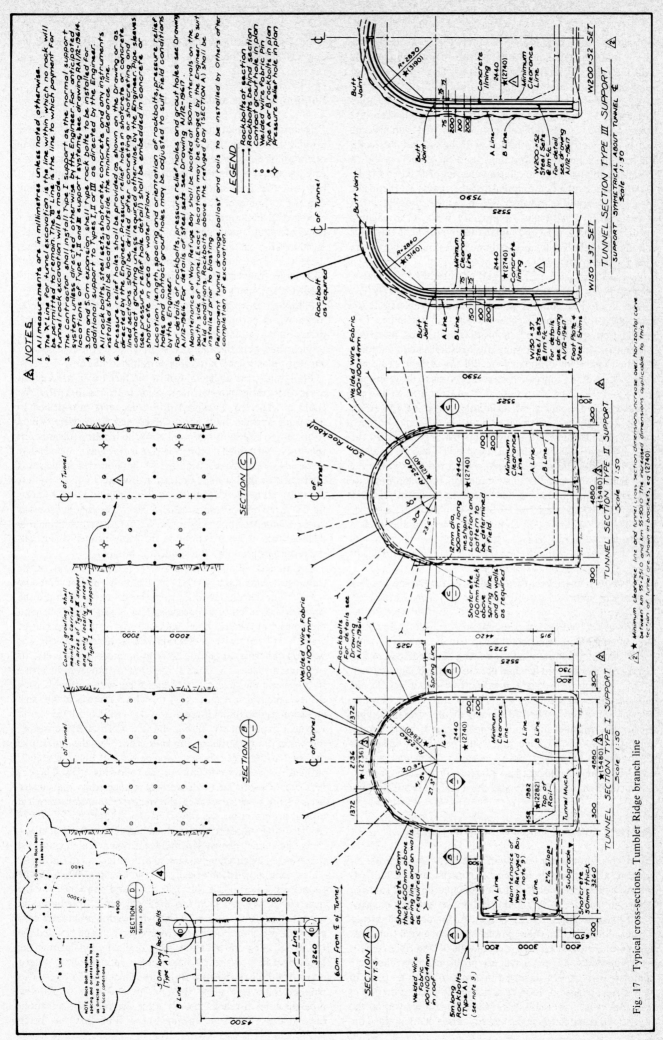

Fig. 17 Typical cross-sections, Tumbler Ridge branch line

53

be remembered if there is any possibility that 5-m steel will be used is that the drill slides should be able to accommodate the 5-m steel when the equipment is ordered. The 5-m steel is not compatible with slides designed for 4-m steel.

All headings used 45- and 50-mm bits; the number of holes varied slightly between headings, but the average was about 112 holes. All headings used burn (shatter) cuts, and each heading had its own preference for the design of the cut, but most used 100-mm relief holes. All headings used the Nonel system to initiate the blasts. The Nonel delay detonator is based on the use of a shock tube (a 3-mm plastic tube coated on the inside with a fine explosive powder). When ignited, usually with a detonating cord ('B' line), a pressure wave is propagated through the shock tube and maintained by the light explosive coating. Both the trunk line and 'bunch' blasting methods were used for hook-ups.

Two headings used dynamite and two headings used water-gel explosives; both work well, but there is noticeably less smoke and fumes from the water-gels and they overcome the headache problem that is characteristic of dynamite. This information applies to the long headings. The most persistent difficulty in drilling and blasting was to establish and maintain a high standard of drilling; there did not appear to be any appreciation of the consequential contribution to the long-term stability of the tunnel that resulted from strict attention to the alignment and spacing of drill-holes. The specifications required a 200-mm step between rounds (the difference between the 'A' and 'B' lines); to achieve this the angle between the drill and tunnel axis, for the perimeter holes, should be about 3.5°. Measuring the angle of the half-holes remaining after the blast gave results up to 9.5°. Constant vigilance and prompting improved the performance, but there were frequent relapses. The specifications must contain some penalty in the event of poor-quality drilling: our contract did not include such a provision, except in a passive sense – there was no pay for any rock broken outside the 'B' line (Fig. 17). This is not sufficient deterrent to make contractors repent.

The short tunnels were excavated by use of the top heading and bench approach, the top heading being completely excavated before the bench was started. Rubber-tyred front-end loaders served both the loading and transport functions; two- and three-boom pneumatic and hydraulic, rubber-tyred or track-type jumbos were used for drilling. This equipment had been used on other jobs and had been maintained, but not well. It was subject to frequent breakdowns, but it served the purpose. Blasting was done with ANFO and electric blasting. To sum up, when applied to tunnels of this size and length range, the top heading and bench method, with similar equipment, is very effective, and would be efficient in tunnels of this section for longer drives, the advantage being the small crew size required, and small investment. If speed is important, this method cannot compete with the method used in the long tunnels.

Shotcrete lining of km 80 and km 86 tunnels

Both short tunnels are lined with steel fibre-reinforced shotcrete and all four portals have poured concrete collars. This was the most successful portion of the work on the short tunnels. Although the pace of shotcreting did not set any new records, it did make steady progress without major delays or break-downs, and the work, when completed, was of a high standard. A dry shotcrete process was used and the 0.75% fibre content by volume (59 kg/m^3) gave no problems. The shotcrete complete with fibres was mixed in a central batching plant in Vancouver, bagged in 1600-kg sacks and shipped to the job in insulated vans; it was still quite warm when it arrived on the job. Stored immediately in the heated tunnels, it maintained the heat, thereby avoiding many of the problems that plagued the application of shotcrete in the winter months in the long tunnels.

Solution caverns and groundwater

Estimation of the amount of water and the location of heavy groundwater inflows that might be encountered in a tunnelling operation is not easy, especially in regions that have a complicated geology. If groundwater is present in large quantities, it presents the possibility of a severe risk in a tunnelling operation. Some of the most catastrophic experiences and expenses in underground works have been caused by heavy flows of water. In our case the potential for water was underestimated throughout the length of the long tunnels – indeed, there was no mention of the possibility of dissolution caverns with large volumes of circulating water. Nor was there any prediction of highly fractured zones with heavy water inflows.

Although the occurrence of these conditions in several locations, in both of the long tunnels, did not, in the event, present any real danger to the workers or the viability of the tunnel, they were the cause of some anxious times, long and expensive delays and miserable working conditions.

Pilot holes were drilled ahead of the face on all headings in areas where the geological information indicated that problems could be expected. Diamond drill holes were also drilled to intercept expected fault zones. These test holes were drilled from refuge bays and ran parallel to the heading advance. In the Wolverine tunnel a trace of H$_2$S gas was encountered early in the advance of the east heading. At that point the railway was instructed to drill a pilot hole to a distance of three rounds ahead on all headings (Table and Wolverine tunnels) and test for further concentrations of H$_2$S gas. This instruction was later rescinded to apply only to the Wolverine tunnel. Pilot hole drilling did, however, continue in Table tunnel when considered appropriate by the resident geologist.

The first large dissolution cavern encountered was in the Table east heading at km 62 + 964, about 1300 m from the portal. The encounter with this cavern came without the slightest indication of its presence. It was just slightly beyond the bottom of the drill-holes, and although a small amount of water was frequently present in the drill-holes, there was nothing abnormal about the amount of water in the holes for this round. When the round was blasted, however, it broke through into the cavern, which was filled with saturated rock debris. Since the invert of this 6-ft high cavern was at the same elevation as the tunnel invert it was not visible until the round was nearly mucked out, although there was a large increase in the water flowing out of the muck pile. As the muck pile dropped at the face this material spewed out into the tunnel. Infilled fissures were present for the following 10 m. There is very little doubt that this cavern is connected to the surface because the flow varies with the weather: approximately 8 h after it begins to rain the flow increases in the tunnel; at times in the spring runoff it has produced more than 2000 l/min.

As the tunnel progressed many inflows were encountered that were a nuisance but which had little effect on the advance. This state changed dramatically around km 60 + 700 just as the tunnel was entering the quartzite zone and continued for the next 200 m. The rock in this area was badly fractured and crystal clear water, about 2°C above freezing and under considerable pressure, poured out of every crack and flooded the tunnel. Drilling and mucking were difficult, but loading the holes became very nearly impossible; water spouted out of every drill-hole in the face for some 75 rounds. Progress was stopped for over a week while pumps and 3 km of 500-mm pipeline were installed. Shortly after the face was advanced beyond the water zone the measured flow that was being pumped from the tunnel through two pipelines, one 500 mm in diameter and the other a 250-mm line, was more than 26 000 l/min. A more dismal and demoralizing place to work than this 200 m of unremitting downpour is difficult to imagine.

In Wolverine tunnel, although the water inflows were greater than had been expected throughout the length of the tunnel, in the final 400 m on each side of the breakthrough the inflow increased to more than 30 000 l/min, evenly distributed between the two headings. On the downgrade end (west heading) the tunnel flooded to a depth of about 3.5 m at the face, drowning the jumbo, the electrics for the sliding floor and the pumps.

In Wolverine tunnel east heading a large solution cavern that crossed the tunnel above the crown delayed the advance for some 29 days while a draining programme was attempted. Here again the cavern was filled with rock debris and during the drainage period some 50 m^3 washed out of the 4-in drains in the face. At the start of the draining period a pressure of 2400 kPa was recorded. After a day or so, however, the pressure began to drop as more holes were drilled in the face. Maintaining flow in the holes was a real problem; after a short time the debris plugged the holes and constant cleaning was required. After draining for about 20 days the pressure had fallen to 200 kPa and at this point it was decided to advance the tunnel. The third round broke into the cavern on the upper right-hand side of the face. The cavern was more than 2 m high and about 1 m wide and extended for some 15 m horizontally and then turned upwards at about 60°. There is very little doubt now that this dissolution channel is circulating waters of surface origin; in addition, judging by some of the larger pieces of debris discharged from the cavern, there is a basis to reason that the channel extends to the surface. There were pieces of coral rock, which is quite common on the surface, in the debris. At this location the depth of the tunnel below the surface is approximately 325 m. Incidentally, the flow from this channel, at only a slightly reduced rate, persists even today. In the next 600 m of this tunnel large torrents of water occur at three other locations and there are many smaller inflows. It is highly probable that these channelways are irregularly and intricately interconnected. Indeed, the outcome of attempts to grout some of these areas produced more water spouts in other places. Pumping grouting materials into the rock achieved very little, notwithstanding the large amount of money that was spent to try to reduce the flow.

In the warmer months the water spouts are an inconvenience, but in the winter months, when every spout turns to a gigantic icicle, the problem becomes formidable. At times trains are delayed, electric catenary cables are pulled down and ice covers the track and generally causes innumerable problems.

Hydrogen sulphide gas in Wolverine tunnel

Another serious problem, peculiar to Wolverine tunnel, is the presence of hydrogen sulphide gas. When first encountered it caused some unpleasant eye irritations and at that time measurements revealed concentrations of up to 35 ppm. An increase in the ventilation reduced and maintained the concentration well within the permissible 10 ppm limit set by the Workers' Compensation Board. Conjecture about the origin of the gas usually leads to the conclusion that it is a by-product of the decay of sulphur-bearing organic materials, but this theory is not universally accepted. There is also a theory that the gas is associated with the water, but this supposition does not satisfy all conditions. Sour natural gas can occur almost anywhere in this region of British Columbia and there are producing fields only 50 km away.

When the contractors removed their fans, on completion of the tunnel, forced ventilation was no longer available. Nature took over, but proved to be an unpredictable and unreliable ventilation method. As the west end of the tunnel is some 45 m higher than the east end, it might be expected that the stack effect would influence the direction of air flow in the tunnel. If it does, there is very little evidence to substantiate that supposition; it changes direction and velocity frequently, sometimes twice a day. There are periods, however, when there is very little movement of air in the tunnel and during such periods the gas concentration increases. This does not cause operating problems, but it may accelerate the corrosion process. A research programme is now in progress to find answers to the problem.

In any case, it is obvious that all the facts have not been collected yet. Nevertheless, it is clear that there will not be a shortage of problems to solve as long as this H$_2$S gas persists. Even now it is causing severe corrosion of the catenary, rails and any other metallic components in the tunnel.

Delays

For the overall Northeast Coal Project to meet the inflexible schedule set for the loading of the first coal ship it was essential that BC Rail be able to deliver the coal to the port. Clearly, this placed BC Rail and their tunnels, and the longer 9-km Table tunnel in particular, on the critical path. There were several instances when progress on the Table east heading ceased or was severely delayed: a labour dispute stopped the work for one month; another three weeks was lost in the area of bursting ground; and time was lost in the shattered quartzite area where the torrents of water poured into the tunnel. These delays set the work back some 700 m and when the west heading reached the end of the contract the east heading still had more than 500 m to go.

To alleviate the damage that this delay would cause, clause 7 of the Supplementary General Conditions, 'Adjustments to tendered tunnel length', was invoked. This clause provides the owner with the right, under certain circumstances, to add to or subtract from any contract up to 500 m of tunnel. The west heading contractor was directed to advance beyond the end of his contract and continue until the two headings met or to 500 m, whichever came first. This action reduced the time to completion by some three weeks.

The several delays in the Wolverine tunnel did not put the completion date in jeopardy.

Conclusion

In conclusion it is notable that, with the exception of the presence of hydrogen sulphide gas and excessive water inflows, the problems that were encountered were less than had been expected.

The part that was played by BC Rail in this large undertaking is a source of considerable satisfaction to the company. The scope of the project and the time limitation provided an unusual opportunity that incited all to do their best.

References
1. BCR Engineering Department. North East Coal Development. A report on the Proposed Railway Branch Line Anzac–Tumbler Ridge. June 1976, 2 vols.
2. Klohn Leonoff Consultants, Ltd. Engineering geology of Hook Lake tunnels. February 1976.
3. BCR Engineering Department. North East Coal Study. Preliminary report, rail access. March 1977.
4. Environment and Land Use Sub-Committee on North East Coal Development. Preliminary environmental report on prepared transportation lines and town sites. May 1977.

5. Klohn Leonoff Consultants, Ltd. North East Coal Study. Geotechnical appraisal of surficial soils. February 1977.

6. Klohn Leonoff Consultants, Ltd. Preliminary design report, Hook Lake railway tunnels. January 1977.

7. Thurber Consultants, Ltd. North East Coal Fields Railway Study. Terrain analysis, Table River–Wolverine River route. October 1977.

8. Klohn Leonoff Consultants, Ltd., in association with Dolmage Campbell & Associates and Canadian Mine Services. British Columbia Railway Tumbler Ridge branch line. Tunnels geological investigation and engineering. April 1981, 5 vols.

Discussion

I. Waugh* asked Hendry and co-workers to expand on the occurrence of rockbursts that delayed the project. In particular, he wished to know (*a*) if the rockbursts occurred only in conjunction with blasting, (*b*) if any extra precautions were taken to safeguard personnel, and (*c*) if the rockbursts were investigated to attempt to determine the reason for their occurrence in one particular length of the tunnel.

D. M. Thompson† congratulated Hendry and co-workers on their excellent paper on a fascinating project. He understood that groundwater emerged into the tunnel at a temperature of $+2°C$ and Fig. 9 (p. 51) showed heavy icing in the tunnel – no doubt owing to groundwater encountering air temperatures well below the freezing point. An explanation of how the plastic membrane that was fastened to the tunnel wall prevented that situation would be welcomed.

J. Buchanan‡ said, with regard to the output of boom-type machines referred to on page 42, that de Mello Mendes and da Silva Amado stated that the average speeds were only 1.6 m/calendar day in the best periods. For a cross-section of about $9 m^2$ that would represent a volume of less than $15 m^3$, which would normally be cut by a boomheader in less than an hour. Perhaps the authors would indicate how the remaining hours of the day were occupied – an average daily or weekly cycle of operations would be a good way of showing that.

He was grateful to the authors for having made clear the administrative problems that were encountered on the project.

T. J. M. Paterson§ said that the severe corrosion caused by hydrogen sulphide gas in the Wolverine tunnel would affect both steel sets and rockbolts and asked Hendry and co-workers if they expected that those would be replaced when corroded or if alternative means of support would be applied.

Grouting of water-bearing zones of the tunnels was described as unsuccessful: he wondered how extensive the grouting programme had been and what grouts had been used, with particular respect to grout additives and lost circulation materials.

J. Svärd** asked Hendry and co-workers to indicate the depth of the drill-holes for the use of 4-m steel with an average advance of about 3.6 m per round and for 5-m steel with an average advance of 4.4 m.

G. C. Burgess†† asked Hendry and co-workers (1) if smooth wall blasting had been undertaken; (2) the average cycle times and how they were made up (i.e. drilling, 55 min; mucking, 45 min; etc.); (3) whether under Canadian law the process of blowing out drill-holes (cleaning) and charging up could take place during drilling; (4) the form of tamping that had been used and if it had proved successful (i.e. if advances had been achieved that were better than those with no tamping); and (5) whether there was the need for 5-m drill steel over 4-m owing to the good penetration (drilling) rate and poor advance achieved with 4-m drill steel (advance 3.5 m with 4-m hole).

The speaker's company offered a smooth wall blasting accessory but, as a result of poor cycle times in charging up,

they were interested in helping contractors to improve that and, at the same time, incorporate their system. With the information that he had requested they might obtain better results.

Authors' replies

Professor F. de Mello Mendes and F. R. da Silva Amado In reply to J. Buchanan, the 1.6 m/calendar day referred to in our paper is an average figure and relates to a period of several years. It reflects times lost owing to the poor quality of the rock mass concerned, as when excavation had to be carried out with great care and it was sometimes necessary to remake the section or reinforce the support, and also time lost when hard rock had to be drilled, when it was necessary to change excavation techniques (in this case to explosives) or when the heads of the machines had to be replaced. Furthermore, the contractual conditions on the basis of which the machines were used, which allowed the initially envisaged time limit to be successively adapted to the partial time limits that the rock mass 'might allow to be complied with', also led to a lowering of that average.

It was these aspects – of poor adaptability of the equipment to the rock mass concerned and of total inadequacy of the contractual conditions for the work in question – that it was intended to bring out in the paper, and it should be stressed that in certain more favourable ground conditions far higher excavation rates were achieved – of about 5 m and, exceptionally, 15 m.

From what has been explained it is considered that to illustrate the low average rates obtained there is not much point in presenting the results of a normal daily or weekly work cycle, as was requested.

The initial contract, based on instructions to bidders, was substituted by a new contract some months after the start of the work, for reasons mentioned in the paper. In this new contract new unit prices were agreed after a proposal from the contractor that was accepted by the client. In particular, as regards excavation costs, they were regarded as variable according to the type of equipment used and the quality of the rock excavated.

As was mentioned above, although an overall execution time had been defined, the contractual conditions allowed this to be adapted to the partial time limits that the rock mass 'might allow to be complied with'. Furthermore, the quality of the rock mass was being defined more according to the time of execution of the work than by more objective criteria of description of the mass, with higher excavation unit costs corresponding to the zones of slower rates of excavation or of stoppages. These facts led to a situation that did little to encourage the contractor to alter his processes for executing the work, and those processes – as referred to in the text – proved not to have been the most suitable; for the client, moreover, the situation was extremely unfavourable as far as his main objectives were concerned – conclusion of the work within the shortest time and at the lowest cost.

This situation was only overcome when, in 1981, the opening of 2.5 km of tunnel was taken away from the contractor and new bids were invited for its execution. The conditions of this competition made it necessary to consider the same price of excavation regardless of the quality of the rock mass, and it was only possible to vary the costs due for the type and quantity of first-phase support applied. Furthermore, an overall time limit was fixed, the contractor being liable to heavy fines if he exceeded that limit.

As far as the initial contractor is concerned, he was not entitled to any indemnification because he had far exceeded the initially envisaged time limits and costs and, according to Portuguese law, this enables the contract to be rescinded.

*Health and Safety Executive, Washington, Tyne and Wear, England.
†Geostore (South Killingholme), Ltd., Whitby, North Yorkshire, England.
‡Sir Robert McAlpine and Sons, Ltd., London, England.
§Geostore (South Killinghome), Ltd., South Killingholme, South Humberside, England.
**Nitro Nobel AB, Gyttorp, Sweden.
††F. Dupré (SA) (Pty), Ltd., Bryanston, South Africa.

R. D. Hendry, F. E. Kimball and V. W. Shtenko In reply to I. Waugh, (*a*) the rockbursts did not occur only with blasting, but the intensity was greatest in the 4 m just blasted and the intensity diminished with distance from the face. Although very little rock was observed to be dislodged in this one specific case, the largest seismic disturbance was some 60 m or so from the face. Bumps that far from the face were rare.

Extra precautions (*b*) were taken – screening of the back, steel sets were installed, scaling was increased and the progress was slowed from some 15 m to about 3.6 m per day. In addition, some experimental stress-relieving was carried out with suspect results.

There was no special investigation to determine the cause of the rockbursting (*c*), but the generally accepted explanation is that the bursting occurred in the very brittle orthoquartzite formation and at a location where this formation has a rather tight fold (this location can be seen in Fig. 2 (p. 47) approximately at station 61 + 888, in the formation designated Om, and continued for about 175 m).

The actual location of this formation was not exactly as shown on this Contract Document profile. It is a point of interest that the tunnel passed through this same formation at two other locations without any signs of rockbursting in either area; we did, however, encounter severe water problems in both cases. The generally accepted theory is that the brittle orthoquartzite rock was left in a state of high residual stress by the tight fold and excavation of the tunnel increased the stress concentration on the rock around the tunnel, particularly at the surface. After a short time this high surface stress readjusted away from the surface and the bumping stopped.

In reply to D. M. Thompson, the plastic membrane is actually a 50-mm sheet of flexible insulation fastened as tight as possible against the rock. This insulation has a thermal resistance equal to about 60 mm of styrofoam; it insulates the rock.

In reply to T. J. M. Paterson, if the rockbolts are installed as they were intended to be – that is, full column resin-grouted, as the Specifications require – they should last indefinitely. The steel sets are another matter: they will have to be replaced when they deteriorate to the extent that they no longer perform their function; fortunately, there are only some 24 of these inside the Wolverine tunnel (12 at each portal).

In the design stage the water problems were manifestly underestimated; as a result, the quantity of cement for grouting was badly underestimated in the 'Schedule of Quantities and Prices', and the contractors spotted the flaw; consequently, the price bid for grout was reflected in the various contractors' appreciation of the situation. For the three successful contractors the price ranged from $3.50 to $7.00/kg. As a consequence, grouting became a profitable activity that they had no incentive to do efficiently. In one location well in excess of $100 000 worth of cement was pumped into the rock without any positive results.

It is important to understand that on more than one occasion when we tried to grout a leak we found that, in fact, we were trying to seal off a solution cavern. One of these caverns was large enough for a man to walk into standing erect and it was about the same width; it was filled with a dense well-graded rock debris. The chance of successfully consolidating the debris and sealing off the water in such situations is rather remote (we tried on more than one occasion to seal off large inflows of water, but the attempts were notable for their cost and lack of success). We now believe that, for most cases, in hard rock tunnels the cost–benefit relationship favours letting the water continue to run. In our case the inflow is diminishing with passing time and the problem caused by the inflow is minor.

The quantities and the cost of grout alone (the cost of delay, packers, valves, and fittings, additives, fillers, etc., is in addition to the cost of the grout) are given in Table 1.

The general feeling in the company, in retrospect, is that if they had it to do again, there would be less emphasis on grouting. There was considerable controversy about the benefits to be gained from grouting while the work was in progress; eventually, this issue was resolved when, after the heading in one of the tunnels had been stopped for almost a month, and cement worth almost a million dollars had been pumped into the rock without success, we decided to drill some 4-in holes into the water-bearing zone to drain it. It was soon evident, from the drop in pressure, that we were able to draw off more water than the make-up. Keeping the drains free of rock debris was the most trying part of the drainage programme; some 50 m³ of debris was removed through the drains. When the pressure dropped from approximately 2400 to < 200 kPa, and we had determined the amount of water involved, we decided to advance the heading.

The third round broke into the cavern. One look at the cavern convinced us that we had chosen the proper course of action. From this point the time and effort that were devoted to grouting were greatly reduced.

It is worth noting that in the 22 months since hole-through the tunnels have dried up considerably, although the flow still varies with the seasons. It is interesting to speculate whether the decrease is caused by autogenous sealing or by a general lowering of the water-table, or some combination of these factors; in any case the trend is in the right direction. It is certainly not causing any special hardships flowing in the ditches to the portal – certainly not enough to make us consider a grouting programme.

Originally, cement was the only grouting material that was mentioned in the Contract Documents, and sand was the only filler or extender mentioned for grouting. Shortly before tenders were called, a mention of chemical and resin grouting was included in the Specifications; however, it is obvious from the following section, taken from that document, that the consultants did not intend to lose much sleep over the use or nonuse of these products!

'*Chemical and resin grouting*
The Contractor shall supply and apply chemical and/or resin grout as required by the Engineer. The type of the chemical and/or resin to be used shall be defined by the Engineer to suit

Table 1

Location	Description	Quantity in tender, kg	Quantity used, kg	Tender unit cost, $	Total cost, $
Wolverine E	Cement for seepage Control grouting	40 000	286 760	3.50	1 003 660.00
Wolverine W		60 000	158 080	5.00	790 400.00
Table E		60 000	52 320	5.00	261 600.00
Table W		40 000	332 440	7.00	2 327 080.00
		200 000	829 600		$4 382 740.00

the field conditions. Payment for Chemical and/or resin grout shall be made in accordance with Clause 13, Force Account Payment, of the General Conditions.'

Nevertheless, several of the resin types that expand when they contact water were tried, but with very limited success. In the area where they were tried the cracks were too large and the pressures too high. The grout expanded very well, but it was washed out of the rock before it had a chance to expand properly. The cracks were caulked, but trying to stop cracks that you can push your arm into with wood wedges against a stream of water with a head of 2500 kPa, at 2°C, is truly a job for a stoic! In addition, there was many metres of crack, much of it in the invert and in the crown, and as the heading advanced a new batch appeared in some areas almost every day; indeed, caulking these cracks was a Sisyphean labour.

As was pointed out previously, the flows have decreased considerably since they were first encountered and we expect this trend to continue for some time, especially in one area where the tunnel passes through the bottom of a quartz formation in a large syncline. The marked drop in pressure at this location supports the position that the water-table is being lowered and this process will continue.

In reply to J. Svärd, although the length of the round varied somewhat from round to round, because of the irregularities of the face, the average was about 3.6 m with 4-m steel. There was some variation in the depth of the hole as well, for the same reasons, especially in the corners, where there is interference between machine and walls. In any case the nominal depth of the hole for the 4-m steel would be between 3.75 and 3.84 m.

For the 5-m steel the depth of the hole would average between 4.75 and 4.85 m, with an average advance of about 4.4 m.

In reply to G. C. Burgess, the specifications called for smooth wall blasting.

'3.6 Controlled perimeter blasting includes, special drilling and blasting methods employed to produce smooth rock faces conforming to the prescribed neat lines and to minimize the occurrence of blast induced fractures in the rock outside of the excavation lines.

Smooth blasting technique will be applied in the underground excavation. Smooth blasting consists of drilling perimeter holes with a suitable burden/spacing ratio, loading all the holes lightly with a small diameter low strength explosive, stemming all holes and then firing them simultaneously as the last delay period in the round.

The Contractor's controlled perimeter drilling and blasting techniques shall be deemed acceptable and in conformity with these specifications if a trace of at least half of the perimeter drill holes of each round is visible on the final rock surface, distributed uniformly, after scaling all loose and shattered rock.

The perimeter drilling and blasting technique for each area shall be as approved by the Engineer and may be varied depending upon the actual results obtained. Perimeter holes along the periphery of the tunnel shall be drilled at 45 cm centre initially.

Measurement for payment under Item 3(3) for variation in the amount of drilling required for effective perimeter blasting in tunnel rock excavations due to changes required by the Engineer from the centre spacing of the perimeter holes specified herein will be made of the actual net increase or decrease in metres in the total length of the holes drilled from the tunnel face to the end of the round.

Payment will be made under Item 3(1) at the unit price per cubic metre stated in the Schedule of Quantities and Prices for tunnel rock excavation, including perimeter drilling at 45 cm centres, excavating, transporting, and disposal of excavated material.'

The cycle times varied with the heading, length of steel, type of ground and length of haul, ranging from 5 to 8 h. The make-up of the cycle, and consistent with the above, is 27% drilling, 57% mucking and 10% loading, the remainder being blowing smoke, blasting scaling, moving floor, jumbo, lights, etc.

Blowing holes would be at the discretion of the foreman, but loading is another matter; the following is taken directly from Industrial Health & Safety Regulations of British Columbia, Canada.

'*Restrictions in blasting area*
(2) No person shall be allowed to conduct or direct an operation, which could affect the safety of the workers in a blasting area, except upon the authorization of the blaster responsible for that area.'
'*Drilling Prohibitions*
46.74. *No drilling shall be done*:
(a) in the socket of an old hole, or
(b) *within 6 inches (15 cm) of any part of any socket, or*
(c) *within 20 feet (6 m) of any part of a loaded hole, or*
(d) *within 2 feet (60 cm) of a misfired hole, or*
(e) on or below any face or slope, or in any excavation until the faces or slopes have been cleared of loose material, as required by regulation 38.22, or
(f) in proximity to underground utility services, except in accordance with regulation 38.04.'
'*Unfired explosives*
46.122. When there is evidence or suspicion of misfired charges or unfired explosives:
(a) no person shall use metallic equipment in the immediate vicinity of the suspected misfired or unfired charges, until after a blaster has directed the hand removal of as much broken material as possible', and then
'*Drilling for re-firing*
46.126. Where an additional hole and charge are necessary for the blasting of a misfired charge, the blaster shall be responsible for directing the angle of the hole, and the depth to which it shall be drilled. No drilling shall be done *within a distance of two feet from a misfired charge*.'

So the answer to question (3) is 'no'.
Tamping is covered thus in the same regulations.

'*Tamping rod restriction*
46.86. Metallic tamping rods, or rods with metallic fittings, shall not be used. All holes shall be carefully tamped, using pressure, not impact.'

Drilling the extra metre hole depth, with 5-m steel, adds only about 15 min to the time to drill off a round, but it increases the advance by some 22% for the same loading, smoke blowing, scaling, moving jumbo out and mucking machine in, cleaning for lifter holes, marking up face, transporting explosives and cleaning up thrown muck as required for a round drilled with 4-m steel. The reason for 5-m steel appears to be obvious, although in one heading the progress with 4-m steel compared favourably with the two headings that used 5-m steel, and they did this by advancing five rounds for every four rounds that the headings with the 5-m steel advanced. It was quite common for this heading, with use of the 4-m steel, to advance five rounds in 24 h.

Session 3 - Concreting

Co-Chairmen: Dr. G. Greschik and J. G. Leeney

Concrete underground in coal mines

Alan S. Bloor
National Coal Board, Mining Research and Development Establishment,
Stanhope Bretby, Burton-on-Trent, Staffordshire, England
Alan Pink
West Midlands and North West Region, Cement and Concrete Association, Manchester, England

Synopsis
A review is given of the use of Portland cement concrete underground in the coal-mining industry, with particular reference to concrete linings and supports to shafts, drifts and roadways. The different types of lining in concrete are described – *in-situ* concrete, precast concrete segments, gunite and shotcrete, fibre-reinforced concrete, grout-filled envelopes and glass-reinforced cement laggings.

Progress in two National Coal Board trials of precast concrete segmental linings in colliery roadways at Cadley Hill, Staffordshire, and Warsop, Derbyshire, is reported.

Portland cement concrete[1] has a long history of successful use below ground in the civil engineering tunnelling industry. Many hundreds of kilometres of tunnels for water and sewage, for railways, roads and pedestrians and for cables have been given a strong, durable and inexpensive lining with one of the many forms of *in-situ* concrete or with factory-made precast concrete segments.

In the United Kingdom in the seven-year period 1970–1976[2] a total tunnelled length of almost 600 km was lined with concrete. The average diameter was just in excess of 3 m and the volume of concrete in the linings was about 1 000 000 m³.

Although it has not been used as extensively as in civil tunnelling, concrete has been employed successfully below ground in the coal-mining industry for some considerable time. Concrete was first used to replace brickwork in shafts: in such a location *in-situ* concrete is ideal, as it is cast in shallow lifts as the shaft is excavated and, being predominantly in ring compression and, hence, free of tensile stresses, it requires no reinforcement in competent ground. The collar and foreshaft structures are likely to be in concrete, now reinforced; the air and fan drifts are generally conventional reinforced concrete box structures; insets, where roadways join the shaft, will normally be heavily reinforced concrete structures changing from box-shaped to traditional horseshoe section.

For roadway (tunnel) linings concrete in the form of precast segments has been used for many years in some mainland European countries – in particular, Belgium – and is now being used on a trial basis in the United Kingdom.

Shotcrete and gunite are used extensively in some British National Coal Board (NCB) Areas to seal the surfaces of gate roads that are subject to spontaneous combustion, and trials with shotcrete as the primary or initial load-bearing lining have been carried out successfully. Shotcrete has also been used in conjunction with traditional colliery steel arches. The facility to improve significantly the load-carrying capacity of steel arches is available with grout-filled envelopes between the arch and the roadway surface.

The United Kingdom coal-mining industry drives more than 500 km of roadways annually,[3] of which about 250 km constitutes roadways that are used primarily for main or district access. These access roadways are mainly in rock, albeit generally weak Coal Measures strata, and are, essentially, civil engineering tunnels.

Shafts

A typical shaft section with the geology and the estimated water flows is shown in Fig. 1.[4] In the United Kingdom shafts are lined with *in-situ* unreinforced concrete cast in purpose-made steel formwork in lifts of about 6 m as the sinking of the shaft proceeds. Sulphate-resisting cement[5] is normally used in concrete with a characteristic strength that ranges from 25 to about 45 N/mm². The higher strengths are the norm nowadays. Typical mixes are given in Table 1.

Bell[6] and Auld[7] have developed elastic and limit state methods for the design of shaft linings. Both recommended designing for the full hydrostatic pressure, which results in wall thicknesses that vary from a minimum of 300 to a maximum of 1400 mm. Shafts are generally of 7.5-m internal diameter, and may be more than 1000 m in depth – the North Selby shafts in the new mine complex in Yorkshire are 1033 m deep.

Table 1   Typical mix designs for *in-situ* concrete shaft linings

Site	Selby Wistow	Selby Riccall	Whitemore
Cement, kg	420 srpc	460 srpc	490 srpc
Sand Zone 2, kg	615	665	685
Sand, % of total aggregate	35	39	39
Coarse aggregate, kg	1140 gravel	1050 gravel	1050 limestone
Water, l	180	186	180
w/c ratio	0.43	0.40	0.37
Admixture	Plasticizer	Plasticizer	Plasticizer
Characteristic strength, N/mm²	45	45	60
Slump	Varies with shaft depth (generally 160 mm or greater)		

In the placement of concrete against frozen ground Bell[8] recommended a minimum thickness of 600 mm. At that thickness the effect of the cement's heat of hydration is sufficient to overcome the effects of the freezing temperatures, and the strength development of the concrete is not retarded significantly (Fig. 2).

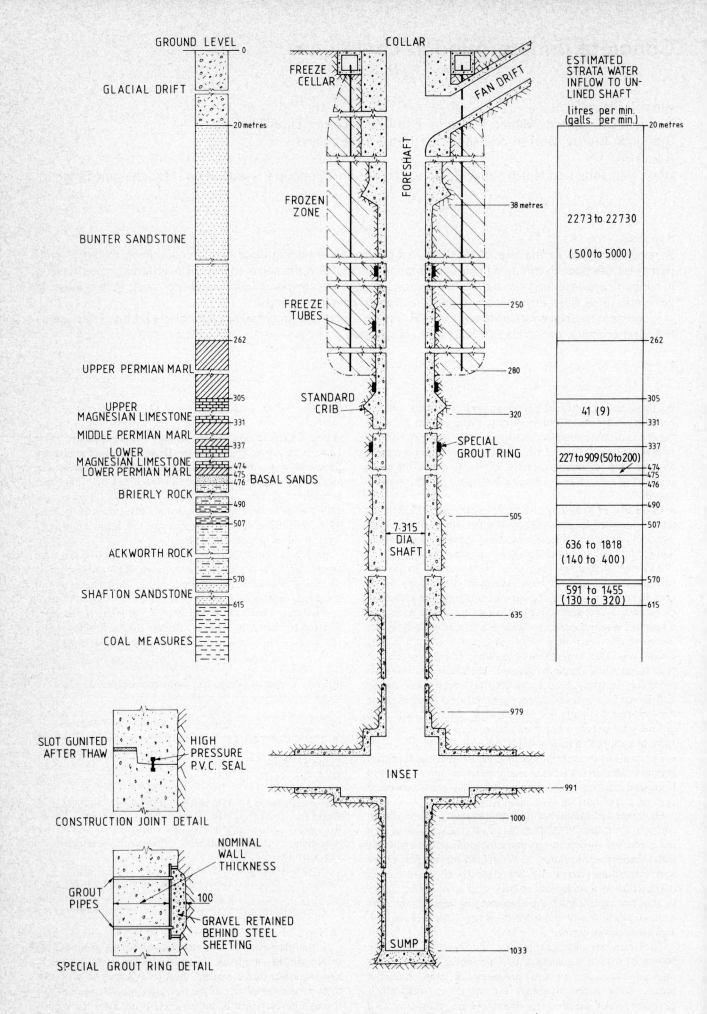

Fig. 1   Shaft section with geology and estimated water inflows, North Selby no. 2 (upshaft) shaft. After Auld[4]

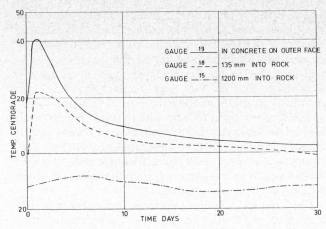

Fig. 2 Temperatures and time from three temperature gauges in shaft in frozen ground

Drifts

In the United Kingdom there has recently been increased use of the inclined drift from the surface to gain access to coal reserves.[3] At the surface there will be a reinforced concrete headwall, pavement and concreted double-arch tunnel section. From the portal to the self-supporting mine strata is the most critical section, i.e. the soft rock tunnel. This section is usually double-arched or supported by closely spaced arches and fully lined with *in-situ* reinforced concrete.

Fig. 3 Hem Heath drift: transfer from arches to circular concrete segmental lining to support drivage through soft marls

As with much work underground, water can be a problem in the driving of drifts, especially when it is combined with near-surface soft swelling marls. Conventional *D*-shaped arches are then not the best linings, a change to circular bolted concrete segments being recommended (Fig. 3). In self-supporting strata the drift lining will be as that for tunnels.

Roadways (tunnels)

The traditional support for roadways in the United Kingdom and mainland European coal mines has been structural steel arches in combination with either timber lagging or corrugated steel sheeting. In Coal Measures strata, where the rock is predominantly sedimentary and relatively weak, the traditional system has the ability to accept large convergences, buckling of the arches giving a visual guide to the need for maintenance.

The disadvantages are the continual expensive maintenance required to keep the roadway operational and the buckling of the arch legs at loads well below their potential strength.

The Mining Research and Development Establishment (MRDE) of the National Coal Board has investigated the use of various types of concrete support in both *D*-shaped and circular roadways, the work being sponsored by the European Coal and Steel Community.[9] The investigations cover the use of precast concrete, shotcrete and gunite, including mesh and glass fibre reinforcement, grout-filled envelopes and glass-reinforced cement (grc) laggings.

Precast concrete linings

Circular precast concrete segmental linings are a standard tool of civil engineer tunnellers, but there is little experience of their use at depth in the United Kingdom in the weak laminated Coal Measures strata. In the Campine coalfield, Belgium, however, over many years there has been considerable use of precast concrete segments as the roadway support system. The roadways at Campine are 600–1100 m deep and in a water-sensitive weak shale. Because of the extreme difficulty in maintaining the traditional timber and steel arch lining in such bad ground better methods were sought, and from 1930 onwards the Belgians have successfully used circular precast concrete segmental linings.[10]

The first concrete linings were rings of between 46 and 90 tapered unreinforced concrete blocks up to 500 mm thick and up to 450 mm wide (Fig. 4). Crushable chipboard packings were between 20 and 40 mm thick. The internal diameters of the roadways were up to 5.4 m. Although rather slow and expensive, this system has proved very successful and has been used to line 500 km of roadway in Belgian coalfields.

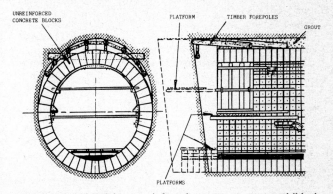

Fig. 4 Original Belgian unreinforced precast concrete multiblock lining

In Czechoslovakia in 1957 a four-piece segmental reinforced concrete lining was used successfully in a mine roadway at a depth of 1000 m. In 1967 the Belgian mining engineers opted for a five-piece reinforced concrete segmental system (Fig. 5). The segments are 200 mm thick and 640 mm wide, and are placed by a segment manipulator, which also places the special floor segment. Special compressed sawdust chipboard packing pieces (total thickness, 50 mm) are used at each joint. There are no bolts in the system. This system has proved both technically sound and economically acceptable and with 17 years' experience of its use in 30 km of roadway it is now the standard system in the Belgian coal-mining industry.

The NCB recently started a trial of the Belgian system at Warsop colliery, north Derbyshire. A 50-m length of an existing roadway, which has been severely squeezed by the soft fireclay strata at a depth of 600 m, is to be relined with the five-piece circular segmental concrete system. A number of segments have had strain gauges cast in so that the performance of the lining can be monitored. A more advanced and much larger trial is under way at Cadley Hill colliery, Staffordshire.

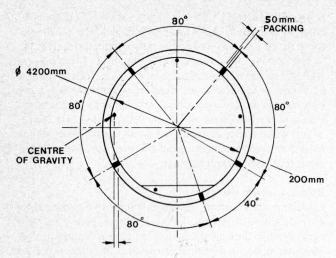

Fig. 5   Current Belgian five-piece reinforced precast concrete lining

An initial 46-m long trial length preceded the main experimental length of 1500 m that is now under way.[11,12] A precast reinforced concrete segmental lining was used to replace a traditional colliery arch lining that had deformed excessively and had needed continuous maintenance.

Table 2   Cadley Hill colliery, West main return, input parameters for roadway closure estimates

Parameter	Value
Diameter of roadway	4.5 m*
Depth of cover	480.0 m*
Cover load	12.0 MPa
Strata properties	
Poisson's ratio	0.24*
Young's modulus	11.9 GPa*
Expansion coefficient	0.2
Compressive strength (laboratory)	38.0 MPa*
Compressive strength (*in-situ*)	8.0 MPa
Triaxial stress factor	2.3*
Support pressure	
Steel arches	0.1 MPa
Concrete lining	2.0 MPa
Cohesive augmentation	0.1 MPa

*Indicates measured values.

The preliminary trial was in the West main return roadway at a depth of 500 m in listricated seatearth mudstones. Table 2 and Fig. 6 give details of the input parameters and the strata. The lining consisted of 75 rings with an internal diameter of

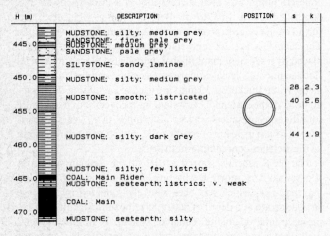

Fig. 6   Cadley Hill: position of roadway in relation to strata (*H*, borehole depth; *s*, uniaxial compressive strength; *k*, triaxial stress factor)

3.66 m, each ring 610 mm long, giving a total length of 46 m. The segments were 240 mm thick and lightly reinforced, and the concrete had a strength of 45 N/mm². Each ring comprised 11 segments and a parallel-sided key piece in the crown. The 12 radial joints had timber packings 14 mm thick and the segments were bolted together. Two rings, number 23 and 51, each situated 14 m from the outbye ends, respectively, were provided with embedded vibrating wire strain gauges, pressure cells between the lining and the rock and reference points to determine the compression of the timber packings. With the configuration of strain gauges it was possible to determine both the circumferential and bending components of strain as a function of time and of angular position.

Fig. 7 ((*a*) and (*b*)) shows the mean strains and strain differences for ring 23 at six time intervals. The strains are plotted in polar coordinates to indicate both magnitude and angular position. The mean strain was compressive (positive), practically independent of the angular position and increased continuously during the life of the lining to a maximum value of 1320 microstrain in ring 51. The estimated failure strain (compressive) was 1300 microstrain.

The bending component of strain, as indicated by the strain difference plot, showed marked variation of both sign and magnitude with angular position and time. The sign convention adopted is that outward bending of a segment with the outward face in tension relative to the inner surface is shown as a positive strain difference.

In ring 23 this outward bending increased more rapidly after 220 days, reaching a maximum in excess of + 5000 microstrain after 345 days, and then decreased, it being concluded that physical failure had occurred. The pressure cells indicated severe non-uniform radial loading from shortly after installation, the pressures on all cells increasing continuously with time.

Maximum compression of the timber packing occurred on either side of the key piece and was 60% of the original thickness after 250 days. The lining eventually partially failed after 450 days, when there was spalling and crushing of the key piece followed by upward movement of the key and adjacent crown segment near ring 23.

The recorded non-uniform pressure distribution mostly resulted from the presence of major cavities in the roof. The primary grouting of these cavities had not been completely effective, and secondary grouting had not been carried out. A contributing factor was the asymmetric loading of the lining from below associated with the massive floor lift previously experienced in this roadway.

The main experimental length (1500 m) of precast concrete lined roadway is well advanced and the results from the vibrating wire strain gauges during the first 600-m drivage are now available. In this drivage the strata consist of sandstones and siltstones at a depth of 450 m. The roadway is being driven by the NCB's purpose-built MRDE tunnelling machine (Fig. 8). The roadway lining is a 5-m diameter × 250-mm thick seven-piece plus key reinforced concrete bolted segmental lining (Fig. 9). In approximately 100 m of the lining each of the seven segments is subdivided into three sub-segments, referred to as the multiblock system. For both types of ring a concrete of strength 45 N/mm² was used. Seven instrumented rings have been erected in the first 600 m of the lining, five containing 22 pairs of gauges and two containing 15 pairs of gauges. Table 3 gives the positions, dates of erection, numbers of segments and gauges and elapsed time for the instrumented rings. Fig. 10 shows the variation of surface strains around ring 101 (a seven-section ring) at 323 days. After erection, the annulus between the concrete ring and the rock was filled with limestone aggregate placed pneumatically. The invert was filled level with debris from the heading to a maximum depth of 1.25 m

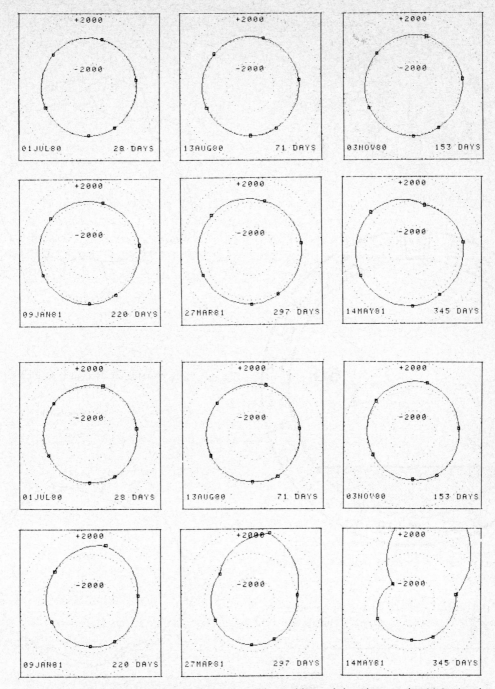

Fig. 7   Variation of mean strain in ring 23 with angular position and time since erection (*a*) (*top*) and variation of strain difference in ring 23 with angular position and time since erection (*b*)

covering gauge positions 9–15 inclusive. The inward bending of the invert segments is evident in the diagram, as is the low mean strain in this region. The bending elsewhere is predominantly outward, apart from two positions in the crown.

Fig. 11 shows the variation of surface strains for the nearby multiblock 21-piece ring 109 at 306 days. The surrounding strata and method of backfilling are the same as those for ring 101. The major difference between the rings is the much lower incidence of bending strains in ring 109, as is shown in the polar diagram. The proportion of bending strains greater than 100 microstrain in magnitude is 18% in ring 109 (62% in ring 101). The multiblock system appears to be more efficient at redistributing the imposed bending moments via the increased number of timber packing pieces.

Various materials were used for backfilling in line with experience gained in the first trial. The original two-shot system of limestone aggregate, followed later by Portland cement grout, was replaced by a one-shot system that utilized 'Anpak' (a mixture of coarse and fine calcium sulphate wetted out at the point of injection). At ring 161 the Anpak was injected after 20 days and it halted the rapid increase in both compressive and tensile strains.

Currently, grouting is being carried out with Archfill 7, a thixotropic Portland cement–PFA grout.

At ring 496 a large roof overbreak of the weak siltstones and coal resulted in large bending strains during the first six days after erection, accompanied by severe cracking of the segment that contained gauges (pairs of) 14 and 15. Grouting took place between 8 and 14 days after erection and resulted in decreased bending strains, considerable reductions in the rates of change of strain and transitions from tensile to compressive strain. At position 15 a crack intersected the intrados gauge, but it continued to function and Fig. 12 shows the decrease in tensile strain as the crack started to close again after the grouting operation. The main conclusions after the completion of 600 m

67

Fig. 8   MRDE tunnelling machine

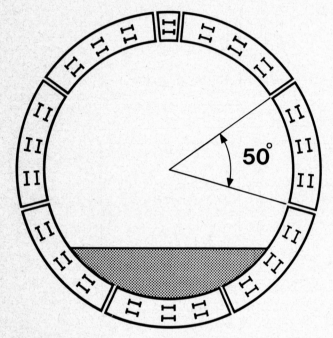

Fig. 9   Cadley Hill precast concrete lining, rings 101, 241 and 380, showing positions of gauges

Table 3   Cadley Hill colliery, northwest drivage, instrumented rings – positions, dates of erection, numbers of segments and gauges and elapsed time

Ring no.*	Date erected	No. of segments	No. of gauge pairs	Days elapsed to 20 April, 1983†
101	26: 5:82	7 + Key	22	329
109	11: 6:82	21 + Key	22	313
161	19: 8:82	21 + Key	22	244
241	16:11:82	7 + Key	22	155
380	27: 1:83	7 + Key	22	83
496	2: 3:83	7 + Key	15	49
525	8: 3:83	7 + Key	15	43

*Equals distance lined in metres.
†600th ring erected on 20 April, 1983.

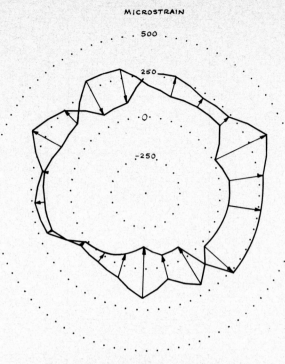

Fig. 10   Surface strains versus angular position for ring 101

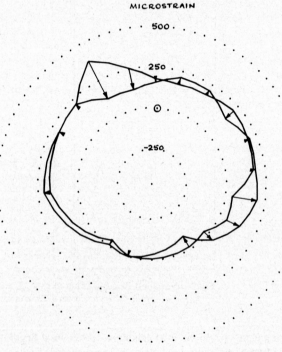

Fig. 11   Surface strains versus angular position for ring 109

of the 1500-m roadway are that the mean circumferential strains are within acceptable limits at less than 200 microstrain, that the multiblock system has developed lower bending strains than the seven-piece standard system, that localized bending strains are often severe and cracking results, and that these bending strains can and should be minimized by adequate and prompt backfilling and grouting.

Given that due account is taken of this last factor, it appears that precast concrete segmental tunnel linings can be used successfully at depth in coal mines in the very difficult strata that are encounted and will reduce very significantly the maintenance costs that are associated with traditional roadway linings.

In some roadways at increased depth a concrete lining may be essential to contain the severe loading. In one of the main spine roads at Selby that is being driven by the Robbins full-face TBM King[13] has commented that at the greater depths (from about 800 m through to 1100 m), and depending on the strata encountered, some form of continuous concrete segmental support may be necessary.

In-situ concrete linings

Traditional *in-situ* concrete tunnel linings have not been used extensively in coal mines, but *in-situ* concrete is used for insets,

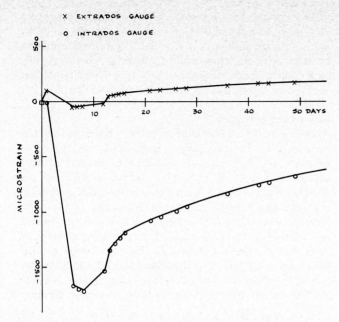

Fig. 12 Strain versus time for gauge position 15, ring 496

spiral chute bunker shafts (for underground storage) for sump tanks and for plugs. Pumping concrete along drifts and roadways is now common practice, as it is in civil engineering tunnelling. The greater restrictions on the transport of materials in a coal mine roadway system make pumping concrete even more attractive, and a special application of concrete pumping was used at Selby in the South drift. A pump station and lodgement, two lengths of arch section roadway and the erection chamber for the Robbins full-face tunnelling machine had to be lined with *in-situ* concrete with minimum interference with other operations.

Fig. 13 South drift at Gascoigne Wood showing finish achieved with special pumped concrete mix

After several months of experimentation[14] a mixing and pumping station was established on the surface and a specially designed sand–cement–PFA mix was pumped a distance of up to 1700 m through a 50-mm diameter pipeline. The concrete mix was designed for a characteristic strength of 30 N/mm² and strengths in excess of 50 N/mm² were obtained: 900 m³ of this mix was used to construct the erection chamber and 2100 m³ was used as the lining in the arch section drifts. The pump station lodgements are watertight and the surface finish is of a very high standard (Fig. 13).

Shotcrete linings

Dry-process shotcrete (gunite) and wet-process shotcrete have been used extensively in the coal-mining industry, the preference in the United Kingdom being for the former (gunite).

Although trials[9] have shown that both dry- and wet-process shotcrete can provide a satisfactory structural lining to a mine roadway, to date, the most extensive use of these materials in United Kingdom coal mines has been to seal gate roadways that are subject to spontaneous combustion. A lining 10–25 mm thick is sprayed on to existing tunnel linings for the sole purpose of preventing the ingress of air into the combustible waste behind the coal face. This application has been very successful, virtually no dust and very little rebound of aggregate arising, even in spraying overhead. The dry process is used in this application, often with prepacked mixes of sand and cement plus accelerator. The 10- to 25-mm layer is sprayed on to steel sheets and timber laggings and is forced into joints, effectively sealing off air flow into the waste.

The same system has been used to line parts of tunnels that have to be fireproofed, such as auxiliary fan houses, and such linings have been applied much more quickly than those which use the traditional manual methods. The NCB now owns and operates more than 100 concrete spraying machines – mostly smaller models of the dry-process shotcrete machines.

In a European Coal and Steel Community funded research project[9] carried out by MRDE in the period 1976–80 there were extensive trials and developments of shotcreted concrete roadway linings. Panels of plain concrete, of mesh-reinforced concrete and of glass fibre-reinforced concrete were included in the trials. The work was carried out underground at two collieries, Brodsworth Main and Abercynon, and at the MRDE's surface test site at Swadlincote. Underground there were 20 panels, which varied in length from 23 to 40 m; three included weld mesh reinforcement; in one glass fibres were incorporated into the concrete mix; and all the remaining panels were unreinforced. In one panel the unreinforced lining is in conjunction with resin-grouted roofbolts. The lining thickness was either approximately 75 or 90 mm.

Fig. 14 General view of shotcreted roadway at Brodsworth Main colliery

The wet-shotcreting process was used for one panel at Brodsworth. All other underground work was carried out with use of the dry process. At Brodsworth Main colliery arches were set inside and close to, but clear of, the shotcrete lining and did not influence the support capability of the lining. At Abercynon the shotcrete was integral with the colliery arches. A typical view of the partially completed roadway at Brodsworth Main

Table 4 Brodsworth Main colliery initial surface trials – typical mix details and type of spraying machine

Mix used					
Cement	Sand	Gravel	Accelerator	Process	Spraying machine
1	2	1	Signite	Dry	Meyco Piccola
1	2	1	Signite	Dry	Aliva 240
2	3.5	1	Sodium silicate	Wet	Putzmeister Pioneer USI 139
1	3	1	Signite	Dry	Reed

is shown in Fig. 14, Table 4 gives details of the concrete mixes and Table 5 some strength test results. The strengths are 28-day equivalent cube strengths from 25-mm diameter × 50-mm long drilled cores from a mix with proportions of two parts Zone 2 sand to one part OPC sprayed on to an open test panel.

Table 5 Brodsworth Main colliery compressive strength test results from sprayed test panels

Process	No. of tests	Compressive strength, N/mm^2 Range	Average
Wet	11	9.8–31.7	20.7
Dry	11	65.3–82.4	71.9
Dry, plus fibres	6	46.5–54.1	49.0

The strengths of the dry-process samples were exceptionally high and have not been achieved again at either colliery. A strength of 40 N/mm^2 is more usual with a 20% difference between the two processes.

The trials at Abercynon followed those at Brodsworth and included four combinations of materials: (1) colliery arch and unreinforced shotcrete, (2) colliery arch and shotcrete-reinforced with weld mesh, (3) colliery arch and shotcrete and grout-filled envelopes and (4) colliery arch and glass fibre-reinforced shotcrete. All the shotcreting was in the dry process (gunite) sprayed by a Markham 'E' continuous spraying machine as used for most of the work at Brodsworth.

The assessment of the results from both sites is that the shotcreted concrete linings have proved to be adequate. The bond of the shotcrete to the rock face has been excellent, except in the one instance where a coal seam appeared in the crown of the roadway. The shotcrete would not adhere to the highly polished coal surface.

Hairline cracks have appeared in the wet-process sprayed shotcrete linings, but these have not been detrimental to the performance of the lining. Very few cracks are apparent in the dry shotcrete linings.

In both dry and wet shotcrete linings there are no signs of compressive failure, and the build-up of load levelled off as had been expected. Closure is generally very low. Theoretical work following Wilson's formula[15] for closure in underground roadways appears to correspond well with the results for the shotcreted roadway. Shotcrete sprayed on to shattered ground demonstrated its ability to fill fissures, thus consolidating a weak mass and preventing any further disintegration of such strata.

When shotfiring was carried out adjacent to the shotcreted concrete lining no serious damage to the shotcrete occurred. The shotfiring was normally carried out on the day after spraying operations, although for a short period at Abercynon the lining was applied during the morning shift and the shotfiring was carried out on the afternoon shift with little damage

to the concrete lining. The ability of shotcrete linings to accept very heavy loading was demonstrated at Thoresby colliery, north Nottinghamshire. A 70-m length of gate roadway had to be driven very close to a major fault and it was successfully lined with a combination of closely spaced colliery arches enclosed in a thick layer of mesh-reinforced shotcrete.

Grout-filled envelopes

Another form of roadway support has been developed and has been on trial for some time – grout-filled envelopes. The envelope fills the irregular space between a standard steel colliery arch and the excavated roadway profile, thereby ensuring that the arch is loaded with a (reasonably) uniform load and significantly increasing the capacity of the arch. Measurements of the load carried by arch legs when yielding indicate that steel arches normally fail by buckling at a load of about 10% of their maximum load capacity. The grout-filled envelopes overcome this disadvantage and, additionally, reduce the amount of necessary back ripping and give immediate support to the strata and induce a pre-stress in the arch.

Fig. 15 Grout-filled envelopes used in surface trial

Fig. 15 shows grout-filled envelopes pumped up in a surface trial. The grouts used have been developed after a number of trials from which it was concluded that a high-strength grout was not essential, 15 N/mm^2 being assessed to be adequate for the system.

After trials of a number of different grouts the grout used in the underground trial at Daw Mill colliery, south Midlands, was produced from a premixed prepacked mixture of equal parts of OPC and PFA with approximately 5% of a long-chain polymer to aid pumpability, and 5% of high-alumina cement to counteract the set-retarding effect of the polymer.

For the envelopes a number of materials were tried – some impervious and some porous. The impervious envelopes were less satisfactory than the porous envelopes and the most suitable materials proved to be a fabric of a porous bonded non-woven thermovinyl PVC fibre with a modified acrylate bonding.

The system of using grout-filled envelopes has been extended from single envelopes filled behind each arch to the utilization of wide envelopes to give full roadway coverage between arches. The Daw Mill colliery underground trial proved that the system was viable, and because the envelope is in intimate contact with all the stratum surface there are no voids that could fill with methane. The additional support of the weld mesh also increased the strength of lagging support and the system has potential in particularly difficult ground where heavy support is necessary.

Glass-reinforced cement laggings

Another new cement-based form of lagging to roadways that has been investigated is glass-reinforced cement (grc). The investigation has shown that a lagging in grc is feasible, but not economical, at the moment.

Of the profiles studied, sandwich panels were found to be the most acceptable, both technically and economically, and it may be that future developments in grc production techniques, coupled with rising costs of timber and steel, will reduce the difference in cost between grc lagging and conventional systems to a more acceptable level, when further development could prove worthwhile.

Current research

At MRDE large-scale testing of precast concrete tunnel linings can be carried out in a specially developed rig (Fig. 16 shows the test rig with a ring of concrete segments in place). Radial force, radial deformation and circumferential concrete strain at two radii are monitored for each test. Direct comparisons are

Fig. 16   Precast concrete tunnel lining under test in NCB rig at MRDE

being made between different designs of concrete linings, i.e. the seven-segment system and the 21-segment system as used at Cadley Hill and the five-segment Belgian system. The effects of loading geometry and the properties of the joint packing materials are also being investigated. Research is being carried out at a number of collieries in association with Newcastle University.[16] At Selby shaft insets at three mines incorporate instrumentation to measure rock deformation prior to casting in-situ concrete, and subsequent pressures, temperatures and concrete strains have been monitored. The results have provided valuable information on the size and distribution of induced strains in the concrete lining and have indicated the importance of pre- and post-construction methods of excavation. The information is being used in the current design of shaft insets.

Early age thermal effects in the in-situ concrete lining to shafts are being investigated via a combination of laboratory research on the basic thermal properties of concrete in conjuction with the Cement and Concrete Association and on-site measurements in mine shafts under construction.

Future developments

In considering possible future developments it has to be kept in mind that coal mining is a hazardous business in which all changes to long-established procedures are, very rightly, not accepted until they have been proved to satisfy the very strict safety regulations. Recent advances in civil engineering tunnelling techniques have to be proved to be absolutely safe in the coal mine before they can be adopted universally.

The application of the design principles of the New Austrian Tunnelling Method (NATM) to capital structures at depth in Coal Measures strata was suggested in the Newcastle University report.[16] The growing requirement for long stable tunnels that carry high-speed conveyors could result in the application of this type of civil engineering approach to the use of concrete. A combination of the advances in rockbolting techniques and sprayed-concrete technology suggests that NATM could be an important technique in the future.

High tensile strength, high modulus inorganic plastics could have useful applications as reinforcement, as formwork or as preformed linings. Alternatively, it has been proposed that a very low modulus concrete would be a valuable and achievable material for deep mining applications.

Further developments in improving the properties of Portland cement based grouting materials would be of significant value to the performance of structural concrete in coal mines.

Whatever developments prove to be the most successful, the future potential use of concrete underground in the coal-mining industry is large, provided that civil engineers and the concrete industry can meet the demanding requirements of the mining engineer.

Acknowledgement

Thanks are due to the Head of the Mining Research and Development Establishment, T. L. Carr, and to the Director General of the Cement and Concrete Association, Dr. R. E. Rowe, for permission to publish this paper. The opinions expressed are those of the authors and not necessarily those of the National Coal Board or the Cement and Concrete Association.

References
1. British Standards Institution. Specification for ordinary and rapid-hardening Portland cement. *B.S.* 12, 1978, 4 p.
2. Craig R. N. and Muir Wood A. M. A review of tunnel lining practice in the United Kingdom. *Transport Road Res. Lab. Supplem. Rep.* 335, 1978, 212 p.
3. King T. I. Tunnelling in British coal mines. In *Eurotunnel '80* Jones M. J. ed. (London: IMM, 1980), 33–45.
4. Auld F. A. Concrete in underground works. *Tech. Pap. Concrete Soc.* no. 105, 1983, 34 p.
5. British Standards Institution. Specification for sulphate-resisting Portland cement. *B.S.* 4027, 1980, 4 p.
6. Bell M. J. The design of shaft linings in Coal Measure rocks. In *Strata mechanics: proceedings of the symposium, Newcastle upon Tyne, 1982* Farmer I. W. ed. (Amsterdam, etc.: Elsevier, 1982), 160–6. (*Developm. geotech. Engng* vol. 32)
7. Auld F. A. Ultimate strength of concrete shaft linings and its influence on design. Reference 6, 134–40.
8. Bell M.J. Concrete in temporarily frozen ground. Paper presented to Concrete in the ground, Concrete Society conference, London, May 1984.

9. National Coal Board MRDE. The development of new and improved types of roadway support. European Coal and Steel Community Research Project 6220-AB/8/801, 1980.

10. Stassen P. and van Duyse H. Development of supports in stone roads in the Campine Coalfield. In *Sixth international strata control conference, Banff, 1977: technical reports* (Ottawa: Canada Centre Energy, Mines Resources, 1977), theme 2, pap. 15, 35 p.

11. Bloor A. S. Deformation of a circular concrete roadway lining in response to strata movement. Reference 6, 223–9.

12. Bloor A. S. Jones R. T. and Zadeh A. M. H. Concrete strain measurements in a circular segmented lining at Cadley Hill colliery. In *Design and performance of underground excavations: ISRM symposium, Cambridge, U.K., 1984* Brown E. T. and Hudson J. A. eds (London: British Geotechnical Society, 1984), 485–92.

13. King T. I. A comparison of heavy duty roadheaders with TBMs in UK coal mines. *Tunnels Tunnell.*, **16**, July 1984, 61–2.

14. Auld F. A. Concrete in deep underground workings: big advances, great potential. *Construction News*, Feb. 16 1984, 32–3.

15. Wilson A. H. The stability of underground workings in soft rocks of the Coal Measures. *Int. J. Min. Engng*, **1**, 1983, 91–187.

16. University of Newcastle upon Tyne, Department of Geotechnical Engineering. Instrumentation of Selby shafts and insets. Final report, European Coal and Steel Community Research Project 7220-AC/814, 1983.

Concrete lining of the Loktak headrace tunnel

G. D. Tyagi
National Hydroelectric Power Corporation, Ltd., New Delhi, India
K. S. Sharma
Loktak Hydroelectric Project, Manipur, India

Synopsis
The Loktak hydroelectric project in the State of Manipur, eastern India, involved considerable tunnelling work. A 6.62-km tunnel with a finished diameter of 3.81 m forms part of the water transfer system: the tunnel was lined with concrete in thicknesses that varied between 250 and 300 mm. In some sections where convergence was noted during the initial stages, the finished diameter had to be reduced to avoid disturbance of the stabilized ground and to reduce the amount of correction that is needed to the supporting system.

To achieve a fast rate of tunnelling the excavation was performed with an Alpine Miner 50 roadheader with support by the New Austrian Tunnelling Method. After completion of the excavation, however, the time that remained for conventional lining of the tunnel was insufficient for commissioning the project within the scheduled period and, therefore, for the first time in India, continuous concreting operations were undertaken. Such equipment as the concrete pumps, agitator cars, a sliding invert shutter and a 60-m telescopic crown shutter had to be imported, but aggregate and batching/mixing plants to supply the ready mixed concrete were available locally. Some difficulties were experienced during the initial stages because the equipment was new to the tunnelling crews, but confidence and expertise were soon developed.

The concreting operations in the Loktak project are highlighted.

The Loktak hydroelectric project included the diversion of 58 m³/s of water from the Loktak Lake to utilize 42 m³/s for power generation, with a gross head of 312 m, and a supply of 16.8 m³/s for irrigation. The water is diverted through a water conductor system that comprises 2.27 km of open channel, 1.073 km of cut and cover and 6.89 km of tunnel, terminating in a penstock manifold. The three penstocks have diameters of 2.286 m and an average length of 1.346 km each. The power plant houses three units, each of 35 MW. Fig. 1 shows a longitudinal section of the scheme.

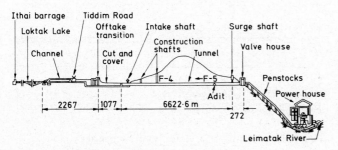

Fig. 1   Longitudinal section of general scheme

Tunnel construction was commenced in 1970 under a private contractor, but in January, 1975, work was stopped after a methane gas explosion. Drivage was later resumed, but although the diameter was relatively small, problems were experienced from side convergence and uplift owing to the complicated, treacherous and generally adverse geological conditions. The strata consist of highly squeezable shales and water-bearing sandstones with numerous faults and folds. The New Austrian Tunnelling Method (NATM) was selected to complete the drivage through the critical 2.6-km section between faces 4 and 5. Excavation was performed by an Alpine Miner 50 and the tunnel was holed successfully on 27 October, 1981.

The significant convergences that were experienced necessitated the correction of the affected supports in parallel with the concreting operations. To achieve a fast rate of concreting telescopic shutters 60 m long were employed to concrete the sides and crown in one-half of the tunnel, whereas in the other half conventional formwork was used. Invert concreting was achieved with a sliding form or guide stakes.

Aggregate and concrete production

For the supply of ready-mixed concrete to face 4 a 50 t/h capacity aggregate processing plant and a 30 m³/h batching and mixing plant were purchased domestically and installed near construction shaft no. 1. The concrete was delivered through a 350-mm diameter vertical steel chute down the 45-m deep shaft. River bed aggregate was used, being processed through the plant to obtain sizes at 40, 20 and 10 mm and sand. The recovery of sand and the other sizes was in the ratio of 30:70. At the face 5 side non-tilting type electric mixers of 750-l capacity were installed outside the adit.

The aggregate processing plant was designed, supplied and commissioned by Marshal Sons and Co., Madras. The raw material – a mixture of sand and gravel with a maximum lump size of 100 mm and a bulk density of 1.6 t/m³ – was fed from tipper trucks to a dump hopper of 25-t capacity. The oversize lumps were removed by hand-picking from a main belt conveyor. The material was delivered from a feed conveyor to the screen unit, which had two sets of vibrating screens, each with a double deck. The first set of screens had 40 mm square holes in the top deck and 20 mm in the lower deck; the second set had 10-mm holes in the top deck and 4.75-mm holes in the lower.

The oversize material >40 mm was fed to crushers, which discharged to a recycle conveyor and thence to the feed conveyor. The raw materials at 40–20 mm, 20–10 mm and 10–4.75 mm were stockpiled separately in bins. The material was drawn from the bins by a 0.3-m³ capacity scraper towards bulkheads (this arrangement ensured that the stockpile height was sufficient to allow a gravity flow through the gate openings into a skip bucket). The skip received measured quantities of aggregates and sand through the bulkhead gates, which were operated pneumatically.

73

The batching and mixing plant was supplied by Millars, Bombay. Two vertically driven pan mixers, each of 500-l capacity, were employed. The cement was supplied by a horizontal screw conveyor installed below two cement silos, each of 30-t capacity. Control was by an automatic cement weighing batcher. The cement silos were filled by a bucket elevator. During mixing the required amount of water was added and the operations were controlled by one man in a central control cabin.

Table 1   Mix composition

	M 200	M 250
Cement, kg	420	420
Aggregate 40–20 mm, kg	429	490
Aggregate 20–10 mm, kg	327	330
Aggregate 10–4.75 mm, kg	265	255
Sand, kg	671	642
Water, l	210	189
Slump, mm	137	100
Water/cement ratio	0.5	0.45

After the concrete was mixed it was discharged through chutes down the shaft to agitator cars at the shaft bottom. The concrete strengths used were M 200 for the crown and sides and M 250 for the invert. The mixes used are listed in Table 1.

The concrete was transported underground in 4.5-m³ capacity NC-4 pneumatically operated agitator cars (transit mixers) imported from Icoma, Italy. These have two loading openings on the drum and the concrete was fed from the chute into each opening in turn. A 15-hp compressed-air motor rotated the drum. An air distribution valve at the forward end of the car controlled the direction of rotation. The cars were hauled by 5.5-t locomotives after being loaded to 80% capacity to allow for voids while mixing. The compressed air required was 6000–7000 l at 5–6 bar. Three or four trains (one car and one loco) were operated according to requirements.

Methods used to install concrete lining

The installation of the concrete lining could not be undertaken concurrently with the driving of the tunnel because of the small diameter, and the support rectification problems would have

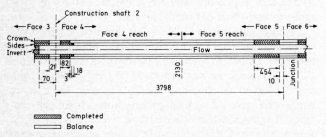

Fig. 2   Position of concrete lining

obstructed rail traffic and delayed the tunnel advance. Concreting was therefore planned to be completed between face 4 and face 5 after holing through. The position of the lining previously completed by the initial contractor is shown in Fig. 2. The length between face 4 and face 5 was 3798 m; of this, 2130 m was allocated to face 4 and 1668 m to face 5. Concreting the adit junction was to be undertaken from face 5. From face 4 the concreting of the invert was to be completed first, followed by the crown. From the face 5 side concreting was planned to be in the reverse order. In fact, at a later stage in the works both invert and crown were concreted simultaneously.

Concreting invert

Several methods were used to concrete the invert. The first system used fabricated guide stakes (Fig. 3), which were positioned on the kerb or on steel chairs. The guide stakes were spaced at 2 m and were prepared in 6-m blocks. They were held together by 25-mm diameter steel rods, threaded at both ends and fitted with double nuts. Wooden planks for radial joints were provided and held against the tunnel sides. A jacking arrangement at each side of the stake was used for levelling. The rail track ended near the last guide stake.

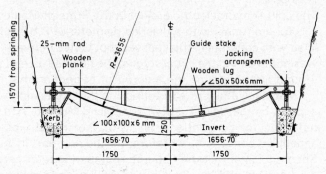

Fig. 3   Guide stake details

Concrete from the agitator cars was discharged either through an open chute or directly (Fig. 4). Vibration was by 35-mm needle-type pneumatic vibrators and the shape was formed by manually operated wooden lugs between the poured invert and the guide stake.

After the first section was poured the agitator car was moved up to the second and then the third, which was poured directly. No problems were encountered as a result of edge slumping at the flat invert angle.

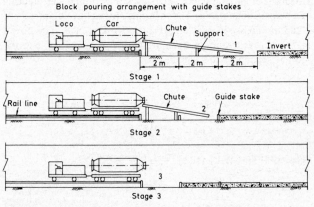

Fig. 4   Block pouring arrangement with guide stakes

While the blocks were being poured excavation and mucking in the next block were in progress from each side and within the rail track without disturbance to the rail sleepers. During the agitator car changes an empty muck trolley was brought in by loco and loaded. It was shunted at a crossing when the next concrete car arrived, this concurrent activity enabling good progress to be made.

After each block had been poured the next 6 m of rail track was dismantled and removed with the wooden sleepers. Any excavation that was required was then performed to the proper level, the guide stakes were fitted and the cycle was repeated.

Concreting invert by slip form

A slip form was employed when the invert was placed ahead of the crown concrete. It was 3 m long and in two pieces joined

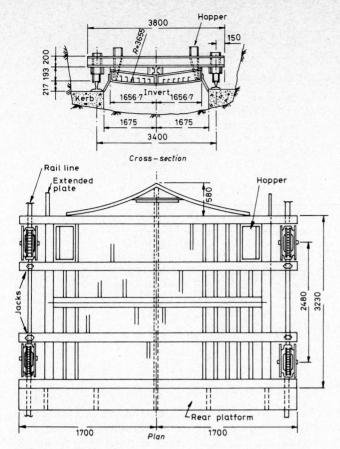

Fig. 5 Invert slip form

in the centre along the tunnel axis. A hopper was provided at each side at the front to fill the invert edges (Fig. 5). To suit the equipment to the tunnel the wheel gauge had to be reduced from 3800 to 3400 mm to allow it to operate in lengths where support legs had moved inwards, although not preventing the minimum concrete thickness specifications to be achieved. The shape of the joint plates was modified to suit the reduced wheel gauge, and they were extended by 0.5 m at the front to prevent the concrete from entering between the wheels when the form was moved. The slope of the edge hopper was made flat and the discharge openings were widened to ensure proper filling at the edges. Four electrically operated shutter vibrators were fixed permanently to the slip form to vibrate the concrete as the slip form was moved. An 80-mm wide platform was fitted to the back of the slip form so that masons could sit over the invert to undertake final finishing.

Rails were laid in advance on the kerb to the correct gauge and level and securely held. In lengths where the kerb had not been poured steel chairs made of rods were fitted, the rails being placed over them. Two 3-t capacity 'max-pullers', one on each side, were provided to pull the slip form: these were pinned to the rail and operated manually, being moved as concreting advanced.

Sections for concreting were prepared in 6-m lengths, being prepared as has already been described. The concrete was poured from the agitator car through an open chute, withdrawing as concreting progressed. The edge hoppers were filled manually by shovel and the slip form was pulled by the 'max-pullers'. Concrete in the edge hoppers was vibrated by pneumatic needle vibrators to ensure good flow and to avoid choking of hopper openings. Every ten days the slip form was pulled ahead over the unconcreted section, thoroughly cleaned, oiled and pulled back.

A jacking arrangement on each side of the slip form over the rails prevented the platform from sticking to the concrete during breaks in the concreting cycle. The slip form was jacked

up over the finished concrete block about two hours after pouring and lowered for restarting.

Maximum progress of around 30 m/day was achieved by slip forming. The major bottleneck was excessive mucking in the cleaning of each block. Track blockage occurred when supports were being rectified at two or three places. Special attention was required to cleaning and greasing the double flange wheels and edge hoppers.

Concreting invert by rail bridge method

In lengths where the crown concreting was placed ahead of the invert a method that used the rail line bridge was employed for the invert, thereby enabling invert concreting to be started at two or three places independently of crown concreting. When crown concreting was completed more working places could be employed with careful planning in the deployment of empty trolleys for mucking out the places.

The method involved the preparation of an 8- to 10-m length with excavation to the required level in the entire area, except near the sleepers, to avoid disturbance of the rail track, which was supported on mechanical jacks at 2-m spacing, placed on girders that rested on the prepared bed. Tie rods kept the track at the required gauge and avoided the risk of any widening. The wooden sleepers were removed before excavation; sometimes, wooden braces were provided to check lateral shifting where the rail track was at a higher level.

Concrete was discharged from the agitator cars into each prepared block and shaped manually by trowels to the required profile. The wooden sleepers were replaced under the rails after a 24-h setting time and nailed in place. The jacks were removed for further use elsewhere. With this system (Fig. 6) the best progress was 40 m/day.

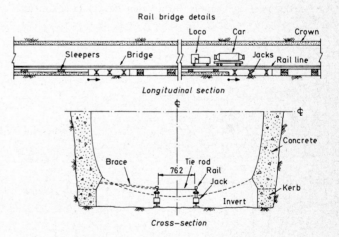

Fig. 6 Rail bridge details

In some lengths invert concreting was performed ahead of the crown by supporting the rail track over the girders placed across the tunnel, resting on the kerbs at either side. These blocks were in 6-m lengths and wooden planks were provided to form the side edges for the radial joint. After the concrete had set the sleeper packing was set and the cross girders were removed.

Concreting crown and sides

The sequence of events in the concreting of the crown and sides is listed in Table 2. Much of the tunnel in the face 4 section was concreted with the use of a 60-m long telescopic formwork, which had ten sections, each of 6-m length, fabricated from 5-mm thick plate, and fitted with a hydraulically operated,

Table 2 Concreting crown and sides

Chainage, m	Width, m	Shape	Formwork	Dates
Face 5				
2130–2290	3.5	Circular	Conventional	25/8/82–3/11/82
2498–2290	3.81	Horseshoe	12-m formwork	25/4/82–15/8/82
2498–2558	3.81	Horseshoe	Erected 60-m form	17/11/81–7/12/81
2558–2986	3.81	Horseshoe	6-m form	20/12/81–25/4/82
2986–3178	3.2	Circular	Special form	9/6/82–10/1/83
3178–3334	3.2	Circular	Special form	9/3/82–23/5/82
3334–3798 ⎫	3.81	Horseshoe	6-m form	
Adit junction ⎭				25/5/82–7/8/82
Face 4				
2130–435	3.81	Horseshoe	60-m telescopic	8/8/82–10/2/83
435–330	3.81	Horseshoe	6-m form	27/8/82–23/10/82
330–215	3.81	Horseshoe	60-m telescopic	11/2/82–13/2/83
215–117	3.81	Horseshoe	6-m	12/11/82–31/1/83

Total concreted
2078 m by telescopic form
1191 m by conventional formwork
　58 m by wooden formwork

3327 m, including junctions

motorized traveller (Fig. 7). This was the first time that this type of shutter had been used in India; the best performance was 400 m, completed in one month in one heading.

The design concrete lining thickness was 250 mm, but in some lengths the finished diameter had to be reduced to enable that to be achieved (Table 2). An existing formwork of 3.9-m diameter was modified in the project workshop to produce a 3.5-m diameter, and another form was made of 3.2-m diameter.

before the telescopic form was used. This was made from mild-steel angles and bars and was 2 m long with an outer radius of 2010 mm. The track gauge was equal to that of the formwork traveller and it ran on the same track. A wooden platform on the top of the jumbo provided access for men. It was moved manually on double-flanged 300-mm diameter wheels (Fig. 8). Whenever ribs would interfere with the telescopic form they were corrected and the work was performed at least 100 m ahead of the concreting.

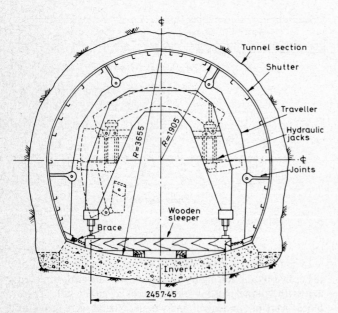

Fig. 7 Telescopic shutter

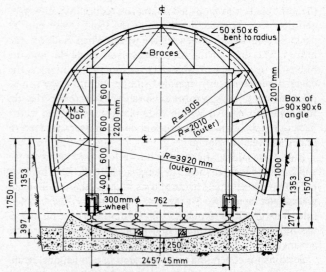

Fig. 8 Jumbo for measurement of encroachment

In the face 5 side a 6-m conventional form was used for much of the work. Concrete was brought in by agitator cars loaded outside the adit from 750-l capacity concrete mixers. A pneumatically operated Pressweld placer of 0.5-m³ capacity was used to place the concrete behind the formwork through the slick line running over the formwork crown. The agitator cars discharged directly into the placer.

An encroachment measuring jumbo was used in the face 4 section to check any inward movement of the stabilizing ribs

The Icoma telescopic shutter was first erected as a 60-m length in the face 5 section (Table 2) and the whole length was then concreted. The adjoining length was concreted (two 12-m lengths at a time) and the rest of the pieces were moved to the face 4 side to commence concreting there (Table 2). The first four pieces were erected in the face 4 section by 4 August, 1982, but operations were delayed for four days by a fall of ground at the left side.

Concrete was pumped by 38 m³/h Schwing BPTF 350 electric

pumps through a telescopic pipe connected to the crown entry hole via a shut-off valve. The pipe was supported and clamped on to flat-bed trolleys positioned at 10-m intervals. The concrete was brought in by agitator cars from the batching and mixing plant and at any one time four trains, each with one car, were operated (Fig. 9).

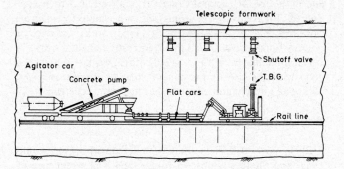

Fig. 9 Concreting arrangement with telescopic shutters

At the commencement of pouring a bulkhead was fitted, but later the set concrete obviated the need for a bulkhead. The shutters from the back were stripped after 16 h, lowered and transported ahead. The concreting was only disrupted when a collapsed shutter crossed ahead and an empty traveller returned after erection for the next shutter to be stripped. While this crossover took place the concrete pipe had to be disconnected, lowered and re-hooked.

The first pour in the face 4 section was of four shutters, the second of seven and, thereafter, the operations were continuous to completion, except for the short lengths from 435 to 330 m and 215 to 117 m (Table 2).

The section near to the shaft was concreted by use of wooden formwork in two stages – the sides followed by the crown. After completion of the sides, niches were fashioned into the sides at 1.5-m intervals and 152 mm by 152 mm RSJs were placed across the span in the niches. These supported the top arch wooden form.

Rail tracks, air and water lines

The rail top was specified to be 397 mm from the completed invert to provide a proper bearing for the wooden sleepers. The sleepers were spaced at 600 mm and their ends were shaped to the invert radius. A steel template was fabricated to the invert shape and the sleepers were prepared in advance of the work. Longitudinal sleepers were also provided to support the cross sleepers.

The central rail track was laid with a gauge of 762 mm throughout the tunnel, with crossings at 1600, 1100 and 600 m chainage. At the sides track for the formwork traveller was laid about 60 m plus 100–120 m in advance; as concreting progressed, rails from the rear were removed and relaid ahead. It was not possible to use dog spikes for these side rails owing to the tapered edges of the sleepers. To hold them securely 25-mm diameter rods and angle irons were therefore welded between the rails and the central rails. As the concreting approached a crossing, the crossing was dismantled and a central track was laid to extend the traveller track.

The air and water lines were installed at the tunnel sides and before shutters could be erected they had to be repositioned. The lines were removed in 220-m lengths and lowered. They were placed between the traveller track and the central track and were joined by a bend to the lines at the side: the bend

position was shifted in advance as concreting progressed. The central track was not dismantled on completion of concreting as it was required for grouting.

Problems

The chief delays experienced were excessive mucking when preparing the invert sections and rectifying encroachments at the sides. It was concluded that more care taken during tunnel excavation would have reduced these delays and, in particular, the support column lengths should have been longer and the rail track laid as low as possible to minimize the chances of muck being deposited. Muck should be cleared away in parallel with other activity and the rectification work carried out while excavation is in progress so that little remains to be done before concreting is begun.

During the concreting of the crown and sides some roof falls occurred and had to be cleared before setting the shutters.

Project conclusion

Grouting was undertaken after the tunnel had been concreted and the project was commissioned successfully on 30 April, 1983. The waters from the Loktak Lake then flowed through the completed tunnel to the Leimatak Valley.

Discussion

N. S. M. Berry* said that he was extremely surprised to learn that the mining industry, having apparently invented precast concrete cement linings in the 1930s, was some 50 years later undertaking its own research into the development of linings suitable for use in roadways in coal mines. In the meantime, however, it had apparently been continuing to use the well-proven system with D-shaped colliery arches, which, although they were not very effective in holding up the roof and did nothing for the floor, had the great advantage that they gave prior warning when about to fail.

Rockbolts were also dismissed as being unsuitable, having apparently not proved effective when used to support a square profile tunnel in the 1950s. He found it very hard to believe that the views of the authors reflected the NCB current policy and, if that were not the case, it was regrettable that such a dated view had been presented of the British mining industry.

The case for the adoption of a circular section, probably with a precast concrete lining, as standard practice for main roadways where there was any possibility of floor movement seemed to be overwhelming and he would make a plea for the coal industry to take advantage of the wealth of experience that existed in the civil engineering industry of modern methods of support.

The case, he believed, was primarily economic. Although the cost of driving and building a circular roadway with precast concrete lining would undoubtedly be higher than for a D-shaped roadway with steel arches, when the cost of maintenance throughout its life was taken into account, both in the actual cost of labour and materials in maintaining the roadway itself, not to mention the effect that that had on the use of the roadway and, thence, production, the overall cost-effectiveness of the circular roadway could surely not be in any doubt. He would be interested to know whether the authors had any comparative cost figures for circular sections as opposed to D-shaped roadways when account was taken of the cost of maintenance throughout their lifetime.

T. J. M. Paterson† said that Bloor and Pink had mentioned that further developments in cement-based grouts would be of significant value in coal mines: he wondered what particular developments the authors had in mind.

He would welcome more details – in particular, the mix design – of the sand–cement–PFA mix pumped over long distances in the south drift at Selby, asking if such a mix was a grout or a concrete.

Dr. J-F. Raffoux‡ asked Bloor and Pink if criteria existed for the selection of roadways in which concrete linings would be used (geotechnical criteria, deformation measurements, etc.). Mention had been made of the NATM and he would like to know the extent of the development in Britain of bolting in roadways, either in rectangular or arch-shaped form.

I. Waugh§ said that trials had been carried out during the 1960s with strata bolts to support roadways of rectangular cross-section. The results had been disappointing owing to the fragmented and relatively weak nature of the strata. If further trials to use strata bolts as the systematic type of support were to be proposed, the strata of the proposed site would need to be of sufficient strength to lend themselves to that method of support.

*Babtie Shaw and Morton, Glasgow, Scotland.
†Geostore (South Killingholme), Ltd., South Killingholme, South Humberside, England.
‡CERCHAR, Verneuil en Halatte, France.
§Health and Safety Executive, Washington, Tyne and Wear, England.

The proposers would, of course, be required to demonstrate that the system complied with the relevant legislation.

F. Rowbottom* sought comments by Bloor and Pink on the use of concrete on remedial work on roadways. He asked if repairs to the floors of roadways that had heaves had involved rockbolts with R.I. concrete to give an improved permanent repair, and if the use of rockbolts and R.I. concrete had been considered, for roadways in seams that were liable to extensive floor heave, as an initial means of support so as to reduce or prevent floor heave, which involved costly remedial work.

He would like the authors to indicate the work that had been done with the use of permanent concrete linings and also rockbolts initially and whether that had been beneficial.

Written contribution

J. Buchanan† Which methods of concreting the invert would Tyagi and Sharma choose in future, and which sequence of invert and arch concreting would they prefer? At what stage in the operations was the kerb laid for both invert-first and arch-first procedures?

Were there problems in achieving the required 'cleanliness' of the invert rock?

Authors' replies

Dr. A. S. Bloor and A. Pink In reply to N. S. M. Berry, in our acknowledgement (p. 71) it was stated that the authors' opinions do not necessarily reflect those of the NCB.

The use of concrete block lining was forced on the Belgian coal industry in the 1930s. The alternative was to abandon the Campine coalfield, as the Dutch did with its extension. Similar blocks were used successfully in extreme conditions in the United Kingdom in the 1950s (or even earlier – we would welcome any information on this point), again of dire necessity.

It must be pointed out that precast concrete liners have disadvantages (cost, handling, transport and slowness of erection) in the mining environment as well as advantages. These are major reasons why they have not been used as standard roadway linings.

The case for circular sections is not 'overwhelming'. Many conventional roadways never need major repair – either because of good strata conditions or short planned life. When installing a strong lining the possibility and consequences of failure must be considered. It is inconvenient to have to trim or 'dint' a conventional roadway, but a failed concrete or steel tube in a coal mine is a serious matter.

The NCB seems to be making increasing and profitable use of civil engineers underground. They are particularly ready to combine their expertise with that of the mining engineer in the sometimes strange world of soft-rock mechanics.

We cannot quote actual figures for circular and D-shaped roadways, but the extra cost of lining the 1500-m Cadley Hill drivage with precast concrete segments was easily offset against projected repair bills over 25 years on conventional supports.

In reply to T. J. M. Paterson, we had in mind a grout that would guarantee redistribution of non-uniform loads around a concrete lining irrespective of the shape of the excavation and differential movement within the annulus. This would avoid the modes of failure described in the paper due to bending strains in circular linings and allow the full compressive strength of concrete to be mobilized.

*Department of Minerals and Energy, Port Moresby, Papua New Guinea.
†Sir Robert MacAlpine and Sons, Ltd., London, England.

F. A. Auld (Cementation Research; see reference 14 on page 72) should be approached for information on the mix design for the Selby long-distance pumping.

In reply to Dr. J-F. Raffoux, it was, rather, a question of selecting a lining for a given roadway situation. There are many other criteria besides the geotechnical ones, which have often already been determined – for example, the type of tunnelling machine, the required lifetime of the roadway, allowable deformation, criticality of its position and, of course, cost-effectiveness.

Considerable caution is apparent in the United Kingdom attitude to bolting as a means of support, particularly as the sole means of support. It must be proven to be safe. This is not an unreasonable attitude in view of the potential consequences of a failure.

In reply to F. Rowbottom, the West Main return concrete segmental lining, described in the paper, was a remedial procedure and, although it eventually failed, it was for more than a year the largest cross-section in the District. Other remedial works with the use of concrete have been more successful (e.g. Haunchwood, Thorne, Calverton and another site at Cadley Hill).

Generally, it would seem that the roadway has to be in a critical position and very poor condition before concrete remedial work is justified, and then concrete blocks seem to be favoured. An important point is that should the concrete repair fail again, it must not make re-excavation more difficult.

It is for this same reason that rockbolts are not, to our knowledge, used in roadway floors. Wooden dowels have been used to control floor heave while allowing floor-trimming ('dinting') at a later date, if necessary.

Rockbolts are often used to secure ground in large excavations, e.g. insets, where changes in cross-section and direction produce potentially unstable situations prior to the placement of in-situ concrete. We do not know of any use of rockbolts before placing concrete segments or blocks in roadways.

G. D. Tyagi and K. S. Sharma In reply to J. Buchanan, we would propose arch first and invert later as the sequence for concreting the tunnel. For invert concreting slip form is the best choice. It can run on rails laid on brackets fixed to the side lining. Invert would follow the grouting. This method avoids dismantling and relaying the track when rolling stock is employed in the tunnel and also checks cleaning of grouting material over the invert.

The kerb laying was started simultaneously with excavation. Whatever stretches were left after daylighting were poured along with arch or invert.

Excessive cleaning, necessary in certain stretches, hampered the invert pouring progress. The operation had to be carried out simultaneously in advance.

Session 4 – Geotechnical studies

Co-Chairmen: Dr. R. Tornaghi and Dr. I. W. Farmer

Finite-element techniques for preliminary assessment of a cut and cover tunnel

D. M. Potts
Imperial College, London, England
M. C. Knights
W. S. Atkins and Partners, Epsom, Surrey, England

Synopsis

Finite-element techniques have been used in preliminary investigations for the design of a cut and cover tunnel proposed as part of the London–Great Yarmouth trunk road (A12) (Eastway to Eastern Avenue section), northeast London. The 20-m wide tunnel will be situated directly below the existing busy A12 trunk road, threading its way between the foundations of Wanstead underground metro station and varied commercial and domestic buildings. It also crosses over the London Transport underground Central line tunnels.

Prediction of the bending moments, stresses and soil/structure movements of the proposed tunnel by conventional limit equilibrium methods would have proved difficult, if not impossible, in view of the complex interaction of the tunnel structure and the short- and long-term behaviour of the London Clay. Finite-element assessment of a number of representative cross-sections of the tunnel were undertaken to gain a preliminary insight into the structural behaviour. Assumptions were varied for identification of the main influences of structural behaviour.

The results of the preliminary analysis for two of these cross-sections are presented and the benefits of this type of prediction are discussed.

The increasing use of cut and cover highway tunnels in urban areas requires that the design investigate the complex construction sequences imposed by existing traffic thoroughfares and neighbouring sensitive structures. The recently opened M25 motorway tunnels have employed cut and cover techniques and the proposed Hatfield (A1) and Ealing Common tunnels will be constructed similarly. It is the intention in this paper to discuss part of the preliminary design procedures for the proposed George Green tunnel in north London.

The Department of Transport, as client, is proposing to carry out improvements to the alignment of a section of the A12 trunk road (formerly known as the Hackney to M11 link road), which will form a connexion between the existing East Cross route at Hackney and the existing M11 southern terminal at Redbridge in northeast London (Fig. 1). The new road will contain multi-span flyovers, a cut and cover tunnel and other major highway structures. W. S. Atkins and Partners have been retained by the client to design this major urban highway scheme.

The section of road between the Green Man roundabout and the River Roding is to be mainly depressed below existing road level and for 300 m the road is to be constructed in a cut and cover tunnel. For the purpose of this paper the tunnel is referred to as the George Green tunnel (GGT). The tunnel is to be built under the full width of the existing trunk road for most of its length. It is essential that traffic flow be maintained along the busy A12 trunk road and adjoining side roads while construction is proceeding. The tunnel is also to be built for environmental reasons since it traverses part of Epping Forest land. This land will be restored to its former state after completion of construction.

The density and the nature of surface structures have imposed a severe constraint on the alignment of the tunnel. In particular, the close proximity of the London Transport (LT) underground station at Wanstead to the south of the tunnel and the accompanying LT running tunnels imposes severe design and construction restrictions on the GGT with respect to surface settlement and sequencing of construction. As a consequence of these restrictions it is felt that either diaphragm or secant pile wall construction followed by casting of the roof slab before the major part of the excavation takes place will be necessary. Such an approach will minimize soil movements and, with careful sequencing of the wall and roof construction, will keep disruption of traffic flows to a minimum. Once the wall and roof slabs are in place, full traffic flow at surface can continue while tunnel construction is carried out beneath existing road level. This method of construction would reduce to a minimum the disturbance to traffic flow on this very busy trunk road.

Design

To assess the feasibility of such a solution a preliminary design was initiated prior to the final design being carried out. In this respect it was necessary to assess both the movements of and the stresses and bending moments in the embedded walls and the road and roof slabs. It was also necessary to predict the likely movements of the soil in and around the excavation. This was particularly important as the twin LT running tunnels cross obliquely under the GGT within a distance of 4 m at the nearest point (Figs. 2 and 3). The close proximity of the LT tunnels also constrained the wall embedment that can be achieved in some places. It is for this reason that a base slab is proposed to provide the necessary restraint to the external walls. The slab will also be designed to resist heave forces under the tunnel excavation.

The proposed GGT is clearly a complex soil structure interaction problem and it quickly became apparent that conventional design approaches were unlikely to be applicable. Consequently, it was decided to adopt a finite-element

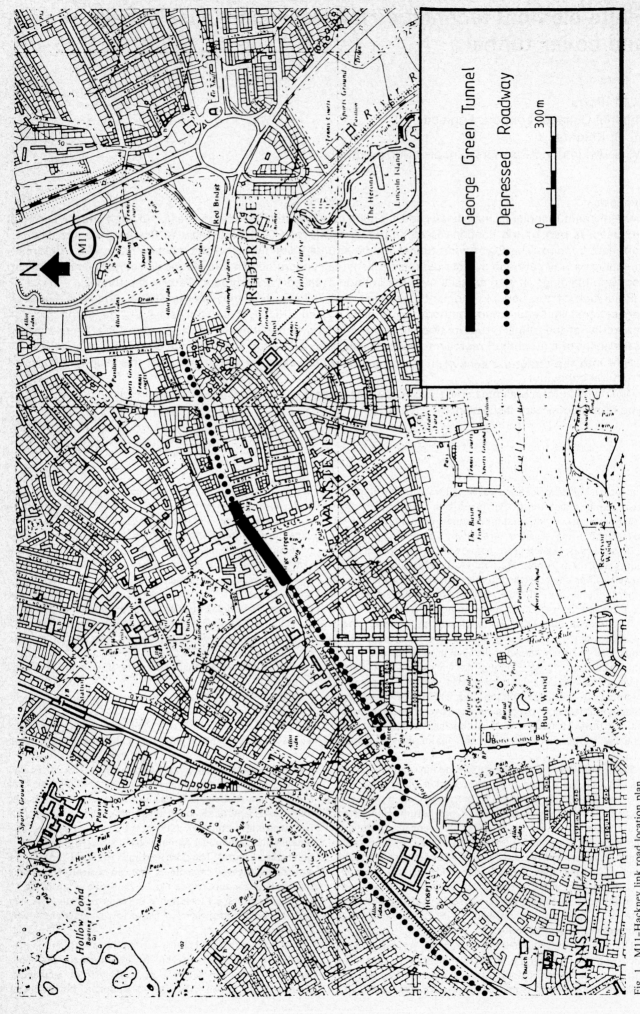

Fig. 1 M11–Hackney link road location plan

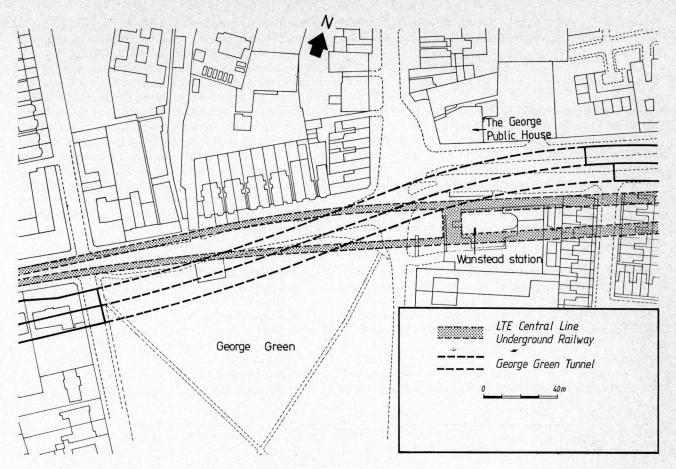

Fig. 2 Plan showing proximity of tunnel to neighbouring structures

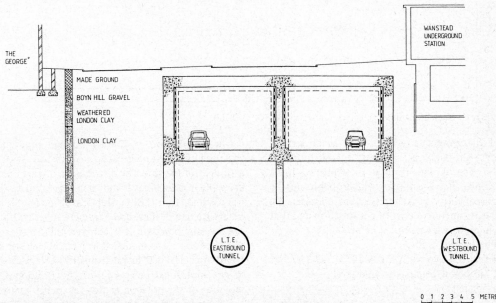

Fig. 3 Proposed cross-section of tunnel adjacent to Wanstead station

approach, which allows the movements and stresses in both the structure and the soil to be calculated from the same analysis. In addition, it is possible to model the construction sequence.

For the preliminary design of the GGT several cross-sections of the tunnel were analysed, but the results of two sections only are discussed here. Comparison of some preliminary analyses, in which the soil was modelled either as an elastic or an elasto-plastic material, indicated that in the former case the predicted displacements and bending moments were smaller. The elastic analyses also predicted tensile thrusts in the road slab in the long term. This is consistent with the results that were presented by Potts and Burland,[5] which indicate that during the dissipation stage of an elastic analysis the wall will try to move away from the excavation. Such results, however, are unrealistic, arising as a direct consequence of the elastic formulation. Following the initial exercise with the use of elastic soil properties the soil was modelled in an elastoplastic manner for all further analyses – a method that results in more realistic predictions.

All finite-element calculations were performed by use of the Imperial College Soil Mechanics Finite Element Package (ICFEP). Eight-noded plane strain elements with reduced integration were adopted and an accelerated form of the initial stress approach was employed to solve the finite-element equations.

Construction

As this is not a 'green field' site, the design of the tunnel will have to take account of construction aspects, which, in turn, will be influenced by (a) existing carriageway traffic diversions, (b) utility diversions, (c) proximity to existing surface structures, (d) proximity to underground tunnels, (e) restricted access to the site, (f) construction of the approach cutting and (g) temporary works.

A realistic simulation of the contractor's likely working method in undertaking construction had to be made for the modelling exercise. The complex phased traffic and utility diversions are the prime factors for consideration, and the temporary propping of embedded walls is also important.

In the following descriptions of two of the sections that were studied by use of computer modelling techniques the assumptions for construction sequencing are listed. They demonstrate the comparative versatility of the use of this method of analysis.

Section 1
Section 1 represents the main part of the GGT. The geometry of the tunnel and the soil conditions are shown in Fig. 4. The

(l) Dissipate excess pore water pressure.

There are possible minor permutations of the above listing, but (a)–(l) is considered to be a conservative procedure.

It was assumed that the roof and road slabs were cast into the embedded walls, forming a joint that could transmit both thrusts and bending moments. During the construction stages of the analysis the London Clay is assumed to be undrained and the Boyn Hill Gravel and made ground to behave in a drained manner. For the final stage of the analyses all the soil was assumed to be drained and the excess pore pressures developed in the London Clay during the construction process were dissipated. As only the excess pore water pressures were dissipated, it was implicitly assumed that the final pore water pressure distribution in the soil returns to that prevailing prior to construction.

The following soil parameters were adopted.

Boyn Hill Gravel and made ground

Angle of shearing resistance, ϕ'	35°	
Cohesion, c'	0	
Angle of dilatation, ν	17.5°	
Bulk unit weight, γ_{sat}	21 kN/m²	

London Clay

Angle of shearing resistance, ϕ'	25°	
Cohesion, c'	0	
Angle of dilatation, ν	12.5°	
Bulk unit weight, γ_{sat}	19 kN/m²	

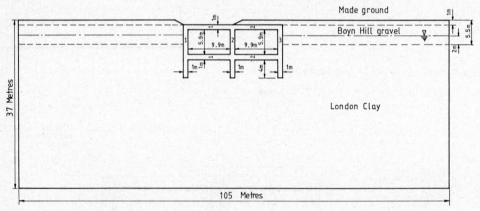

Fig. 4   Sketch of tunnel geometry for section 1 (not to scale)

tunnel consists of three embedded walls – to be installed prior to any excavation. Although the geometry of the tunnel is symmetric about a vertical plane through the centre wall, the construction sequence that is adopted will probably not be symmetrical. Consequently, it is necessary to consider the whole section. The assumed sequence of construction and that simulated in the analysis were as noted below.

(a) Construct all embedded walls.

(b) Excavate soil between two walls (i.e. walls 1 and 2 in Fig. 4) to a depth of 3 m below original ground level.

(c) Construct roof slab 1.

(d) Excavate soil between walls 1 and 2 to a depth of about 9 m below original ground level.

(e) Construct road slab number 1.

(f) Backfill 1 m above left-hand portal roof and apply a surcharge loading to the surface of the fill of 10.5 kN/m² to represent traffic loading.

(g) Excavate soil between walls 2 and 3 to a depth of 3 m below original ground level.

(h) Construct roof slab 2.

(i) Excavate soil between walls 2 and 3 to a depth of about 9 m below original ground surface.

(j) Construct road slab 2.

(k) Replace 1 m of soil above right-hand portal and apply traffic surcharge of 10.5 kN/m².

The distribution of drained Young's modulus is based on that used by Potts and Burland.[5] A Poisson ratio (M) of 0.2 was assumed for the soil. The distribution of earth pressure at rest, k_0, in the London Clay is shown in Fig. 5 and a value of $k_0 = 0.5$ was assumed for the Boyn Hill Gravel and made ground. Unless otherwise noted, these soil parameters were obtained from the site investigation data. The concrete that forms the walls, road and roof slabs was modelled as isotropic elastic with $E = 28 \times 10^5$ kN/m², $M = 0.15$ and density of 24 kN/m³. In the modelling of the undrained behaviour of the London Clay the bulk modulus of the pore water was set to 10^7 kN/m³.

Results from the analysis are given in Figs. 6, 7 and 8. Vectors of accumulated displacement at various stages of construction are presented in Fig. 9. It should be noted that the vectors that are shown in Fig. 9(e) are drawn to half the scale of those in Fig. 9(a)–(d). These plots clearly show that during construction the movements are not symmetrical, but after dissipation of excess pore pressures (Fig. 9(e)) an approximately symmetrical displacement pattern is predicted.

Predicted horizontal movements and bending moments in the three walls and the slabs are shown in Fig. 6. Wall 1 is subjected to the greatest movement and bending moments. For the outside walls (1 and 3) the maximum bending moment occurs after completion of undrained construction, whereas for wall 2 the bending moments are greatest after construction of

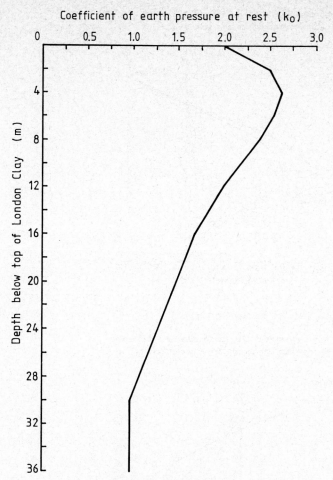

Fig. 5 Variation of coefficient of earth pressures at rest, k_0, with depth in London Clay

roof slab 2. In all cases the maximum bending moments are reduced during the dissipation of excess pore water pressures. It should be noted that at times wall 2 is subjected to appreciable bending moments – a result that might not have been expected if the construction sequence had been ignored.

Bending moments in the roof and road slabs are given in Figs. 7 and 8, respectively. The sign convention assumed for the figures is that sagging leads to positive bending moments. In all cases for the roof and road slab the maximum bending moments are predicted in the long term after dissipation of excess pore water pressures.

Thrusts in the structural components of the tunnel, and distributions of stresses and pore pressures in the soil, were also obtained. Table 1 gives the thrusts in the roof and road slabs.

The finite-element analysis having been set up, it is a relatively easy task to vary such input parameters as the material properties, soil conditions, depth of wall embedment and construction procedure. In addition, a separate finite-element analysis was carried out in which the LT running tunnels were

modelled with respect to the GGT. This was done to enable heave predictions of the LT tunnels to be observed.

Conventional design procedures for embedded walls[1,3,4] do not allow for supports that apply an unknown moment restraint as well as a lateral restraint, and it is difficult to see how these methods could take account of the construction sequence. Potts and Fourie[6] have also shown these procedures to be questionable for propped walls in stiff overconsolidated soils.

Section 2

In the immediate vicinity of the east portal of the GGT the road cutting is to be supported by embedded walls, which are propped at road level by the road slab itself. In the final configuration a wall propped at mid-height is required (Fig. 10). Application of conventional design approaches based on limit equilibrium type calculations is difficult, if not impossible. Such approaches rely on an assumed mechanism of failure. For the present geometry it is difficult to decide on a failure mechanism and the following alternatives appear possible – (1) the wall rotates away from the ground with respect to the position of the road slab, generating active conditions behind the top of the wall and in front of the wall and passive conditions behind the bottom of the wall, or (2) the wall rotates in towards the ground with respect to the position of the road slab, reversing the zones of active and passive pressure in (1).

If the wall had been loaded by backfilling behind it, mechanism (1) might be thought to be applicable. In the present situation of an embedded wall where excavation occurs, however, it is not obvious which, if either, of the two mechanisms is applicable. Present design codes provide no guidance here. For example, Padfield and Mair[4] stated that conventional limit equilibrium methods are only applicable to cases where the prop is close to the top of the wall. The permissible distance of the prop from the top of the wall is not quantified. The situation becomes even more complicated when the actual construction procedure is considered. Although the wall can be made stable once the road slab is cast, it is impractical to provide a temporary support at this level during construction. In the case of GGT it is envisaged that some excavation would be carried out before insertion of a temporary prop close to the top of the wall. The remainder of the excavation would then be completed and the road slab cast before this temporary prop was removed. The insertion of a temporary prop followed by its subsequent removal at a later date will clearly affect the final movements and stresses in the wall. Application of limit equilibrium type calculations that take no account of construction procedure is therefore questionable.

The finite-element approach can overcome these shortcomings. No prior assumption of a failure mechanism is required as this is actually predicted by the analysis. In addition, the construction procedure may be followed closely. As an example of the use of the finite-element approach some results obtained for the GGT are presented. The geometry and

Table 1 Predicted thrusts in road and roof slabs for section 1 per metre

	After completion of left-hand side tunnel		After construction of roof slab 2		After construction of right-hand side tunnel		In long term	
	Left-hand side, kN	Right-hand side, kN	Left-hand side, kN	Right-hand side, kN	Left-hand side, kN	Right-hand side, kN	Left-hand side, kN	Right-hand side, kN
Roof slab 1	− 536	− 536	− 524	− 524	− 660	− 660	− 80	− 80
Road slab 1	—	—	+ 49	+ 103	+ 304	+ 620	− 562	− 586
Roof slab 2	—	—	—	—	− 463	− 463	+ 24	+ 24
Road slab 2	—	—	—	—	—	—	− 782	− 750

Negative values indicate compression.

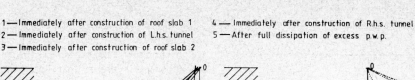

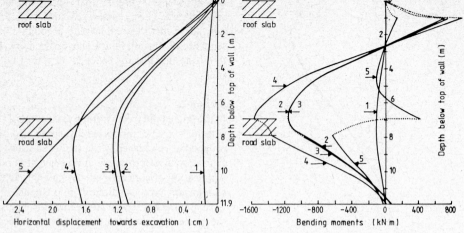

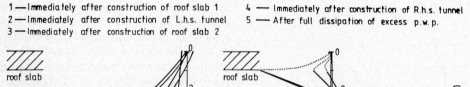

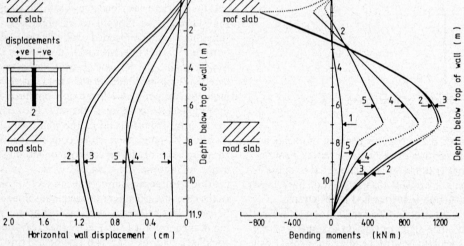

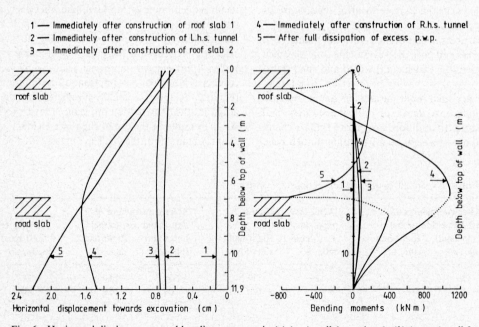

Fig. 6   Horizontal displacements and bending moments in (a) (top) wall 1, section 1, (b) (centre) wall 2 (centre wall), section 1, and (c) (bottom) wall 3, section 1

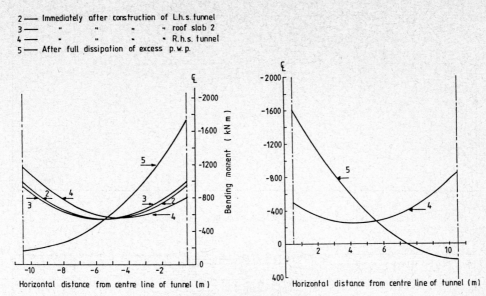

2 —— Immediately after construction of L.h.s. tunnel
3 ——   "   "   "   " roof slab 2
4 ——   "   "   "   " R.h.s. tunnel
5 —— After full dissipation of excess p.w.p.

Fig. 7   Bending moments in roof slabs 1(a) (*left*) and 2 (b) (*right*), section 1

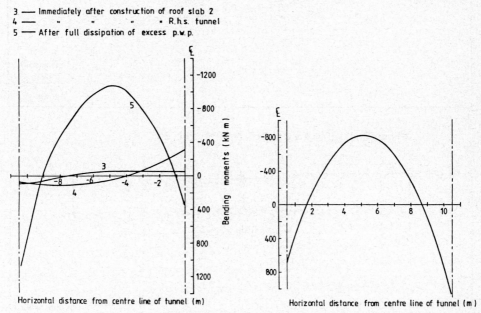

3 —— Immediately after construction of roof slab 2
4 ——   "   "   "   • R.h.s. tunnel
5 —— After full dissipation of excess p.w.p.

Fig. 8   Bending moments in road slabs 1(a) (*left*) and 2(b) (*right*), section 1

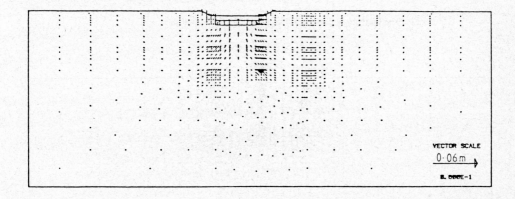

a) Immediately after constructing roof slab 1

Fig. 9—*See page 90*

soil conditions are given in Fig. 10. The same soil and concrete properties as were assumed for section 1 were adopted and the head deposits were modelled with the same properties as the Boyn Hill Gravel and made ground. The following construction sequence was assumed and simulated in the analysis.

(a) Construct embedded walls.
(b) Excavate soil between the diaphragm walls to a depth of 4 m below the original ground surface.
(c) Install temporary rigid prop at 1 m below the top of the walls.

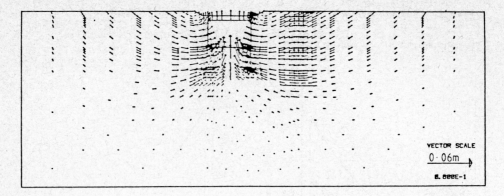

b) Immediately after construction of L.h.s. tunnel

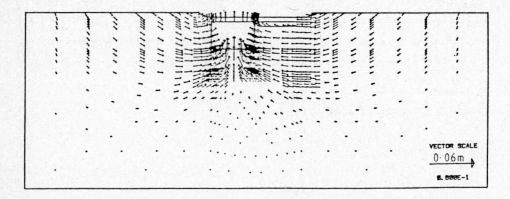

c) Immediately after construction of roof slab 2

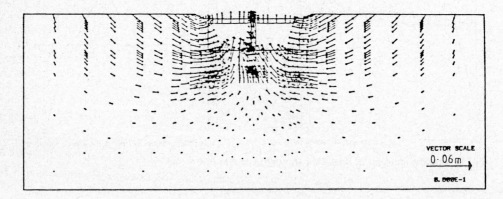

d) Immediately after construction of R.h.s. tunnel

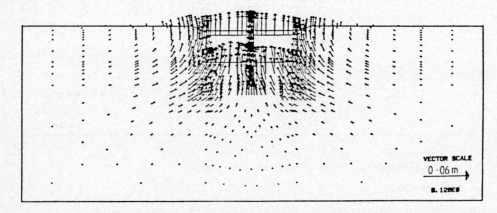

e) After full dissipation of excess p.w.p.

Fig. 9   Vectors of accumulated displacement, section 1

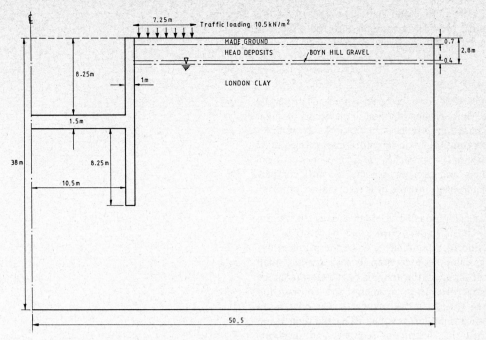

Fig. 10   Sketch of tunnel geometry for section 2 (not to scale)

(d) Excavate soil between the diaphragm walls to a depth of 9.75 m below original ground surface.
(e) Construct road slab.
(f) Remove temporary prop.
(g) Impose traffic loading of 10.5 kN/m² to ground surface immediately adjacent to diaphragm walls.
(h) Dissipate all remaining excess pore water pressures.

During stages (a)–(g) the London Clay was assumed to behave in an undrained manner, whereas for stage (h) drained behaviour was assumed. The made ground, head deposits and Boyn Hill Gravel were modelled in a drained manner throughout the analysis.

An example of the prediction of horizontal displacements is shown in Fig. 11. The associated bending moments predicted in the wall are presented in Fig. 12. The road slab applies both a horizontal and rotational restraint to the wall and its effects on the wall behaviour are evident from the predictions. The maximum bending moment in the wall occurs after full excavation has been completed and before removal of the temporary prop. In the long term, after dissipation of excess pore water pressures the sign of the bending moment changes over the top part of the wall.

Several analyses of this section were performed, different amounts of pore pressure dissipation being allowed to occur

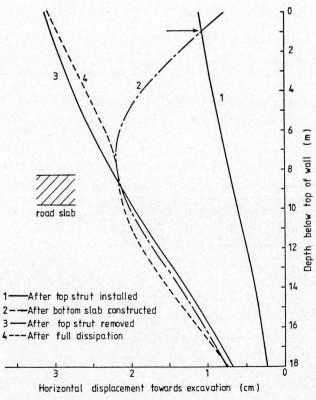

Fig. 11   Horizontal wall displacements for section 2

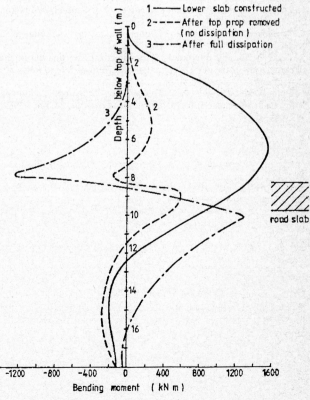

Fig. 12   Wall bending moments for section 2

prior to construction of the road slab. Comparison of the predictions obtained provided an insight into the effects of drainage resulting from a delay in construction of the road slab.

Conclusions

The two examples that have been presented illustrate the application of the finite-element method to the design of a real soil–structure interaction problem. In both these examples conventional limit equilibrium design procedures proved to be inadequate. Such simple approaches consider elements of the structure separately and take no account of such complex interaction and, moreover, provide little information on likely soil movements.

The finite-element approach has much greater flexibility, allowing both the construction sequence and the complex soil–structure interaction to be simulated. Once the problem has been set up on the computer it is relatively easy to make small adjustments to the input. In the analysis of the George Green tunnel the material properties, geometry and construction procedure were all varied. In this manner it was possible to identify the significant parameters that affect the tunnel, i.e. embedment of the wall, construction sequence and the short- and long-term soil properties. It is hoped that this improved understanding of the tunnel structural behaviour will assist the designers during the final design.

Acknowledgement

The authors wish to thank the client, the Department of Transport, Eastern Regional Office, Bedford, for permission to publish this paper. They also wish to acknowledge comments by members of Imperial College Department of Civil Engineering, W. S. Atkins and Partners and the client.

References
1. *Earth retaining structures* (London: Institution of Structural Engineers, 1951), 224 p. (*Civil Engineering Code of Practice* no. 2)
2. Jardine R. J. *et al.* The importance of small strain behaviour in the analysis of soil structure interaction. Publication in preparation.
3. United States Naval Facilities Engineering Command. *Design manual–soil mechanics, foundations and earth structures* (Washington D.C.: NAVFAC, 1971). *Rep.* DM-7.
4. Padfield C. J. and Mair R. J. Design of retaining walls embedded in stiff clays. *CIRIA Rep.* 104, 1984, 146 p.
5. Potts D. M. and Burland J. B. A numerical investigation of the retaining walls of the Bell Common Tunnel. *Transport Road Res. Lab. Supplem. Rep.* 783, 1983, 40 p.
6. Potts D. M. and Fourie A. B. The behaviour of a propped retaining wall: results of a numerical experiment. *Geotechnique*, **34**, no. 3 1984, 383–404.

Use of NATM in soft ground near Tokyo, Japan

T. Fujimori
Chiba Prefectural Office, Chiba Prefecture, Japan
C. Uchiyama
Chiba Prefectural Office, Chiba Prefecture, Japan
H. Kunimi
Shimizu Construction Co., Ltd., Tokyo, Japan
H. Takasaki
Shimizu Construction Co., Ltd., Tokyo, Japan

Synopsis
The basin of the Kokubu River near Tokyo, Japan, has recently been undergoing drastic urbanization and the risk of flood damage has increased. Accordingly, a drainage tunnel 2555 m long and 60 m² in cross-sectional area has been designed to drain part of the water that is discharged in times of flood.

Private houses, roads and farms, as well as underground conduits, exist above the tunnel and the cover soil is 5–20 m thick. The fine sandy soil was formed during the Quaternary period and the level of free groundwater is near the tunnel crown. Under the invert there is an impermeable clay layer beneath which lies a layer of fine sand that contains confined groundwater. The tunnel, which passes through much difficult ground, is being constructed by the New Austrian Tunnelling Method (NATM), which offers advanced technology and cost-efficiency. To lower the groundwater level dewatering by the deep-well system is used and the in-tunnel well-point system is employed as an auxiliary method.

The work is being undertaken with a design that utilizes the finite-element method, which provides careful supervision by measurement of the surroundings of the tunnel together with flexibility for safer and economical construction.

Project plan outline

Flood control along the Mama River basin has deteriorated markedly with rapid urbanization and the corresponding increase in the flow of rain. There is a limit to the flood control improvements that can be made on the Kokubu River – a tributary of the Mama River, because the former runs through highly developed metropolitan areas. Because of these circumstances an extensive plan for water control of the Mama River was established, one part of which is the construction of the Kokubu diversion channel tunnel, which will discharge some flood water into the Edo River, which runs through Matsudo City, above Ichikawa City.

The planned site of the tunnel is shown in Fig. 1 and data in regard to the diversion channel plan are presented in Table 1.

Table 1   Plan of diversion channel

Drainage area, 19.44 km²		
Length of diversion channel, 3467 m	Open channel	400 m
	Tunnel	2555 m
	Culvert	512 m
Planned discharge	100 m³/s	
Longitudinal slope	1/800	

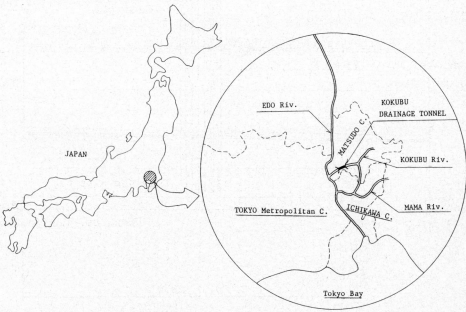

Fig. 1   Location of Kokubu drainage tunnel

This paper presents data on the design planning, construction and measurements of the upstream 282-m length. This section is intended as a test pilot tunnel.

Topography and ground conditions

The topography in the diversion channel area can be divided into two plains – one with an elevation of about 25 m and the other of about 5 m. These two plains are at the end of Hokuso plain, which covers a broad area of the northern part of the Chiba prefecture. The tunnel would run underneath this plain, the area near the portal of the tunnel forming a steep cliff.

The ground over the tunnel route is covered mainly with roads. The surface of the land downstream on the tunnel route, for 780 m, is a densely built-up area with narrow roads. The central part of the route, for 1300 m, has wide roads, most of which are complete. The surface upstream of the tunnel route for 475 m is used for farming and there are a few factories. The overburden is 5–20 m thick throughout the length of the tunnel.

The soil is characterized by a wide Narita stratum – mainly a Quaternary sand layer. The area is covered by Kanto loam with a maximum thickness of 10 m and an average thickness of 5–7 m in the upper level of the Narita stratum.

A drawing of the longitudinal section of the upstream section for 282 m is shown in Fig. 2. The soil comprises, from top to bottom, fine sand (Ds_1), clay and silt (Dc_2) and, beneath, a

further fine sand stratum (Ds_2). The Dc_2 stratum is the impermeable layer, and there is free groundwater in the Ds_1 stratum, which overlies Dc_2. There is 100 kN/m² of confined groundwater beneath the Dc_2 layer.

The tunnel will be constructed by excavation of the area under the groundwater level of Ds_1. The standard penetration test indicates that this area's N-value is about 30, and the area is a loosened layer with about 6% of a small binder constituent (clay and silt). The uniformity coefficient is of small value, which means that the diameter of the sand is small and uniform.

Therefore, from the point of view of tunnel technology, the following three points were considered at the time of planning.
(1) As the bearing capacity of the ground is small, the stabilization of the ground–tunnel interaction system must be ensured, and restoration of groundwater level after completion must be taken into consideration in the design, although the level of underground water might be lowered during the execution time. As a matter of course, a construction method that did not loosen the ground should be employed.
(2) The sand in the Ds_1 stratum flows out easily with water and it is possible to lift the tunnel invert section by the confined groundwater in the Ds_2 stratum at the time of excavation. Therefore, a plan must be developed to lower the groundwater level in the Ds_1, with simultaneous dewatering to decrease the pressure of underground water in the Ds_2.
(3) Although dewatering is being attempted, it is predicted that the time during which the face can be self-supporting may be

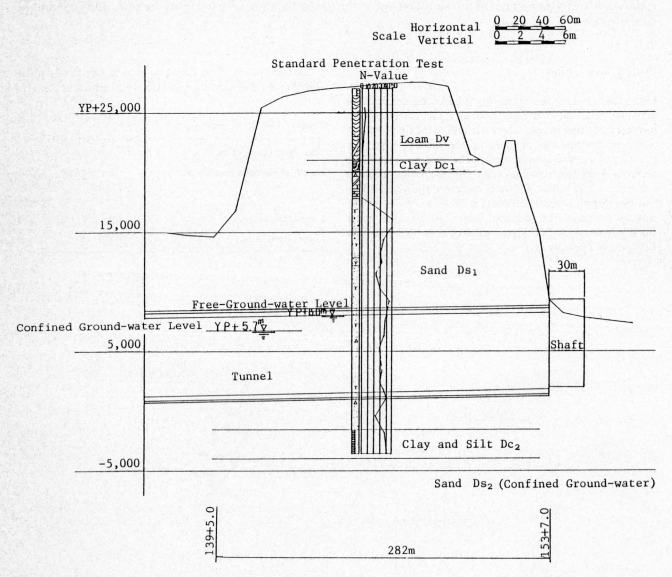

Fig. 2   Longitudinal section of tunnel and soil stratum

short, so countermeasures to stabilize the face must also be planned.

Design planning

At the design planning stage the application of the slurry pressurized shield method was studied, but because of advances in design and construction technology, as well as cost considerations, the so-called New Austrian Tunnelling Method is being employed. The special feature of this method is to obtain structural stabilization of the tunnel by the formation of a thick cylinder with the ground surrounding the tunnel and the supporting members, use being made of the bearing capacity that the ground around the tunnel possesses naturally. Accordingly, it is necessary to plan exactly how the design and execution should be carried out so that a supporting ground arch is formed that makes use of the surrounding ground.

For the construction of this tunnel the design is being prepared in line with these principles so that the equivalent force of excavating will be supported by the surrounding ground arch and the first lining, and the water pressure will be supported by the second lining. The reason for supporting the water pressure with the second lining is for groundwater condensation for the security of the surrounding environment (for example, to prevent wells from drying up) after the tunnel is completed. While the tunnel is being built it is possible to dewater.

The applied design technique employs, mainly, the finite-element method (FEM) and static and seismic analyses were conducted. The second lining, which supports the water pressure, was designed by use of the framed structure analysis.

Analysis of ground–tunnel interaction system by FEM

Expression of non-linear deformability and failure criterion
Generally, the fracture envelope of soil is uniformly expressed as a parabolic shape. Therefore, the fracture criterion is established by equation 1

$$\left(\frac{\tau}{\tau_R}\right)^n = 1 - \frac{\sigma}{\sigma_t} \tag{1}$$

where τ_R is shear strength, σ_t is apparent tensile strength and n is failure envelope index.

The method proposed by Hayashi and Hibino[1] is adopted for the expression of non-linear deformability of soil. This method is based on the relation between Mohr's working stress circles and the failure envelope (Fig. 4). An index R $(0 \leq R \leq 1)$, which is called the failure severity, is defined as in equation 2 and by using R as a parameter the non-linear deformability of soil under an arbitrary stress condition is mathematically expressed by equations 3 and 4

$$R = \min\left(\frac{d_1}{D_1}, \frac{d_2}{D_2}\right) \tag{2}$$

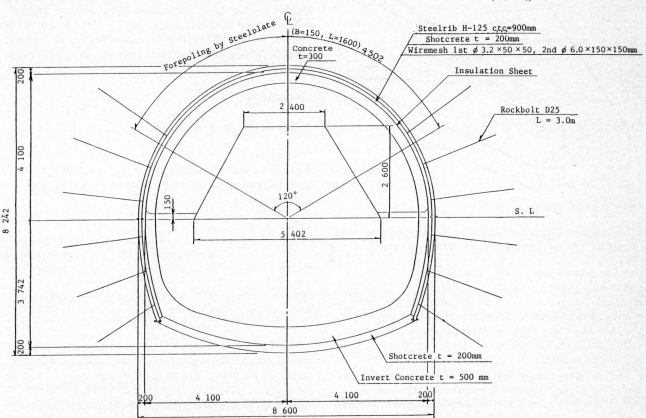

Fig. 3   Standard support system

The standard support system is shown in Fig. 3. In the initial lining the shotcrete is 20 cm, H-125 steel support is 90-cm pitch, and 12 rockbolts 3 m long are installed on the side wall. Four rockbolts in the top heading were considered at the design stage, and other rockbolts needed to improve security. In the second lining the invert is 50 cm and the others are 30 cm (of reinforced concrete construction to bear the water pressure). Excavation is carried out by the short bench cut construction method, dividing it into top heading and bench (bench length, 18 m).

$$D = (D_0 - D_f) R^a + D_f \tag{3}$$

$$\nu = (\nu_0 - \nu_f) R^b + \nu_f \tag{4}$$

where D, ν are modulus of deformation and Poisson's ratio, D_0, ν_0 are values for the initial state, D_f, ν_f are values for the failure state and a and b are deformability indices.

Mechanical models of shotcrete and rockbolts
To simplify the structural model shotcrete is modelled by use of the rod element of an elastic body. Moreover, as the

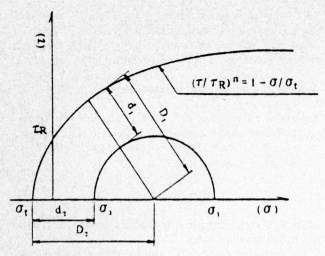

Fig. 4 Fracture criterion

modulus of elasticity and strength of shotcrete at an early age exhibit remarkable changes, the modulus of elasticity for shotcrete is to be evaluated on the basis of its age at the time.

A mechanical model of a rockbolt is adopted as shown in Fig. 5, based on the philosophy that a rockbolt is a rod element

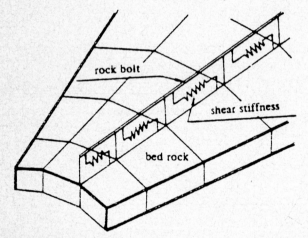

Fig. 5 Mechanical model of rockbolt

of an elastic body, shear stiffness being used to express the interaction between natural ground and the rockbolt.[2]

Relation between face advance and timing of timber installation

Although the earth pressure that acts on timbering is mainly influenced by the release of the face constraining force owing to face advance, the execution process – that is, the sequence and timing of timber installation – is considered to be one of the important factors.

The analytical method that deals with the delay effect in timbering installation and earth pressure facing advance speed, as a model of a plain strain problem, is believed to make possible an expression by substituting the strain transition of natural ground by face advance to a function of creep, as proposed by Tsuchiya.[3] This method is based on the relation between the tunnel wall deformation or ground deformation after the passing of the face and the distance from the face. The transition is like a function of creep, and is expressed by using the Ross model in which the creep strain converges with the passing of time. Moreover, the creep factor α is expressed by equation 5. The creep factor β is expressed by equation 6 and is based on the relation between distance from the face, when strain ϵ after passing of the face becomes almost a constant state, and rate of advance of the face. But the modulus of deformation, $\bar{D}$, used to calculate strain, ϵ_θ, at the

time of the passing of the face is obtained from equation 7

$$\alpha = \epsilon/\epsilon_\theta \qquad (5)$$

$$\epsilon = \epsilon_\theta \cdot \alpha \cdot (1 - \epsilon^{-\beta t}) \qquad (6)$$

$$\bar{D} = D \cdot (\epsilon_\theta + \epsilon)/\epsilon_\theta \qquad (7)$$

where t represents days when ϵ becomes almost constant and D is the modulus of deformation of the ground. Hence, the delay effect of the timbering installation can be expressed as a step in the timbering installation creep calculation.

Analytical steps and input constants

Since the tunnel is symmetrical left and right, the right-hand portion only is used for analysis, and one side and the lower part are considered as about five times the tunnel excavation diameter in the analysis steps. A finite-element mesh for the ground and input constants are shown in Fig. 6. Fig. 7 shows the analytical steps used to model the construction process.

The creep coefficient, α, is defined here by making the strain in the first period, until the time the face is passed, 35% of the total strain. β is found by assuming that 90% of the strain will be produced as the face advances a distance equal to twice the length of the excavation width at an excavation speed of 1.8 m/day.

Analytical results

The shotcrete stress during the excavation of the top heading and during the final stabilization time, and the ground's principal stress distribution, are shown in Figs. 8 and 9. The shotcrete stress is 5300 kN/m^2 at most, but can be allowable to 6860 kN/m^2. The ground's failure zone extends 1–2 m from the tunnel wall.

Construction

A view of the tunnel is shown in Fig. 10.

Dewatering

A pumping test was conducted in the plain area to determine the necessary hydraulic constants in the Ds_1 and Ds_2 strata (Table 2).

Table 2 Hydraulic constants by pumping test

Stratum	Coefficient of permeability, cm/s	Coefficient of storage
Ds_1	0.007	0.07
Ds_2	0.02	0.0002

The pumping test determined that the 45-m pitch of staggered spacing for the deep wells, as originally planned, would not reduce the groundwater to the specified level, so the design for the staggered spacing was changed to 20–25 m (about twice that in the original programme). For the section in which deep well working time would not be adequate the vacuum deep well method was employed in part. The arrangement of the deep wells in relation to the tunnel sectional direction is shown in Fig. 11. The deep well is set 8 m away from the tunnel centre, i.e. 3.7 m away from the excavation side. Three sets of deep wells were drilled in this 282-m trial length against the Ds_2 to lower the head of the confined groundwater below the impermeable layer about 2.5 m under the tunnel invert.

Because of this impermeable layer some 2.5 m under the tunnel excavation invert the deep well to lower the level of free groundwater will be drilled, but only in the upper part. Because of the rise of the hydraulic gradient line, caused by the distance between the deep well and the tunnel, the lowering of

Soil Stratum	Modulus of Deformation (Tangential) Do (kN/m²)	Poisson Ratio (Initial) νo	Modulus of Deformation (Failure) (kN/m²)	Poisson Ratio (Failure) νF	Cohesion (kN/m²)	Internal Friction Angle (deg.)	Unit Weight (kN/m³)	Coefficient of Lateral Pressure
Loam (Dv₁)	9,800	0.40	200	0.45	100	21	15.2	0.6
Loam (Dv₂)	5,400	0.40	1,100	0.45	50	7	16.7	0.6
Fine Sand (Ds₁)	44,100	0.35	8,800	0.45	10	37	17.6	0.6
Clay & Silt (Dc₂)	28,400	0.35	5,700	0.45	70	30	18.1	0.6
Fine Sand (Ds₂)	46,100	0.35	9,200	0.45	0	43	18.6	0.6

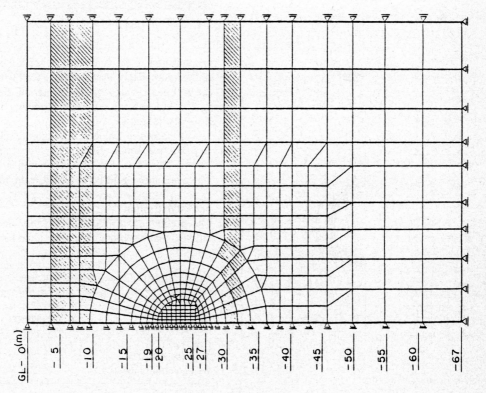

Fig. 6 Finite-element mesh and input constants of soil

Step		1	2	3	4	5	6	7
Model		no support			creep	bench no-support		creep
Elastic Modulus of shotcrete (kN/m²)	Top heading	—	1.96×10^6	1.96×10^6	14.70×10^6	14.70×10^6	14.70×10^6	14.70×10^6
	Bench						1.96×10^6	14.70×10^6
Rockbolt		—	—	bring-in $\phi 24^{mm}$, $L=3^m$	—	—	—	take-out
Steelrib		—	—	—	—	—	—	—
creep time (day)		0.23	0.08	5	7	0.29	5	12.4

Fig. 7   Analytical steps

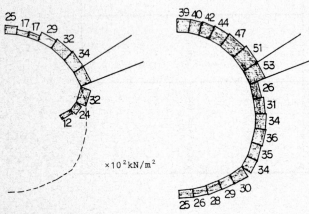

Fig. 8   Shotcrete stress

Fig. 10   Front view of tunnel

Principal Stress

0   100   200 (×10²kN/m²)   ▨ Failure Zone

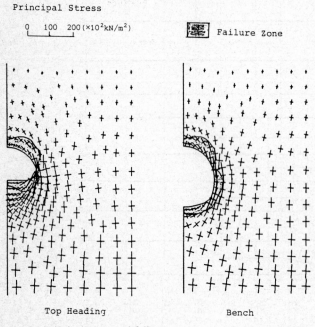

Top Heading   Bench

Fig. 9   Principal stress and failure zone

groundwater to the tunnel invert section could not be accomplished completely. Accordingly, for the residual water level, the well point is set from the bench rail elevation, as is shown in Fig. 11, with the staggered spacing a 1.8-m pitch on both sides of the tunnel.

As is shown in Table 3, the quantity pumped from the Ds_1 stratum was small. But in Ds_2, beneath the impermeable statum, there was abundant groundwater. Thus, the change in water pressure could be observed from 500 m away.

Face stabilization

The preliminary drilling investigation indicated that it was unlikely that a self-standing face could be sustained. Hence, a

Table 3   Pumped quantity by dewatering

Dewatering	Numbers	Pumped quantity, l/min
Deep well (Ds_1)	29	300–600
Deep well (Ds_2)	3	800–2400
Well point in tunnel (Ds_1)	60–320	100–340

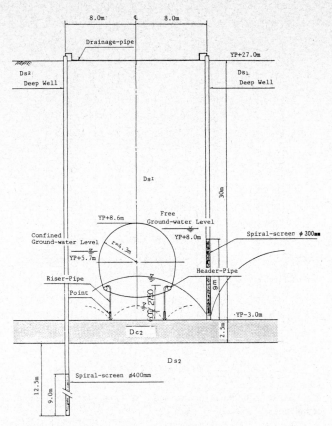

Fig. 11   Plan of deep well and well point

ring-cut was planned for the top heading, but in the actual execution the stability was still poor and various steps were

Fig. 12   Forepoling with steel plates at face

taken to improve the situation. To make the face self-standing in the initial construction stage straight cutting was avoided and the face was inclined, shotcrete was applied on the face and forepoling by a single pipe ($d = 47$ mm) was undertaken.

Among these countermeasures, the inclination of the face and the application of shotcrete had a significant effect, but the fall of sand from the spaces between the mini-pipes became pronounced, the face cracked and large-scale sinking of the surface was observed, which threatened to bring down the whole face. Steel plates were used to hold the ground (Fig. 12), which made it possible to control sand falling from the crown, to form the arch zone of the ground and to decrease the overbreak excavation. In addition, for the most destabilized areas of the face rockbolts were driven into the face to provide reinforcement.

A few minor falls of about 3–8 m³ did occur, but they were corrected by filling with mortar.

Investigation, measurement results and back analysis

Since this 282-m stretch was designated a test section, it is maintained in an observable condition. The control items, to which special attention was paid during execution, include the level of underground water, the stress in the support elements and the strain in the ground. These can be estimated by measuring the convergence and crown deformation in the tunnel, surface settlement and underground deformation.

Fig. 13   Automatic measuring and data processing system

Because there are so many measurements, an automatic measurement data processing system was introduced that involved, mainly, the use of a microcomputer and printer/plotter. Energy and time are therefore saved in the measurement data processing (Fig. 13).

Soil investigation
The results from soil sampling and tests on samples at the face every 20 m at the time of excavation are shown in Table 4. Both the uniformity coefficient and the binder component (clay and silt) are very small. The water content falls as the crown is approached. At the small crumbling area described above the uniformity coefficient was less than 1.5, binder component $\leq 5\%$ and water content $\leq 11\%$. When the water content is about 20% cohesion appears to increase. For that reason at the bench excavation near the area where the groundwater was reduced the face shows good stability and self-supporting properties.

Measurement results
The principal results from measuring a representative measurement section, 120 m away from the portal, are shown diagrammatically. Fig. 14, which shows the distribution of vertical

Table 4   Soil survey during excavation

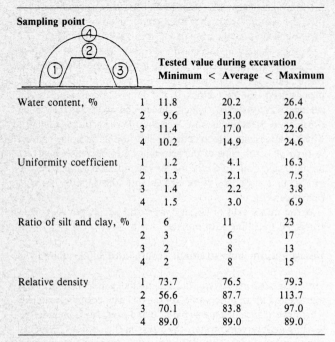

Sampling point		Tested value during excavation		
		Minimum	< Average <	Maximum
Water content, %	1	11.8	20.2	26.4
	2	9.6	13.0	20.6
	3	11.4	17.0	22.6
	4	10.2	14.9	24.6
Uniformity coefficient	1	1.2	4.1	16.3
	2	1.3	2.1	7.5
	3	1.4	2.2	3.8
	4	1.5	3.0	6.9
Ratio of silt and clay, %	1	6	11	23
	2	3	6	17
	3	2	8	13
	4	2	8	15
Relative density	1	73.7	76.5	79.3
	2	56.6	87.7	113.7
	3	70.1	83.8	97.0
	4	89.0	89.0	89.0

deformations in the ground, indicates that the effect of excavation around the part of the crown starts to show from 23° in front of the face and, passing through the face at 26 mm, accounts for 45% of the total deformation.

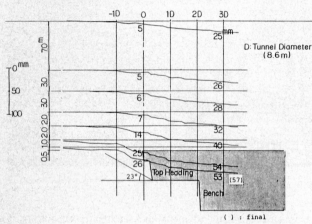

Fig. 14   Vertical deformation of ground (longitudinal section)

Figs. 15 and 16 show the horizontal deformation in the ground near the tunnel: it is small – less than one-half of the perpendicular deformation. The maximum shear strain is 1.1%. From these results we can determine that the principal strain in the tangential direction near the tunnel wall, ϵ_θ, is assumed as $\epsilon_\theta \doteqdot u/r$ (u is tunnel wall deformation, r is tunnel radius). From this relationship the following figures can be obtained: near the crown area $\epsilon_\theta = 57/4300 = 1.3\%$; at the side wall section $\epsilon_\theta = 20/4300 = 0.5\%$.

Fig. 17 shows the changes of horizontal deformation towards the tunnel longitudinal direction according to the distance from the face. Among the various measures taken to stabilize the face, the stiffness in the tunnel longitudinal direction is the most effective, and the figure could remain within a small value.

Back analysis

It is common for design forecasts to differ from actual measurement results. The equivalent elastic modulus for support members and the modulus of deformation of the ground can,

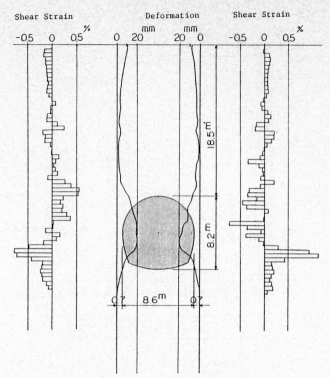

Fig. 15   Horizontal deformation and shear strain near tunnel wall at completion

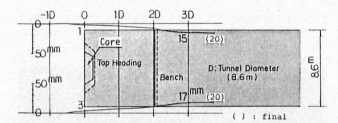

Fig. 16   Horizontal deformation near tunnel wall (sectional)

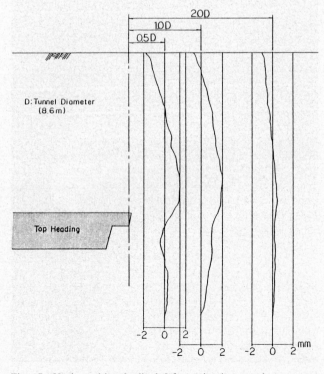

Fig. 17   Horizontal longitudinal deformation in ground

however, be obtained by use of back analysis based on actual measurements and then used to prepare the next design.

The equivalent elastic modulus of the support members (shotcrete with steel support member) can be determined from the increased amount ϵ_θ' of strain in the tangential direction, after the setting of support material, and from the stress produced in the support material. The average of ϵ_θ' in the vicinity of the tunnel wall is 0.48% (Figs. 14 and 16). The average axial force, P, of the shotcrete equals 197 kN/m, the steel support members carry 400 kN/m. The actual load working on the total supporting members was therefore 597 kN/m. Hence

$$E = \frac{P/A}{\epsilon_\theta'} = \frac{597/0.25 \times 1.0}{0.0048} \doteqdot 5.0 \times 10^5 \text{ kN/m}^2$$

Various methods have been used to determine the modulus of deformation of the ground from the measurement results. Here the modulus of deformation is determined from the absolute deformation amount from the time before tunnel excavation, considering the setting period of the supports and the support reaction force.

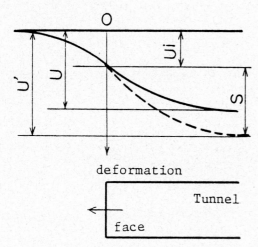

Fig. 18   Deformation distribution dependent on tunnel advance

Generally, the absolute deformation from the original ground changes with the advance of the face of the tunnel (Fig. 18). When the tunnel support is not set it will be changed as shown by the broken line in Fig. 18 after it reaches the face. With this in mind, the modulus of deformation will be found by following the procedure below in regard to the two-dimension FEM elastic model, full-section instantaneous excavation and instantaneous installation of the supports.
(1) Using the measurement position's supporting pattern as a model, find the modulus of deformation equivalent to the variation amount $(U - U_i)$.
(2) Using the modulus of deformation obtained in (1), find the variation amount, S, in the no-support case during which support is not considered.
(3) Find the entire deformation amount U', adding the first-stage deformation amount, U_i, to the variation, S, obtained in (2).
(4) Find the ground modulus of deformation at the no-support status, equivalent to the entire deformation about U'.

The result of the analysis is shown in Fig. 19, which (a) shows the relationship between the modulus of deformation and deformation of the tunnel crown, with the consideration of support, and (b) those without the consideration of support. By use of this graph and by finding the ground modulus of deformation by following the above steps, Ds_1, the fine sand stratum's modulus of deformation, can be determined as $D = 33\,000$ kN/m^2.

This result approximately matches the value used in the design - a value determined by the borehole loading test. The

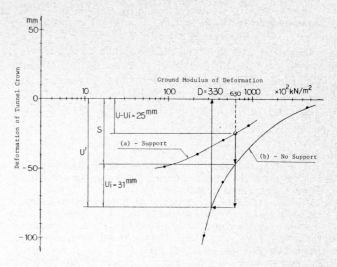

Fig. 19   Relationship between deformation of tunnel crown and ground modulus of deformation calculated by FEM

reasons for this good match are that the ground deformation in the first stage was considered, at the time of deciding the elastic modulus of the supporting member the equalled elastic modulus that utilized the actual measurement values was used and the ground is relatively homogeneous.

Conclusions

An actual case of NATM application for sandy ground has been reported, the major conclusions being listed below.
(1) In a fine sand stratum, consisting of loosened even-diameter sand, with presence of groundwater, excavation by NATM is possible. The 60-m^2 tunnel area was excavated by the short bench cut method, divided into an upper and a lower part – top heading and the bench. The tunnel was stabilized by closing the section with an extra 18 m behind.
(2) The free groundwater is treated by arranging a deep well on both sides of the tunnel at a pitch of 20–25 m. The residual water at the invert section is lowered by the well point in the inside of the tunnel, and positioned with a 1.8-m pitch on both sides. To prevent uplift in the invert section confined water under the impermeable layer at the lower part of the tunnel was decompressed by the deep well.
(3) Dewatering was successful, but there was instability at the face, which could be resolved for many sections by forepoling, ring cut, inclination of the face, shotcrete and rockbolts to the face and the use of steel plates along the crown of the face.
(4) Self-support of the face was especially weak when the water content $\leq 11\%$, the uniformity coefficient ≤ 1.5 and the binder component (ratio of clay and silt) $\leq 5\%$.
(5) The deformation of the ground, including deformation in the initial period, was 57 mm within the tunnel crown and 20 mm at the side wall. The maximum shear strain of the ground was 1.1% and the tangential direction principal strain on the wall of the tunnel crown was 1.3%. Thus, the ground–tunnel system was stabilized.
(6) When there are differences between design forecasts and measurement results the back analysis that is proposed with use of the two-dimensional elastic FEM application can determine the ground modulus of deformation. Such coefficients can be fed back and used to design the next tunnel.

Japan's metropolitan areas are mostly constructed on soft ground strata and the conventional tunnelling technique has been the shield method in such conditions. The alternative NATM was introduced for tunnel work because it saves money and is effective. This successful experience with the NATM will be used for our next tunnel and underground projects beneath residential areas.

Acknowledgement

The authors wish to extend their profound gratitude to the members of the Kokubu River Construction Work Study Committee, Technology Center for National Land Development, under the chairmanship of Prof. Dr. Masami Fukuoka. The tunnel work is progressing successfully thanks to excellent Committee advice and support.

References
1. Hayashi M. and Hibino S. Progressive analysis of relaxation around underground excavating space. Central Research Institute of Electric Power Industry Report, 1968.
2. Takasaki H. and Kusumoto F. Study on peripheral behavior of tunnel during tunnelling in soft rock by NATM. In *Weak rock: soft, fractured and weathered rock, proceedings of the international symposium, Tokyo, 1981* Akai K. Hayashi M. and Nishimatsu Y. eds (Rotterdam: Balkema, 1981), vol. 2, 951–6.
3. Tsuchiya T. Research for design of system rock-bolt tunnelling method. Reference 2, vol. 2, 1063–8.
4. Akada M. *et al.* Estimation of ground modulus of deformation based on tunnel behavior observation. In *Proc. 39th Ann. Conf. Japan Soc. civ. Engrs,* **3,** 1984, 431–2. (Japanese text)

Significance of the unsupported span in tunnelling

M. Baudendistel
Tunnel Consult, Ettlingen, Federal Republic of Germany

Synopsis
For a tunnel the face area is crucial with regard to stable and economic execution. Depending on the prevailing rock conditions, smaller or larger breakout steps are possible and to support the rock intensive shoring, to be placed near to the tunnel face, or a light follow-up shoring of a structural nature must be placed.

Many years ago practical experiences were collected by Lauffer for general application in a standing time diagram. A report is now given on three-dimensional investigations that attempt to deal by calculation with the processes in the area of the tunnel face.

Depending on the length of the unsupported span, varying stresses will occur in the rock mass both in the calculation and in reality, and greater or lesser loads will act on the support. These processes are described by means of stress release and so-called load factors as a result of the three-dimensional computations, which are depicted as curves in the diagrams. By use of these load factors the stresses and deformations in the rock mass, as well as the internal forces in the support, can be determined in a two-dimensional computation of stability.

The results and practical application of the investigations are considered. By use of an actual example - the 7.3-km Dietershan tunnel of the New Rapid Rail Transit Line Hannover-Würzburg, Federal Republic of Germany - a solution is suggested that takes into account the practical procedures for design and execution and permits a usable calculated estimate of the stresses in the rock mass and in the support dependent on the actual unsupported width of span.

The tunnel face is a vital part of the tunnel in regard to its stable and economic execution. Depending on the prevailing rock conditions, a smaller or larger unsupported span between the tunnel face and the supported part of the tunnel is possible during the excavation (Figs. 1 and 2). To support the rock intensive shoring near the tunnel face or light follow-up shoring of a structural nature is necessary.

The engineer must decide at the design phase on the unsupported span that will be possible under various rock conditions - both in relation to the excavation methods and the excavated cross-section. Different unsupported spans will cause different stresses in the rock mass and rock loads on the support. The smaller the unsupported span, the higher is the rock load on the support and the smaller the stresses in the rock mass. By increasing the unsupported span these conditions are reversed - the rock load on the support decreases and the stresses in the rock mass increase (Figs. 3 and 4).

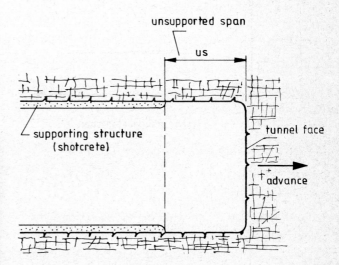

Fig. 2   Definition of unsupported width of span

In addition to the static effect, the length of the unsupported span and the related instalment time of the supporting measures also play an essential role in the estimation of construction time and costs for the tunnel. The unsupported spans used during the construction obviously affect actual construction time and costs.

Because of the importance of the tunnel face Lauffer[1] - to mention but one of the well-known engineers in this field - has presented practical experiences in the form of a standing time diagram. To apply this diagram the standing time of the rock mass should be known or estimated.

Fig. 1   Tunnel face with unsupported width of span

The following text describes research by use of computational methods to calculate the processes at the tunnel face, 'characteristic lines of stress release and load factors' being presented. With the aid of these curves and factors the imposed

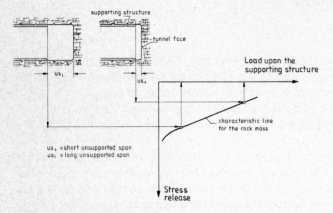

Fig. 3   Supporting structure loading corresponding to stress release

rock mass and support stresses can be calculated for a range of unsupported spans. In contrast to the standing time of the rock mass, which is difficult to estimate, the unsupported span is used here as it has, in any event, to be chosen in relation to the rock conditions and defined in the design and tender documents.

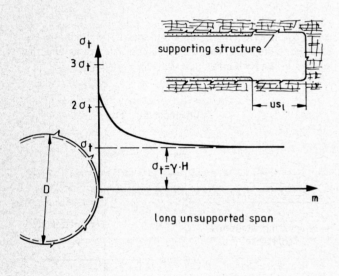

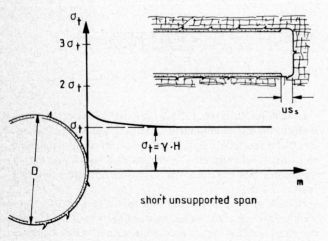

Fig. 4   Rock stress, σ_t, corresponding to long or short unsupported spans

Investigations

From observations in completed tunnels it is known that deformation-monitoring instrumentation installed in the area of a tunnel section ahead of the excavation indicate movements even before the tunnel face has reached the measurement section (Fig. 5). Deformations appear when the tunnel face is at a distance of one-half to one tunnel diameter from the measurement section. When the tunnel face reaches this section some 25–30% of the total deformation during the tunnel

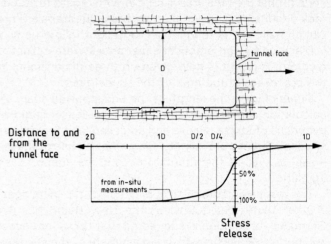

Fig. 5   Stress release corresponding to site of tunnel face

advance has taken place. When the tunnel face is at a distance of approximately one and a half to two tunnel diameters beyond the measurement section virtually no further increase in deformation can be observed.[2-6] To obtain a deformation (≙

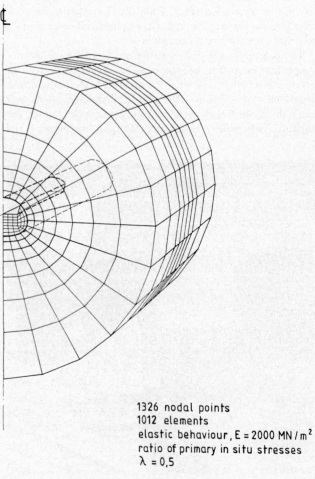

1326 nodal points
1012 elements
elastic behaviour, E = 2000 MN / m²
ratio of primary in situ stresses
λ = 0,5

Fig. 6   Finite-element network (three-dimensional)

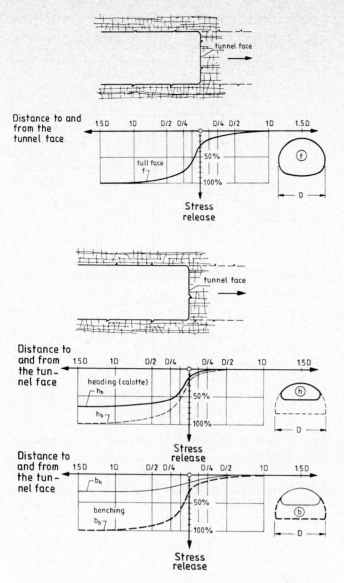

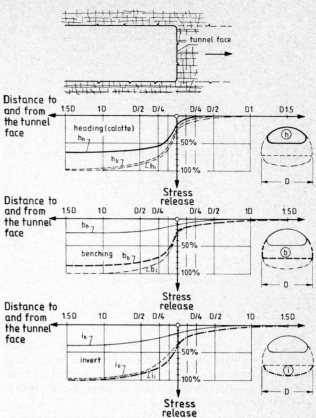

Fig. 7   Characteristic lines of stress release ((a) (*top left*), full-face; (b) (*bottom left*), heading and benching; (c) (*above*), heading, benching and cutting of invert)

It is clear why in most cases only a part of the overlying load has an effect on the structure, and it follows that in many cases the rock mass – not the tunnel support – has to absorb the major part of the load. This knowledge is essential to enable the bearing capacity of a tunnel to be judged. The characteristic lines of stress release have been developed from a computer model with the maximum depth of $H = 100$ m. At greater tunnel depths the curves will probably show a somewhat flatter shape and cause an even greater rock mass stress release in the area of excavation. This view should, however, be confirmed by additional research.

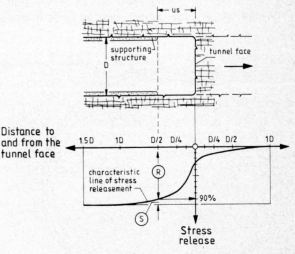

Fig. 8   Stress release acting on unsupported and supported rock mass

stress release) characteristic for the tunnel face with which the stress release or rock loads can be defined quantitatively at any place behind the tunnel face the present author – inspired by case histories and with the aid of three-dimensional finite-element calculations (SAP IV FEM program[7] with isopara-metric prismatic elements and variable-element stresses, elastic behaviour, ratio of *in-situ* stresses, λ, = 0.5, Fig. 6) – has formulated characteristic lines of stress release for a variety of headings (full face; heading and benching; heading, benching and cutting of invert; Fig. 7). The latter are required for the larger cross-sections that are now fairly frequent.

The curves, which relate exclusively to the change in the stiffness of the tunnel face, depending on the geometry, for various steps in the excavation, indicate deformations about one tunnel diameter ahead of the tunnel face. This result is in accordance with *in-situ* measurements.[3,5,8] Directly at the tunnel face 20–30% of the total deformation has taken place. Half a tunnel diameter, D, behind the tunnel face about 90% of the stress release of the rock mass has occurred. Thus, if a support is installed $0.5D$ behind the tunnel face, only about 10% of the stress release would have a rock load effect (Fig. 8). As a result of the interaction between rock mass and support a part of this load effect would be absorbed by the rock mass.

About $1.5D$ behind the tunnel face the rock mass has released (fully elastic) 100% of its stress. A support erected at this particular point is not placed under a rock load as a result of the total elastic stress release. Occasionally, some residual load may be imposed by changes in stress of longer or shorter duration.

105

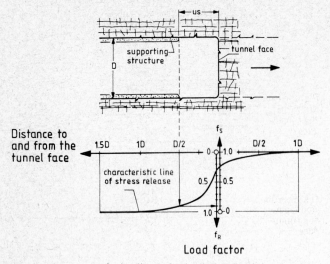

Fig. 9   Load factors for rock mass and supporting structure

f_R Loading factor for the unsupported rock mass
f_S Loading factor for the supported rock mass

With respect to computations for tunnels, where assumed loads have to be applied to calculate the rock mass and support stresses, load factors f_R and f_S (Fig. 9) have been derived from the stress release curves (Fig. 7: e.g. stress release of 100% is identical to $f_R = 1.0$).

In computations for tunnels these factors have to be multiplied by boundary nodal forces that have been derived from the primary stresses. These nodal forces are assumed in the initially unsupported tunnel and, in the next step of the computation, in the structure. In this way the three-dimensional effect of the tunnel face can be taken into account and can be reduced to a more simple two-dimensional computation. The load factors relate explicitly only to the three-dimensionally effective process of stress release near the tunnel face – to enable this process to be described separately. Various depths, primary *in-situ* stresses, rock mass strength and deformation characteristics, stress redistribution as a result of excessive loading and the stiffness of the structure are substituted in the two-dimensional computation, as in other cases.

Practical application of results of investigations

The practical application of these investigations and their results is exemplified by the Dietershan tunnel, which is being constructed as part of the Hannover–Würzburg New Rapid Rail Transit Line. The tunnel has an approximately

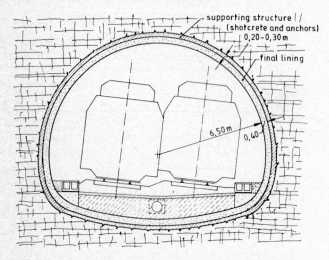

Fig. 10   Cross-section of New Rapid Rail Transit Line tunnel

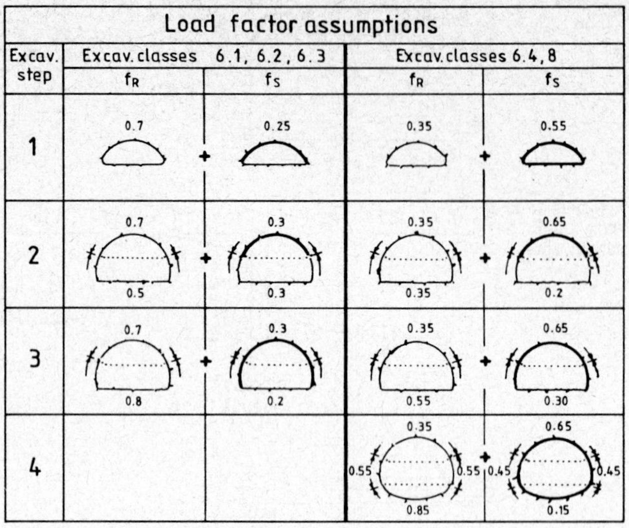

Load factor assumptions				
Excav. step	Excav. classes 6.1, 6.2, 6.3		Excav.classes 6.4, 8	
	f_R	f_S	f_R	f_S
1	0.7	0.25	0.35	0.55
2	0.7 / 0.5	0.3 / 0.3	0.35 / 0.35	0.65 / 0.2
3	0.7 / 0.8	0.3 / 0.2	0.35 / 0.55	0.65 / 0.30
4			0.55 / 0.35 / 0.55 / 0.85	0.45 / 0.65 / 0.45 / 0.15

Rock mass assumptions	
Excav.classes 6.1, 6.2, 6.3	Excav. classes 6.4, 8
$E = 330 – 750$ MN/m²	$E = 100 – 330$ MN/m²
$c = 0.5$ MN/m² (cohesion)	$c = 0.15$ MN/m²
$\varrho = 40°$ (friction)	$\varrho = 27.5°$
$\gamma = 24$ kN/m³	$\gamma = 24$ kN/m³
$\lambda = 0.25$	$\lambda = 0.25$
$E_{shotcrete} = 15\,000$ MN/m²	

Fig. 11   Load factors related to tunnelling excavation classes (Dietershan tunnel)

140-m² excavated cross-section (Fig. 10) and is located in sandstone of Triassic age – basically an interbedded sandstone–claystone sequence. The maximum tunnel cover is about 85 m.

For the calculations the finite-element method was used. In addition, deformation and stresses were measured during the construction.

As is usual during the design phase of tunnel projects, the excavation technique, cross-section and rate of tunnel advance and the relevant methods of construction were selected and defined for the tender in the form of tunnelling excavation classes. An analysis of the stability for the tunnel was then made that took into account the selected design criteria (Fig. 11). The load on the structure was calculated by use of the load factors f_R and f_S (Fig. 11). Depending on where the supporting structure was placed in relation to the face, which, according to the rock quality, would be selected by the engineer and not by computation, the load proportions in both the unsupported and the supported tunnel were defined.

The example that is taken from the monitoring of the excavation of the calotte – the initial heading – shows ($H = 25$ m) that at about 70% ($f_R = 0.7$) a high proportion of the stress release was estimated for the unsupported rock mass, and only some 30% ($f_S = 0.3$) for the support (Fig. 12). These figures were derived from the characteristic line of stress release for an assumed length of unsupported span of approximately 3 m; they correspond to various rock conditions (excavation classes 6.1, 6.2 and 6.3, Fig. 11). As a result of the interaction of rock and tunnel support, part of the residual load (30%) imposed on the support is absorbed by the rock. For poorer rock conditions (excavation classes 6.4 and 8, Fig. 11) smaller lengths of unsupported span are considered. Here the stress release before erection of the support was smaller (say, 35%) and the remaining stress release on the support ($\triangleq$ load) larger (say, 65%). The computation is carried out as follows. As the first step 0.7 times the total load at the margin of the unsupported

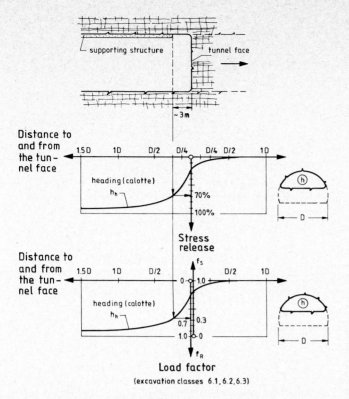

Fig. 12   Load factors for calotte advance (Dietershan tunnel)

calotte is estimated by means of nodal forces (with the aid of the computer program the nodal forces are derived from the primary *in-situ* stresses, $\lambda = 0.25$). Next, 0.3 times the residual load that acts on the support, now included in the calculation, has to be considered (Fig. 13).

With this load assumption both the stresses and deformations in the rock mass as the internal forces in the support are calculated for the excavation of the calotte, to which the description is restricted here. The benching and cutting of the invert was calculated in a similar way.

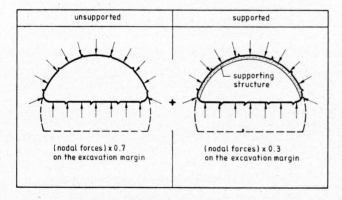

Fig. 13   Loading assumptions for calotte

Comparison of the measured deformations in the roof and the characteristic line of stress release derived from the investigations indicates a good agreement in the deformations ahead of the tunnel face and in the sharp increase directly at the tunnel face, as well as in the gradual decrease in the deformations at one to two tunnel diameters behind the tunnel face (Fig. 14). The stress release in the rock mass, taken as 70% as derived from the characteristic line, should have had a value of 60% according to the measured deformation of the tunnel roof. This difference is acceptable, even though a slightly too low support loading had been assumed in the present example.

Comparison of the radial stresses between rock and support as calculated and as measured with pressure gauges for the

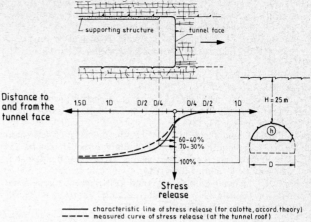

Fig. 14   Stress release (deformation): comparison between theoretical work and *in-situ* measurement on Dietershan tunnel

excavation of the calotte, taken in sections, and with a tunnel coverage of $H = 25$ m, $\gamma = 24$ kN/m^3, shows a calculated mean radial pressure of 0.044 MN/m^2 and an identical measured value (when statistically a mean value is established whereby the high values of the measurement points 1 and 6 in Fig. 15 are eliminated). If all the measured values are taken into consideration, the mean radial pressure increases to 0.07 MN/m^2.

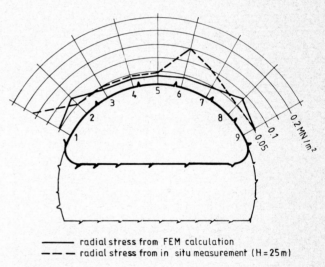

Fig. 15   Radical stresses between rock mass and supporting structure: comparison between FEM calculation and *in-situ* measurements on Dietershan tunnel

In the cases not described here the calculated and measured radial pressures between rock and support also agree very well.

Concluding remarks

The comparison between calculation and measurement shows that the magnitude of the assumed loads, applied in the calculations by use of the load factors f_R and f_S, derived from the unsupported width of span, agrees very well with reality. In tunnelling this is a remarkably good result.

The practical application of the unsupported span, which can be fixed in advance and which can be measured, allows consideration in the calculations of the conditions in the tunnel during excavation, even when the cross-section is excavated in several steps. Not only is the support taken into consideration but also (with loads and stresses) the rock mass – which, basically, is the most important component of a tunnel structure.

References

1. Lauffer H. Gebirgsdruckklassifizierung für den Stollenbau. *Geologie Bauwesen*, **24**, no. 1 1958, 46–51.

2. Baudendistel M. Wechselwirkung von Tunnelauskleidung und Gebirge. *Veröff. Inst. Boden- Felsmechanik, Univ. Karlsruhe* no. 51, 1972.

3. Kramer J. Einfluß von Tunnelbauten auf die Geländeoberfläche. *Straße-Brücke-Tunnel*, no. 9, 1974.

4. Lögters G. Das räumliche Verformungsgeschehen beim Vortrieb oberflächennaher Tunnelröhren. *Veröff. Inst. Boden- Felsmechanik, Univ. Karlsruhe* no. 59, 1974.

5. Mörscher J. and Baudendistel M. Probevortrieb im Dietershantunnel der Neubaustrecke Hannover–Würzburg, Eisenbahnbau für das 21. Jahrhundert. Streckenausbau bei der Deutschen Bundesbahn, Bahnbauzentrale Frankfurt (M), 1984.

6. Sauer G. Spannungsumlagerung und Oberflächensenkung beim Vortrieb von Tunneln mit geringer Überdeckung. *Veröff. Inst. Boden- Felsmechanik, Univ. Karlsruhe* no. 67, 1976.

7. Bathe K. *et al.* SAP-IV Beschreibung und Benutzerhandbuch. *Mitt. Inst. Konstruktiven Ingenieurbau, Ruhr-Univ. Bochum* 75-14, 1975.

8. Axhausen K. Ein Beitrag zur Erfassung der Bauzustände bei der Berechnung von Tunnelbauten. Institut für Bauingenieurwesen I, Universität München, 1980.

Discussion

A. Hayes* said that Fujimori *et al.* made a comparison of the NATM and shield alternatives on the basis of quality, cost and safety. Perhaps the authors would explain why the NATM method was shown as not being as safe as the shield method. Details of the main factors that were considered in safety and accident statistics for the period of time in which the tunnel was driven would be appreciated.

G. Fudger† asked Potts and Knights to comment on the possible variation in efficiency of the moment joints – especially the base slab to wall joints. It might well be that the problems of constructing such a joint at the bottom of a deep, possibly muddy, excavation would prevent the easy competition of a full moment joint. Some examples of the predicted movements in the London Transport running tunnels would be welcomed since the vehicle gauge in those tunnels was very tight.

Dr. M. Gysel‡ said that Baudendistel's proposed concept of characteristic stress release curves or deformation curves and the derivation of load factors could perhaps be adapted for cases of swelling rock, provided that the total deformation curve, including the swelling, could be measured or predicted suitably. It would be expected that at least the clay mineral type swelling rock could be handled by a similar type of load factor concept since the relatively quick process of swelling in that case might result in a substantial percentage of swelling deformation before the tunnel lining became active.

Written contribution

J. N. Shirlaw§ Several short lengths of tunnel have been constructed in soft ground by use of the NATM on the Hong Kong MTR. Extensive use was made of rockbolts on the first few drives, but observations on site indicated that the rockbolts gave rise to more problems than they solved. Subsequently, seven drives have been completed without rockbolts. At a recent lecture in Hong Kong** Golser said that in his opinion bolts were unnecessary in soft ground tunnels at depths of less than 30 m.

Comment by Fujimori *et al.* on whether their monitoring data allow them to assess the value of the bolts that were used in their tunnel would be appreciated.

Authors' replies

Dr. D. M. Potts and M. C. Knights In reply to G. Fudger, the use of either diaphragm or secant pile construction for the tunnel walls clearly complicates the formation of full moment joints – particularly those with the tunnel base slab. The main difficulties occur as a result of the construction tolerances that are required to build these walls, and especially in placing the wall reinforcement to an exact level.

It is expected that the moment connexion with the base slab will be formed by linking the wall and slab reinforcement by use of couplers, although other methods are still under consideration. The couplers would be fixed into the wall-reinforcing cage prior to casting the walls, and subsequently exposed after excavation inside the tunnel. Clearly, these couplers can only be placed to within a certain tolerance of the required level, and therefore the base slab design must take this into account.

We do not expect any particular problems with this form of construction, similar techniques having been adopted successfully elsewhere.

The expected maximum long-term movement of the London Transport running tunnels is of the order of 30 mm, as predicted by finite-element techniques. The accompanying cross-sectional distortion of the running tunnels was predicted as a 4-mm increase of the vertical diameter and a 1.5-mm shortening of the horizontal diameter.

T. Fujimori, C. Uchiyama, H. Kunimi and H. Takasaki In reply to A. Hayes, it was not intended to suggest that the NATM is dangerous whereas the shield method is safe. Both methods are safe if adequate design and construction procedures are followed.

In ordinary designs that involve the use of the shield method in Japan the ground surrounding the tunnel is always considered to be an external force. On the other hand, one of the principles of the NATM is that the ground surrounding the tunnel supports the tunnel when supporting rings are built around the tunnel, and that the ground also acts as an external force. Hence, if the ground surrounding the tunnel loosens during excavation, the NATM will be affected adversely.

In reply to J. N. Shirlaw, measurement of rockbolt axial force has shown that the tension force is as low as 0–30 kN (small value), and compressive forces were widely apparent. In addition, it was technically difficult to obtain a large anchoring force. Experience suggests that pattern bolting is unnecessary for the soil layer in homogeneous ground. Instead of rockbolting, it may be preferable to let the tunnel stabilize by employing the sectional shape that prevents stress concentration, early closing of the section, etc. But significant results can be obtained if several rockbolts are installed around the part of the leg on the top heading to reduce the stress concentration caused when the tunnel sinks and to restrain the horizontal convergence of the top heading during bench excavation.

The use of so many rockbolts is explicable in terms of safety.

Professor M. Baudendistel In reply to Dr. M. Gysel, the characteristic lines of stress release and load factors that were proposed are based on an elastic behaviour of the rock mass. A similar method, considering the swelling of clay material before and after the installation of the tunnel lining, as proposed in Gysel's contribution, is, in my opinion, possible. Further examinations, however, are then necessary and time intervals should be substituted in the place of the free unsupported span that is used for the characteristic lines and load factors.

---

*Health and Safety Executive, Leicester, England.
†Department of Transport, London, England.
‡Motor-Columbus Consulting Engineers, Inc., Baden, Switzerland.
§Formerly Mass Transit Railway Corporation, Kowloon, Hong Kong; now MRT, Singapore.
**Discussion (unpublished) following lecture by Professor J. Golser ('Austrian tunnelling method') to Geotechnical Group, Hong Kong Institution of Engineers, 22 October, 1984.

Session 5 – Major projects

Co-Chairmen: Dr. J-F. Raffoux and D. N. Simpson

Sakhahuaya – principal design aspects of an underground power plant in the Andean Range

O. G. Koch
Hidroservice · Engenharia de Projetos Ltda., São Paulo, Brazil
G. Rico
Empresa Nacional de Electricidad – Ende, Bolivia
R. J. Zalszupin
Hidroservice · Engenharia de Projetos Ltda., São Paulo, Brazil

Synopsis
A small but extremely complex hydroelectric development is to be implemented in the moderately seismic Bolivian Andean Range. The completed plant will generate 76 MW. Some very specific adverse conditions that were encountered on this project are described in regard to topography, geology, water resources and construction facilities.

The topographic conditions of the Andean region, with very high and steep mountains cut through by colluvium-covered deep valleys, make access to the several worksites extremely difficult. The presence of colluvium on slopes hampers the construction of roadways even more.

Four intakes were needed owing to the scarcity of water resources. Two 3.0-m diameter TBM-excavated tunnels with a total length of 12 000 m will convey water to a 2.3-m diameter steel-lined pressure tunnel, dropping 400 m and excavated at a 45° angle. A manifold furnishes 20 m³/s to two Pelton turbines, housed in a cavern.

The main features of the project are presented and the principal difficulties that were encountered and the means that were employed to overcome them are described.

General description of project

The Sakhahuaya project, although of small installed capacity, is a good example of the complexity that is encountered in the design of a power plant in a region of scarce water resources and very difficult topographic and geological conditions. These conditions resulted in a design that comprises an underground power house for two 38-MW Pelton turbines, water (20 m³/s) being conveyed along 12 km of tunnels (Fig. 1).

The principal hydraulic circuit consists of two main catchments (Chaco and Taquesi), low-pressure tunnels converging at the surge tank and a pressure tunnel dropping therefrom some 700 m to a manifold that feeds the two units.

The main components of the project are therefore the Chaco dam, the Taquesi catchment, 12 km of low-pressure tunnels, the surge tank, the pressure tunnel, the power house with outlet and ventilation tunnels and the sub-station.

An excavation was designed to form a platform for the sub-station at elevation 1720.00 and a 300-m vertical shaft of 4.40-m diameter will connect the power house and sub-station, housing electrical cables and serving ventilation purposes.

Main components

Chaco dam
The Chaco dam (Fig. 2) is a gravity-type concrete dam 69.30 m long and 42.00 m in height as measured from crest to foundation level. Impounding the Unduavi River waters will form a reservoir about 70 m in width and 800 m in length. The worksite is located in a deep stretch of the valley the sides of which are covered with colluvial soil, except for some stretches in which slate outcrops occur. The bottom of the valley has a thick layer of alluvium, which will be removed and substituted by concrete.

The dam body was divided into three blocks by means of construction joints placed in such a manner that the end blocks are based mostly on rock, whereas the central block rests on the concrete wedge that results from substitution of the alluvium. The spillway is in the block on the left bank, its crest corresponding to the maximum normal level of the reservoir (elevation 1872.00).

The central block houses the bottom spillways, which consist of four galleries with a cross-section of 3.00 m × 4.50 m, closed downstream by sector gates. Besides assisting in the control of exceptional floods, the bottom spillways are designed to remove material, silt and loose rocks that have accumulated against the upstream facing. The emergency sluice gate and the water intake for the Chaco–Huajilaya tunnel are in the block on the right bank.

Taquesi water intake
Water will be impounded from the Taquesi River, for supplying the tunnel, by means of a small gravity-type concrete dam 29.00 m long and 12.00 m in height as measured from the crest of the spillway to foundation level. Over its entire length the dam has a spillway-type cross-section.

On its left bank the Taquesi River valley has barely consolidated alluvial material with an outcrop of slate, where the dam axis is located. On the right bank there is a rock outcrop with an almost vertical slope. The river bed is composed of a thick layer of alluvial material, which will not be removed owing to the small size of the dam.

The heterogeneous foundation (rock at the extremities and alluvium in the central part) necessitated a dam behaviour study by means of a three-dimensional analysis by the finite-element method. Consolidation grouting was specified to reduce water seepage through the layer of alluvium beneath the dam.

The Taquesi intake (Fig. 3) has two canals for the cleaning out of fine material and rocks that accumulate against the upstream face and in the water intake of the tunnel. In view of

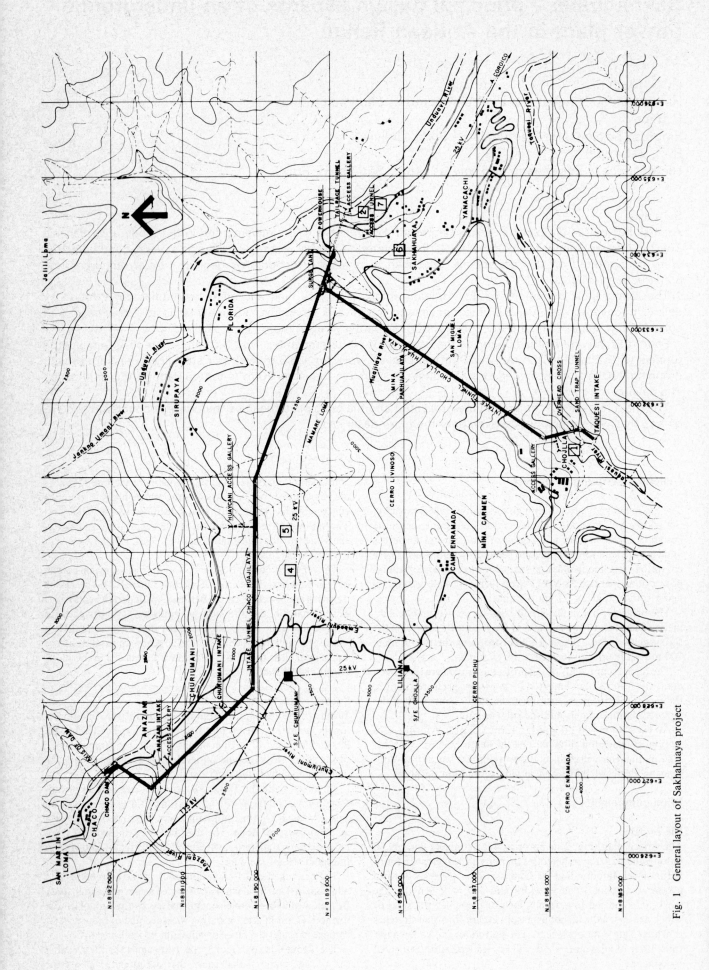

Fig. 1 General layout of Sakhahuaya project

114

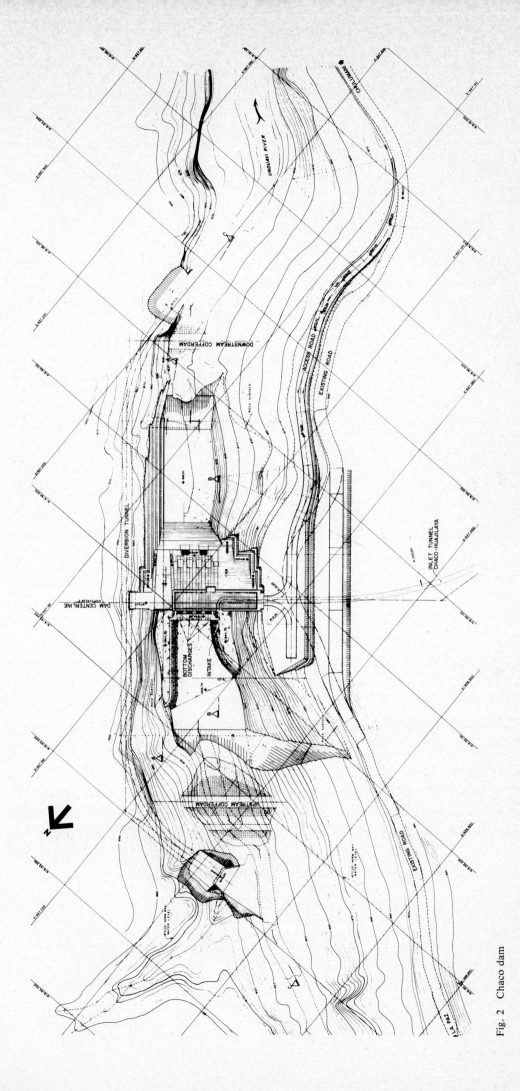

Fig. 2 Chaco dam

115

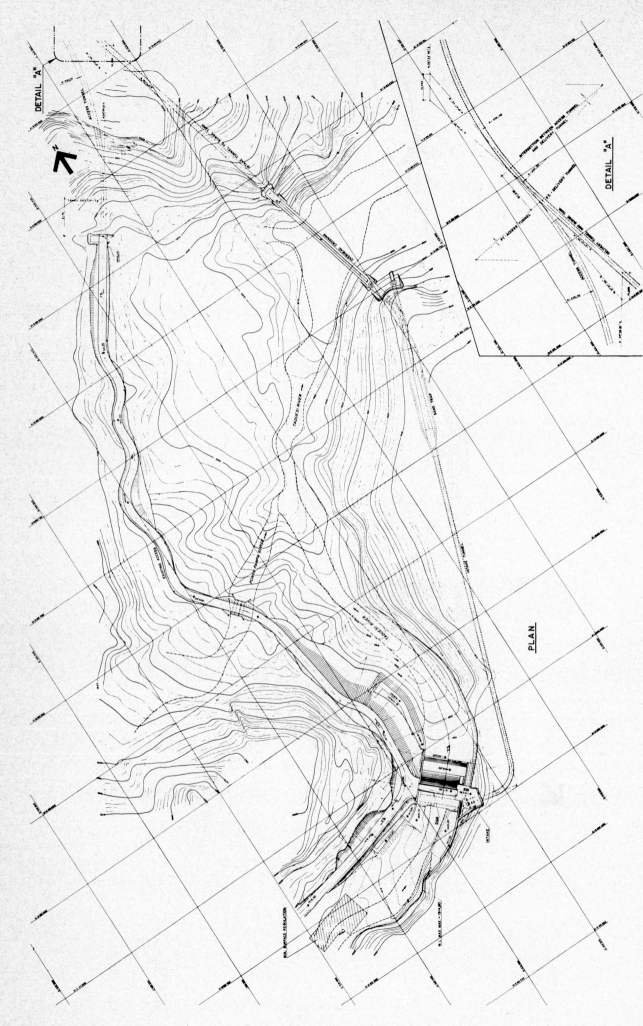

DETAIL "A"

DETAIL "A"

PLAN

Fig. 3   Taquesi intake and overhead crossing

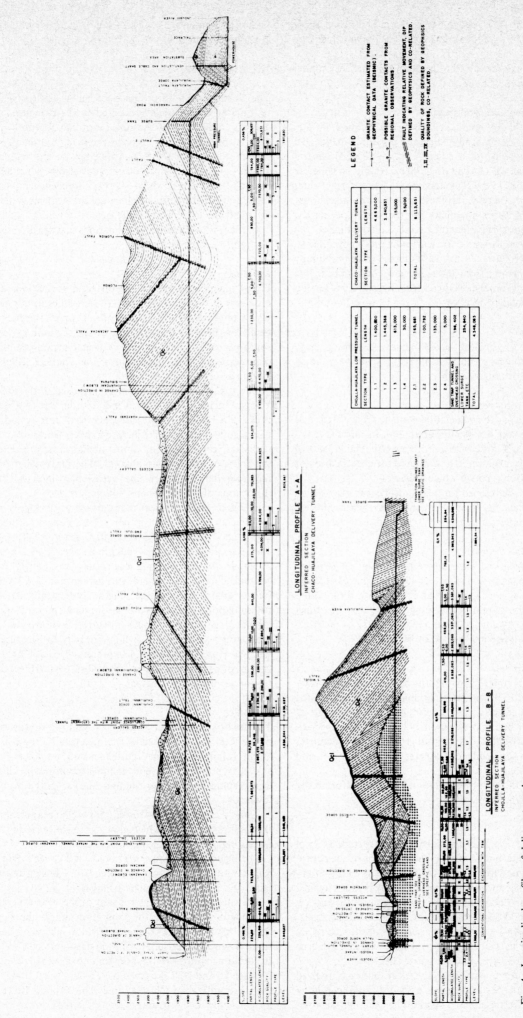

Fig. 4 Longitudinal profiles of delivery tunnels

117

the very irregular flow regime of the Taquesi River a small reservoir will be formed the variations in level of which will be very great.

The water intake for the Chojlla–Huajilaya delivery tunnel is located on the right bank.

Overhead crossing and sand trap

The Taquesi delivery tunnel, close to the Taquesi intake, crosses a deep valley in a 1.50-m diameter pressure pipeline. To provide a solution for this overhead crossing (Fig. 3) a metal truss was designed with a span of 74.00 m, resting on concrete supports embedded in the rock mass of the left and right sides of the valley. In their upper part these concrete structures house the hydraulic transition chambers for the steel pipe, with a typical cross-section corresponding to that of the tunnel.

Because it was not feasible for scaffolding to be installed to erect the metal structure, a truss was designed to be built up by incremental launching from the sides and connecting in the centre. Upstream from the overhead crossing, the cross-section of the tunnel is altered to allow for a sand trap 50 m long.

Delivery tunnels

The water delivery system of the Sakhahuaya complex (Fig. 4) consists of two branches – the Chaco–Huajilaya delivery tunnel and the Chojlla–Huajilaya tunnel.

Chaco–Huajilaya tunnel

The tunnel begins at the water intake at the Chaco dam and ends at the surge tank – a distance of 8113 m. Its internal cross-section diameter is 3.00 m, with a shotcreted final lining of 0.10 m, which is reinforced or not according to the classification of the bedrock section through which it passes.

The design was developed for mechanical excavation with a tunnel-boring machine, except in fault areas where the excavation must be performed by conventional methods.

Chojlla–Huajilaya tunnel

The tunnel begins at the water intake at the Taquesi dam and ends at the surge tank – a distance of 4300 m. Its cross-section is arch-rectangular in shape, with an internal width of 2.20 m and a shotcreted non-reinforced lining of 0.10 m. The tunnel will be excavated by conventional methods as far as the overhead crossing and beyond that point by TBM.

High-pressure tunnel

The high-pressure tunnel (Fig. 5) is the penstock to carry water to the power house. It consists of a tunnel, which begins at the surge tank at an elevation of 1811.50 and falls at an angle of 45° to the power house at elevation 1425.80 with an approximate length of 705.00 m. Its internal cross-sectional diameter is 2.30 m, with a non-reinforced concrete facing of 0.30 m and lined with steel.

Excavation of the high-pressure tunnel is to be performed by conventional methods.

Power house

The power house (Fig. 6) is an underground structure 51.75 m long, 14.80 m wide and 25.80 m high. The floor of the cavern is covered by a foundation slab of varying thickness (minimum, 1.00 m). This slab is anchored to the underlying bedrock against the uplift forces. The walls of the cavern are faced with reinforced concrete 0.50 m thick to the generator floor at elevation 1434.50. Above this level the surfaces of the cavern are not lined, except in their upper part, which, excavated in arch form, is supported by a concrete barrel shell.

At one end of the power house a vertical shaft was inserted for connexion with the sub-station to provide for the ventilating system and the electric cables. This shaft has an internal cross-sectional diameter of 4.40 m and is faced with reinforced concrete 0.30 m thick. It is 300 m in height.

Regional geology

The North and South provinces of Yungas in the Department of La Paz (the project is located in the province of South Yungas) cover two of the seven morphostructural units that exist in the Republic of Bolivia – the Real or Oriental Range to the southwest and the Subandean belt or the region of the Yungas. A third geomorphic unit may also be considered – the region of the valleys, which is a transition between those of the main units of the country which are the Andean system to the west and the low plains to the east.

In the following only the formations that are directly related to the project are described.

Lithology

Fig. 4 makes mention of the different formations and lithologies that form a direct part of the studies in question. The visible physiography in the area of the Yungas is principally the result of the deforming action of the tectonic cycles to the southwest of the Real Ranges. Volcanic action resulted in the deposition of large batholiths – the Taquesi, Illimani and Unduavi formations.

The stratigraphic series that are exposed in the area of the Yungas include Ordovician and Silurian up to Quaternary rocks superjacent to the sequence that corresponds to the Cretaceous–Tertiary – the intrusive rocks. Outcrops of igneous rocks are very limited in number and size and are generally in the form of small granite dykes. The Ordovician is mainly represented by dark grey slate, occasionally interstratified with thin bands of quartzites and siltites.

The area of the project is composed of dark grey slates of Ordovician age, probably a part of the Yungas formation, on subjacent intrusives of granite–granodiorite of Tertiary age. The slates are the principal rocks in the area; they are dark grey in colour, fine-grained and moderately stratified. The stratification is defined as fine-grained, lighter-coloured layers being rich in quartz and sericite. Siltstone interstratification is encountered occasionally. Another lithologic unit comprises the granitic rocks of the Taquesi intrusive, composed of granite, granodiorites and aplites, which are only to be found in the Chojlla–Huajilaya tunnel. The granite is usually light grey in colour, of a granular, coarse, hard, abrasive texture, composed of quartz, mica and feldspar.

Tectonics

The area of the project is located within the southwest sector of the Real Range – a sector characterized by the presence of highly folded and faulted anticlines and synclines. From the structural point of view the synclines generally coincide with the topographic heights and the anticlines with the topographic lowlands.

The principal structural formations of the area are the result of the Taquesi intrusive, which gave rise to the local and regional fracturing, principally with the formation of normal faults.

The principal traits are (a) homoclinal cover – San Miguel Ridge and Sakhahuaya Syncline; (b) northeast–southwest faults; (c) northwest–southeast faults.

The characteristic structural trait of the zone (a) consists of a homocline that reaches the point of forming a 'dip-slope', i.e. the topographic slope coincides with the incline of the strata. In the Taquesi River valley zone the strata reflect a preferential strike close to north–south, maintaining the dip to the northeast between 25 and 70°; the low dips (25–30°) are found mostly in the surroundings of Chojlla mine. The Taquesi River runs at a right angle to the strata, meeting the dips downstream.

The northeast–southwest faults system stands out clearly in the geomorphologic landscape and is recognized easily in the aerial photographs, mostly constituting the watercourses of the main canyons.

The faults of the northwest–southeast system result mainly from stratification. Their strikes vary between N30 and 40°W and the dips are similar to the stratification.

Quaternary
Unconsolidated deposits are represented by materials of alluvial, colluvial and glacial origin. The alluvial deposits consist of certain sands and gravel found in the river beds, terraces and fan deltas. The colluvial deposits, very frequent in the area of the project, vary greatly from slope debris to slides of fine material. The formation of these deposits, which have a tendency to slide, is favoured by the high rate of humidity and rainfall, in addition to the natural joints of the rocks. The glacial deposits do not occur in the area of the project.

Seismology
According to data from the Department of La Paz seismicity study, which was undertaken by the San Calixto laboratory, the seismic events of 1947 and 1956 caused panic and anxiety among the inhabitants of the provinces of North and South Yungas, the intensities reaching above grade V (of the Modified Mercalli scale). The provinces of North and South Yungas are included in the zones of intensities V to VI (Modified Mercalli scale).

Based on 63 years of seismological instrument records and a $1° \times 1°$ grid the distribution coefficients for the average annual frequencies of maximum accelerations on each point of the grid were calculated. Calculation was then made of maximum probable intensities and seismic risk (probability percentage of 5% of gravity acceleration, equivalent to an approximate intensity of VI to VII (Modified Mercalli)). Both maximum probable intensity and seismic risk were calculated for a 50-year period. The maximum probable intensity for the area of the project is V (Modified Mercalli) for a period of 50 years and the seismic risk (probability of 5% of gravity acceleration) is 40–50% (also for a period of 50 years).

The entire area of the project is considered to be moderately seismic and it should be noted that the San Calixto Observatory has stated that the Department of La Paz may be considered as a region in which it is necessary to employ earthquake-resistant techniques.

Rock mass classification
Methods of classifying rock masses are generally based on experience that has been acquired during the supervision of the performance and analysis of the results of excavation instrumentation. Available methods include those of Bieniawski,[3] Barton and co-workers[2] and Wickham and co-workers.[4] These methods have an empirical formulation and the classification of the mass is achieved by attributing 'weights' to the various characteristic factors of the rock that affect the stability of the excavation – for example, the mechanical characteristics of the rock mass, usually determined by discontinuities and properties of the material, the initial state of stress, the hydrogeological characteristics of the formations, the dimensions of the works and the works construction phases (excavation process, type and timing of lining placement, etc.).

Rock mass characterization techniques usually present limitations with regard to linear works, such as tunnels, as they provide information on points that are spaced sufficiently far apart that can be extrapolated to the rest of the massif.

All the classification methods that have been developed in recent years follow an empirical course (a combination of experiments and theoretical approximations) and are applicable principally to underground works. A geomechanical classification should divide the rock massif into a number of classes so that the behaviour of the massif within a class is homogeneous with respect to the excavation. In underground works the number of classes should be such that all possible types of behaviour in the massif crossed by the tunnel are represented in the classification.

Analyses of characterization data on the rock massifs obtained from surveys led to the conclusion that none of the known methods alone would satisfy the requirements of the design. The application of any of these classification methods would require a series of other parameters to be inferred, which would impose a very subjective character on the classes into which the massif would be divided.

It was therefore decided to use a classification that consisted of four large groups such that in the classification of the massif each group would cover a large number of sections of rock with similar characteristics. The results of rock quality measurements (RQD), degree of fracturing and alteration of test samples, the results of geophysical measurements, the large ranges of geomechanical parameters obtained from laboratory tests and experience in similar works and knowledge of local conditions were taken into consideration in the following classification.

Class I – Excellent-quality rock: RQD, 75–100%; little or no alteration; slightly fractured; practically impermeable; longitudinal wave propagation velocity greater than or equal to 4000 m/s.

Class II – Good-quality rock: RQD, 50–75%; slight or moderate alteration; moderately fractured; low permeability; longitudinal wave propagation velocity, 3000–4000 m/s.

Class III – Average- to low-quality rock: RQD, 25–50%; signs of alteration; fractured; moderately to highly permeable; longitudinal wave propagation, 2000–3000 m/s.

Class IV – Fault zone: RQD, <25%; highly altered; fractured or heavily fractured; possibly filled with clayey material.

Geomechanical parameters

Underground works
The geomechanical parameters were estimated from the results of 45 tests on drill-core samples performed by the Technological Research Institute, São Paulo, Brazil (IPT), on geophysical measurements of seismic refraction and 44 geological survey drill-holes. Published reference information was also taken into account, together with geological field surveys and a visual analysis of drill-core samples.

Modulus of elasticity
Tests on drill-core samples by IPT indicated modulus of elasticity values between 80 000 kgf/cm^2 and 300 000 kgf/cm^2. Experience and previous publications have shown, however, that all rock masses, account being taken of possible heterogeneity, fractures, joints and other imperfections as well as the scale effect, show a modulus of elasticity somewhat below that obtained by laboratory tests performed on samples of the same rock.

The dynamic moduli of elasticity were also evaluated, based on geophysical measurement data. These measurements showed a wide range of variation in the longitudinal wave propagation velocities (between 1500 and 7200 m/s).

The determination of static moduli of elasticity representative of the rock massif was arrived at by use of a correlation curve between the results of seismic tests and the result of on-site tests proposed by Deere.[6]

Finally, publications on the subject were consulted. Values indicated in the literature, which also vary with the direction of stratification, show moduli of elasticity of between 240 000 and

119

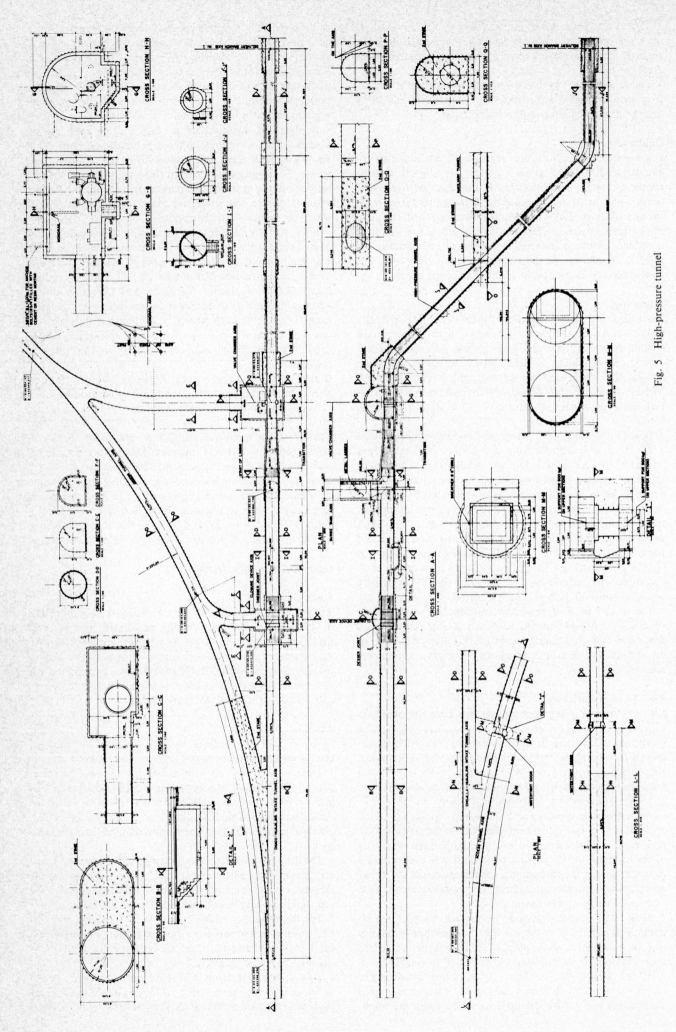

Fig. 5   High-pressure tunnel

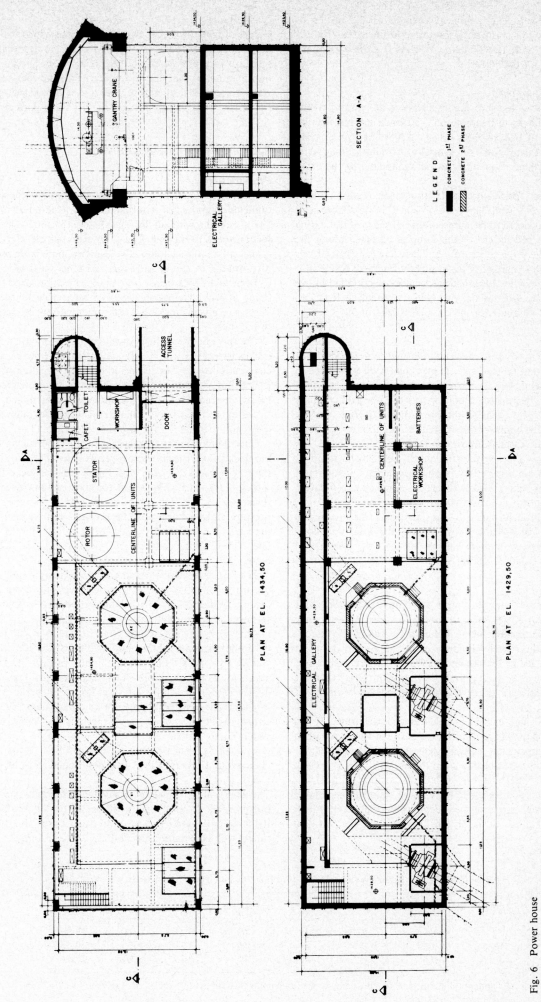

Fig. 6 Power house

300 000 kgf/cm^2. The combined analyses of the results of seismic tests and a study of the literature produced the following values: class I, 180 000 kgf/cm^2; class II, 90 000 kgf/cm^2; and class III, 30 000 kgf/cm^2.

Internal friction angle

Protodyakonov-type shearing tests showed 44 pairs of points on three different test samples and indicate internal friction angle values of between 38 and 44°. According to published data studied for rock massifs consisting of mudstone or slate, the average value of the internal friction angle is of the order of 30°.

Values taken for the internal friction angle of class I and II rock massifs (43° and 38°) were obtained directly from tests and were considered to be representative of the massif, bearing in mind that the failure of the samples occurred along the weakest planes – the stratification. The value for class III was estimated by extrapolation based on laboratory data and also bearing in mind the published information mentioned above owing to the lack of tests of this type. This analysis led to an internal friction angle for the class III massif of 30°.

Cohesion

The tests previously described also indicated cohesion values of between 150 and 180 kgf/cm^2. These values were considered to be too high and, hence, not representative of the entire rock massif, since the intrinsic characteristics of the massifs that are more affected by cohesion than by other properties are not represented by small samples tested in the laboratory. These values should represent maximum limits.

The extrapolation to the rock massif, bearing in mind its irregularities, represented by fractures, whether filled or not, type of filling, alterations in this rock, joints or stratification and other features, obviously lead to lower values.

Taking published data into consideration, where cohesion values of between 0.4 and 30 kgf/cm^2 are indicated, the following values were estimated: class I, 40 kgf/cm^2; class II, 15 kgf/cm^2; and class III, 3 kgf/cm^2.

Compressive strength

Tests on samples showed values of compressive strength of between 800 and 1900 kgf/cm^2. In the compression test, when the rock is not homogeneous, failure occurs along the discontinuities of the sample. In these cases failure can occur by shearing or even by tension and is therefore not representative of the entire massif. It should be borne in mind that the compressive strength of the mass also depends on continuity of conditions.

There are therefore no established and confirmed correlations that can be used directly to transform values obtained in the laboratory into values representative of the massif.

Also, taking into consideration the average values given in publications, which also vary with the disposition of the stratification (from 500 to 800 kgf/cm^2), the following estimated values for simple compressive strength values were established: class I, 700 kgf/cm^2; class II, 500 kgf/cm^2; and class III, 300 kgf/cm^2.

Final remarks

Values obtained for the geomechanical parameters (Table 1), despite their being based on tests, consist of generally conservative forecasts owing to the difficulty of converting them into parameters that are representative of the rock massif. It was recommended, therefore, that during the excavation work site tests should be performed to verify these parameters.

Special design considerations

Pressure tunnel

As was mentioned in the general description, the pressure tunnel is composed of a horizontal section about 30 m long, a 537-m section with an inclination of 45° and a horizontal section about 100 m long. The internal pressure level within this tunnel will require a lining of steel plates, both from the aspect of resistance to forces and from resistance to abrasion.

To have the rock bear a part of the inner pressure a concrete lining is provided. Even when the magnitude of the tensile stresses results in cracking, axial forces will still be transmitted to the rock.

The form both for the hydraulic profile (lining) and for the excavated profile will be circular, steel and concrete forming concentric layers. The diameter of the hydraulic profile was established at 2.3 m and the thickness of lining concrete (and, hence, the radius of the excavation) was determined by consideration of the internal and external pressures plus effects of creep and thermal deformations in the concrete.

Once the possibility of cracking in the concrete is assumed, the thickness of the concrete layer will have little influence on the forces that act on the steel lining and the rock. This was therefore established as 0.3 m for construction reasons. The thickness of the lining was dimensioned for the internal pressure and buckling was checked as a function of external pressure. A calculation was performed of additional stresses due to creep of the concrete and the thermal expansion of the plate.

The final thicknesses obtained for the lining were 8 mm ($\frac{5}{16}$ in) in the initial section to about halfway down the inclined section, and 16 mm ($\frac{5}{8}$ in) in the second half of the inclined section and for the final horizontal length.

Analyses of the steel lining, concrete and rock with regard to deformation compatibility and stress distribution were performed by a fully automated computer process. The method makes use of the 'three-pressures' theorem and allows analyses of structures that comprise several layers, integral or cracked.

The effects of external pressure were calculated to determine critical depth – also by means of specially developed computer programs.

Analysis of Unduavi River diversion tunnel close to Chaco dam

The diversion tunnel will be excavated in predominantly good-quality rock. Its total length will be 300 m, the axis being for the most part parallel to the natural course of the river. The tunnel will have an arch-rectangular cross-section 5.5 m wide

Table 1   Characteristic parameters of rock mass for underground works (predicted)

Class	E, kgf/cm^2	E, kgf/cm^2	ϕ, °	σ_r, kgf/cm^2	ν	γ, t/m^3	RQD, %
I	180 000	40	43	700	0.22	2.71	75–100
II	90 000	15	38	500	0.25	2.71	50–75
III	30 000	3	30	300	0.35	2.60	25–50

E, Young's modulus; ϕ, internal friction angle; σ_r, compressive strength; ν, Poisson's ratio; γ, specific weight; RQD, rock quality designation.

and 5.0 m high. The lateral cover over the tunnel (to the natural side of the slope) will be variable along its length (minimum cover, 13 m). With excavations for building the dam this minimum cover will be reduced to 9.0 m, which will result in relieving the stresses in the neighbourhood of the tunnel.

Calculations were then made to verify the stand-up capacity of the rock in this region, as it would be of interest to build the tunnel without lining owing to its being of a temporary nature. A section located in a fault region with medium-quality rock was taken for the calculation. The model adopted was that of a plate of uniform thickness conforming to the suppositions of deformation planes and elasto-isotropic material. The process used was the finite-element method. Simulation of excavations was achieved by means of evolutionary calculations in three stages, plus a fourth stage to simulate tunnel operation.

Stage 1 consisted of geostatic generation of the initial vertical stresses, taking a confinement coefficient, K_0, of 1 for the initial horizontal stresses. Stage 2 consisted of excavating the tunnel and stage 3 of excavating the slope. Stage 4 corresponds to operating the tunnel under extreme conditions, in which it was flooded with a piezometric level corresponding to the crest of the upstream coffer dam.

Analysis of the fields of displacements and of stresses from the evolutionary calculations led to the following findings.
(a) No tensile stresses were found during tunnel excavation and excavating the slope only resulted in some few points with localized tensions. As regards compressive stresses, no existence of such states of stress was found, which could indicate the formation of plasticized zones at any position.
(b) The stresses at the edges of the excavations, which were obtained by extrapolation, confirmed the total non-existence of plasticizing.
(c) Displacements of the internal contour of the tunnel were limited to 2 mm and excavating the slope should result in a sideway displacement of about 1 cm at positions close to the slope.
(d) The influence of the assumed confinement coefficient value ($K_0 = 1$) could be analysed against the results of the readings, by which adoption of that value was confirmed as being the most critical for the case under consideration.
(e) The calculations were effected on the basis of medium-quality uniform material. As the predominant material is of good quality, it is to be expected that, in the greater part of the tunnel, the conditions should be better than those which have been calculated.
(f) The influence of internal pressure in the tunnel is small, hardly affecting the fields of stresses and displacements resulting from excavations.

The conclusion that could be reached was that the results confirmed the feasibility of the location adopted for the tunnel and showed that the greater part of the tunnel does not require lining or systematic support. As there is a fault of about 15 m in width, however, the parameters of which are unknown, a lining was designed that would be extended along the entire fault zone.

Stability analysis of slopes excavated in rock in proximity of Chaco dam

The Chaco dam will have part of its foundations on slopes excavated in rock on both banks of the Unduavi River. These slopes will have a gradient of 10:1 with intermediate berms. The geological data consisted of a map of the surface and of maps of two galleries (one on each bank of the river). These data were analysed by means of stereographic projections prepared by computer to establish potential failure mechanisms.

An attempt was first made to evaluate the geomechanical parameters, starting with the potentially unstable formations in

the natural slope. This failed, however, in that, according to the stereograms prepared, there were no unstable formations. It was therefore necessary to adopt parameters obtained from similar sites for potentially unstable planes.

The excavated slope was then analysed and revealed several potentially unstable formations. The safety of these formations (plane failure, toppling, wedges, etc.) was quantified by means of computer programs to check the stability of a plane or of a block of any shape and, where necessary, make it possible to calculate reinforcement for the slope.

The conclusion that was reached by these analyses was that the slope would be safe as long as it was drained sufficiently, and a drainage design was therefore prepared for each bank.

Cavern calculation

The Sakhahuaya power house (Fig. 6) is located in a cavern that measures 51.75 m $\times 14.6$ m $\times 25.8$ m and is situated at a depth of 300 m. To establish the field of stresses that will result in the rock massif as a result of excavating the cavern and adjacent tunnels a series of calculations was made by computer, with the finite-element method. In addition to determining the stresses in the massif, these calculations established the level of pressures that would be applied to the concrete dome, as well as enabling the need to use anchor bolts and tie-rods to be assessed.

The principal cavern calculation comprised a simulation of a cross-section by means of a two-dimensional finite-element model, the stages of excavating in rock and of concreting the dome being taken into consideration.

One of the major problems was, as is usual, the lack of data on the parameters of the rock massif, both as regards the *in-situ* installed stresses and the rheology of the material (the existence or not of anisotropy, values of the moduli of elasticity, non-linearity characteristics, strength criteria, etc.).

To compensate for this deficiency some calculations were made by varying these parameters to determine the factors that would most directly affect the behaviour of the rock mass. The construction stages are shown in Fig. 7. The final calculation was made by grouping these stages into five phases: *phase 1* – initial condition of the rock mass (*in-situ* stresses); *phase 2* – excavation of tunnels (construction stage 1); *phase 3* – excavation in the dome region up to the level 1442.00 (construction stages 2 and 3); *phase 4* – dome concreting and lowering excavation to the level 1434.50 (construction stages 4, 5 and 6); and *phase 5* – final excavation to the level 1423.40 (stages 7, 8 and 9).

The calculation in question is evolutionary, which means that the phases described above are automatically taken into consideration by the finite-element program used, by activating and deactivating elements, once the final state of stresses of one phase is taken as the initial state of stresses of the next.

As for the rock massif, it was assumed as behaving under perfect elastoplastic condition, which signifies that, once plasticized, it is no longer able to absorb new stresses. The Mohr–Coulomb yield criterion was adopted.

With respect to the state of initial stresses of the massif (*in-situ* stresses), three possibilities were calculated:

$$K_0 = \frac{\sigma_H}{\sigma_V} = 1 \tag{a}$$

$$K_0 = \frac{\sigma_H}{\sigma_V} = 1.5 \tag{b}$$

$$K_0 = \frac{\sigma_3}{\sigma_1} = 1.5 \quad \text{(plus principal stresses with relationship} \tag{c}$$
to horizontal of $\pm 10°$)

It was concluded that the variance in the value of K_0 was largely responsible for the significant alterations in the final

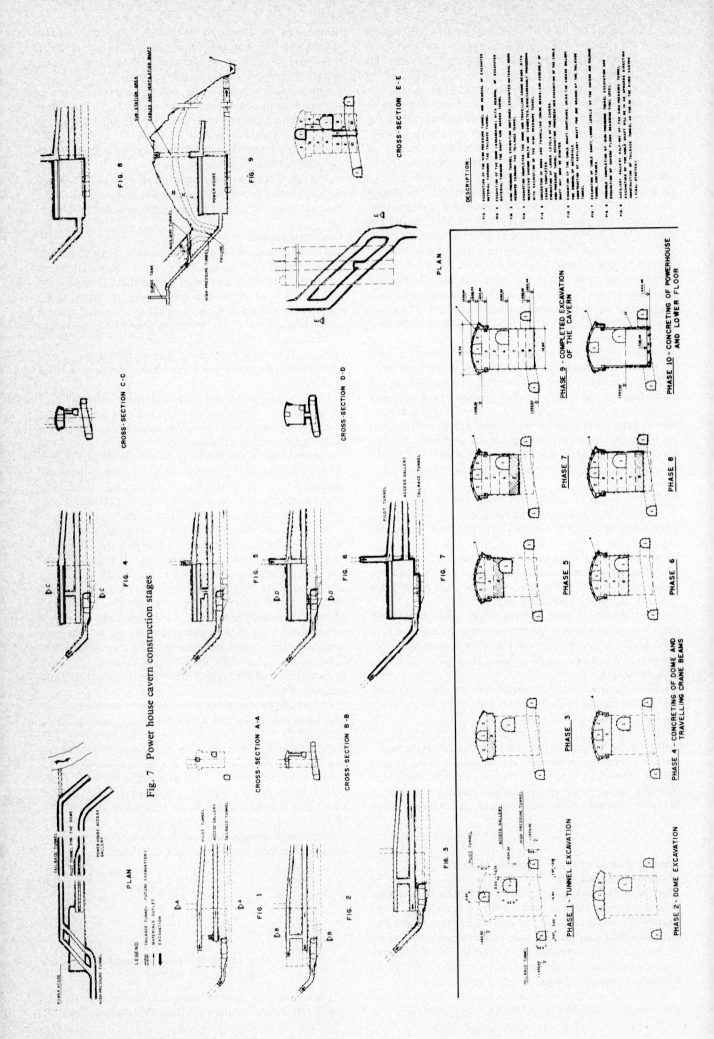

Fig. 7 Power house cavern construction stages

field of stresses obtained, (*b*) having been adopted as the dimensioning factor.

As is usual, these calculations only seek to supply an initial idea of what may be expected in terms of the behaviour of the massif. Instrumentation of the works is planned for comparison of the effects obtained with those predicted and to permit revision of the analysis where this is considered to be necessary.

Sand trap design

Given the unusual dimension and low temperature of inflowing water from the Taquesi River, special consideration was required for the lining design. The internal forces in the concrete lining were calculated by means of the finite-element method, assuming a plane strain condition. The effects of internal pressure and temperature gradient were found to be the most critical loads. The relieving effects of excavating were presumed not to be reflected in the lining as they will materialize long after the excavation. In the mathematical model that was used interaction of the lining with the surrounding massif was taken into consideration.

The effects of temperature were studied against the possibility of a thermal rate of change in the lining owing to the difference in temperature between the rock massif and the water in the sand trap during thawing. Because of the reduction in temperature the lining tends to contract, creating tensile stress in the concrete–massif interface and in the concrete itself. These stresses can reach values that are capable of breaking the interface or the lining. Both factors therefore give rise to immediate relief in the stresses that result from heat, whether by eliminating the external restraint or by a reduction in the rigidity of the part. Of the two mechanisms described, one will reach breaking point before the other.

If the concrete–massif interface is destroyed, a gap will result between the two materials. In this case, on superimposing the effects of internal pressure, there will no longer be an interaction between lining and massif and the former will be required to absorb the resultant stresses on its own. Thus, for a lining not in contact with the rock owing to the presence of the gap, the maximum stresses under maximum water pressure were found to be, for the arch-rectangular section, the horizontal base, assumed to be simply supported on the rock, and for the circular excavation section elastic supports in the radial direction in the lower half circumference, making an iterative calculation eliminating the elastic supports when subject to tensile stress.

The stresses obtained for internal pressure were used to dimension the sections, care being taken to distribute reinforcement in an appropriate manner so that, should cracking occur, it would be distributed uniformly throughout the member.

Tunnel excavation and lining

Both conventional (drilling and blasting) and mechanized (TBM) methods were studied and compared for the tunnel excavation. The use of a TBM would result in a more regular rock surface, thereby allowing shotcrete lining to be placed, even though the Chaco tunnel is a pressure tunnel.

Hydraulic studies were carried out to determine the roughness and diameters for both cases and comparative cost analyses were carried out. The technical aspects considered included the rate of excavation, the reduction in damage to rock and elimination of overbreak by use of a TBM, the reduction in temporary support, safety aspects, the use of shotcrete lining for TBM-excavated tunnels and of concrete for conventional excavation and costs and construction schedules, conventional techniques indicating major problems.

Against these advantages the greater initial investment, the reduced use of local labour and the greater outlay of hard currency were noted.

The economic/technical analysis led to the recommendation of the use of a TBM for the tunnel excavations.

Acknowledgement

The authors wish to express their thanks to the Empresa Nacional de Electricidad for permission to publish data relating to the Sakhahuaya Development and to Hidroservice-Engenharia de Projetos Ltda. for the support that has been given. Appreciation is also expressed for the help and assistance willingly given by the following colleagues: Eng. Israel Burman, Eng. Ivan Collares Werneck, Eng. Sérgio E. D. Monteclaro Cesar and Geol. Sohrab Shayani.

References

1. Rzhevsky V. and Novik G. *The physics of rocks* (Moscow: MIR Publishers, 1971), 320 p.
2. Barton N. Lien R. and Lunde J. Engineering classification of rock masses for the design of tunnel support. *Rock Mechanics*, **6**, 1974, 189–236.
3. Bieniawski Z. T. Rock mass classification in rock engineering. In *Symposium on exploration for rock engineering, Johannesburg, 1976*, vol. 1, 1976, 97–106.
4. Wickham G. E. Tiedemann H. R. and Skinner E. H. Support determinations based on geologic predictions. In *Proceedings North American rapid excavation and tunneling conference, Chicago, 1972* Lane K. S. and Garfield L. A. eds (New York: AIME, 1972), vol. 1, 43–64.
5. Hoek E. and Brown E. T. *Underground excavations in rock* (London: IMM, 1980), 527 p.
6. Deere D. U. Geological considerations. In *Rock mechanics in engineering practice* Stagg K. G. and Zienkiewicz O. C. eds (London, New York: Wiley, 1968), 1–20.
7. Gudehus G. ed. *Finite elements in geomechanics* (New York, etc.: Wiley, 1977), 588 p.

Design and construction of large underground caverns – a Himalayan experience

R. L. Chauhan
R. S. Chauhan
Himachal Pradesh State Electricity Board, Shimla, India

Synopsis

Design and construction aspects of large underground caverns that have been or are being built in the Himalayan Mountains are discussed. The caverns, which house underground hydroelectric power plants (Chibro, Chukha, Bhaba, Tehri and Chamera) are widely scattered: one project is located in the eastern Himalayas, two are in the outer part of the central Himalayas and two are in the inner part of the western Himalayas.

Experience with the projects has confirmed that Himalayan geology is both difficult and unpredictable. The Himalayan formations are necessarily fractured, numerous joints and shear planes being accompanied by the occurrence of seams and pockets of weak materials. At Chibro, which was the first project to be constructed, load estimation was carried out by use of Terzaghi's empirical method and the roof arch was supported with built-up steel sets along with blocking concrete. In the later projects, however, the introduction of new rock mass classification systems, such as those of Bieniawski, Barton and Wickham, the concept of support design had changed and there is a significant trend towards the use of rockbolts to support the rock. There are reports that Barton's system is not applicable to Himalayan geology, but on the basis of experience of caverns already constructed, it is suggested that, except for strata that are exceptionally adverse, the method can be used advantageously even in the Himalayas, provided that weak seams and pockets are specially treated as and when they occur.

The Himalayas are the youngest fold mountains and they present very complex geological conditions. The snow-capped mountains feed several perennial rivers with steep bed slopes in their upper reaches where they negotiate loops and bends, rendering them ideal for power generation. Several power projects have been constructed on these rivers, but the potential of Himalayan rivers remains untapped. The development of hydroelectric power in the Himalayas, where slopes are unstable and glaciers could cause problems to surface power stations, involves the construction of large underground caverns to accommodate power plants and other structures. The several underground power houses that have been or are being constructed in the Himalayan region include Chibro, Chukha, Bhaba, Tehri and Chamera. In this paper design and construction aspects of the large underground caverns of these projects are discussed with special emphasis on the Bhaba power plant complex.

The cavern of the Chibro underground power plant, which was the first to be constructed in the Himalayas, was supported by use of steel sets, but the modern approach of using shotcrete and rockbolts has been adopted to support the arches of later caverns.

Doubts have been expressed by some authors as to the applicability of Barton's system of classification for supporting the rock mass in the Himalayas, but we have used the system to advantage in designing the supports for the Bhaba underground caverns. The rockbolting pattern has, however, to be adjusted to suit the pattern of the rock wedges formed by the various joint sets. This support system has been supplemented by the grouting of rock to a predetermined depth. Nevertheless, in certain segments where pegmatite intrusions occurred in kaolinized form, resulting in collapse and cavity formation, steel ribs with backfill concrete had to be used.

Chibro power house cavern

The first large underground cavity to be constructed in the Himalayas was for the Chibro power house, which was put into operation in March, 1975. This power house is an underground station with an installed capacity of 240 MW, utilizing a drop of about 124 m on the River Tons (a tributary of the Yamuna). The main cavern houses generating machines and transformers in a linear arrangement. The erection bay and control room are also contained in the same cavern, which is 113.2 m long, 18.35 m wide and 32.5 m high at the point of maximum excavation. The shape of the cavity is rectangular and the roof arch is circular with a rise to span ratio of about 0.27. The layout of the complex is shown in Fig. 1.

Geology

The power house cavern is located within a limestone band that overlies a major shear zone. This shear zone is, however, below the bottom of the cavern at a depth of not less than 10 m from the lowest level. The rock is closely jointed and a series of shear zones exists, varying from about 2 to 50 cm in thickness and running parallel to the bedding planes. Such geological features are not uncommon in the Himalayan formations.

Support system and construction of cavern

During the excavation of the ventilation tunnel, which joins the power house arch at the crown (Fig. 1), two cross joints combined with a minor shear zone were observed that resulted in a rockfall between these joints. Because of the presence of shear zones with highly crushed and water-laden material combined with an erratic joint pattern, it was thought to be much safer

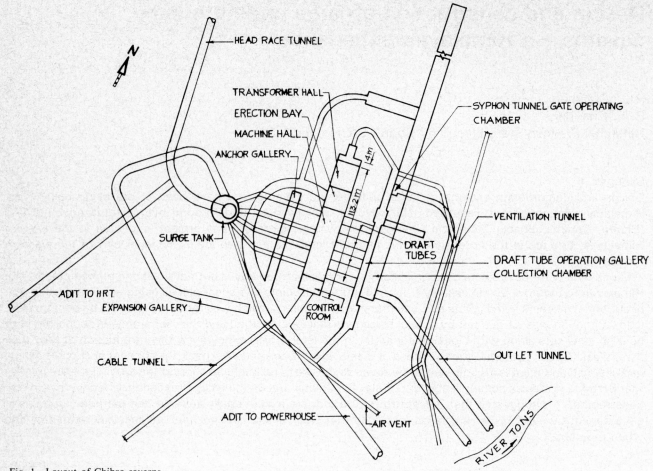

Fig. 1 Layout of Chibro caverns

and more desirable to provide positive rock supports by erecting steel sets and by providing blocking concrete concurrently. The steel sets were designed for a rock load of 8 m, estimated by use of Terzaghi's empirical method. In addition, the self-load of concrete arch, a temperature variation of 10°C, a rock dilatation of 7 mm and a rib-shortening effect of 10% were also taken into consideration. No water pressure was considered as that was released through a suitable rock drainage arrange-

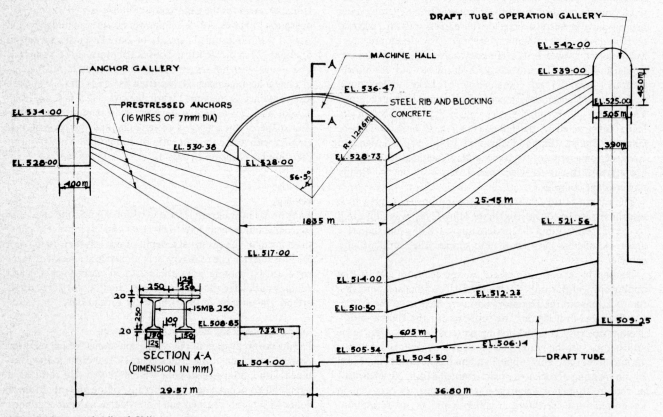

Fig. 2 Support details of Chibro caverns

ment. The steel ribs used were 250 mm × 125 mm, reinforced with flange plates 250 mm × 20 mm along the extrados and 150 mm × 20 mm along the intrados. The steel sets were provided at 250-mm centres. Thus, the top flange plates were continuous and no formwork was required for the placement of blocking concrete (Fig. 2). The space between the intrados and extrados of the ribs was filled with hand-packed gravel, which was grouted in position to ensure water-tightness and cross bracing of ribs. To hold the gravel in position steel fabric was welded on the inside of ribs and a layer of shotcrete and gunite was laid over the ribs (this also served the purpose of protecting the ribs from weathering effects). Contact grouting was carried out at a pressure of 1.75 kg/cm^2, after 21 days of placement of blocking concrete, through 38-mm diameter holes placed at 3.5-m centres. These holes were drilled through 50-mm diameter pipes, which were earlier embedded in the roof arch steel set and blocking concrete. Later, through the same pipe holes 38 mm in diameter and 5 m in length were drilled for consolidation grouting, which was carried out at a pressure of 3.5 to 5.25 kg/cm^2. After consolidation grouting 8-m drainage holes were drilled with NX bits at 6-m centres in the gap between two adjacent ribs.

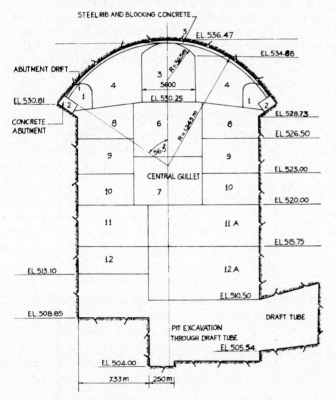

Fig. 3   Excavation sequence for Chibro

The sequence of excavation (Fig. 3) was planned to, first, construct two drifts along the upstream and downstream haunches of the roof arch. These were D-shaped, 2.5 m high and 2 m wide. A central drift of 5.6-m width was also driven, which made it possible to carry out the construction of the arch simultaneously at more than one place along its length. The muck from rock pillars between drifts was removed in stretches of 1.5–2.0 m, support being by use of steel sets and blocking concrete.

The entire power house roof arch was completed within one year in April, 1968, a total of 423 steel sets involving about 1200 t of steel being used. The side walls of the power house cavern were supported by means of prestressed anchors. During the excavation of the cavern a number of medium and minor shear zones were encountered: it was felt that these, if combined with the adverse jointing pattern, might cause sliding

of the long walls of the power house cavern. Because of the existence of the shear zones, slip planes and joints in an erratic pattern, it was decided to support the side walls of the power house by means of prestressed grouted cables both on the upstream and downstream faces (Fig. 2). On the upstream face an anchorage gallery 4 m wide and 6 m high was excavated parallel to the main cavity, a cover of 18 m being maintained. The anchorages were designed for the component of the rock load that has a tendency to slide inside the cavern. On the downstream the draft tube operation gallery, which is located 25 m from the power house cavern, has been utilized as an anchorage gallery. The excavation of the cavern below haunch level was planned in such a manner that the excavation and prestressing of cables could be carried out simultaneously. The muck was removed through an adit at erection bay level. Overbreak was limited by using line drilling along the sides. The muck from levels below the erection bay was moved up by means of a ramp with a combination of shovel and dump trucks. Later, the muck ramps were cut and muck was lifted to erection bay level with the help of a crane.

The entire excavation work on the power house cavity, from commencement of abutment drifts to zero stage concreting, was completed in thirty months.

Chukha power house cavern
The second underground power station that is being constructed in the Himalayas is the Chukha power station, which will have an installed capacity of 344 MW. The project is located in the eastern Himalayas in Bhutan and construction work is being carried out by the Government of India. The power house cavern, which houses the generating machines, the transformers and inlet valves in a composite arrangement, is 24.5 m wide, 136.75 m long and 41 m high. The cavity has already been excavated and supported and the erection of units is presently in progress (Fig. 4).

Geology
The power house cavity is located some 230 m below the ground in granite gneisses with minor bands of schist and occasional shear zones that range in thickness from 5 to 50 cm. The foliation planes of the gneisses around the cavity generally strike N30°W–S30°E to N40°W–S40°E, i.e. into the hill. The long axis of the cavity is almost at right angles to the strike of the granite gneisses.

The granite gneisses in the area of the cavity are traversed by several sets of joints. Six principal and most prominently developed joint sets have been identified. These joints govern the stability of the power house cavity and are responsible for the development of the rock loads by the formation of different wedges in the crown and the walls of the power house.

Design of support system
Interpretation of geological data indicated conditions that could cause rockfalls from the crown as well as from the side walls if they were not supported adequately.[5] For the six identified major joint sets stereo plots were made that combined the various joint sets to identify unstable rock wedges in the roof and side walls of the cavern. It was revealed that unstable rock wedges occurred in the downstream and front walls that had a tendency to slip and slide into the cavern. The maximum size of the potential unstable blocks for these walls was estimated to be 2 m × 2 m × 1 m. Large, unstable rock wedges were expected near the junction of the roof arch and the downstream wall – a problem that was compounded by the pressure of seepage water encountered. These wedges were specially supported by the provision of rockbolts 13.5 and 9 m deep in two rows. Very high in-situ vertical stress conditions presented the problem of a few loosely jointed, deep rock

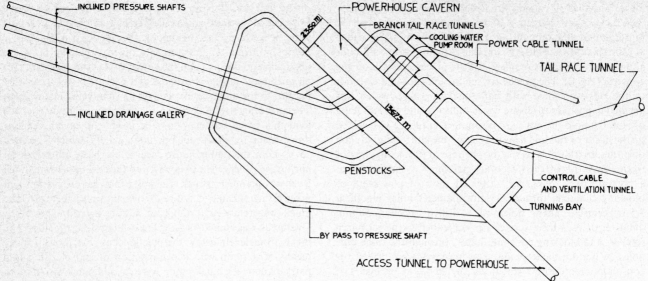

Fig. 4   Layout of Chukha caverns

blocks falling loose and dropping into the cavern. At a distance of 90 to 104 m, measured from the front wall, shear zones 5–50 cm thick were encountered on the roof and upstream wall. There was a major rockfall and dome formation in the crown that had to be backfilled with cement concrete and supported with closely spaced steel ribs. The general pattern for supporting the roof arch was with rockbolts 10 m long and 25 mm in diameter at 3-m centres in a staggered formation (Fig. 5). Along the side walls 8-m rockbolts at 3-m centres in a staggered formation were provided. A gunite layer (150 mm), together with 150 mm square mesh of 3.25-mm diameter welded wires, was provided on the surface along with the rockbolts concurrently with excavation. The steel ribs provided are I sections 300 mm × 200 mm, which have been laid on suitably designed abutments that, in turn, are anchored into the rock by two anchor bolts of 25-mm diameter spaced at 3-m centres. To

prevent the ingress of seepage water, which could add significantly to the loads acting on the roof and side walls of the cavern, a drainage gallery has been provided all around the cavern at the springing level of the roof arch. The observation of extensometer readings did not indicate any significant movement in the side walls of the power house cavity.

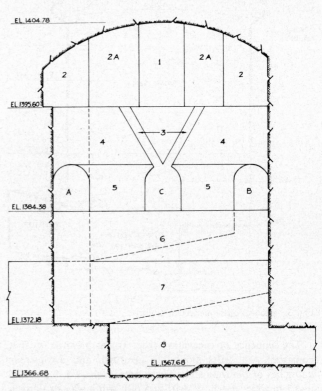

Fig. 6   Excavation sequence for Chukha

Fig. 5   Support details of Chukha cavern

Construction work on the Chukha power house cavity was planned in the following manner (Fig. 6). The permanent access tunnel, which joins the cavity at its one end at the erection bay level, was constructed first. Tunnel A was constructed along the upsteam at a slope of 1 : 6 upwards to approach the arch portion and a second tunnel (B) along the downstream side was laid at a slope 1 : 6 downwards to reach EL 1372.18 m and excavate the horizontal portion of the penstock tunnels (Fig. 6). Central tunnel C along the full power house length was also excavated horizontally. Tunnel *A* having been constructed, arch unit one was built in its full length and supported with rockbolts and shotcrete simultaneously. Thereafter, arch unit 2, followed by arch unit 2*A*, was completed, the work of rockbolting and shotcreting being carried out simultaneously. At the same time shaft 3 was excavated, which proved useful for dumping muck to the lower level. Excavation of portion 4 was then taken up by benching and disposing of the muck through shaft 3, removing it by means of tunnel *C*. Portion 5 was excavated by enlarging tunnel *C*. The excavation below EL 1384.38 m (erection bay level) of portions 6 and 7 was carried out by benching and slashing, muck being removed through ramp *B*, into the access tunnel. The excavation below EL 1372.18 m, i.e. portion 8, was done by smooth blasting and muck was removed through the tail race.

Sanjay Vidyut Pariyojna–Bhaba power house caverns

The third underground power station that is scheduled for construction in the Himalayas is the Bhaba power house, which is a 120-MW (peak) hydroelectric station located in the inner Himalayas in Himachal Pradesh, India. The excavation and

pegmatite has a tendency to disintegrate and pulverize under the influence of water. A kaolinized pocket that has rendered the rock mass into a powdery state has been encountered in the last 17 m reach of the power house, which has resulted in chimney formation during excavation.

The vertical and horizontal *in-situ* stresses determined in a drift close to the power house by flatjack tests were observed as 53.9 and 39.4 kg/cm^2, respectively. According to field tests conducted for augen gneisses, the Barton classification[1] is 13. Eight major joint sets have been identified in the power house drift.

Design of support system
The orientation of the caverns has been checked with respect to the joint sets. The worst joint set crosses the cavern normally and other minor joint sets traverse the caverns obliquely. Care has been taken to avoid any joints running parallel to the long axis of the caverns, which have also been located with an adequate rock cover of more than three times the width of the cavern in every direction to the slump line of the slope. Rock pillars equal to the average width of two adjoining caverns have been provided between them.

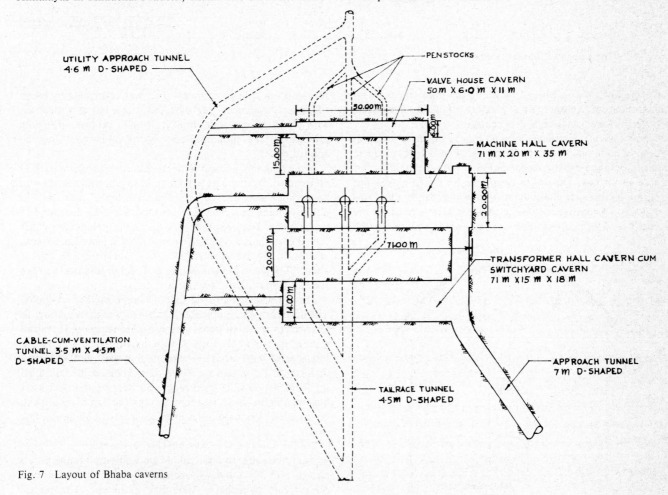

Fig. 7 Layout of Bhaba caverns

support of its underground caverns are currently in progress. The following major caverns in the power house complex run parallel to one another (Fig. 7): machine hall (20 m wide, 71 m long and 35 m high), the transformer and switchyard cavern (SF-6 switchgear; 15 m wide, 71 m long and 18 m high) and the main inlet valve gallery (6 m wide, 50 m long and 11 m high).

Geology
The power house caverns lie under a rock cover of some 300 m. All three caverns are located within a band of augen gneiss, heavily jointed and intercepted by pegmatite bands and pockets that vary in thickness from a few centimetres to about 3 m. The

Rock support for the Bhaba power house caverns comprises, basically, rockbolts and shotcrete, applied shortly after excavation. In the roof arch portion pre-tensioned, grouted, rock wedge type rockbolts, made of mild steel bars, have been provided. For this rock (Barton classification number 13) rockbolts of 6-m length are specified at a spacing of 1-m centres, but after analysis of the eight set of joints for wedge formation it has been decided to have systematic rock support with 6.5-m long × 25-mm diameter grouted rockbolts spaced at 2-m centres. These are interspaced with 5-m long × 25-mm diameter bolts at 2-m centres (Fig. 8). The rockbolts help the jointed rock to stay together and form a natural arch, which

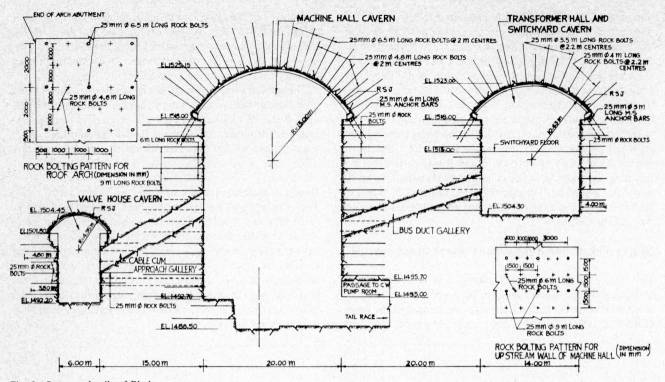

Fig. 8   Support details of Bhaba caverns

will be further strengthened by filling the joint crevices with consolidation grouting, at a pressure of about 5 kg/cm², through holes 5 m deep at 3-m centres.

Subsequently, drainage holes 60 mm in diameter and 8 m deep at 6-m centres are to be provided to ensure adequate drainage to prevent the accumulation of water behind the roof arch so formed. The design is suitable for augen gneiss, but pegmatite has been encountered in wider bands than was expected. A massive rockfall in the drift excavated along the upstream abutment was encountered, which resulted in the

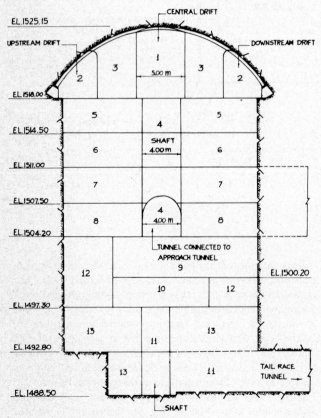

Fig. 9   Excavation sequence for Bhaba

formation of a large chimney. This was controlled by back-filling with concrete. Steel ribs, 300 mm × 140 mm, built up with plates 12 mm × 300 mm at 300-mm centres, are being provided in the kaolinized zone as rockbolts could not be applied.

In the remaining length some steel sets are being provided in addition to rockbolts as pegmatite in small erratic bands was appearing almost everywhere. The provision of steel sets was also psychologically helpful to workmen after the formation of the chimney. The size of the steel sets in the arch portion other than the kaolinized zone is 250 mm × 125 mm placed at 300-mm centres. In the transformer hall cavity, where the arch span is about 17 m (24 m in the machine hall cavity), the steel sets are fixed at a spacing of 500-mm centres.

The side walls are also planned to be supported by rockbolts. The upstream wall is unstable because of wedge formation, as analysed by means of stereo nets. It has been proposed to install grouted bolts 9 m deep and 25 mm in diameter at 3-m centres interspersed with grouted rockbolts 6 m deep and 25 mm in diameter at 1.5-m centres. The 6-m rockbolts will be installed at the earliest possible opportunity, but not later than 24 h after blasting to give immediate support until the 9-m rockbolts can be installed. Drainage holes are also proposed along the side walls.

For the purpose of excavation (Fig. 9) the machine hall arch was approached through a cable-cum-ventilation tunnel at the crown level. Two drifts – one each along the upstream and downstream haunches – were first excavated. The central tunnel was then excavated, all being supported with rockbolts. Abutments for steel ribs were also laid along the upstream and downstream drifts in advance. Meanwhile, the access tunnel meeting the machine hall cavity at erection bay level was also completed and connected to the roof arch by a vertical shaft at the centre of the hall, which made it possible to doze muck downwards. The intervening rock pillars were then proposed to be cleared off in stretches of 2–3 m and supported with rockbolts. As required, steel sets were also provided and backfilled with concrete concurrently. The excavation below springing level to erection bay level will be lowered in stretches of about 3 m and rockbolt and shotcrete support will be applied concurrently. The muck is being dumped into the shaft and removed through the permanent access tunnel. Major quantities of muck from below the erection bay level will be raised by means of ramps, the remainder being moved out through the tail race tunnel.

Tehri power house caverns

Recently, construction work on the Tehri dam project[5] has been begun in the Himalayas. The dam is located in a narrow gorge, on the River Bhagirathi – a tributary of the mighty Ganges – near Tehri, Uttar Pradesh, India. The Tehri power house is an underground station with an ultimate installed capacity of 2000 MW (8 × 250 MW). It comprises the following

house caverns have been so aligned that the crown and side walls for most of the length lie within Grade I phyllites, which are the most competent type of rock in the area.

Rock pillars of adequate width have been kept between adjoining caverns (Fig. 11), the width being not less than the sum of the width of the two adjoining cavities because the strata are not very competent. It has been decided to keep the width of caverns to the minimum possible: for this reason the valves, machines and transformers have been placed in separate chambers. The largest width is that of the machine hall, which is 22.5 m – the minimum requirement for a 250-MW machine.

Excavation work on the Tehri power house caverns has not yet been commenced and the design of supports has still to be finalized. It is proposed, however, to support the roof arch by

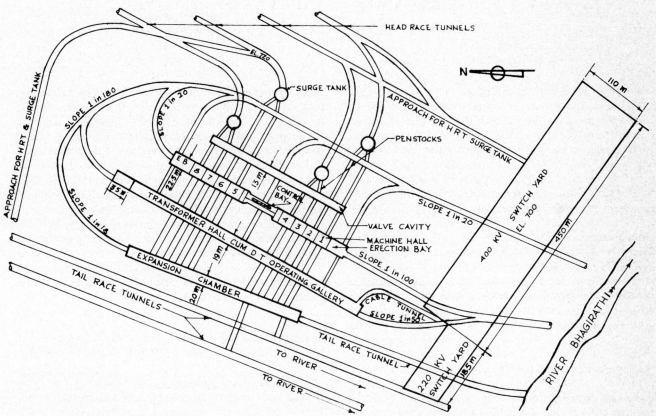

Fig. 10   Layout of Tehri caverns

major underground caverns, which run almost parallel to one another (Fig. 10): machine hall cavern (22.5 m wide, 326 m long and 50 m high), valve house cavern (13 m wide, 250 m long and 42 m high), transformer hall cum draft tube gate operation gallery (19 m wide, 470 m long and 18 m high) and collection chamber cum expansion gallery (20 m wide, 300 m long and 20 m high).

Geology
The rock formations at Tehri power house site are generally banded phyllites, which have been broadly grouped into three categories (Grade I, Grade II and Grade III) on the basis of their argillaceous and arenaceous contents and tectonic status. Shear zones and fractures also occur in between the various types of rock bands. The rock is highly jointed. Five sets of joints and three shear zones criss-cross the rock at the power house location.

Stability of underground caverns
The orientation of major caverns in the power house complex has been kept nearly normal to the strike of the rock foliation, which is considered structurally sound. Moreover, the power

means of rockbolts and shotcrete or steel ribs with blocking concrete, or by a combination thereof, depending on the quality of rock encountered from reach to reach. The wall supports are proposed to be designed by marking out prominent shear planes, joint planes and slip planes in the cross-section and longitudinal section of the underground caverns. Supports will be designed to resist the sliding rock wedges formed between different slip planes – rockbolting with shotcrete will be provided for this purpose. If the strata in certain locations prove to be extremely bad, prestressed anchors with shotcrete may be used.

In the Tehri power house it is proposed to provide adequate drainage both in the roof arch and along the side walls by means of purpose-drilled holes.

Chamera power house caverns

The Chamera project[6] has recently been authorized for construction with Canadian assistance and, currently, infrastructure works are in progress. It is located in the western Himalayas on the River Ravi in the State of Himachal Pradesh, India.

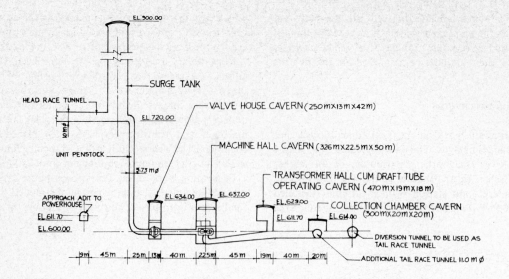

Fig. 11   Cross-section of Tehri caverns

The power house complex consists of three caverns – a valve house cavern, a power house cavern and a tail race gate operation cavern. The power house cavern, which houses three machines, each of 180 MW, is 112 m long, 15.5 m wide and 44 m high.

The power house complex is located within the volcanics, which consist of vescicular and amygdaloidal basalts accompanied by bands of shales and quartzites, which are heavily foliated and jointed. It is expected that rockbolts will be utilized to support the power house caverns.

Conclusions

Some experiences in the design and construction of large caverns in hydroelectric projects in various parts of the Himalayas have been outlined. In all the projects, as is true of the entire Himalayas, the geological conditions have been difficult and unpredictable. The rocks are fractured and have numerous joints and shear planes, which, coupled with the erratic occurrence of weak seams and pockets, make construction of large underground caverns hazardous, time-consuming and expensive. Of necessity, investigation work in the Himalayas should be both detailed and extensive to enable, as far as is possible, problem zones to be avoided. Secondly, the layout of a project should be inherently flexible to permit changes in the event of adverse geology being encountered.

The experience of constructing large underground caverns in the Himalayas covers only some 15 years. The first underground cavern was the Chibro power house, with an installed capacity of 240 MW; the latest, under construction, is the Tehri power house, with an installed capacity of 2000 MW. This is, however, merely the beginning of an activity that will occupy many decades. The development of a support system that is economical and well suited to Himalayan conditions is therefore essential.

On the earlier project (Chibro) emphasis was laid on the building of artificial arches of steel sets and blocking concrete to resist rock loads, which were estimated primarily by means of Terzaghi's empirical method. On more recent projects, however, there has been a significant trend towards the use of rockbolts and the application of Barton's method to estimate rock loads, which gives lesser values. In addition, the various wedges formed by different combinations of joint sets are identified with the help of stereo plots and the length and pattern of bolting are determined accordingly. The accent is on developing a natural self-supporting rock arch capable of withstanding *in-situ* stresses and stress concentration on account of

cavity formation. The excavated section is expanded gradually, rockbolts being applied concurrently. The rockbolts prevent the jointed rock from disintegrating and, ultimately, a natural self-supporting rock arch is developed. This can be further enhanced by filling the joint crevices with grout. In comparison with steel rib support and concrete blocking methods shotcrete and rockbolts tend to minimize final loads in that they allow a controlled amount of deformation that is sufficient to develop arching but insufficient to allow loosening.

Sometimes, however, in the Himalayan geology, as in the Bhaba machine hall cavern, where kaolinized pockets of pegmatite rendered the rock mass into a powdery state in some reaches, it is impossible to install rockbolts. In such locations it is essential to use steel ribs and to scoop out weak material and to backfill with concrete.

References

1. Barton N. Lien R. and Lunde J. Engineering classification of rock masses for the design of tunnel support. *Rock Mechanics*, **6**, 1974, 189–236.
2. Terzaghi K. Rock defects and loads on tunnel supports. In *Rock tunnelling with steel supports* Proctor R. V. and White T. L. eds (Youngstown, Ohio: Commercial Shearing and Stamping, 1946), 17–99.
3. Tandon G. N. and Agrawal C. K. Excavation of Chibro Power House cavity. Paper presented to All India symposium on economic and civil engineering aspects of hydroelectric schemes, Roorkee, April 1978.
4. Operation and maintenance manual, Yamuna Hydroelectric Project Stage-II-Part-I.
5. Gupta J. P. Jain K. P. and Singhal M. M. Layout of Tehri Power House complex and stability of underground cavities. Paper presented to Workshop on Tehri Dam Project, Dec. 1979.
6. National Hydroelectric Corporation Ltd. (A Government of India Undertaking). Information on Chamera and Dhauliganga hydroelectric projects.

New methods of constructing tunnels for new routes for the German Federal Railway (DB)

Heinz Distelmeier
Stephan Semprich
Bilfinger + Berger Bauaktiengesellschaft, Mannheim, Federal Republic of Germany

Synopsis
The German Federal Railway is currently planning two new routes – between Hannover and Würzburg and between Mannheim and Stuttgart – that represent a total length of 427 km, of which 146 km is in tunnel. At present 51 tunnels with a total length of 112 km are under construction; seven tunnels with a total length of 9 km have already been completed and 16 tunnels with a total length of 25 km are to be started in the near future. To date, nearly all tunnels have been constructed by use of the drill and blast technique. New technical developments that have been employed during the construction procedure are described: these include monitoring of the excavation profile, new shotcrete methods and the use of waterproof concrete for the inner concrete linings. The decision not to use a full-face tunnel-boring machine is explained – despite the large amount of tunnel length with virtually constant cross-section that would appear to have justified such a machine.

Project background

The German Federal Railway celebrates its 150th anniversary in 1985. Its line network has remained virtually unchanged for more than 100 years and it was not until 1970 that a programme was submitted to the Government for the comprehensive modernization and extension of the outdated network. The two outstanding features of this programme are the new Hannover–Würzburg and Stuttgart–Mannheim routes (Fig. 1) – owing, primarily, to the fact that the main traffic flow routes of the country have changed as the result of the division of Germany from what was a west–east direction to today's north–south direction.

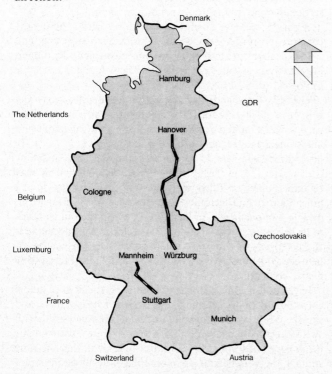

Fig. 1   New routes established by Deutsche Bundesbahn

Work on the new routes was begun, somewhat tentatively, as early as the 1970s. Towards the end of that decade the efforts of the German Federal Railway received more support as a result of an increased government awareness of environmental considerations and overall energy economics. Progress in planning and execution was held up in only a few sections by official protests by those who lived near the planned routes. Tunnel construction engineers do not generally complain about delays caused by local residents, however, as such delays tend to result in longer underground sections!

In the early 1980s construction work was intensified on an increasingly broad front and it is now expected that the routes will be opened to railway traffic early in 1991.

Line routing and extension criteria

The two routes pass through central hilly areas that, by German standards, are thinly populated.

Railway routes constructed in earlier years in these areas generally followed the bends of the rivers, but the speeds at which trains are now required to travel no longer permit this. The new routes are to be designed for train speeds of 250 km/h and they therefore require a much straighter route both in regard to line location and gradients. The essential criteria for the route are

Minimum radius, R_{min} = 5.100 m
Maximum slope, s_{max} = 1.25%
Track spacing, a = 4.70 m

On the basis of these criteria it was necessary to plan numerous tunnels, bridges, cuttings and embankments (Fig. 2). The overall tunnel length, 146 km, represents an extremely large proportion (one-third) of the entire line length. The 74 individual tunnels will require cross-sectional areas of between 105 and 145 m^2 to suit current operating requirements and to allow for later extension plans (Fig. 3).

At the present time 63 tunnel contracts have been awarded for 58 tunnels (Fig. 4), Bilfinger + Berger having been selected in 12 of these cases.

Hanover ⟷ Würzburg: 327 km

Tunnels	Cuttings	Bridges	Embankments and surface tracks
116 km	93 km	36 km	81 km
36 %	28 %	11 %	25 %

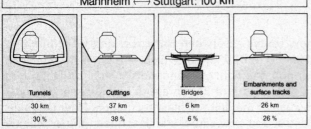

Mannheim ⟷ Stuttgart: 100 km

Tunnels	Cuttings	Bridges	Embankments and surface tracks
30 km	37 km	6 km	26 km
30 %	38 %	6 %	26 %

Fig. 2 Per cent of tunnel construction for new routes

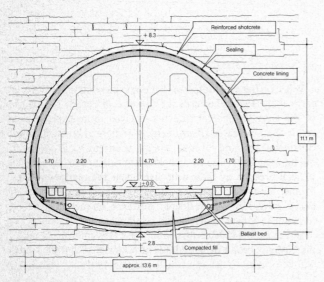

Fig. 3 Typical cross-section

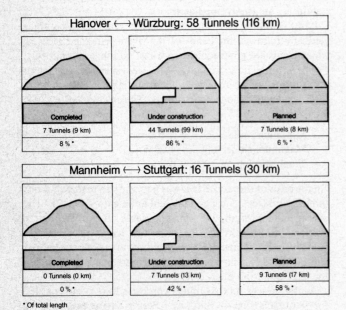

Hanover ⟷ Würzburg: 58 Tunnels (116 km)

Completed	Under construction	Planned
7 Tunnels (9 km)	44 Tunnels (99 km)	7 Tunnels (8 km)
8 % *	86 % *	6 % *

Mannheim ⟷ Stuttgart: 16 Tunnels (30 km)

Completed	Under construction	Planned
0 Tunnels (0 km)	7 Tunnels (13 km)	9 Tunnels (17 km)
0 % *	42 % *	58 % *

* Of total length

Fig. 4 Tunnel construction status, January, 1985

Geology

The tunnels of the two new lines lie mainly in Triassic strata. They thus cut through virtually all the bedding layers of the New Red Sandstone, the Muschelkalk and the Keuper Series (Fig. 5).

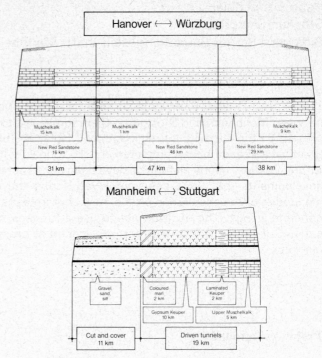

Fig. 5 Major geological profiles for tunnel sections

The characteristics of the rock range from firm rock formations suitable for the use of explosives through relatively soft rock to loose rock. The tunnel structures lie sometimes above and sometimes below the groundwater-table. A detailed description of the geological conditions would be beyond the scope of this paper, but it is necessary to describe a few special features to explain the reasons for the choice of construction methods that were used.

As no experience was available with tunnels of large cross-sectional area in the rock conditions in question, it was necessary to conduct a comprehensive investigation before the construction project was begun. This comprised drilling and field and laboratory tests and was supplemented by pilot tunnels in zones that presented particularly difficult and unpredictable geological problems.

The New Red Sandstone at considerable depth is generally firm and thickly bedded. In passing beneath intermediate valleys with a limited overburden, however, the sandstone and mudstone strata frequently thin out and may lead to the 'coffin lids' feared by miners. In certain areas the New Red Sandstone is characterized by large, near-vertical fissures, which may be either open or filled with silt (Fig. 6). Bedding joints, other fissures and tectonic faults pose problems in regard to driving – in particular, in locations in which the tunnel needs to be driven near to a ground surface slope. The sandstone is characterized by uniaxial compressive strength values of between 20 and more than 60 MN/m^2 and has up to an 85% quartz content.

In general, the Muschelkalk poses more difficulties to tunnel construction than the sandstone. It is leached, karstic and subject to falls. At certain points it contains residual strata with swelling clay minerals. With an ingress of water, softening of the unpaved bed would be inevitable. In general, the limestone strata in the Muschelkalk are more solid – the mudstone strata less so.

Fig. 6 Quarry face of New Red Sandstone (Jossa quarry)

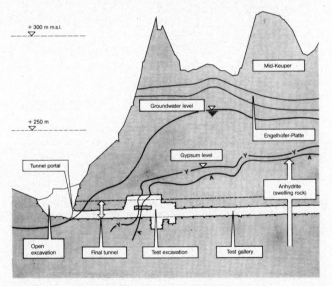

Fig. 7 Part of geological section, Freudenstein tunnel

In the Keuper Series special tunnel construction considerations arise primarily in the middle stage (gypsum Keuper Series). In one section of the Mannheim–Stuttgart line the route of the tunnel lies alternately in the gypsum, in the anhydrite and in the leached zone (Fig. 7). In this case it should be noted – in particular, with regard to the durability of the finished structure – that the rock volume may increase by approximately 60% as a result of water ingress at the transition points from anhydrite to gypsum.

The Upper Permian formation beneath the New Red Sandstone contains thick saline strata in the centre and northern section of the Hannover–Würzburg line in certain areas and these strata have been dissolved locally by groundwater, which

was able to enter through fractures. Erosion resulted in subsidence and sink holes, which, with diameters of more than 100 m, also pass through the New Red Sandstone and are filled with debris. Such pipes create problems during driving and the subsequent construction.

Detailed descriptions of the geological conditions are available for each individual tunnel structure and the responsible authorities will allow interested parties access to this information (the addresses of the authorities are listed in the Appendix).

Design principles

The cross-section (Fig. 8) shows the structure clearance that is required for the tunnel when it is in operation. This means minimum effective cross-sectional areas of 82 m² with a straight track and a maximum of 94 m² in the area of the overhead conductor tensioning equipment over a curved track.

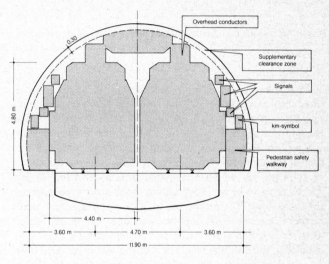

Fig. 8 Typical tunnel cross-section clearances of new routes

The contract specification requires a twin-shell configuration, the inner lining of which is to be either a waterproof membrane with a largely unreinforced concrete or a waterproof reinforced concrete.

The shape and size of the excavated cross-section depend on the required effective cross-section, the static requirements (which determine not only the shell thickness but also whether a curved invert is necessary), the selected sealing concept and, not least, the planned excavation method.

Construction methods

Full-face mechanical driving
At this point it is useful to report on a development that did not, in fact, take place – full-face shield driving. This development did not proceed beyond the planning phase and no machine was tested in prototype form.

In the country of origin of the shield-driving method it will not be easy to understand why, in partially friable rock, 74 tunnels with approximately the same cross-sectional area were driven conventionally, even though individual sections are up to 11 km in length. For this reason it is perhaps necessary to describe the five main decision criteria that made the use of a giant shield undesirable.

Construction time
Long tunnels normally justify the use of a TBM. In this case, however, all the long tunnels were on the critical path as regards overall completion time and it was necessary to make careful

137

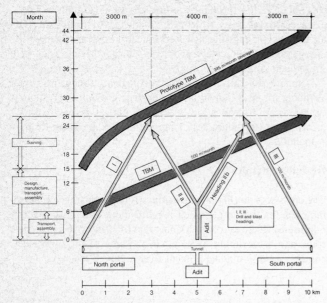

Fig. 9   Comparison of construction time (TBM versus drill–blast)

comparisons between the times necessary for shield driving and those for conventional driving. In areas that permit simultaneous working from both ends and outwards from the middle the rate of working of a TBM must be high for it to be competitive with drill–blast times. A comparison was made for the typical 10-km tunnel shown in Fig. 9. An average performance of 20 m per day would be required from a TBM for similar overall times to be achieved. Owing to the protracted delivery times necessary for prototypes of such machines, and since neither contractor nor supplier had one readily available, analyses based on previous experience showed that, even optimistically, the time that would be required would be 18 months greater than that for conventional driving, allowance having been made for the necessary design and mobilization times.

Excavated cross-section

The circular cross-section, preferred in regard to alignment control, rotational excavation and segment lining, is, however, 10–20% less favourable than an excavation form that is suited to conventional cutting methods, depending on the required profile. Even though the machine manufacturers endeavoured to produce a non-circular profile by the introduction of mechanical innovations (in Fig. 10 an elliptical profile by inclining the cutting head), it was not possible to achieve any significant improvement in economic performance.

Depreciation

The investment for the major equipment necessary for drill–blast excavation at a single face is, based on recent experience, approximately DM 5 000 000. Expenditure on a fully mechanical shield machine of corresponding diameter capability, complete with related mucking-out equipment, would be approximately DM 40 000 000, according to manufacturers' quotations. To write off the full capital value economically would require at least 20 km of operation. On a drill–blast basis, however, it is possible to obtain eight sets of equipment for the same outlay. This confers greater flexibility of shape variation, facilitates simultaneous working at eight locations and implies a significant residual equipment value at the end of the contract.

Financing

Since the payback period for such a machine would be between four and five years, the manufacturer, the contractor or the

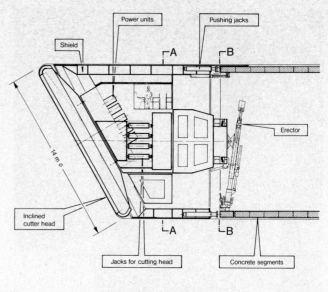

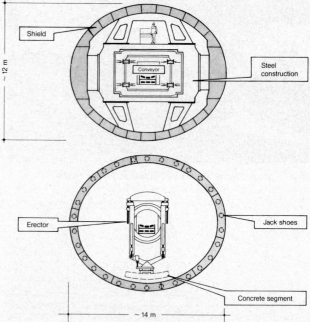

Fig. 10   TBM proposal by Mannesmann–Demag: (*a*) longitudinal section and (*b*) cross-sections

employer must provide advance finance for the machine: such financing is complex from the contractual and legal points of view and, of course, costs extra.

Failure risk

A fully mechanical TBM with its ancillary equipment is sophisticated and has a necessarily specialized range of application. It is therefore subject to the risk of failure if the rock conditions change unexpectedly. By contrast, it is easier to make alternative arrangements if problems occur with conventional driving methods. This argument may well have been one of the reasons for the client's preference for drill–blast techniques.

There are, of course, good reasons in favour of the use of a large full-face TBM – for example, reduced labour costs and greater accuracy of profile. These advantages, however, were either not economically justifiable or the related technical aspects could not be evaluated sufficiently in the short tender period that was available. The longest of all the new tunnels will be the Landrücken tunnel. The same mountain had to be penetrated by a double-track tunnel for the old route in 1910. Bilfinger + Berger were the contractors for this Distelrasen

Fig. 11   Distelrasen tunnel shield (Schlüchtern, 1910)

tunnel (Fig. 11). Safety considerations led those responsible to opt for a shield.

Use of non full-face mechanical driving

A fully mechanized shield machine is to be used to construct the pilot gallery in the 7-km Freudenstein tunnel. The pilot gallery is required in this case for the Mannheim–Stuttgart route in the gypsum Keuper Series to pretreat the transition areas between gypsum and anhydrite in such a way that water ingress into the unleached rock will be provoked neither during construction nor ultimately (Fig. 7). Area by area, the pilot gallery simultaneously serves a pre-drainage function and, in subsequent profile extensions, serves the purpose of test-dimensioning for a lining that will be able to cope with otherwise unpredictable swelling pressures when in use. A full-section machine is to be used in a blade shield, which is able, if necessary, to allow for swelling pressures by mechanically reducing its diameter. Bilfinger + Berger have already acquired valuable experience with a similarly designed Robbins machine in the construction of the Stillwater tunnel in Utah, U.S.A. (Fig. 12). On the Freudenstein pilot gallery the lining is of extruded concrete. This design simplifies profile extensions and the demolition of the pilot tunnel lining during main tunnel construction. In addition, this form of construction means that the pilot tunnel can be made waterproof or it can be used section by section as a drainage conduit. A compressed-air

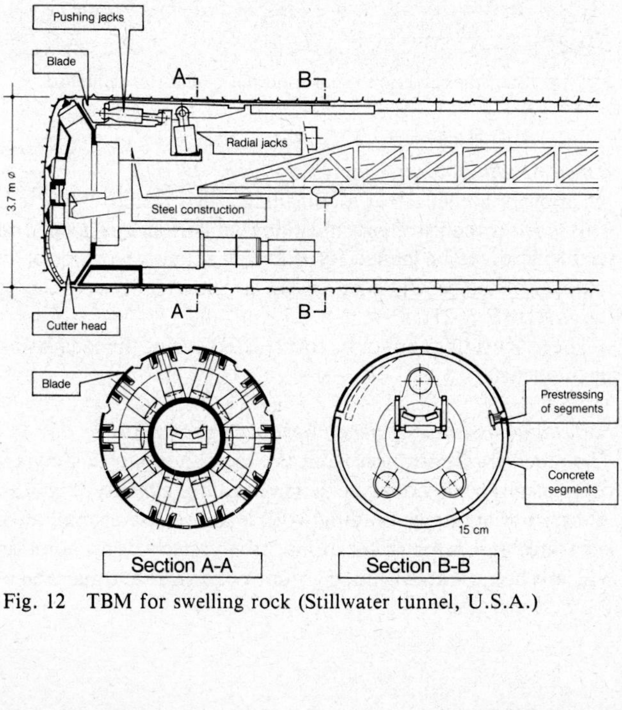

station and airlocks will be installed, in addition to a deep well-point system, to permit careful control of the transition zones without incurring residual water problems.

Roadheaders were used only rarely in the construction of the new routes. Their performance is lower than that of drill-blast methods in harder rock formations and they also create more serious dust problems. One roadheader that was being used in softer strata to construct an access adit had to be withdrawn after a short driven section because its tracks sank into the soft bed owing to the weight of the machine. In addition, the fact that excavation and support work could not be carried out simultaneously without mutual hindrance in the narrow adit decreased performance greatly.

Another roadheader has been used successfully in conjunction with drill–blast techniques. A reduced cross-section, produced initially by drill–blast methods, was then enlarged to the required profile by use of the roadheader (Fig. 13).

Fig. 13   View of roadheader (railway tunnel, Stuttgart)

Standard method

Generally, the tunnels of the new routes to be constructed are being driven with drill–blast methods on the basis of the principles of the New Austrian Tunnelling Method and supported with reinforced shotcrete, steel ribs and rockbolts. Owing to the large dimensions, even in fully stable rock, the face is generally worked in sequential excavation operations. The cross-section height of approximately 12 m is subdivided into top and bench headings followed by invert excavation (Figs. 14 and 15).

Fig. 12   TBM for swelling rock (Stillwater tunnel, U.S.A.)

Fig. 14   Drill jumbo at tunnel face

139

Fig. 15   Drill jumbo for bench excavation

The construction contracts schedule the use of excavation method classifications for payment of construction work. These definitions of rock classes recognize the working procedure, the subdivision of the cross-section, the round length and the type and time of use of support measures.

The inner lining is either a membrane seal with a largely non-reinforced concrete shell or a reinforced waterproof concrete shell (Fig. 16).

The new tunnel construction developments thus include no dramatic overall changes in technique – rather, the innovations are numerous improvements of detail, some of which are described below.

Fig. 16   Travelling formwork for concrete lining

Detailed developments

Sequences for staged excavation
To drive the tunnel into loose material the contract documents foresaw a variety of possible excavation subdivisions, such as preceding side wall drifts or sectionalized top heading, in addition to the simple subdivision into top, bench and invert excavation. In the past contractors were able to formulate modified proposals to optimize their economic performance. Such variations include shotcrete wall plates and rockbolts (Fig. 17) in place of a temporary invert in the top heading or installing a longitudinal foot block beneath the roof ribs. This speeds up the installation of the roof ribs and permits a reduction to be made in the number of lower side wall ribs (Fig. 18).

The efficiency and economy of the whole driving operation is heavily dependent on the sequence of working for top and bench headings. Three examples of such sequences are given below for different ground conditions.

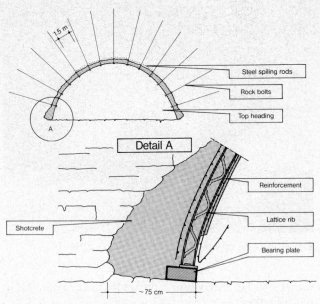

Fig. 17   Example of increased temporary support – top heading

Standard solutions for changing rock conditions
Half-bench heading simultaneous with top heading, with use of a side ramp for the transport of excavated muck from the top heading: subsequent half-width excavation and concreting of the invert is carried out immediately or later, depending on the quality of the rocks (Figs. 19 and 20).

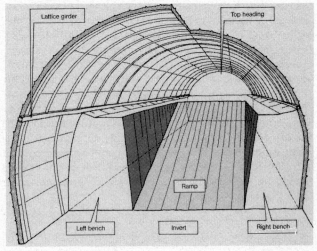

Fig. 18   Staged excavation – unsupported bench slot sequence

Bench heading in loose material
An appropriate length of top heading is driven and supported. This work is then stopped and side wall slots are excavated to enable access to be gained for side wall support work prior to removal of the central core and excavation and concreting of the invert (Fig. 21).

The top heading cannot be constructed during the excavation of the bench.

Simultaneous top and bench heading in solid rock
The muck transportation from the top heading is made via a centre ramp while both side bench headings advance (Fig. 18). At appropriate times heading work is halted and a small team excavates and reforms the ramp progressively. This solution will only be permitted in good ground conditions and guarantees the best progress.

140

Fig. 19   One-sided bench excavation

Fig. 20   One-sided bed plate placing

Drilling

Twin-boom drill jumbos with an additional service platform are normally used. Even if the cross-sectional area justifies the use of four drilling booms, two twin-boom jumbos are preferred instead of a four-boom rig. All drilling equipment

Fig. 21   Drilling for rockbolts in side wall slot

operates electrohydraulically. Equipment produced by Tamrock, SIG and Atlas Copco (Fig. 21) leads the market, technical and price differences being slight.

Use of explosives

Even though approximately 10 000 t of explosives will ultimately have been used for the construction of the new routes, the explosive materials themselves have not, to date, been modified. The most frequently used explosives are Ammongelit 3 in the form of cartridges and Dynacord 100 explosive cord in the perimeter holes in conjunction with millisecond delayed electric caps. Only approximate blasting schematics are provided, the details being defined by the relevant blasting foreman regarding rock quality and profile.

Profile monitoring

In the use of drill–blast methods conformity to profile is crucial to efficiency and economy. A long depth of round can generate rapid progress, but at the expense of excessive overbreak. Backfilling overbreak cavities with concrete is very expensive! It is even more expensive, however, to have to go back to remove material belatedly and it is better to remove too much 'to be on the safe side' than to resort to expensive trimming. Conventional profile measurements are made as infrequently as possible since they are time-consuming, necessitate interruptions in driving operations and, hence, cost more.

For these reasons Bilfinger + Berger made a study of rapid profile monitoring techniques on the basis of the complete equipment and methods then available. This study included tests of all equipment and methods for rapid profile monitoring available on the market and the equipment and methods were evaluated. Subsequently, the company decided to order a system that was developed by Professor Stolitzka in Vienna as an equipment prototype and to use it parallel with conventional monitoring methods in the construction of the 5.5-km long Mühlberg tunnel. In conjunction with Professor Stolitzka the system was further developed on site to the series production stage.

Fig. 22   Profile measurement instrument

The system consists of an instrument, mounted on the tunnel floor, that is capable of the rapid measurement by laser of the distances from the instrument to predetermined grid points on the tunnel surface. An inbuilt computer is then programmed to record and compare in printout form the relationship between the tunnel profile as cut and as required.

141

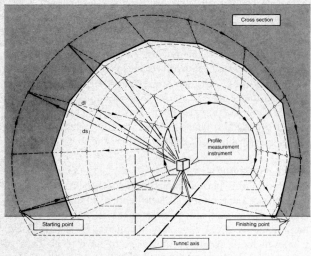

Fig. 23   Reference points for profile monitoring

The system operates automatically. In addition to the 'software' that needs to be created for each construction task, it comprises equipment components for measurement, marking, calculation and result output. The computing devices, as well as the power supply system, are protected against shock in a monitoring vehicle (Fig. 22).

The measuring equipment is assembled in the supported section close to the newly cut face. It determines its own location via a reflector, which is installed up to 300 m behind it. The unit then records the tunnel wall surface at points spaced as required via a motor-driven swivelling head with the aid of a laser radar distance meter and simultaneous automatic angular recording. The data entered via a hand terminal and the

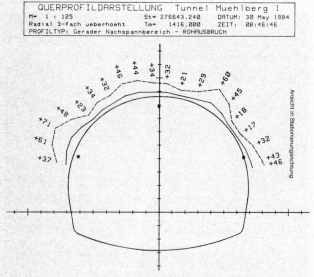

Fig. 24   Direct print-out of theoretical and actual profile

pre-recorded data are processed by the control and evaluation computer. Measured cross-sections are then displayed by graphical and digital comparison between the required and actual values via a monitor and the results can then be plotted and filed (Fig. 24).

The unit is able to record up to 30 points per minute automatically and, in addition to profile monitoring, is also suitable for recording the data of completed tunnels, for measurement subsequent to payment and for convergence measurements. The device is capable of working to an accuracy of 1 cm.

Use of shotcrete

The production and use of shotcrete are subject to influences that are far more difficult to monitor than those which arise with conventional vibrated concrete in formwork. The quality of the final product was frequently found to be unsatisfactory when the traditional dry spraying method was employed – primarily because the addition of water and setting accelerators is difficult to monitor. An associated result is high rebound and, hence, high material costs. Not least, the great quantities of dust produced and the rebounding coarse grains pose health risks during work for the nozzle operator. All three factors – quality, cost and risk – became even more important with the great quantities involved in those railway tunnels and because more items of equipment needed to be used simultaneously. For these reasons, various contractors and machine manufacturers have, during the last few years, made strenuous efforts to develop new methods. Various systems are now ready for competitive production and clear improvements are evident.

Fig. 25   'Spritzbüffel' wet shotcrete equipment by Putzmeister

One development has been to project the wet shotcrete in a dense stream (Fig. 25). Concrete pumps manufactured by Putzmeister or Schwing are used for this process.

The concrete, pumped in a dense stream, is accelerated at the spray nozzle by compressed air. The units are mounted in a compact form on carrier devices with single or multiple spray booms.

Working conditions and economy are considerably better than is the case with conventional dry shotcrete methods. As regards concrete quality, however, other risks apply since the method requires the addition of large quantities of waterglass. Even though Bilfinger + Berger use the wet shotcrete method, the company has, nevertheless, vigorously promoted the development of an alternative system – in conjunction with the supplier, Intradym.

For the dual mixed shotcrete method (Fig. 26) the fine-grained material of the aggregate is mixed together with cement and water outside the tunnel to produce mortar and is then transported by concrete agitators to a carrier unit with a Mohno pump and spray booms. The coarse aggregate is transported separately into the tunnel, deposited in a container and discharged by a screw conveyor to a conventional dry shotcrete

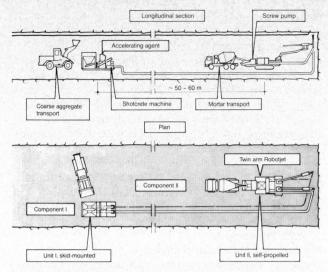

Fig. 26   Dual mixed shotcrete method, B + B/Intradym

Fig. 27   Field tests for dual mixed shotcrete method: (*a*) (*top*) Mühlberg tunnel I (Gemünden) and (*b*) Richthof tunnel (Fulda)

machine. The accelerating agent is added to the dry coarse aggregate. Both components are routed together near to the nozzle, mixed by the air–aggregate stream and applied as shotcrete. The method has been proved on the basis of large-scale site tests (Fig. 27) to be economical, clean and more susceptible to efficient and accurate quality control. Use of this method is currently planned for the construction of the 7.5-km long Mündener tunnel.

Steel ribs

The popularity of lattice girders has increased continually as compared with conventional ribs. With a similar section

Fig. 28   Installation of lattice girders

modulus they are easier to handle and shotcrete embedment can be achieved more completely and securely (Fig. 28).

Loading and mucking equipment

Since the large cross-sections permit easy two-way traffic, loading and mucking out are done with conventional wheeled

Fig. 29   Mucking out, top heading

equipment that complies with German safety regulations relating to underground use (Fig. 29).

Lining concrete

In the production of the inner lining of waterproof concrete new precedents were set by German standards, since no such structures of such large dimensions had previously been constructed – nor had such structures been conceived in conjunction with the relatively irregular profiles that result from drill–blast methods (Fig. 30). Experience gained during the manufacture of such inner linings is currently being documented for future publication.

Fig. 30 Irregularly shaped excavation line in New Red Sandstone, Einmalberg tunnel (Gemünden)

Appendix

Addresses of responsible authorities
Control of all new railway routes: Bahnbauzentrale–Hauptverwaltung der Deutschen Bundesbahn, Friedrich-Ebert-Anlage 43–45, 6000 Frankfurt (Main)
For the three sections of the route Hannover–Würzburg
Deutsche Bundesbahn, Bundesbahndirektion Hannover, Projektgruppe H/W Nord der Bahnbauzentrale, Joachimstraße 4–5, 3000 Hannover 1
Deutsche Bundesbahn, Bundesbahndirektion Frankfurt (Main), Projektgruppe H/W Mitte der Bahnbauzentrale, Baseler Straße 27, 6000 Frankfurt (Main)
Deutsche Bundesbahn, Bundesbahndirektion Nürnberg, Projektgruppe H/W Süd der Bahnbauzentrale, Stromerstraße 12, 8500 Nürnberg 70
For the route Mannheim–Stuttgart
Deutsche Bundesbahn, Bundesbahndirektion Karlsruhe, Projectgruppe M/S der Bahnbauzentrale, Bahnhofstraße 5, 7500 Karlsruhe 1

Concluding remarks

In addition to the extension of existing lines, 426 km of new lines is being constructed in the 1980s for high-speed trains for the German Federal Railway. This necessitates driving 74 tunnels with an overall length of 146 km. Although no spectacular large-scale changes have been made to established practice, tried and tested items of equipment in conjunction with numerous detailed innovations are helping to complete the construction project on time at favourable cost and in accordance with qualitative requirements. The German construction companies and the representatives of the German Federal Railway expect that this undisputed success will be conducive to speeding up Government decisions to continue the planned programme of construction.

References
1. Wagner H. Erfahrungen mit Gebirgssicherungsmaßnahmen am Beispiel des Tunnels Altengronauer Forst. *Tiefbau-BG*, no. 5 1983, 351–72.
2. Linkerhägner W. and Blind W. Die Realisierung der Neubaustrecken der Deutschen Bundesbahn. *ETR–Eisenbahntechnische Rundschau*, **33**, no. 7/8 1984, 575–84.
3. Naumann G. Halbzeit beim Bau des Landrückentunnels. *Bundesbahn*, **60**, no. 10 1984, 747–50.
4. Maak H. Bauaufgaben an den Neubaustrecken der Deutschen Bundesbahn. Offprint of *Mayreder Zeitschrift*, **27**, June 1982, 2–7.
5. Engels W. and Thöne K. H. Begleitende Planung von Fachbehörden bei der Neubaustreckenrealisierung. *Bundesbahn*, **57**, no. 10 1981, 795–9.
6. Schrewe F. and Blütling H.-H. Erkundungsmaßnahmen für die Tunnelneubaustrecke Hannover–Würzburg zwischen Hannover und Kassel. *Bundesbahn*, **59**, no. 10 1983, 645–54.
7. John M. and Pöttler R. Entwurf und Standsicherheitsbetrachtungen für die Eisenbahntunnel der Neubaustrecke Hannover–Würzburg. *Felsbau*, **2**, no. 2 1984, 70–7.
8. Harpf R. and Gais W. H. Vortrieb im Lockermaterial und im aufgelockerten Material. *Felsbau*, **1**, no. 1/2 1983, 1.

Discussion

Dr. J-F. Raffoux* said that, for economic reasons, Distelmeier and Semprich had decided to use conventional drilling and blasting techniques to drive the German Federal Railway tunnels rather than to use tunnelling machines. He would welcome further comment on that decision and also on whether the authors thought that the drilling and blasting method could still be improved. He would like to know the operations that were thought to be on the 'critical path' of the method and those on which R and D should be concentrated.

G. C. Burgess† noted the extensive unlined underground drill and blast activity in India and his own interest in the blasting products that were used and the techniques that were adopted. Details on the following aspects would be welcomed: (*a*) types of explosives used, (*b*) the use of pre- or post-splitting or a smooth wall blasting method (with information on system and products), (*c*) whether future large-scale projects were planned and (*d*) whether tamping was used (type of product and its effectiveness).

Turning to the paper by Distelmeier and Semprich, he said that he was not familiar with Ammongelit 3 explosive cartridges and would like to know if any type of smooth wall blasting was carried out and what was used.

South African contractors often complained about blasting cycle times and, in proportion to the number of people at the face, could not meet the efficiency of European contractors. Details of the cycle times, the number of personnel involved and the methods that were used to achieve such good turn-around times would be appreciated.

If German and neighbouring (Austrian, Swiss) contractors used tamping materials, details of the type and why they were chosen, together with more information on the profile monitoring equipment developed by Professor Stolitzka, would be welcomed.

Dr. M. Gysel‡ said that in the Chibro cavern stabilization of the vertical side walls had been achieved by prestressed anchors fixed in separate galleries that ran parallel to the axis of the cavern. Apparently, the prestressed tendons did have a permanent function over the lifetime of the power plant. He asked if there were Indian regulations or standards on the use of permanent prestressed anchors with respect to the long-term behaviour (including corrosion protection) that had to be fulfilled by the design and the anchor product used. In addition, it would be interesting to know whether a technical/economical comparison between the anchor solution that had been selected and the alternative solution of curved side walls and a complete concrete lining had been made.

M. C. Knights§ said that Distelmeier and Semprich referred to pilot tunnels as part of the investigative work: more details of those (sizes, excavation methods, tests) would be welcomed, as would the authors' comment on whether the results from the trial tunnels reflected the conditions when the main tunnel was driven.

Authors' replies

Dr. R. L. Chauhan and R. S. Chauhan In reply to G. C. Burgess, for the most part we use special gelatin of 60% and 80% strength designations. To ensure the smooth profile of the

wall surface we use both pre-splitting and smooth blasting techniques according to the availability of suitable drilling equipment.

For smooth blasting drill-holes of 40- to 46-mm diameter, spaced 200–400 mm apart, are drilled in a line for wall blasting and on the arch periphery for the roof arch of the cavern. These holes are lightly loaded with explosive and adequate stemming in between the explosive cartridges is carried out. The charge is thoroughly tamped and blasting is done with the last delay detonators provided in these holes.

In pre-splitting drill-holes of 60- to 75-mm diameter are drilled 400–500 mm apart. Alternate holes are lightly loaded with explosive (special gelatin of 40–60% strength, no stemming). Zero delay is used in these holes. The order of firing for the rest of the holes is as normal.

In smooth blasting and pre-splitting it is only after a few trials that the next combination of drill-hole spacing and quantity of explosive used is determined.

Most of the projects in the Himalayan region will have underground power houses: two such projects are to be executed shortly – Nathpa Jhakri (1020 MW) (power house cavern, 140 m × 25 m × 44 m; transformer hall cavern, 128 m × 18 m × 16 m) and Chamera II (273 MW) (power house cavern, 85 m × 25 m × 42 m; transformer hall cavern, 75 m × 17 m × 21 m).

Tamping is done by a wooden stick. The explosive charge is laid first, clay cartridges filling the holes and being tamped with the stick.

As Dr. M. Gysel notes, in the Chibro caverns stabilization of the vertical side walls has been achieved by prestressed anchors. Each of the prestressed tendons consists of 16 7-mm diameter high-tensile steel wires placed within a watertight sheath. Holes 75 mm in diameter were first drilled, washed and grouted at a pressure of 4 kg/cm^2 to consolidate the rock. After pre-grouting, the holes were washed again and the sheathed cables were put into position. Steel anchors were provided at the two ends supported on shotcrete pads 750 mm × 750 mm × 75 mm thick and the cables were tensioned and anchored, element by element, after which the holes were grouted for their entire length. The tendons have a permanent nature, as for prestressed concrete. The sheaths are watertight, special care being taken for tightness at the joints. This arrangement will ensure protection against corrosion. Moreover, the quality of wires used is such that these are not susceptible to stress corrosion. The relevant Indian Standards are *Code of practice for prestressed concrete* (IS: 1343) and *Specification for plain and hard drawn steel wire for prestressed concrete* (IS: 1785, pts I and II).

As the Chibro power house was completed in 1975 it is not possible to provide the technical/economic comparison between the prestressing arrangement and the alternative solution of curved side walls.

H. Distelmeier and Dr. S. Semprich The main reasons that led to the decision in favour of conventional drilling and blasting techniques, mentioned by Dr. J-F. Raffoux, were referred to in the section *Construction methods*. With this method the drilling work for the blast-holes and applying the shotcrete lay on the critical path.

In reply to G. C. Burgess, tamping is used for all drilling and blasting operations when driving tunnels. The spacing between the cap holes is between 40 and 60 cm. The total number of boreholes for excavating the roof section with an excavation cross-section of approximately 55 m^2 is some 100. Conventionally, the wedge-cut method is used.

In the cup area a Dynacord fuse with 100 g of explosive per metre run is used, and in the centre area Ammongelit 3 in cartridge form is used. Ammongelit 3 is a gelatinous ammonium nitrate explosive that can be used without restriction even in wet

*CERCHAR, Verneuil en Halatte, France.
†F. Dupré (SA) (Pty), Ltd., Bryanston, South Africa.
‡Motor-Columbus Consulting Engineers, Inc., Baden, Switzerland.
§W. S. Atkins and Partners, Epsom, Surrey, England.

boreholes. Today, Ammongelites are the standard explosives for numerous blasting applications – driving tunnels, in quarries and opencast mining.

In the large majority of tunnels the driving teams work round the clock. A driving team comprises, basically, 10–13 miners and the team leader. One or two rounds are achieved per shift, depending on the rock in question and the necessary safety and support work.

The scope of and time taken for the individual operations for a round depend on the relevant sub-stratum conditions and the time taken can only be specified in relation to individual cases.

In general, no special requirements are made as regards tamping the boreholes. Tamping is carried out with wet rock cuttings, which provide a high degree of resistance to the blasting gases owing to the significant mutual friction of the grains and the crystals and friction with respect to the borehole walls.

Professor G. Stolitzka will present a detailed description of this method at the STUVA Conference '85 (Hannover, 25–28 November, 1985). The text will appear in the 'Forschung und Praxis' series of books, published by STUVA.

In reply to M. C. Knights, several trial tunnels were excavated for the tunnelling work for the new Hannover–Würzburg and Mannheim–Stuttgart routes. The trial driving work for the Dietershan, Rollenberg and Freudenstein tunnels is described in greater detail below.

Trial tunnel Dietershan

A 600-m trial tunnel was driven into the New Red Sandstone in connexion with the 7.3-km Dietershan tunnel for the new route Hannover–Würzburg. The horseshoe-shaped cross-section of the trial tunnel (dimensions, width/height approximately 5 m/ 4.5 m) was expanded over an overall length of some 100 m to the size of the roof cross-section for the planned tunnel. Measurements and tests conducted in the sections (levelling, convergences, extensometers, inclinometer, concrete pressure cells, anchoring pressure cells, triaxial tests on large borehole samples, plate-loading tests and anchoring tensile tests) permitted both the excavation method and the supporting and lining measures to be optimized for the final tunnel structure, which is at the present time under construction.

Trial tunnel Rollenberg

Early in 1984 an approximately 1500-m trial tunnel with a horseshoe-shaped cross-section and with a width and height of 3.5 m was completed for the Rollenberg tunnel of the new route Mannheim–Stuttgart. In addition, in two sections, each 100 m long, the tunnel was extended to the planned tunnel profile with width/height dimensions of approximately 14 m/12 m. The trial tunnel was driven through the various strata of the leached gypsum Keuper Series.

The trial tunnel permitted a continuous investigation of the rock characteristics, including the important geohydrological conditions. Deformation and tension measurements in the expanded sections (by use of pressure cells) permitted economical dimensioning of the supporting elements and the lining of the final tunnel structure. In this respect the required transition between gradients of the arched floor was of importance.

Trial tunnel Freudenstein

Currently, a pilot tunnel 1500 m long is under construction for the ~7-km Freudenstein tunnel of the new route Mannheim–Stuttgart. This tunnel is being driven by a tunnel-boring machine (diameter, 5.2 m). As a supplement to the information that has already been provided, explained below is the trial programme for assessment of the effects of swelling of anhydrite (see Fig. 7, p. 137) as regards economical and safe dimensioning of the final tunnel lining.

Circular and mouth section shaped cross-sections with various degrees of transition between floor gradients were driven in individual extended sections with widths of 10 m and an overall length of several hundred metres. In addition, lining thicknesses between 40 and 80 cm and anchoring arrangements were varied for trial purposes in these sections. Swelling of the anhydrite is intentionally initiated by artificial irrigation of the anhydrite that surrounds the cavities. The water is fed in via boreholes. The stress to which the concrete facing and the surrounding sub-stratum are exposed is determined with the aid of measuring facilities, such as levelling points, convergence measuring sections, multiple extensometers, concrete pressure cells, anchoring pressure cells, geophones and check boreholes.

Session 6 – Major projects

Co-Chairmen: S. Babendererde and O. M. Bevan

Submarine tunnelling in poor rock

Anders Carlsson
Swedish State Power Board and Royal Institute of Technology, Stockholm, Sweden
Tommy Olsson
Uppsala Geosystem AB, Uppsala, Sweden
Håkan Stille
Royal Institute of Technology, Stockholm, Sweden

Synopsis
The geological prerequisites, site investigations, tunnelling and support works for four sub-aqueous rock tunnels are described. The tunnels are located within an area of about 2 km² and all pass through a 200-m wide regional zone of tectonic disturbance. Driving of the tunnels through the zone has now been completed and the experience of the actual conditions that was acquired during tunnelling illustrates the unreliability of all forecasts of rock conditions and of the need to adopt the 'design as you go' method. The driving experience also showed, however, that well-planned site investigations and the feedback of experience contribute greatly to realistic solutions of the problems that are encountered during construction.

The Forsmark power station is situated on the east coast of Sweden some 130 km north of Stockholm. It is a nuclear power station with three units, two of which are in operation; the third unit is under construction. The cooling water from the units is discharged through two sub-aqueous rock tunnels – one for units 1 and 2 and one for unit 3. The tunnels run under the sea, the Baltic (Fig. 1), for most of their length.

Work has now been started on the world's first reactor waste repository (referred to here as SFR) below the sea-bed offshore from the Forsmark power station (Fig. 1). The two parallel access tunnels of the repository are now being excavated.

Hence, four sub-aqueous rock tunnels have been excavated in one and the same area, all the tunnels having intersected a regional zone of tectonic disturbance called the Singö fault. The object of this paper is to describe the geological prerequisites, tunnelling and support work for the tunnels, with particular reference to the driving through the Singö fault.

Site investigations

A comprehensive site investigation programme was carried out that included both regional and detailed investigations. The regional investigations were started with a review of earlier geological studies of the area, these studies then being supplemented by a geological survey to elucidate the regional stratigraphy and the local rock distribution and occurrences of zones of weakness. Detailed studies were then instituted, with a network of seismic profiles, after which the zones of weakness indicated by the regional and seismic investigations were examined closely by means of rock drilling. The seismic investigations were then intensified, further networks of seismic profiles being made, and the intensity of the rock drilling was increased. The seismic profiling and the core drilling were performed from the ice-covered sea and from drilling platforms. Nine diamond drill holes, of a total length of 860 m, were sunk for the discharge tunnel for units 1 and 2, and 18 were sunk for the unit 3 tunnel, for which the total depth drilled exceeded 2500 m. Nine drill-holes were sunk along the line of the SFR tunnel. In addition to standard core logging routines, water injection tests were performed in the drill-holes, and falling head tests were also carried out in the drill-holes for the SFR tunnel. The results from the different site investigation phases have been presented in a number of reports, including those by Larsson and Moberg[1] and Hagconsult.[2]

The tunnelling work has been followed continuously by engineering geology surveying that consisted of investigations of the structural geology, fractures, water inflows, etc. The results of the geological follow-up have already been presented.[3-6] Pilot-hole drilling was also employed in the tunnel for unit 3 (a total of 1300 m of percussion drilling and about 300 m of coring). These holes were used to locate sections of inferior rock ahead of the face and to assess the need for grouting. In the driving of the SFR tunnels continuous pilot-hole drilling was performed, three 20-m holes being sunk at each drilling point. In addition, two diamond drill holes, 100 and 120 m long, were drilled horizontally from the tunnel face. The location of DS101 is shown in Fig. 2.

Inspections of the tunnels for assessment of the permanent support required were made in step with driving, and observations were noted in records that specified the type and extent of support in each area. The examinations were made by an engineering geologist and a designer and countersigned by the work supervisor responsible for the relevant section of tunnel.

Geology

Schistose, Svecocarelian intrusive rocks, the so-called gneiss granites, as well as mica gneisses and mica schists (here termed paragneiss), make up the main part of the rocks in the Forsmark tunnels. The rock that is traditionally called gneiss granite is, from the engineering-geological point of view, an orthogneiss with rather well-defined schistosity and anisotropy. Dykes of amphibolitic composition in the gneiss granite, as well as dykes and basic layers in the paragneiss, occur quite frequently, as do dykes and small massifs of pegmatite.

The Forsmark power station is situated between two major regional fracture zones, of which the northernmost, the Singö fault, is intersected by the tunnels (cf. Fig. 1). The width of the zone, approximately 200 m, consists of mylonitic rocks and breccias. This brecciated gneiss granite contains numerous

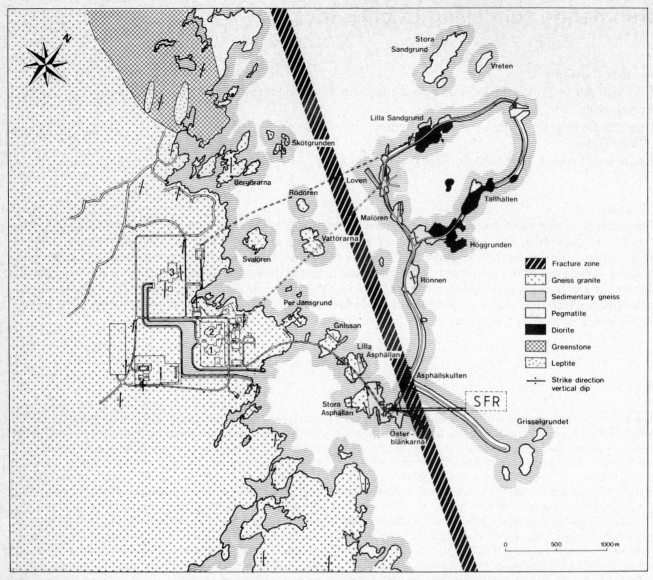

Fig. 1 Sketch map of geology in Forsmark construction area showing locations of power plant discharge tunnels and reactor waste repository (SFR) access tunnels. Fracture zone intersected by tunnels is called the Singö fault

clay-filled fractures and the rock is locally heavily clay-mineralized and weathered. On the other hand, from a rock construction point of view, most of the Singö fault may be described as good rock.

Singö fault in tunnel for units 1 and 2

In the discharge tunnel from units 1 and 2 the width of the Singö fault is estimated to be about 200 m. The rock shows various phases of tectonization, with intermediate calcite and quartz dissemination of the crushed rock. The frequency of open fractures within the brecciated zone increases greatly along a 50-m section, and most are filled with clay, the material being mainly illite and quartz, and with a maximum fracture width of 500 mm.

The tunnel also intersects another zone of weakness. In all, about 60% of the water leakage into the tunnel comes from these zones, the total length of which along the line of the tunnel is approximately 450 m. These properties give a rate of leakage of about 4 l/min per metre of tunnel (l/m m^{-1}) for the zones of weakness, which may be compared with a rate of leakage in the rest of the tunnel of only 0.8 l/m m^{-1}. Owing to its length, the Singö fault is the most productive of the four tectonic zones and about 25% of the total flow into the tunnel has its origin here. Within the Singö fault, the leakage is very variable: half of the zone is dry, the flow being concentrated in the other half.

Part of Singö fault in unit 3 tunnel

About 350 m to the west the Singö fault was penetrated a second time by the unit 3 discharge tunnel. The width of the zone at this point is about the same as in the tunnel for units 1 and 2, i.e. 200 m. The zone may be divided into two main parts. Within a 175-m long section of the zone the rock is a red, fine-grained porphyritic or pyroclastic leptite with intrusions of folded phyllite, as well as amphibolites and pegmatites. Fracture frequency is about five fractures per metre. The remaining part of the zone reveals a heavily fractured, brecciated and clay-mineralized leptite. The rock mass may be characterized as fragments of good rock separated by layers of weathered, unconsolidated rock. In one 15-m section the rock has, to a great extent, been mineralized into clay. Analyses of the clay were made on nine samples from this section and, as in the remainder of the tunnel and in the unit 3 tunnel, no swelling clays were found. The rate of water leakage was very moderate and was estimated to be about 1 l/m m^{-1}.

Singö fault in SFR tunnels

About 1500 m to the east the two access tunnels to the nuclear waste repository cross the Singö fault, which is about 120 m wide here. The geology of this zone is similar to that of the tunnels mentioned above. One part may be characterized as

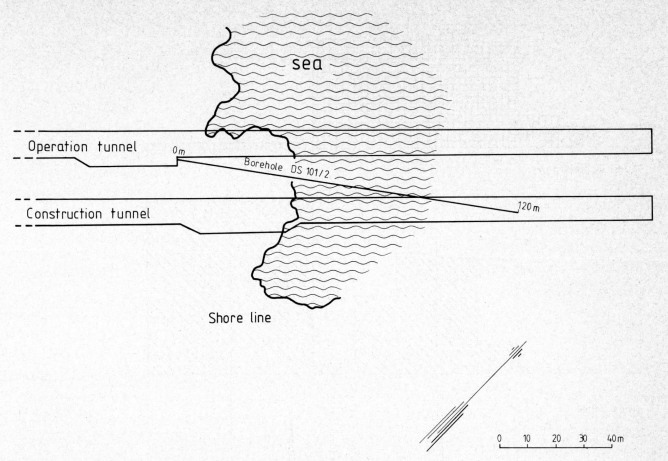

Fig. 2   Location of pilot diamond drill hole DS101 in operational SFR tunnel

having an irregularly blocky rock mass with a number of steeply dipping clay-filled fractures. The width of the fracture filling varies between 10 and 150 mm. Another part of the Singö fault shows a slaty rock structure. Locally, the rock is heavily fractured and clay-mineralized.

The part of the Singö fault that is encountered in the SFR tunnels reveals a similar hydrogeological pattern to that in the discharge tunnels of the Forsmark units (shown in Fig. 3). The hydraulic properties vary considerably across the zone, heavily fractured, water-bearing zones being interfoliated with blocks of intact and dry rock. Hence, the variation in hydraulic properties is most pronounced across the Singö fault, whereas the pattern is more similar along it. Only minor differences in the hydraulic properties have been recorded in the four tunnels. It seems reasonable to assume that the Singö fault is composed of elongated blocks of intact rock embedded in a crushed, fractured and altered rock matrix.

The hydraulic testing performed in the investigation holes and in the four tunnels gave a hydraulic conductivity of about $1-2 \times 10^{-6}$ m/s for the Singö fault as a hydraulic unit. The unit value is composed of blocks with very low conductivity ($< 10^{-10}$ m/s) and of conductive portions.

Tunnels, tunnelling and equipment

The tunnel for units 1 and 2 has a total length of 2300 m; its cross-sectional area is 80 m², with a top heading of 50 m² and a bench of 30 m². The tunnel is about 75 m below sea-level, the rock cover being approximately 55–60 m.

Tunnelling was started simultaneously on two fronts – at an opening onshore at a surge basin and at an opening on Loven Island (Fig. 1). The top heading was driven with Avelin–Barford trucks equipped with six Tampella RP 625 booms. The rigs were also provided with charging cradles. In good rock the average rate of driving per round was about 3.5 m.

The tunnel for unit 3, 3000 m long, connects the mainland to Lilla Sandgrund Island, and reaches a maximum depth of about 70 m. The tunnel is 10 m wide and 6.3 m high, giving a theoretical cross-sectional area of 55 m².

Tunnelling was carried out on two faces and was driven to full section on each with a hydraulic Montabert four-boom rig mounted on a Euclid R27 on one face and a pneumatic Atlas Copco four-boom rig equipped with a Tampella L400 on the other face. The rigs were equipped with charging cradles and pilot steering of the booms and drills.

According to Swedish State Power Board practice, full-time working was employed during the tunnelling, part of the workforce being engaged in drilling, charging and blasting and also assisting in mucking out, but additional truck drivers were also available.

Caterpillar 988A machines were used for mucking out and CAT 769B trucks were used for rock haulage. An Atila scaling machine equipped with a Montabert BRH 125 was used for scaling after each round. For rockbolting an Atlas Copco Boltec 540/22 was used that allowed the installation of rockbolts 3.8 m long.

The average rate of driving per round was 4.9 m from the sea end of the tunnel and 3.8 m from the land end. The difference in the rates of driving is related to the use of different drilling machines at the two faces, but the rock structure also had an effect.

In regard to the SFR access tunnel, the length of each of the two parallel access tunnels is about 1000 m and, at an inclination of 1 in 10 from Stora Asphällan Island, they end about 50 m below the sea-bed (Figs. 1 and 4). The cross-sectional areas of the tunnels are 65 and 49 m². The tunnel with the larger cross-section will serve as an operational tunnel for transport of the containers to the repository, and the other will act as a temporary construction tunnel.

Work was started simultaneously on the two tunnels, for

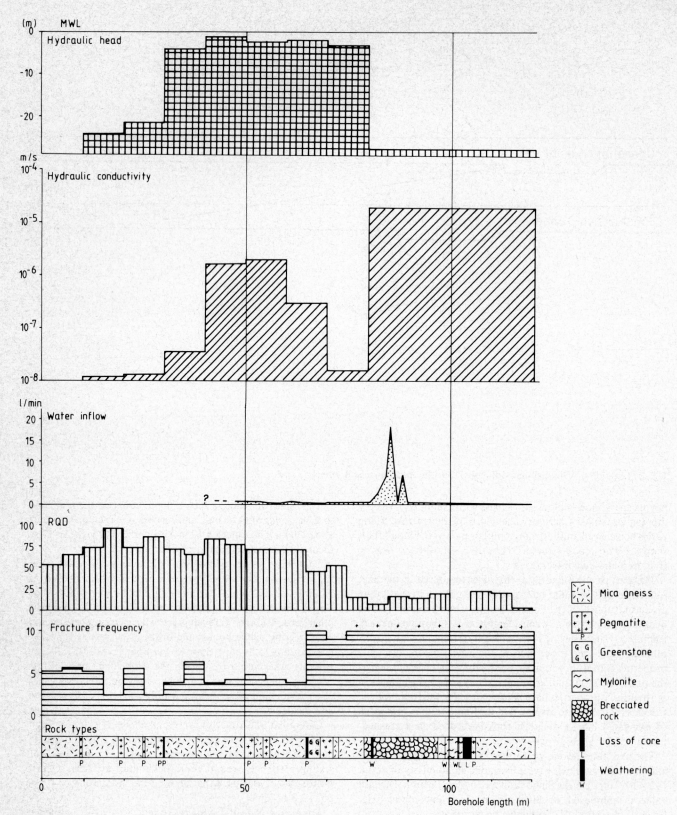

Fig. 3 Hydraulic evaluation of pilot drill-hole DS101, SFR. Evaluation based on reports by Moberg[8] and SGAB[9]

which three rigs are being used (Atlas Copco Promec TH531 drilling jumbos equipped with BUT35 booms fitted with an 18-in 'feed', and COP 1038 HD rigs). Each rig is fitted with a charging cradle on a hydraulic boom (Fig. 5). Two electrically powered Bröyt X-4 excavators are used to muck out rock and eight Engson 666B trucks, two Kiruna K250 trucks and one Kiruna K501 truck for rock haulage. The two scaling machines are a Liebherr 941A and an Åkerman H9M equipped with a Montabert BRH 125.

As for the unit 3 tunnel, an Atlas Copco Boltec 540/22 is being used for the rockbolting operations (Fig. 5). Full-time

working is also being employed in the SFR tunnels.

The average rate of drilling is 4.9 m per round in good rock, the work being performed as contour blasting with an average damage zone tolerance of 0.3 m in the operational transport tunnel and 0.6 m in the construction tunnel.

Tunnel support

Units 1, 2 and 3 tunnels

The temporary support work required for the driving of the tunnels for units 1, 2 and 3 consists of pre-grouting, rockbolting

152

Fig. 4   Aerial photograph of construction site for SFR access tunnels

and shotcreting. On the basis of the observations made from the pilot-hole drilling, pre-grouting with 67 000 kg of cement was carried out in 2500 m of drill-holes in the unit 3 tunnel, 122 000 kg being used in pre-grouting in about 4000 m of drill-holes in the tunnel for units 1 and 2.

Fig. 5   Atlas Copco Promec TH 531 drilling jumbo and Boltec 540/22 in operation in SFR tunnels. Photograph by A. Markgren

The permanent rock support consisted of grouted rockbolts, which were used both systematically and selectively, and unreinforced mesh reinforcement and reinforced shotcrete, normally between 80 and 200 mm thick. In all, shotcrete was applied along 43% of the length of the tunnel for units 1 and 2 (35% for the unit 3 tunnel). Shotcrete arches covered about 4% of the tunnel length in both tunnels. No *in-situ* concrete was used in the tunnel for units 1 and 2, but concrete arches were required along 2% of the total length of the unit 3 tunnel.

There is a significant difference between the two tunnels in regard to support work within the Singö fault. In the tunnel for units 1 and 2 the clay-filled fractures were supported by reinforced shotcrete arches as well as mesh-reinforced arches. The advance of the tunnelling operations was not affected significantly. The rock problem encountered was concentrated on the support of these clearly defined clay-filled fractures.

The driving through the first 100 m of the 200-m wide Singö fault in the unit 3 tunnel proceeded without any major disturbance, and the predicted rate of driving seemed to be achieved. Several clay-filled fractures were passed, but, as in the tunnelling for units 1 and 2, no significant problems occurred. After a

round had been fired at section 2/545, however, there was a tendency for rock to break away above the theoretical roof of the tunnel, so a singly reinforced arch of shotcrete approximately 2 m wide was constructed and singly reinforced shotcrete was also placed back up the tunnel, over a distance of about 10 m from the arch, to protect those working in the area. Several clay-filled fractures were located in this section but, in addition, the rock mass as a whole was to a large extent heavily clay-mineralized. The rock mass ahead of the face was investigated by drilling a 23-m long pilot hole collared just above the bottom of the tunnel. On the basis of the observations made from the pilot hole a decision was taken to blast a new, 4.5-m deep round. The holes for the round were located 1 m inside the theoretical contour of the tunnel section and the size of the charge was reduced.

After the round had been fired the drilled holes could be seen clearly, but the rock started to give way after about 3 h. Rock falls started at the tunnel face, then from the roof and, finally, from the walls. All surfaces were shotcreted, but rockfalls continued and overbreaking started. A decision was then taken to make steel arches. Shotcreting was carried out on three shifts while the arches were being made, and the overbreak was stabilized after a time. Further falls were observed, however, and before the steel arches were placed in position clearing work was carried out and the bottom slab for the arches was cast.

Fig. 6   Rockfalls after erection of steel arch within area of Singö fault in unit 3 tunnel. Photograph by A. Markgren

One 4-m section of steel shuttering was erected and casting could be started, but new falls occurred, of which the largest involved 200 m³ of rock from the face from the left-hand side of the tunnel (Fig. 6). The shuttering was cleaned and further

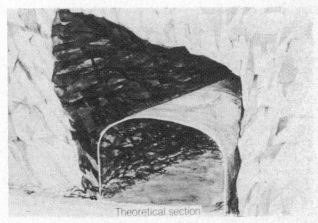

Fig. 7   Maximum overbreak in Singö fault amounted to 7.5 m above theoretical roof of tunnel

153

falls were prevented by filling the overbreak with concrete. At the worst point the overbreak extended 7.5 m above the theoretical line of the tunnel roof (Fig. 7). The final cover of rock at this section amounted to about 58 m.

The area ahead of the steel shutter was filled to the upper edge of the shutter with rock and the ends of the structure to be cast were covered with timber shuttering constructed between the steel shutter and the arch of shotcrete at the tunnel roof. Several concreting pipes were introduced into the area of overbreak and it was filled with concrete. Supporting work was carried out about 7 m ahead of the steel shutter, with reinforced shotcreting of the roof and walls, down to the bottom of the tunnel. After the concreting, excavation was performed to release the shutter and the shotcrete support was continued down to the bottom of the tunnel. The steel shutter was removed and excavation was started in stages, alternating with shotcreting. The concrete inside the section of the shutter was removed by careful blasting. Bolts were fixed in a radial pattern from the face of the tunnel at an upward angle of 45° from the horizontal. Three pilot holes were drilled, of which two were in the sides and one in the middle of the tunnel. The shotcreting unit was in position and a new steel shutter was ready before driving was continued. The next round was carried out with careful blasting with a rate of advance of 2.5 m. After the round had been fired the steel shutter was erected and the unreinforced concrete arch was immediately cast. The remaining driving through the zone was achieved without noteworthy problems.

knowledge of the actual conditions acquired during tunnelling, this assessment may now be regarded as having been too optimistic. When the assessments were made, however, only the engineering geological forecast was available as a basis for decision-making. The forecast was based on the results of the site investigation and the positive experience gained from the driving of the tunnel for units 1 and 2 and, taking this into account, the decision that was taken may be regarded as realistic. At the same time, the driving experience from the unit 3 tunnel shows the inherent uncertainty of all geological forecasting. Well-planned site investigations, however, not only reduce the amount of financial risk taken but contribute significantly to the realistic solution of problems encountered during construction.

SFR tunnels

Experience gained during the tunnelling of the discharge tunnels provided a good basis for the planning of and preparation for the driving of the SFR access tunnels, especially where they pass through the Singö fault, ranging from relatively good rock conditions to inferior, local zones of weakness, and, hence, of experience ranging from relatively moderate support works to solid, in-situ cast structures.

At present, only 500 m of both tunnels has been driven – about one-half the distance to be tunnelled. The width of the Singö fault in this area is about 120 m.

Based on information from the continuous pilot drilling, pre-grouting was carried out from the tunnel face, with a double

Table 1   Supported tunnel length as percentage of total length of Singö fault (200 m)

Type of support	Bolts, ϕ, 25 mm; L, 4 m	Shotcrete Unreinforced T, 100–200 mm	Reinforced T, 80–90 mm	Arches of shotcrete, T, 200 mm	In-situ cast concrete	Grouting
Units 1 and 2 (top heading)	67	65	4	16	—	10
Unit 3	66	36	24	17	17	13

The total amount of rock support work carried out within the Singö fault in each discharge tunnel is shown in Table 1 (the compilation does not claim to be exact, but the figures represent the approximate amount of support; they only represent the rock within the Singö fault (200 m), whereas the previous text refers to total tunnel lengths).

In summary, it may be said that the result of the driving through the Singö fault was good, with the exception of the passage through an isolated local geological defect on a section of the unit 3 tunnel in the Singö fault. This very local zone of poor rock required extensive support work in the form of in-situ cast concrete arches, which significantly hampered the rate of driving.

It is apparent that it is difficult to define clearly and forecast zones of the type described above. The results of site investigations and feedback of experience from the driving of the tunnel for units 1 and 2 formed the basis of the type and method of support and preparation of equipment for the installation of supports in the unit 3 tunnel. The level at which this preparedness is set depends on a number of factors, such as the probability of a certain event occurring and the consequences of such an event for safety, the progress of the work and financial considerations. In the unit 3 tunnel, on the basis of the observations, the probability of an event occurring that would result in long stoppage of tunnelling was judged to be small. Against this background it was decided not to make steel arches as a contingency measure.

Driving of the tunnel has now been completed and, with the

curtain at the crown and a single curtain at the bottom. When the Singö fault was reached the rate of driving per round was also reduced from 4.9 to 3.0 m. The temporary support that was required consisted of systematic bolting and unreinforced shotcreting; reinforced shotcrete arches were installed as quickly as possible after the rounds had been fired, followed by pre-bolting of the next round. The permanent support works comprised systematic bolting in roofs and walls, and the construction of shotcrete arches containing reinforcing bars. In addition, prefabricated steel arches were available for immediate use, but it was never necessary to use them.

The method of driving the access tunnels, with pilot drilling, pre-grouting and pre-bolting of the next round, reduced the rate of driving per round. Mechanical scaling, flushing and fibre shotcreting proved to be successful. No serious rockfalls have occurred along the zone and there have been no stoppages, so it has been possible to drive through the zone according to plan. Table 2 indicates the total amount of support work performed in the two access tunnels. Such work – bolts, shotcrete, arches of shotcrete and pre-grouting – is significantly higher in the SFR tunnels than in the discharge tunnels. This does not necessarily mean, however, that the rock conditions in the SFR tunnels were inferior – on the whole, the rock quality is about the same in the four tunnels. Owing to the natural heterogeneity of the rock mass, there are small, local parts of rock that are of poor quality, such as that which required the massive support in the unit 3 tunnel in the form of in-situ cast concrete arches. To avoid problems such as that which was

Table 2 Supported tunnel length as percentage of total length of Singö fault (120 m)

| Type of support | Bolts ϕ, 25 mm | Shotcrete* | | Reinforced T, 100 mm | Arches of shotcrete, T, 200 mm | Pre-grouting | Pre-bolting |
		Unreinforced T, 30–50 mm	Fibre-reinforced T, 50–80 mm				
Operational tunnel	100	—	68	33	28	30	82
Constructional tunnel	100	10	67	20	26	21	86

*Fibre shotcrete and reinforced shotcrete occasionally occur in combination.

encountered in the unit 3 tunnel unusually large allowances were made for the driving of the SFR tunnels, which proved to be successful. Another factor that is also reflected in the figures is the function of the tunnels. The SFR tunnels are transportation tunnels, whereas the discharge tunnels are water tunnels – a difference that has an effect on the support measures that were taken.

Field measurements in SFR tunnels

Deformation measurements
Deformation measurements were performed to check the stability of the SFR tunnels within the Singö fault. A detailed discussion of the measurements has been given by Stille and

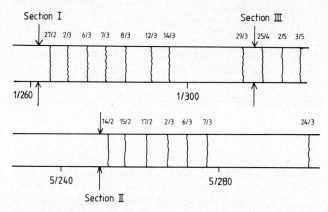

Fig. 8   Plan showing deformation measurement sections with dates for different excavation rounds

Delin[7] and results were also presented by Christiansson and Eriksson.[6]

The measurement sections were installed in the central part of the Singö fault, where the rock mass is of poor quality, at section 1/262, in the operational tunnel and at section 5/250 in the construction tunnel. The third section (1/317) was located in a part of the fault that shows a rock mass of good quality to enable comparative measurements to be made. Fig. 8 shows the measurement sections, with dates for rounds that were difficult to excavate.

Tunnel convergences were measured with a Distometer, and tunnel deformations were also measured with 2-m and 6-m long extensometers. The principal measurement section is shown in Fig. 9. In the section at 1/262 further points were installed in the roof for convergence measurements and extensometers, together with devices to measure the loads in the rockbolts and the permanent shotcrete lining. These measurements are still in progress and the results will be published later.

The results of the deformation measurements are interesting in regard to the central part of the Singö fault. The vertical deformations of the roofs were small (1–2 mm), but the wall deformations were much larger (convergence, 7 mm). The two

parallel SFR tunnels are divided by a rock pillar approximately 15 m wide. The deformations of the walls of the pillar are larger and not so superficial as those of the outer walls. One reason for this may be that the pillar is of poorer quality than the rock in the outer walls; another could be that destressing in the horizontal directions makes the behaviour of the pillar more flexible than that of the more fixed outer wall.

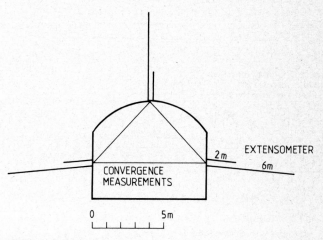

Fig. 9   Section showing principle used to make deformation measurements in SFR tunnels

Deformations in the third section were much smaller (about 1 mm), which is a quite normal deformation for a shallow tunnel in fair to good rock. The rock cover here is 20 m. The measurement results from the three sections are shown in Fig. 10. In section 1/262 it may be seen that the convergence exhibits an unstable condition with a tendency to creep. Additional, heavier supports were therefore installed.

Hydrogeological measurements
A pilot diamond drill hole was drilled in the operational tunnel in a wide section of the tunnel (Fig. 2). It was directed slightly upwards (2°) and at a 9° deviation from the tunnel axis, and extended a total length of 121 m. The core was logged with respect to rock type, weathering, fracturing, fracture filling and *RQD*. During drilling, the water inflow was carefully recorded and, after drilling, the total inflow was measured at 25 l/min (Fig. 3).

Water injection tests were performed in addition to the water flow measurements. The tests were carried out in 10-m sections, with simultaneous recording of the water head in the drill-hole. The hydraulic tests were performed as injection tests with a constant injection pressure. The injection was continued for 60 min, followed by a 60-min pressure fall-off test. The tests were carried out as double-packer tests, except for the innermost part of the drill-hole. At a depth of 80 m the hole was blocked and the testing was performed as a single-packer of the innermost 40 m.

Section I 1/260

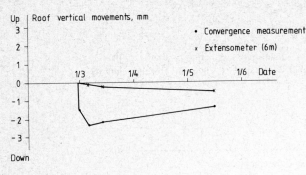

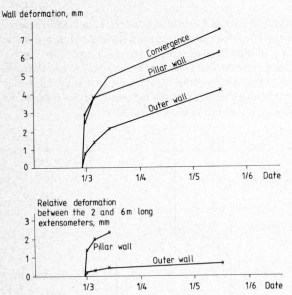

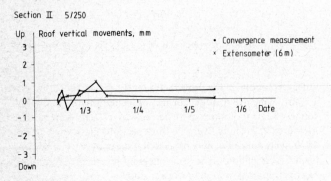

Section II 5/250

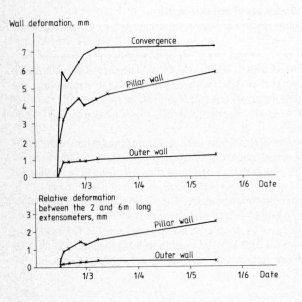

Section III 1/317

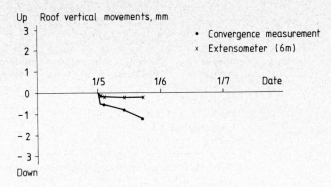

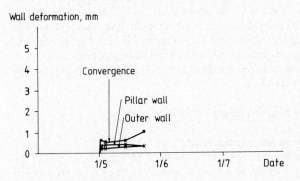

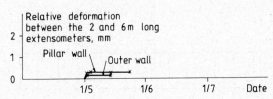

Fig. 10 Deformation measurement results from three sections in SFR tunnels

These tests gave information on the following hydraulic parameters: hydraulic conductivity, piezometric head, skin effect, effective drill-hole radius, radius of influence, fracture conductivity, fracture length and hydraulic boundaries.

The hydraulic conductivity is relatively high, 2×10^{-5} m/s in the central part of the Singö fault, in comparison with -10×10^{-8} m/s for the adjacent, more intact rock.

The piezometric head is governed by the sea-water level, but is already affected by the tunnelling in some sections. This is especially pronounced near the mouth of the drill-hole and in the inner, conductive part of the hole.

The results show that the rock mass in the Singö fault is strongly water-bearing and could cause problems – water inflows, erosion and, consequently, stability. The continuous pre-grouting was in this respect successful, however, and no problems occurred during the excavation of the tunnels.

Acknowledgement

The Forsmark power station has been built and is being operated by a limited company, Forsmark Kraftgrupp AB, which is owned by the Swedish State Power Board and Mellansvensk Kraftgrupp AB. Forsmark Kraftgrupp AB has commissioned the Swedish State Power Board as the main contractor for the plant.

The discharge tunnel for units 1 and 2 was designed and the project was administered by the Swedish State Power Board. Hagconsult AB was the consultant on permanent supports. The contractor for the tunnelling was AB Forsmarkstunnlar, a joint venture between AB Armerad Betong and AB Vägförbättringar.

The design, the tunnelling work and the assessment of the permanent support for the discharge tunnel for unit 3 were undertaken by the Swedish State Power Board.

The repository for reactor waste (SFR) is owned by the Swedish Nuclear Fuel Supply Company, which has commissioned the Swedish State Power Board to plan, design and build SFR, and the tunnelling work is now being carried out by the Power Board. The consultant for geological follow-up at the site is VIAK AB.

References

1. Larsson W. and Moberg M. Forsmark Kraftstation, aggr. 1 och 2. Avloppstunneln. Grundundersökning 1971–1973. (Forsmark Power Station, Units 1 and 2. Discharge tunnel: site investigations 1971–1973.) *Tek. rapp. Statens Vattenfallsverk*, Stockholm, 1973.

2. Hagconsult, SFR-Forsmark. Bergtekniskt utlåtande över undersökningar för tillfartstunnlar. (Rock mechanics report on investigations for access tunnels.) *Tek. rapp. Hagconsult*, Stockholm, 1982.

3. Carlsson A. and Olsson T. Water leakage in the Forsmark tunnel, Uppland, Sweden. *Sver. geol. Unders*. C734, 1977, 45 p.

4. Carlsson A. and Olsson T. Geological prediction and reality during construction of two subaqueous tunnels. In *Proceedings international symposium on engineering geology and underground construction, Lisbon, 1983*, vol. 1, III. 77–85.

5. Carlsson A. Characteristic features of a superficial rock mass in Southern Central Sweden: horizontal and subhorizontal fractures and filling material. *Striae*, Uppsala, vol. II, 1979, 79 p.

6. Christiansson R. and Eriksson K. Statens Vattenfallsverk. Forsmarksarbeten. SFR1. Byggnadsgeologisk uppföljning. (Forsmark works. SFR1. Engineering geological follow-up.) *VIAK Rep.* 3, Stockholm, 1984, 7 p.

7. Stille H. and Delin P. Measurements at the Singö fault. *Tek. rapp. Dep. Soil Rock Mechanics, KTH, Stockholm*, 1984.

8. Moberg M. Forsmark SFR1. Kärnborrhål DS101. Resultat. (Diamond corehole DS101: results.) *Tek. rapp. Statens Vattenfallsverk*, Stockholm, 1984, 16 p.

9. SGAB. Vatteninjiceringstester i ett kärnborrhål vid SFR-lagret i Forsmark. (Injection of water into a core-hole at the SFR in Forsmark.) *SGAB IRAP*, 84015, Uppsala, 1984, 22 p.

Lake tap – the Norwegian method

B. Berdal
Ing. A. B. Berdal A/S, Sandvika, Norway
B. Buen
Ing. A. B. Berdal A/S, Sandvika, Norway
J. Johansen
Dyno Konsulent A/S, Gullaug, Norway

Synopsis
Of the order of 500 successful submerged tunnel piercings have been performed in Norway since the 1900s – mostly to create economical drawdown reservoirs for hydroelectric power plants. The deepest piercing is at 105 m at Lake Jukla and the largest (95 m²) at Rygene. A piercing is located where rock quality is favourable and soil overburden limited. Exploratory drilling, grouting and careful blasting are used to bring the tunnel close to the rock surface. The final blast has at least two parallel hole cuts and high-strength water-resistant explosives are used. Specific charge varies between 3 and 8 kg/m³, depending mainly on cross-section and depth. In the most common piercing method an air cushion is established below the final plug to reduce shock waves on gates and bulkheads.

Submerged tunnel piercing, the process of piercing the bottom of a lake with a tunnel, has been a regular practice in Norway for more than 75 years. During this period it has been undertaken somewhere between 300 and 500 times. The firm and documented number is approximately 300, but from the number of hydroelectric power schemes that are in existence, and in view of the haphazard way in which the early cases were registered, the estimate of 500 is considered fairly accurate. The final blast for a lake tap and the opening after drawdown are shown in Fig. 1.

One reason for the failure to register lake taps is probably the fact that nobody considered it to be a feat that merited reporting – it was merely common construction practice. To date, the practice has involved the piercing of a lake bottom at a depth of 105 m and the breakout of a tunnel with a cross-section of 95 m². A list of some of the more noteworthy piercings is given in Table 1.

The main use of submerged tunnel piercings is that of lake taps, but the principle has found application for some tailrace tunnels and for sewer outfalls.

The large number of lake taps that have been executed in Norway relate to the combination of topography and econ-

Fig. 1 Lake Rembesdal during blasting and after drawdown (depth, 25 m; cross-section, 54 m²; plug thickness, 2.5–7 m; soil cover, 3–5 m)

omics. The economic part is the possibility of creating a reservoir by drawdown of a natural lake or by combining a low dam and a drawdown. The topographic element is that the many small lakes in high valleys and in the mountains lend themselves to such a solution.

Table 1

Location	Hydroelectric power scheme	Depth, m	Cross-section, m²	Year
Skjeggedal	Tysse	—	—	1905
Tverrelvvatn	Simavik	—	—	1913
Storglomvatn	Glomfjord	—	16	1920
Krokvatn	Skarsfjord	—	4	1922
Tafjord	Tafjord I	—	—	1923
Storbotnvatn	Svelgen IV	70	8	1971
Jukla East	Folgefonn	80	13	1973
Jukla West	Folgefonn	105	10	1973
Jukladalsvatn	Folgefonn	93	60	1977
Selbusjøen	Bratsberg	10	65	1977
Nidelven	Rygene	9	95	1977
Lomvivatn	Lomi	70	17	1978
Ringedalsvatn	Oksla	86	40	1980
Tyee Lake	Tyee Hydro	50	8	1983

The process of tapping a lake can be divided into the design of the tunnel system, the excavation of the tunnel and the design and execution of the final blast.

Design of tunnel system

The main components in an intake tunnel system are shown in Fig. 2. The rock trap will contain the debris from the final plug and prevent rock fragments from being swept far into the tunnel and even jamming and damaging the gate. Temporary bulkheads are used when work is still proceeding in the downstream tunnel system or if the installations cannot take the blast shocks. In many cases the ordinary gate can be used during the blasting.

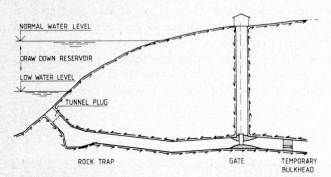

Fig. 2 Typical layout for lake tap

The gate shaft to the surface shown in Fig. 2 is, of course, not a requirement. A gate chamber in the rock connected to a suitable surface location by a tunnel is a much used alternative.

The depth of the piercing in a hydroelectric power reservoir is determined mainly by the hydrology and the topography of the basin. Restrictions on the drawdown, both on rate and depth, may be imposed by unstable slopes in sediments and in tallus slopes. Rapid changes in pore pressure might trigger slides. The slides in themselves can be a problem and the slide-generated waves can also be unacceptable. Other factors are wave erosion on newly exposed surfaces and the erosion taking place in the tributaries to the reservoir now at a lower base level. A submerged tunnel piercing is therefore often accompanied by erosion-protection work in the reservoir.

A very important factor in the design is to determine the location of the piercing. Extensive geological mapping, soundings, refraction seismic surveys, exploratory drilling, inspection by divers and core drilling serve to assess the suitability of a site with respect to overburden and rock mass quality. Fairly competent rock and limited overburden are sought. The main problem during the construction of a lake tap is usually that of leakage, so sites with faults and open joints are avoided, if possible. A piercing can be done through some soil overburden, but an overburden larger than the tunnel diameter is usually considered to be risky. A limited overburden of 1–3 m will, on the other hand, often help to seal cracks and joints and may therefore be a benefit. The erosion of soil into the tunnel during drawdown may also pose a problem and will require an oversize rock trap. For this reason rock slopes fairly free of overburden are considered to be those most suitable.

Two basic types of piercing are normally applied, the differences between open- and closed-system piercing being shown in Fig. 3. In an open-system piercing the gate or bulkhead is placed on the downstream side of the gate shaft, leaving a direct communication between the tunnel face and the atmosphere.

To prevent rock debris from reaching the gate it is essential to fill the tunnel partly with water prior to the blasting. The

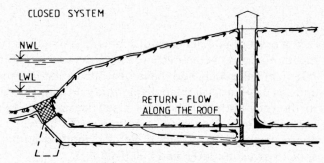

CONDITION 1: $H_2 < H_1$ TO PREVENT SQUEEZING OUT OF AIR CUSHION
CONDITION 2: $H_4 > H_3$ TO PREVENT SURGE TO REACH THE GATE HOUSE (C = 0,7 – 0,9)

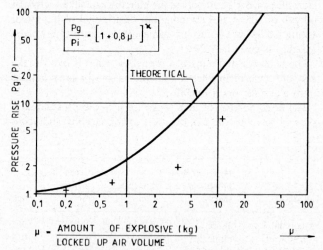

Fig. 3 Open and closed systems of submerged tunnel piercing. In the first the trapping of plug soil is easy; in the second it is difficult. After Solvik[1]

degree of filling must be weighed against the upsurge in the shaft, which should not be allowed to reach the floor of the gate house (condition 2, Fig. 3). This upsurge can be calculated quite accurately. When filling the tunnel before piercing an air pocket must be left against the tunnel face to prevent any harmful shock from being transmitted to the gate. This will normally restrict the level to which the tunnel may be filled to avoid the air in the pocket being squeezed out through the plug into the atmosphere (condition 1, Fig. 3). The pressure conditions in this air pocket just after the detonation are presented in Fig. 4 (both theoretical pressures and some recorded data).

$$\frac{Pg}{Pi} = \left[1 + 0.8\,\mu\right]^{\varkappa}$$

THEORETICAL

μ – AMOUNT OF EXPLOSIVE (kg) / LOCKED UP AIR VOLUME
Pi AIR CUSHION PRESSURE BEFORE BLASTING
Pg GAS PRESSURE IN AIR CUSHION JUST AFTER DETONATION
+ APPROX. MEASURED Pg

Fig. 4 Gas pressure in air pocket (open piercing). After Solvik[1]

To obtain an air pocket of the required volume the final plug is usually situated at the end of a short shaft. Very often, the tunnel is excavated at a gentle incline close to the breakthrough. In a closed-system piercing the gate or valve is placed so that the tunnel volume is confined from the atmosphere. This system requires a relatively long stretch of tunnel between the

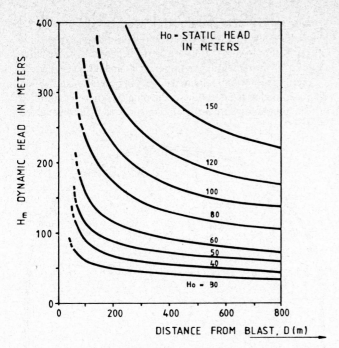

Fig. 5   Dynamic pressure, H_m (closed piercing). After Solvik[1]

plug and the gate to prevent damage to the closing structure from the maximum pressure produced by the detonation. Fig. 5 shows how this dynamic pressure, H_m, from inrushing water against the gate decreases with increasing tunnel length.

Closed piercings can be made with empty or partially filled tunnel. There are records of closed piercings in which the increase in pressure was so high that the closing structure was damaged. Even if the results have normally been good, closed piercings are used less frequently than open piercings and they have more frequently required model tests during the design stage.

Construction

Construction of a tunnel system for a submerged piercing is done by drill and blast methods. Because extensive drilling of exploratory holes is required and because grouting is generally necessary, only drill and blast methods have the required flexibility and space at the face.

When the tunnel is approaching the location of the piercing a systematic drilling of exploratory holes is begun. This drilling starts when the tunnelling under the reservoir begins or when the tunnel reaches to 30–100 m of the breakthrough, depending on local conditions. The main objective is to detect water-bearing faults and joints ahead of the face. For this percussion drilling of three to five holes is used. The drilled length is dependent on round length and available equipment, but the rock mass one round ahead of that which is being drilled and blasted should always be explored (Fig. 6).

Major leakages are grouted ahead of the face, minor leaks not seriously affecting working conditions being left untreated. Fast-setting cement-based grouts are commonly used. Special coarse-grained types are used to plug large leakages. Chemical grouts of types that react and expand on contact with water have proved of value, especially close to the surface where only low grouting pressure can be applied. The use of low grouting pressure close to the surface is important because too high a pressure will jack open joints and faults.

Close to the surface the round length is reduced and, if necessary, the drilling pattern is changed to produce a light breakout. When close to the surface a number of holes that depends on the cross-section is drilled through to the surface to locate it exactly. On this basis the final trimming, design and drilling out of the final round are done.

The rock trap is excavated carefully after the drilling of the final round – the rock trap precludes the use of heavy equipment at the face without the installation of heavy ramps and scaffolding.

Conditions at the face are very often wet and the water is cold, so survival suits can be a necessity. To push a packer into a drill-hole jetting ice-cold water at high pressure is almost impossible without the right protection and equipment. At lower pressures the holes can be plugged by long tapered wooden plugs, but at higher pressures packers or even large 'drill-through' packers have to be used.

Design of final blast and blast control system

The final blast is a crucial part of the tunnel piercing. A failure can lead to long delays because part of the old tunnel system may have to be sealed off and a new approach constructed and new gates may have to be installed. This can be very costly in terms of construction and because of the delayed start-up of the project. For this reason detailed planning of the final blast is done and special water-resistant explosives and detonators are used. The explosive used is of a high-strength gelatine type. Before use in a piercing samples are taken from the batch and tested. The standard test requirement is failsafe and full-strength detonation after a 72-h storage in water at a depth equivalent to the final blast.

Electric detonators of the millisecond delay type are used. The detonators have heavy-duty insulation. The test requirement for detonators is the same as that for the explosives.

The drilling pattern is designed on the basis of the tunnel cross-section, the plug area as mapped by exploratory holes, the thickness of the plug, the rock type, the thickness of the overburden, the water pressure and the water leakage. Parallel-hole cuts are used and the minimum number of cuts is two (in large cross-sections three). There are usually four large-diameter unloaded holes in each cut. The holes are drilled 0.3–0.5 m short of breakthrough.

The blast holes are loaded and tamped for maximum density. Depending on the factors mentioned above, the specific charge will typically vary between 3 and 8 kg/m^3. This is, as a rule, 50–100% more than the usage in normal tunnelling. The high specific charge gives high shock loads on gates and bulkheads. To reduce the specific charge would, on the other hand, increase the risk of full or partial failure and, as the lesser of two evils, high charges are used.

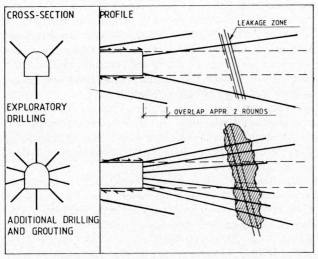

Fig. 6   Exploratory drilling and water-sealing procedure

Double and independent ignition systems are used. One detonator is placed in the bottom of the hole and the other in the outer part of the hole.

Present-day piercings are usually of the 'open-system' type, and the tunnel system is designed to entrap an air volume to act as cushion. If this volume is not sufficiently large, additional air is pumped in by compressor. Compressors are also kept at standby to replenish any air leaking out of the tunnel. The water level in the tunnel is monitored by a simple device where the water short-circuits two sensors – one for high and one for low water level.

Detailed descriptions of two piercings, Tyee Lake and Lake Lomi, at depths of 50 and 70 m, respectively, are given in Appendix 1 and Appendix 2.

Conclusion

Underwater piercing is a proven method of obtaining economical reservoirs for hydroelectric power projects. A successful breakthrough is dependent on a well-selected site, a carefully planned and executed construction and a well-designed final blast. With these requirements fulfilled, the hitherto maximum depth of 105 m and a maximum cross-section of 95 m² are not the limits of this method – often termed the 'Norwegian method'. Most lake taps to be done in the future – and there are many planned in Norway, and there is no reason why they should not be used elsewhere – will, however, be in the intermediate range both with respect to cross-section and depth.

Reference
1. Solvik Ø. Underwater piercing of tunnels. In *Fjellsprengningsteknikk* (Trondheim: Tapir, 1983). (Norwegian text)

Appendix 1

Plug blasting

Lomi hydroelectric power plant
General description   The Lomi hydroelectric plant is located in the northern part of Norway, approximately 100 km east of Bodø. The headrace tunnel was connected to Lake Lomi by the 'lake-tap' method. The static head on the plug was 75 m. The cross-section of the final plug was 18 m² and the thickness of the plug about 4.5 m. The plug was covered by 2–3 m of loose deposits. The distance between the plug and the gate shaft was

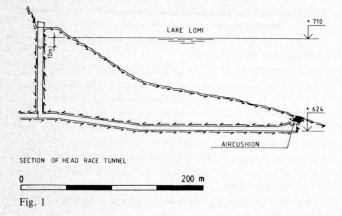

Fig. 1

280 m (Fig. 1). The rock type was quartzitic mica schist. Leakage of water through the rock close to the final plug was insignificant.

At the time of blasting the gate was closed, and the tunnel system was filled with water to 10 m below the level of the lake. Below the plug an air cushion was established. A high-strength gelatine explosive and millisecond delay detonators were used for the final blast.

Drilling pattern   The drilling pattern was based on the use of parallel holes with three separate parallel-hole cuts. In each of the parallel-hole cuts there were four uncharged 5-in diameter large holes, the remainder being 45-mm diameter holes (Fig. 2).

There were 80 45-mm diameter charged boreholes and 12 5-in diameter uncharged boreholes. The plug thickness was 3.9–5.0 m. The boreholes were drilled 0.5 m short of breakthrough of

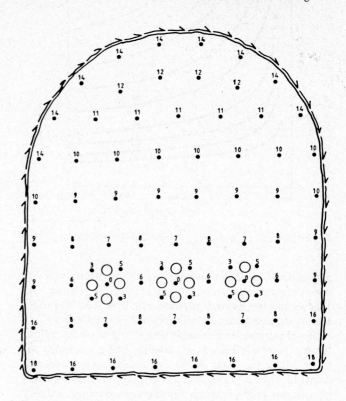

CROSS SECTION FINAL PLUG
NUMBERS SHOW PERIOD OF DELAYS
○ UNCHARGED
• LOADED

Fig. 2

the plug, i.e. the average length of the boreholes was 4.0 m.
Charging and ignition system   The boreholes were loaded with 35 mm × 600 mm cartridges in plastic film with 60% NG explosive (trade name, 'Extra Dynamit'). The charge concentration was calculated to be 1.4 kg per metre of borehole. In all loaded holes 2-ms delay detonators with identical delay number and normal sensitivity were used. One detonator was placed in the bottom of the hole and one in the middle of the outer part of the hole. The detonators had protective sheaths over the lead wires and the wire length was 6 m.

The unloaded part of the holes (0.3 m) was stemmed with expanded polystyrene plugs. A wooden conical dowel with a precut opening for the detonator wires was used to keep the charge and stemming in place. Details of the ignition system and charge are given in Table 1.

The round was split into two circuits, i.e. 80 detonators in each circuit with the bottom detonators in one circuit and the detonators in the outer part of the holes in the other circuit. The circuits were connected in parallel. The blasting machine was placed at top of the gate shaft, and the shot was fired immediately after the water in the gate shaft had reached a level 10 m below the lake level.

Table 1 Delay detonators - charges*

Delay no.	No. of holes per interval	No. of short-delay detonators	Loading length, m per interval	Extra Dynamit 35×600, wt of explosives, kg/interval
0	3	6	10.3	14.4
3	6	12	20.6	28.8
5	6	12	20.6	28.8
6	4	8	14.5	20.3
7	6	12	21.0	29.4
8	8	16	28.8	40.3
9	10	20	36.5	51.1
10	8	16	29.8	41.7
11	5	10	18.4	25.7
12	4	8	15.0	21.0
14	10	20	37.5	52.5
16	8	16	28.1	39.3
18	2	4	7.4	10.4
	80	160		403.7

*Total quantity of rock, 80 m³; total explosives required, 404 kg; powder factor, 404/80 = 5.1 kg/m³.

Appendix 2

Plug blasting

Tyee Lake hydroelectric power plant

General description The Tyee Lake hydroelectric plant is located near the town of Wrangell in Southern Alaska. Breakthrough of the final plug was carried out in September, 1983. The static head on the plug was 50 m and the distance between the plug and the gate shaft was 85 m. The plug cross-section was 8 m² and the plug thickness was 2.5–3 m.

The rock type was granodiorite and extensive grouting was necessary to seal the plug area.

Drilling pattern The drilling pattern was based on the use of parallel holes with two separate parallel-hole cuts on the symmetric line through the centre of the tunnel face. In each of the parallel-hole cuts there were four uncharged 76-mm diameter holes, the remainder being 35-mm holes (Fig. 1). The boreholes were drilled 0.3 m short of breakthrough of the plug, i.e. the average length of the boreholes was some 2.5 m.

Charging and ignition system The boreholes were loaded with 25 mm × 200 mm cartridges, containing 60% NG explosive ('Extra Dynamit'). The charge concentration was calculated to be 1 kg per metre of borehole.

In all the loaded holes there were 2-ms delay detonators with identical number and normal sensitivity. One detonator was placed in the bottom of the hole and the other was used in the middle of the outer part of the hole. The detonators had protective sheaths over lead wires and the wire length was 4 m.

Table 1 Delay detonators - charges*

Delay no.	Interval, ms	No. of holes per interval	No. of short-delay detonators per interval	Loading length, m per interval	Explosives, 25 × 200 mm, kg/interval
1	25	2	4	4.4	4.4
4	100	4	8	8.8	8.8
6	150	4	8	8.4	8.4
7	175	1	2	2.2	2.2
8	200	4	8	8.8	8.8
9	225	2	4	4.4	4.4
10	150	2	4	4.4	4.4
11	275	4	8	9.0	9.0
12	300	6	12	13.2	13.2
13	325	2	4	4.4	4.4
14	350	8	16	17.6	17.6
15	375	8	16	17.0	17.0
16	400	8	16	17.6	17.6
17	425	5	10	17.0	14.5
18	450	7	14	13.3	13.3
		67	134		143.6

*Total quantity of rock, $1.6^2 \pi \times 2.8 = 22.5$; total explosives required, 143.6 kg; powder factor, 143.6/22.5 = 6.38 kg/m³.

A wooden conical dowel with a precut opening for the detonator wires was used to keep the charge in place.

Details of the ignition system and charge are presented in Table 1. The round was split into two circuits, 67 detonators in each circuit, the central detonators being in one circuit and the detonators in the outer part of the holes in the other.

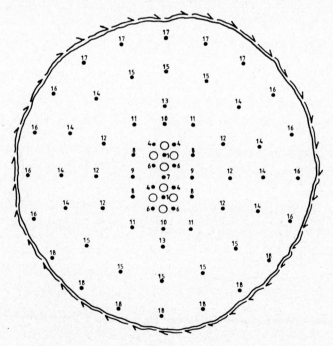

CROSS-SECTION FINAL PLUG

DELAY PATTERN USING MS DELAYS
NUMBERS SHOW PERIOD OF DELAYS
O UNCHARGED
• LOADED

0   3m

Fig. 1

Low-cost protection against water and frost in road tunnels

Jon Krokeborg
Knut B. Pedersen
Norwegian Road Research Laboratory, Public Roads Administration, Oslo, Norway

Synopsis
A large proportion of Norwegian road tunnels are situated in areas that are subject to severe frost. Problems invariably arise in that part of the tunnel's frost zone in which the leaks do not freeze dry. The accumulation of ice along walls and ditches often blocks drainage paths, causing water to spill on to the road, where it freezes, making driving hazardous and increasing the difficulties of maintenance.

The problem of water leakage has been solved by the Norwegian Road Research Laboratory by means of shielding. Since the first shielding sections were developed in the early 1970s more than 25 km of shielding has been mounted in Norwegian road tunnels. Various types of shielding were tested in an experimental tunnel, the most efficient types proving to be insulated panels of aluminium and a sandwich structure of fibre-reinforced polyester.

Another method that has proved to be suitable, especially for use against limited areas of leakage and in old narrow tunnels, is the use of PE foam. Sheets of the foam are pressed directly against the rock crown on to rockbolts.

The protection systems used and experience over the past ten years are described.

Of the more than 700 road tunnels in Norway, some 450 are on the primary national road network, the remainder being on country or secondary roads. Less than 3% of the total tunnel length has zones with *in-situ* concrete lining. In many tunnels the cost of permanent support amounts to 40–50% of the total costs, which include water and frost protection, some scaling, plus the drainage system and road construction. Normally, water and frost protection comprises the greater part of the initial expenditure, which can equal the cost of excavating the tunnel by drilling and blasting.

Various forms of shielding are mounted, first and foremost, in tunnels that are difficult and expensive to insulate by means of injection, and where considerable demands are made in terms of insulation tightness. One prerequisite is that the rock be sufficiently stable that it is not necessary to line it with concrete and a membrane. It is therefore of great importance that unstable rock be reinforced with bolts, bands and, if necessary, netting. Reinforcement of the rock must be thorough: once the shielding has been erected it is no longer possible to examine the rock with a view to supplementary reinforcement.

To ensure the stability of the structure and its appearance the shielding should cover the whole tunnel profile from the base of one drainage ditch to the other. The simplest building method, and the most secure, is obtained in tunnels of circular cross-section, but the method can be applied to any cross-section. The sheets or elements that are used are uniformly curved, and this simplifies the mounting process, ordering and storage.

Materials

Shielding materials should be corrosion-resistant and fireproof. Aluminium has proved to be suitable and is the material that is most widely used in Norwegian road tunnels, but some steel and plastic materials can also be employed. The thickness of the sheets ought not to be less than 0.5 mm, the aluminium sheets that are used in Norway having a thickness of 0.71 mm.

The aluminium has a relatively high content of magnesium to make it resistant to salt water. The sheets are also treated with aludin and coated with baked enamel for additional protection against corrosion from copper-containing water.

The aluminium sheets that are used have sine corrugation – a principle that should also be adopted if steel or plastic materials are used. Leakage water is carried away and this form is also easily adapted from a geometrical point of view during erection, especially on bends.

Hot-galvanized steel and aluminium can be used for bearing rails – the latter is the most commonly used material because it is easier to handle and mount. If different types of material are used in combination, it is necessary to consider the possibility of galvanic tension.

The materials that are used most widely as sandwich elements are glassfibre-reinforced polyester with polyurethane as the insulation core. With these structures it is particularly important that fire-resistant additives be used. The polyester should display satisfactory resistance to fire and to the spread of flames (aluminium trihydrate is also favourable in this respect). In general, it is important not to use halogenized polyesters in any situation in which fires would produce poisonous chlorine and bromine compounds. Polyurethane insulation must not drip during fires, and materials must qualify as being self-extinguishing.

A third method of shielding arises from the use of PE foam (polyethylene). Extruded PE foam has several properties that render it suitable for water and frost protection purposes, the most important of which are its good insulating capacity and the low moisture absorptiveness. The head conductivities of the materials that are used are in the region of 0.033–0.055 $W/m^2 K$.

Types of structure

Aluminium shielding

Two types of aluminium shielding have been developed: one is

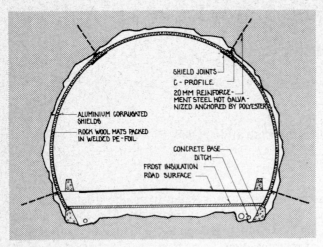

Fig. 1 Double lining of aluminium with frost insulation between

single, uninsulated sheeting for use in frost-free zones; the other, the double sheeting, is made by two sets of corrugated sheets mounted with a 10-cm insulation-filled gap, the sheet on the roadside being held rigid by means of bow-shaped steel pipes.

The bearing section of the shielding consists of bearing rails of aluminium, C profile, which are fixed by means of key-headed bolts (dowels) 20 mm in diameter. The location of the bearing rails is indicated in Fig. 1. The rails must be mounted very precisely, the location being determined by means of measuring equipment, including a specially constructed template. Each single sheet is mounted on seven bearing rails; for the double shielding four bearing rails are used, plus two

Rivets are used to fasten the corrugated aluminium sheets together and to the bearing rails. To prevent leakage around the rivet holes sealed rivets with steel nails are used. The automatic machines that are now available simplify riveting work and enable greatly increased productivity. Thread-forming (Drilkwik) screws have been tested, but they proved to be unsuitable for fastening sheets on to bearing rails.

The sheets that are used in Norway are 871 mm wide and about 6000 mm long, and are profiled to the correct radius of the individual tunnel profile. The sheets are laid so that two corrugations overlap and are riveted together. In mounting the double sheets the inner sheet is erected ahead of that nearer to the road; at the same time the insulation is placed between the two. To date, mineral wool mats (Glava, Rockwool) have been used for insulation purposes. The thickness of the mats is 10 cm and to protect the material against dampness it should be enveloped in 0.15-mm polyethylene foil.

The sheet that is away from the wall is fastened in such a way that, in principle, it is self-bearing. To make the shielding rigid, bow-shaped pipes are mounted every 3 m: they are fastened to the foundation rail and can be tightened so that they follow the radius of the shielding completely. The curved pipes can also be used to hang lighting equipment.

Sandwich shielding

Sandwich shielding is constructed in such a way that two half-bows are fastened together on to the roof (Fig. 2). The separate roof hanging is constructed as indicated in Fig. 3. The shielding itself consists of an insulation core of 50 mm of polyurethane foam, cast into approximately 2 mm of glassfibre-reinforced

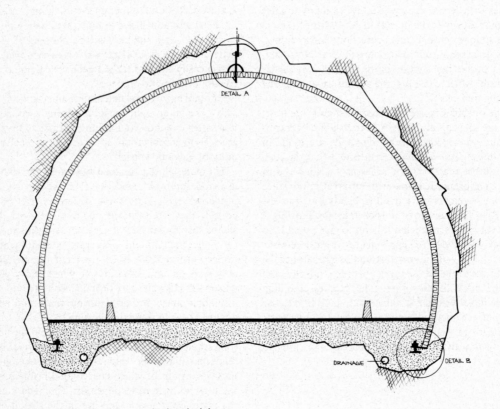

Fig. 2 Sandwich structure – basic principle

foundation rails mounted 50 cm below the road surface. The foundation rails must be grouted in place by separate foundations every 3 m.

polyester. Both in the choice of insulating material and polyester the emphasis is on self-extinguishing and fire-resistant materials.

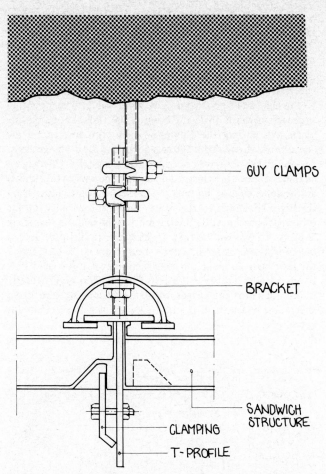

Fig. 3 Detail A: roof hanging of sandwich structure

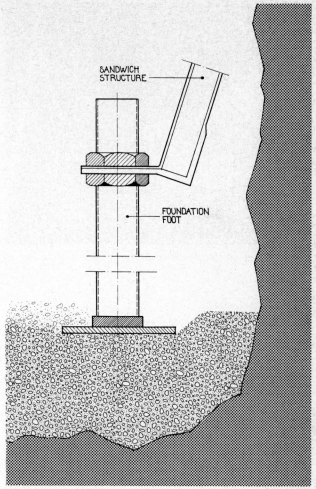

Fig. 4 Detail B: foundation footing of sandwich structure

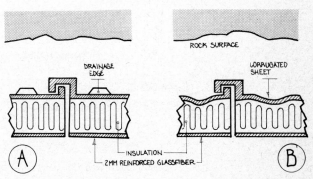

Fig. 5 Joints of sandwich elements: two ways of excluding water from joint

Shielding in frost zones is mounted in a manner that corresponds to that of the insulated aluminium sheeting – on foundation rails 50 cm below the road surface. Foundation rails must be grouted in place every 3 m, but it is also possible to use 'foundation feet' on the jacking principle (Fig. 4). The sheeting is fastened to a 'jack', which enables the height to be adjusted during foundation laying. After the sheeting has been set in place the jack must be grouted in place or fastened to a grouted foundation with bolts.

Joints along the elements have a watertight construction and to prevent frost penetration polyurethane foam is sprayed in (Fig. 5).

The installation of sandwich shieldings can be carried out effectively with a truck-mounted hydraulic grab (Fig. 6). In less than 6 h three men can install about 15 m of shielding.

The elements of the sandwich are supplied in various sectional shapes adapted to the tunnel section. The width of the elements varies from 1500 to 2400 mm. Joining together the elements along the length takes place in such a way that it is possible to mount the elements on bends with a radius down to 300 m.

Plugging up ends

With both types of shielding the gap between the rock and the sheeting must be plugged at the ends so that cold air does not enter behind the sheeting. The basic principle is that the heat of the rock must be retained so that water leakage can drain frost-free into the drainage system.

Two methods are currently employed to plug the ends of the shielding: the first is based on the use of plastic-covered rockwool mats. The mats are packed into the gap between rock and sheeting and held in place with rockbolts and steel wire. The second method employs mats of PE foam, which are bolted to the rock about 500 mm in front of the edge of the shielding.

The mats are then bent down against the shielding and forced into place with L-profile aluminium brackets (Fig. 7). The mats are cut into shape so that they follow the profile of the shielding. To cover the whole section of the profile the mats are laid with an overlap.

Experience to date indicates that the latter method seems to be superior both in terms of function and appearance.

PE foam

The two previously described methods give total protection against water and frost when they are correctly dimensioned and mounted. As a supplement to these methods a simple technique that does not offer complete watertightness has been developed for use, in particular, in old narrow tunnels and for the diversion of leakages over limited areas.

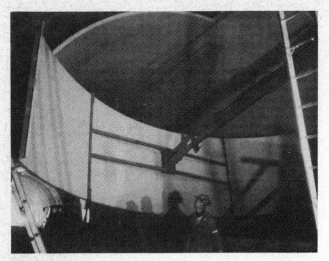

Fig. 6   Mounting of sandwich elements

Extruded PE foam has several properties that make it suitable for water and frost protection purposes. It is essential that the material exhibit low moisture absorptiveness, and flexibility and tensile strength are also very important.

The various PE foam manufacturers supply the material in sheets of somewhat varying size, but it is a simple matter to glue or fuse the sheets together to achieve the desired size. For ease of transportation and installation experience has shown that sheets of about 15–20 m² are suitable. They can be glued or fused together at a separate site or can be supplied ready for use by the manufacturer.

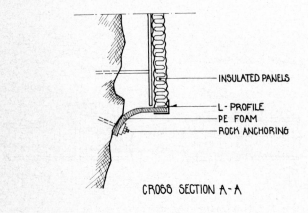

CROSS SECTION A-A

— INSULATED PANELS
— L - PROFILE
— PE FOAM
— ROCK ANCHORING

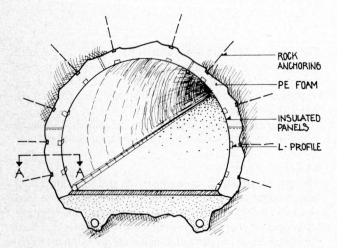

Fig. 7   Plugging ends by PE foam

168

The foam sheets can be mounted directly on to the tunnel lining by being pressed on to bolts set in the rock or by piercing the material and installing the bolt after it has been positioned. The number of bolts depends on the evenness of the rock contours and the size of the sheets, but it is important that the sheets fit snugly against the rock. In practice, it is apparent that five to eight bolts per 16.5 m² give good results. The mounting proceeds upwards from the base of the wall. To enable the water to seep into the drainage system without freezing the sheets must extend about 500 mm down into the drainage ditch.

After the sheets have been mounted, the ditch is filled again so that the sheets are clamped up against the wall of the tunnel. At the upper edge of the mat bolts are set in about 200 mm from the edge. The sheets are then pressed against the wall by means of a washer and nut. Before the nut is tightened the next sheet is placed to overlap the first. If the whole tunnel profile is to be covered, one can build up the sheets from both sides, fixing the roof last. To make the construction even more rigid steel bands are added between the bolts (Fig. 8). This is particularly important on the outer edges, where the space between rock and sheet must be filled either with rockwool or with pieces of PE foam.

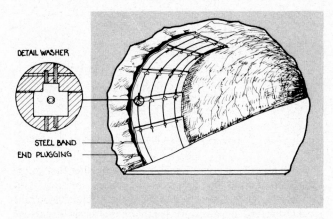

DETAIL WASHER

STEEL BAND
END PLUGGING

Fig. 8   PE foam – basic principle

If one is to cover areas that are longer than the length of the sheets, they must also be overlapped lengthwise. If the tunnel has a slope, the overlapping principle must be applied along the downward slope.

The greatest weakness of the method lies in the insertion of the bolts through the sheets: to date, no good method has been discovered to pierce them without leakage. Work is being undertaken on this problem and exploitation of the properties of laminated sheets offers the possibility of better results. There is also a hope of finding materials that can be used for filling around the bolts to remove or reduce the leakage problems.

Estimation of fire hazard
Polyethylene foam is a plastic material and, as such, inflammable. The risk of fire has been assessed on the basis of a literature survey, our own experience and statistics that relate to car fires in Norwegian road tunnels. In 1982 the Norwegian Road Research Laboratory cooperated with the Norwegian State Railways in a realistic fire experiment in a disused railway tunnel. It was noted that the element of risk increased very little in relation to the development of temperature, gases and smoke that occurs in a car fire.

Most of the materials can be supplied in so-called flame-reducing or self-extinguishing varieties. If halogens are used as additives, bromine and chlorine, in particular, will be released by fire. We have concluded that these heavy poisonous gases may increase the hazard. As such, we have not recommended the use of any of these materials.

Costs

The cost of shielding varies considerably from one site to the next, but the average cost of a fully mounted shielding unit is of the following order:

Single sheet of aluminium   Approx. NOK 5000/m (£500)
Double sheet of aluminium   Approx. NOK 8500/m (£850)
(Insulation included)
Sandwich sheet   Approx. NOK 8500/m (£850)
PE foam   Approx. NOK 250/m^2 (£25)

For the aluminium and sandwich sheet the cost of plugging the ends must be taken into account (about £500–£800 for each end that is plugged).

Labour and materials costs are approximately as follow: aluminium – materials, 35%; labour, 65%; sandwich – materials, 90%; labour, 10%; and PE foam – materials, 35%; labour, 65%.

Experience to date

During the past decade the number of motor vehicles has doubled and the transport of goods on Norwegian roads has increased by an average of 5% per annum. Thus, the proportion of larger and heavier vehicles has increased steadily. A larger percentage of new tunnels are therefore being constructed with the greatest cross-section described in Norwegian Road Tunnel Standards. In combination with the additional traffic, this has caused an increased dynamic strain on the shielding, and in recent years it has been necessary to carry out reinforcement of the structure and also a revision of the construction details to meet present-day requirements.

Three or four years ago damage to the aluminium shielding, especially the single, uninsulated type, was reported. Five reasons for this damage emerged from a detailed investigation: (1) damage caused by cars and lorries; (2) damage caused by ice (uninsulated shields mounted in the frost zone); (3) incorrectly mounted shields; (4) the rivets that were used were too weak; and (5) insufficient stability.

As was mentioned earlier, points (2)–(5) are soluble by reinforcement and revision of detail. Point (1) is not so easily avoided, but the best protection of the shielding is to make use of a solid guardrail to prevent vehicles from leaving the carriageway.

Experience with sandwich structures to date is very good, despite the relatively short observation period, and we expect that the use of sandwich shielding will increase.

With regard to PE foam, it may be said that a successful result is very dependent on an exact and reasonable mounting. The method is most suitable for leakages over limited areas, but it has also been used successfully on larger areas.

References

1. Krokeborg J. Ekstrudert PE-skum i vegtunneler. Beskrivelse av brannforsøk. Norwegian Road Research Laboratory, Oslo, internal report no. 1045, 1982.
2. Krokeborg J. and Pedersen K. B. Platehvelvtyper. Oppfølgings-rapport. Norwegian Road Research Laboratory, Oslo, internal report no. 1102, 1983.
3. Pedersen K. B. *et al*. Vann- og frostsikring av vegtunneler med platehvelv i aluminium. Norwegian Road Research Laboratory, Oslo, internal report no. 1096, 1982.

Discussion

J. Buchanan* sought the opinion of Carlsson and co-workers on the economic balance between the realistic decision taken for unit 3, which subsequently incurred some additional cost and delay and the 'unusually large allowances . . . made for the driving of the SFR tunnels' when 'on the whole, the rock quality is about the same'.

He asked Berdal and co-workers if the drawdown of the lake always exposed the lake tap and if the very thorough grouting that was required created any problems for the blasting (that was perhaps the reason for the three cuts used for the last plug).

He wondered if the problem of the rock travelling along the tunnel, as shown in Fig. 3 (p. 160), could be overcome by lengthening the rock trap in the invert.

T. J. M. Paterson† asked Berdal and co-workers if any failures had occurred in the construction of lake taps and, if so, how a failure to blow the rock plug was dealt with. He enquired if excavation of overburden at a lake tap site had ever been carried out underwater.

Perhaps Carlsson and co-workers would state how much time was spent in negotiating the Singö fault in each of the tunnels and whether that time could be broken down into specific stages in the case of tunnel no. 3.

It was interesting to compare the methods of tunnel support that were used in different countries. He suspected that in Britain tunnels that crossed such a major fault zone would have been lined with *in-situ* concrete – at least the discharge tunnels. The confidence of the designers of those tunnels in other forms of tunnel support was demonstrated by their decision to omit such an *in-situ* lining.

Authors' replies

Professor A. Carlsson, Professor T. Olsson and Professor H. Stille We regret that the economic balance sought by J. Buchanan cannot be discussed realistically.

It is not possible to answer T. J. M. Paterson's questions as the Swedish State Power Board was both the owner and the contractor. Tunnels for nuclear power plants are of great public interest and support measures may be carried out that are based on factors other than rock quality. It may be assumed that problems of a normal nature in the driving of hydroelectric tunnels, etc., would be judged in a considerably different light if the same type of problem were to occur in these nuclear power tunnels.

B. Berdal, B. Buen and J. Johansen In reply to J. Buchanan, the annulus is not always exposed: this may be impossible, for example, in the case of a tailrace tunnel entering a downstream lake or river. If possible, however, a reservoir is drawn down for inspection and cleaning of the area around the intake – especially desirable when the lake tap has penetrated a large soil overburden.

Blasting and, in particular, drilling and charging are considered to benefit from thorough grouting. It is believed that the grouting, in filling joints and fissures, gives a better energy transfer and prevents single charge holes or part of the round being sheared off, thereby creating a misfire.

The number of cuts (two or more) is to ensure a failsafe blast.

A closed-system piercing, as shown in Fig. 3 (p. 160) is, as a rule, complex and model tests are recommended in each case. Various kinds of rock traps have been tested – long as well as short and deep. In general, short and deep traps can be said to have produced the best results. This can probably be ascribed to the energy that is dissipated in turbulence by the abrupt and large change of tunnel cross-section.

In reply to T. J. M. Paterson, a few failures have been reported, being broadly due to (1) excessive pressure in the tunnel system (gates/valves/penstock), (2) debris blocking or damaging gates and (3) misfire or blocking of openings.

If for some reason the breakthrough has not been clean, but an opening has been established, scaling and blasting can be performed by divers or in the dry if the reservoir can be drawn down.

Only one complete blocking has been reported: moraine with large boulders blocked the opening completely and rendered it watertight. A concrete bulkhead was erected to seal off a part of the tunnel close to the original piercing and a new piercing could then be undertaken.

In cases where a bulkhead could not be erected a completely new tunnel would have to be constructed, starting from a position behind the gates.

Excavation of overburden at lake tap sites has been carried out in a number of cases. According to material and depth, dredge grabs or pumps have been used.

*Sir Robert MacAlpine and Sons, Ltd., London, England.
†Geostore (South Killingholme), Ltd., South Killingholme, South Humberside, England.

Session 7 – Machine tunnelling

Co-Chairmen: Dr. G. Sauer and T. I. King

Practical results of cutting harder rock with picks in United Kingdom coal mine tunnels

A. H. Morris
National Coal Board, Tunnelling and Transport Branch, Mining Research and Development
Establishment, Stanhope Bretby, Burton-on-Trent, Staffordshire, England

Synopsis
Since the introduction of roadheaders to the National Coal Board in 1961 and their subsequent development the traditional method of cutting rock in British coal mines has been with the radial or point attack pick. Roller cutters and discs have been used on particular installations, but the application has not been widespread. The NCB requirement is for fairly mobile machines that are capable of operating in relatively short tunnels and of being transferred from site to site as required. Machines that are equipped with cutter picks lend themselves more readily to this type of overall operation.

As part of an agreed R & D policy the Mining Research and Development Establishment set out to develop means of applying picks to rock in such a way that the machine capability was raised and much harder strata could be tackled. Two separate approaches were made. The first concerned the development of machine tool philosophy by which cutter picks are held rigidly to their task with high unit force and the minimum possibility of vibration, which necessitated the design and development of a boom, cutting head and power transmission with four to five times the torque and traversing forces that are available on current heavy-duty roadheaders, and the means of anchoring the boom turret rigidly in the roadway. This approach has led to the production of the MRDE circular shield and boom machine that is currently operating at Cadley Hill colliery, and the Eimco–NCB machine currently on trial at Middleton limestone mine.

The second approach has been the application of high-pressure water jets to assist mechanical cutting on roadheaders. A joint development project (National Coal Board–United States Bureau of Mines) has, over the past few years, resulted in the practical application of this technique to light- and medium-duty roadheading machines. Trial results are now available from a prototype that has operated at Middleton limestone mine and also from machines that have worked underground in collieries. A significant improvement in cutting capability, dust suppression and a reduction in pick usage has been measured.

Also mentioned is the parallel development of CAD cutterhead design, and some automatic control and instrument indication, since these are essential ingredients of the success of the major projects.

The United Kingdom coal industry will drive, each year, some hundreds of kilometres of tunnel. Some of these are in coal or part coal, but a large number are in cross-measure strata, in certain of which abrasive and often homogeneous strata can be encounted that test to the limit the ability of any roadheading machine that employs cutter picks.

The roadheader is the machine that is normally employed by the National Coal Board for rock heading, some hundreds being available for use in various forms. Great Britain has a large roadheader-manufacturing capability, partly based on the large home market, and since 1961, when the NCB purchased a PK3 machine from Russia, the roadheader-type machine has undergone considerable development. This development has been along the classical line of light- and then medium-duty machines into heavier and more powerful examples, on the assumption of higher operational capability and increased reliability. As a result we now have caterpillar-tracked machines that range from about 25 t in weight to 120 t. In addition, we have at least one example of a roadheader-type boom and turret mounted in a shield that is around the 150-t mark. Fig. 1 gives an indication of this variation.

For some considerable way along the curve of increased power and weight there does not appear to be a proportionate increase in the ability of a machine to cut harder rock or, more precisely, to cut economically and without an insupportable loss of cutting picks and without damage to the machine itself. In recent years, however, refinements in engineering application have improved this situation and two major changes in design approach have had a significant effect on cutting capability – the application of a different order of pick speed and torque at the cutting head with associated changes in traversing forces and machine stabilization and the use of high-pressure water to assist mechanical cutting.

Route 1 – more power and more weight

The roadheader is designed for flexibility in operation, an ability to cut almost any shape of roadway and manoeuvrability in cutting roadway junctions, etc. The engineering limitations that result from the achievement of these needs are well known. Clearly, in the earlier breed of lighter machine the degree of success in cutting even medium-hard rock was limited and the possibility of vibrating a machine to a degree that destroyed picks and often the machine itself was considerable.

As the machines have been developed into the heavy-duty category the geometry of the elements that urge the cutting head into the rock has been improved to give better engineering stiffness and, of course, structural and power transmission changes have been made. In British mines the trend has been to accept a certain loss of operational flexibility by using larger, wider-bodied machines for more rigidity, and a more consistent application of tool to rock. This has led to design and use of gearboxes and hydraulic components with reliability factors well in excess of those which were obtained previously. For

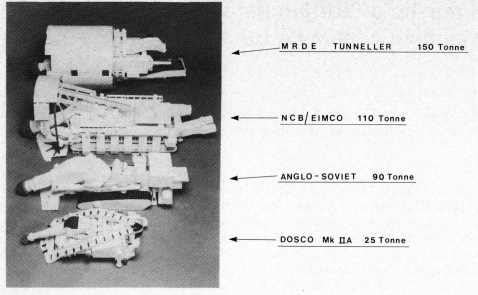

Fig. 1   Range of roadheaders – top machines

example, NCB guidelines to manufacturers with regard to the cutter gearbox are now for design based on a 50 000-h wear life at full load rather than the previously accepted 12 500-h life.

Operational results did not, however, fully match the NCB requirement and some time ago it was agreed, as part of the NCB's R & D policy, that MRDE should develop a machine that was capable of cutting any rock that an NCB engineer was likely to encounter. This decision is now reflected in two machines, one designed and manufactured at, and the other sponsored from, MRDE. Following the years of research into the factors that affect the ability of picks to cut rock, a major test rig was constructed to verify the philosophy derived from that research, i.e. we should be looking at much higher unit pick forces, slower linear pick speeds, greatly increased cutting head torque and high application forces via the slewing and elevating

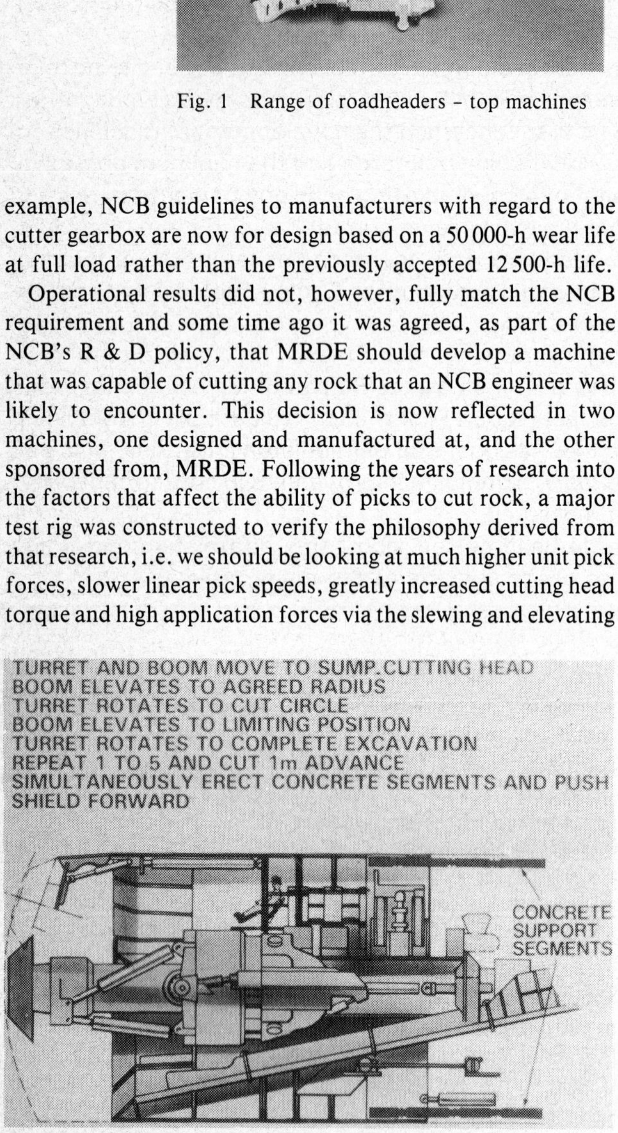

TURRET AND BOOM MOVE TO SUMP. CUTTING HEAD
BOOM ELEVATES TO AGREED RADIUS
TURRET ROTATES TO CUT CIRCLE
BOOM ELEVATES TO LIMITING POSITION
TURRET ROTATES TO COMPLETE EXCAVATION
REPEAT 1 TO 5 AND CUT 1m ADVANCE
SIMULTANEOUSLY ERECT CONCRETE SEGMENTS AND PUSH
SHIELD FORWARD

CONCRETE
SUPPORT
SEGMENTS

Fig. 2   Bretby tunnelling machine

cylinders. The test rig work led to the conclusion that a suitable machine could be built, provided that we added another factor – anchoring of the machine in the roadway, as is common in civil engineering. Subsequently, a circular machine was built (Fig. 2). In simple terms it is a boom within a shield, but where the forces applied for cutting are of the order of five times greater than those which are normally employed on heavy-duty roadheaders (a very rigid 'stiff' boom powered by a 225-kW motor, secured to a turret, mounted in slides in the shield). The rather special epicyclic gearbox has a 210:1 reduction. The

cutting head speed is therefore very low and the output torque very high (312 kN m). The force at each individual pick is approximately 1 t and the hydraulic forces that urge the cutting head into the rock can generate up to a 50-t thrust.

Anchorage is achieved by the use of a horizontally split shield, which can be set hydraulically to the roof.

Because these high forces have to be reacted back through machine elements to the shield, and because the shield is designed for a circular excavation of 5.5 m, total machine weight is around 150 t. The ancillaries, mounted on sledges that are towed behind the machine, weigh, approximately, a further 100 t. The machine has now operated at Cadley Hill colliery to produce more than 1200 m of roadway. Part of the drivage has been through rock of + 200 MPa in compressive strength: this was dealt with successfully, though at a slow rate of excavation. Rock at more than 100 MPa has been dealt with more often and without any great difficulty.

Although the rigid anchoring of the boom and turret and the provision of high-output torque with massive thrust produce the correct result in terms of cutting ability, operation of the machine has also revealed some interesting mechanical problems in that every transient force and every inducement to vibration are rigidly resisted and all reflected loads have to be absorbed in the machine elements. This has highlighted any design weakness in the overall machine.

At a later stage in the development of the circular machine Eimco became the main contractor for a machine that is based on the same principles for rock removal but aimed at the more conventional shape of NCB roadways – the arch or D shape. A MRDE-type boom and turret have been supplied for use on an Eimco-designed machine, which accepts the turret in machine slides that are assembled on a track-mounted chassis. The design and operational requirement results in a road-header-type machine, but which has the same cutting capabilities as the circular machine. A further parallel with that machine is a facility for anchoring the machine rigidly in the roadway. In this case the anchor mechanisms are fixed at both sides of the machine and can be reacted against the roadway between the set arches (Fig. 3).

The surface trials at Middleton limestone mine have already demonstrated the high level of cutting capability, and underground trials are expected to confirm this.

Because of the general and natural desire to achieve near-continuous operation out of a relatively high capital investment

Fig. 3   NCB–Eimco tunnelling machine

a roadway support transporter and setting device has been developed and applied (Fig. 3) that should permit the 'building' of a loosely bolted arch, on the body of the machine, while cutting and loading are undertaken. The arch can then be mechanically transported and set with minimum downtime, and just behind a canopy that ensures improved safety during the setting, strutting and lagging operations.

Route 2 – high-pressure water jets to assist mechanical cutting

The alternative solution to the problem of cutting hard rock with picks, also pursued at MRDE, has been the application of high-pressure water to assist mechanical cutting. In this project MRDE sought to find a means of applying significant extra energy at the cutting head of a roadheader without increasing machine weight and size. To do so it was necessary to apply the energy without increasing reactive forces: this can be achieved by the provision of fluid power to the cutting head. Following research into this subject (based on earlier work by the South African Chamber of Mines), MRDE was able to show in its own laboratories and at the Health and Safety Executive laboratories in Buxton that the use of water pressures of up to 700 bar could

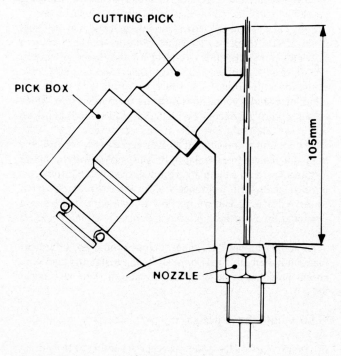

Fig. 4   Position of nozzle relative to cutting pick

reduce significantly the forces, both lateral and normal, that were required to make a pick cut at a certain penetration and at a certain level of debris removal in particular rocks (Fig. 4).

A collaborative project between MRDE and the U.S. Department of Energy was then arranged and concentrated on the engineering development necessary to apply this technique to a light-duty roadheader (Dosco Mk.2A) in such a way that water at 700 bar could be released in trial combinations covering some or all of the picks on the cutting head. This was done via development of an intensifier, rotating seals to transmit high-pressure water and redesign of the boom and cutting head itself so as to make the transmission of the high-pressure water safe and efficient. The trials of the modified machine at a test site in Middleton limestone mine showed that much better extraction rates could be obtained, wear on the picks was reduced considerably and, for some reason that was not understood at that time, machine vibration was reduced. Not only was this reduction in vibration apparent by sight and touch but it was measurable via recordings of electrical and hydraulic power levels that were made with the machine in the 'jets on' and 'jets off' condition.

There was also an early indication that dust suppression was improved and it looked as though the incidence of frictional sparking was at least reduced.

At this stage it was agreed that MRDE would hand over to selected British and U.S. firms the technical information that would allow them to make production prototypes as an addition to the MRDE programme. Anderson Strathclyde and Dosco responded and have produced trial equipment that has already been put to use. Indeed, including a MRDE machine, three light- to medium-weight roadheaders have now been operated on underground production, the results obtained confirming those which were yielded by the original development trials at Middleton limestone mine, i.e. the high-pressure water, applied to cutter picks in critical positions on the cutting head, definitely improved the machine's ability to operate in the harder strata. Rock as high in compressive strength as 160 MPa and in bands 1.2 m thick has been tackled successfully. The rate of pick usage has been reduced significantly and the incidence of incendive sparking in abrasive conditions is minimized. In addition, one 'spin-off' that is assuming a greater importance than had been expected is the dust-suppressing characteristic of this technique. In the early trials at Middleton it appeared that dust-suppression efficiency increased up to applied water pressures of around 140 bar (cf. normal dust-suppression water pressures of 15–20 bar) and then tended to level off. Colliery experience in mudstones, siltstones and sandstone associated with Coal Measure strata has, however, tended to show a continuing improvement in dust suppression up to water pressures of 500 or 600 bar.

As was stated previously, an unforeseen advantage is the reduction in vibration on machines: this has a beneficial effect not only in reducing machine damage but the improved stability must contribute to improved cutting efficiency.

MRDE monitored and instrumented trials on one of the production machines have shown that, on average, specific energy requirements were reduced by 32% and excavation rate in medium-strength and harder rock was increased, on average, by 50%. Dust make was also reduced progressively through the water pressure range, and at maximum pressure was only 30% of that produced with the use of water at normal pressure levels (e.g. 20 bar). Average pick consumption was very low at 0.6 pick/m advance.

The experience that has been gained on prototype trials at Middleton and three underground trials under production conditions does not yet provide the full story, but the project objectives have clearly been met and there is no doubt that the technique will be further refined and applied. This work will

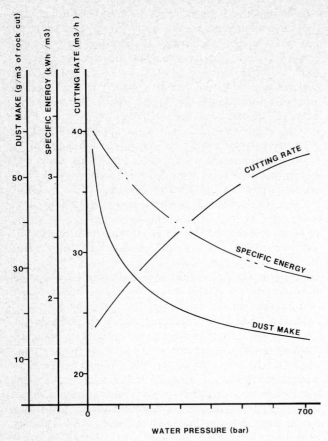

Fig. 5 Performance improvement with high-pressure water jets

now be in the hands of the manufacturers who have taken the technology from MRDE, and they will be applying production technology to the design of various elements of the system. It is hoped that they will also be encouraged by early results to undertake further development work on their own behalf (Fig. 6).

Fig. 6 Production prototype machine

Future MRDE activity will be concerned with basic engineering research into materials and technology that will enable water to be applied at pressures of around 1400 bar, and also with the very difficult materials and design problems that are associated with the application of phasing devices. This work will have as its objective the release of water only in the direction of cutterhead attack so as to limit the amount of water that is released in the overall heading operation.

Automatic control and instrumentation

A major limitation to the use of roadheaders in United Kingdom coal mines has been the difficulty of matching machine capability to constantly changing strata conditions. The application of the machine and attempted rate of excavation are normally dependent largely on the discretion and aptitude of the machine operator. Over-cautious operation gives too shallow a cut with limited penetration, which results in a high rate of pick wear. An attempt to achieve too great a penetration in hard and difficult rocks results in actual damage to picks, and sometimes to the machine as a consequence of frequent stalling of the cutting head, and generally erratic performance.

It was recognized that the forces that come into play on the MRDE and the Eimco tunnelling machines could not be adequately controlled by the normal fixed-displacement hydraulic pump and circuit with pressure compensation. A load-control system based on measurement of electrical cutting power, which was then used to determine the angle of the swash plate in a variable-delivery pump, was devised and has operated on the circular machine for two years. Early experience showed that it was better to split control into two levels, the lower level being rate control. This was arranged by allowing the operator to determine manually traverse speed by reading the power level, from a kilowatt meter and using his pilot hydraulic control lever accordingly. Above a power level fixed below full rated motor load the auto control takes over and replaces the operator's judgement on matching traverse speed with indicated load (Fig. 7).

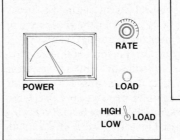
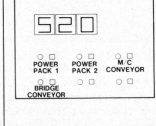

Fig. 7 Load/rate control unit and boom readout

The value of this type of control and protection was very quickly evident, and more sophisticated systems are now being developed with the aid of Sheffield University and others.

Figs. 2 and 3 show the vertical mounting of boom in the turret of the MRDE tunnelling machines: elevation of the boom to a set radius and subsequent rotation of the turret generate a precise circular profile – full circle in one case and half-circle at the top in the other. Transducers positioned at the boom-elevating cylinder connexions measure the boom angle, which is indicated to the operator on a digital readout so that he can set the cutting radius precisely to suit conditions.

For the Eimco machine it is also necessary to control the boom movement to cut a flat floor: this is done with the aid of a system based on a template tracing device, which, after comparing signals from transducers, gives incremental movement to servo valves to control oil flow to cylinders, and hence a combination of turret rotation and boom elevation, to cause a flat sweep.

Although, on both machines the operator is positioned for maximum visibility, it is unlikely that satisfactory and consistent profiling could be achieved without these instrument aids.

CAD – cutterhead design

For many years we have had to accept the design of the cutting head of a roadheader as the best that a designer could do based on experience and empirical rules. Now we have a much greater understanding of the design requirement. A number of research and test programmes into picks and their application in rock have come to fruition and, perhaps most important of all, CAD programs have been developed. Originally used to check existing cutterhead designs, they are now expanded to take account of the above-mentioned research input and can provide design layouts for cutting heads that are correctly balanced with maximum breakout efficiency, the most suitable pick lacing and best positioning of picks for durability and debris loading.

So far as the NCB is concerned, the research work has been allied to practical trials with full-scale cutting facilities in a limestone mine and then verified on production machines in collieries. The optimum attack angles, pick lacing and line frequency for different types of strata have been largely established, and the computer programs are constantly updated to take account of this practical input. The CAD system allows the intervention of both design engineer and research scientist to produce the best compromise result between ideal operational layout and engineering practicality.

At all stages during the design process it is possible to check that all picks have roughly equal duty and that the breakout pattern eliminates side rubbing of picks and grooving. Picks and pick boxes in the computer memory can be retrieved and positioned to ensure welding practicability without overlapping, water nozzles can be fitted in the most suitable place and loading vanes can be engineered for efficiency and manufacture.

A feature of great value is the ability to check the traversing and vertical force components on a cutting head operating through 360°. Out of balance forces are identified by this method and, if eliminated, can help the cutterhead to operate in very hard or inconsistent strata with a lower incidence of those vibrations which can be reflected through the boom and gear transmission and cause machine damage.

The design of cutting heads for the MRDE tunnelling machine and for the high-pressure water jet assisted roadheaders was a critical factor in the success of the projects, and the availability of CAD programs as an aid to this was particularly beneficial.

Cutter picks

During the evolution of light-duty machines into heavy-duty the cutting pick was quickly identified as a weak link. The first roadheaders utilized the normal radial pick that is used on shearers to cut coal. This was, of course, eventually found to be inadequate, particularly when applied with higher unit force and without any precise control of the way in which it was done. The three major lines of pick development within the NCB have been the forward attack pick, the point attack pick and the very large radial picks used on the MRDE and NCB–Eimco tunnelling machines.

A notable feature of the development of the point attack pick has been the recognition that wear can be evened out by allowing, or even initiating, rotation of the pick during cutting. This appears to be a significant factor in lengthening the time between pick changes.

There has been some debate on the relative cutting efficiency of radial and point attack picks, but there is now agreement that in conditions in which a high rate of heavy impact can be expected the point attack pick, which accepts the load axially, is probably stronger.

The MRDE tunnelling machine can use either the large radial pick originally developed by Greenside–MacAlpine or point attack. To date, most operations have been with the large

radial, although the limited experience obtained with point attack has been reasonably satisfactory.

Both forward attack and point attack picks have been used on the water jet assisted roadheaders with equal efficiency.

Conclusions

Based on many years of rock sampling and testing at MRDE it is concluded that probably 75% of the strata that will be encountered in coal mine drivage will be of a compressive strength of 100 MPa or below. The rest will have a higher compressive strength of up to +200 MPa and, relatively infrequently, +275 MPa. This broad classification by compressive strength ignores fracture count, abrasivity, tensile strength and specific energy measurements, but it does give some general indication of the scope of our rock-cutting requirements. The fact that this is not generally as difficult as that encountered in the more extreme civil engineering conditons is probably the reason why the NCB has concentrated more on the use of cutter picks rather than discs or other rolling cutters (which require larger and more expensive machines for their operation).

It now appears that there is at hand the means to tackle almost all of the strata that are likely to be met, machines equipped with picks being used.

In the longer tunnels, in which higher capital machine investment can be accommodated, larger, more powerful machines, such as the MRDE and the NCB–Eimco machines, will pass through rock at +200 MPa, albeit more slowly and probably with the use of a large number of picks. The application of high-pressure water to medium-weight roadheaders is already showing significant advantages and rock at more than 140 MPa, which would normally be outside their economic range, has been excavated successfully. The associated better dust suppression, reduced incendive sparking and protection of picks and machine are valuable additional benefits.

The experience now gained with computer-aided design of cutting heads shows a significant contribution to the efficiency of all machines of whatever size and with whatever cutting assistance they may receive. That contribution should not be underestimated.

Better control of machines in tackling difficult rocks is essential. Work already done on automatic load control indicates not only the practicability of this aspect of development but also the considerable advantages that are to be obtained.

The general picture is encouraging.

Acknowledgement

The author would like to thank T. L. Carr, Head of Mining Research and Development, for permission to present this paper. The views expressed are those of the author and not necessarily those of the National Coal Board.

Design and construction of Bristol Southern foul water interceptor – stages 2 and 3

T. N. Plenty
City of Bristol District Council, Bristol, England
M. V. M. Law
Bovis Civil Engineering, Ltd. (now A. E. Farr, Ltd.), Westbury, Wiltshire, England

Synopsis
For more than 20 years the City of Bristol has been progressing a regional drainage scheme that, when complete, will eliminate all discharges of crude foul sewage into the River Avon. The design of one £7 000 000 section of the sewer network and details of the working methods adopted by the contractor are described and information is provided on rates of progress achieved with the tunnelling systems and on some of the problems that were encountered.

From the earliest stages of its development Bristol, in common with many other industrial cities, had taken advantage of natural water courses as a cheap and convenient method of disposal for the waste, both human and industrial, that such development created. By the middle of the 1950s the situation had deteriorated to such an extent that during the summer periods, when river flows were at their lowest, up to 200 t per year of chlorine was being pumped into the rivers to counteract the obnoxious smells.

The River Avon has one of the largest tidal ranges in the world and the large volume of water ebbing and flowing on each high tide might be considered adequate to cleanse this section of the waterway. Unfortunately, the true situation was that much of the effluent that travelled down on the ebb tide could not reach the Bristol Channel and would return on the following tide, combining with the sewage that was then discharging.

The Regional foul water scheme (Fig. 1) was established with the objective of eliminating all discharges of crude foul sewage to the River Avon by the construction of a system of sewers and pumping stations that would convey the effluent to a new sewage treatment works to be constructed at Avonmouth. It was intended that the scheme should deal not only with the sewage from the city but also with that from adjoining districts within the catchment area and enable isolated treatment works to be closed down.

The regional scheme, which was begun in 1959, was phased to provide a new major sewage treatment works at Avonmouth as a priority, together with the construction of the main trunk sewer from Lawrence Weston to Portway. The regional scheme pre-dated the reorganization of the water industry in 1974, which established Wessex Water Authority as the responsible authority for such initiatives. The scheme has continued to be developed by Wessex, Bristol acting under an agency agreement.

In January, 1978, stage 1 of the Southern foul water interceptor was complete and the effluent from 80% of the city's population was then being treated at Avonmouth.

Design

The areas to be served by the Southern interceptor include Hartcliffe, Windmill Hill, Totterdown, Knowle, Brislington, St. Anne's and Bath Road industrial estate. The low-lying areas will continue to discharge via the existing nineteenth century brick barrel sewers to a pumping station at Ashton Avenue, which was commissioned in 1971.

The route and gradient of the proposed interceptor were dictated by (1) the levels of existing sewers, (2) minimizing the number of pumping stations and future maintenance costs, (3) ensuring self-cleansing velocities for each completed length and (4) providing sufficient capacity for future development.

The population of this area amounts to 140 000, which, together with 125 hectares of industrial site, produces a daily dry weather flow of 960 l/s. The majority of the existing sewers in the catchment were constructed during the nineteenth and early twentieth centuries as a combined system of drainage. The interceptor therefore has to be capable of carrying storm and dry weather flows, a total capacity of 5500 l/s being required.

It was originally intended that the complete section from Ashton Avenue pumping station to the Bath Road industrial estate would be constructed as a single project. Financial restrictions required that the scheme be phased over several years and awarded as a series of separate contracts. The physical restraints that were imposed by the geography of the area and its development dictated that a minimum of four stages would be economically viable within the financial provision allowed. Stages were determined so that the appropriate level of benefit accrued after construction of each phase.

The first stage – from Ashton Avenue pumping station to Dean Lane (1680 m × 2.59 m internal diameter) – was awarded to Bovis Civil Engineering, Ltd., in 1975 and completed in January, 1978.

The second stage – from Dean Lane to Victoria Park (614 m × 2.74 m) – and the third – Victoria Park to St. Anne's (2393 m × 2.44 m and 460 m × 1.2 m) – were combined to include all remaining tunnel construction and are the subject of this paper (Figs. 2 and 3).

The interceptor was designed with a gradient of 1 in 2500, which required strict tolerances during construction to avoid reverse gradients. The specification for stage 1 had required the installation of a single-pass precast concrete segmental lining. Difficulties were experienced, however, both with level control to specification and damage to the lining – in particular, the invert sections, which required extensive remedial works. To overcome these problems the specification for stages 2 and 3 was for a primary precast concrete lining with a secondary lining of in-situ concrete (Fig. 4).

Stage 4, which is now under construction, consists of two pumping stations, together with associated rising mains, which will intercept and pump into the main sewer from the low-lying areas of St. Anne's and the Bath Road industrial estate.

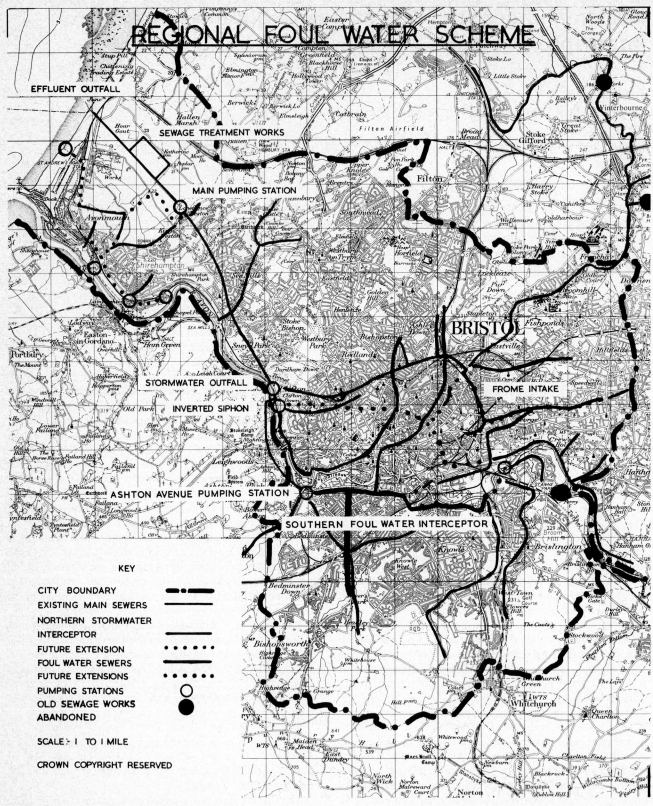

Fig. 1 Regional foul water scheme

Inverted syphon

Stage 2 of the interceptor commences at Dean Lane, Bedminster, and crosses the densely developed valley and flood plain of the Malago Stream. The topography of this section was such as to suggest construction to be by box culvert laid in open-cut trench with a 100-m length of inverted syphon to traverse existing large-diameter sewers and a busy urban highway.

Ground investigations confirmed that the excavation for the box culvert would be in very weak alluvial material that contained peat bands over its entire length. The culvert would have

needed to be supported on piles founded on competent rock at 6-m depth. In addition, the excavation would require substantial temporary support by well-strutted sheetpiling. The predicted noise from sheetpiling operations and the disruption to local traffic by necessary road closures would, it was decided, be unacceptable to the owners of adjacent properties. Furthermore, the works would also necessitate extensive and costly service diversions and highway reinstatements. It was therefore decided to construct the entire section as an inverted syphon and locate the horizontal leg in competent rock at an average

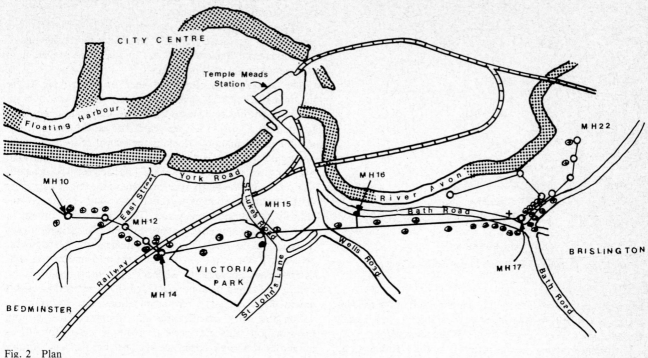

Fig. 2 Plan

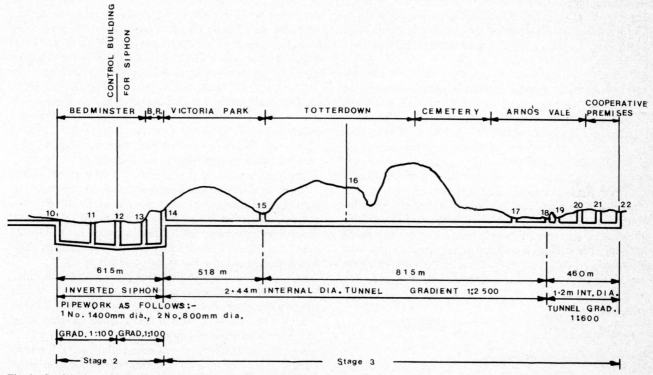

Fig. 3 Section through tunnel (approximate length, 3.5 km; average depth, 30 m)

depth below ground of 25 m: this increased the length of tunnelling that could be constructed by the same technique by an additional 614 m, thereby effectively reducing the unit cost.

An essential feature of any syphon structure is that velocities of flow are sufficient to ensure self-cleansing of the system under all operational conditions. In this instance three pipes are required – two of 800-mm diameter and one of 1400-mm diameter (Fig. 5) – which can be utilized singly or together by controlling flow. A control building located midway between inlet and outlet contains electrically operated valves that operate on time switches and by over-riding electrodes under storm conditions. For maintenance purposes it was considered

essential to provide a permanent pump installation within a dry well at the base of the centre shaft. The possibility of a permanently submerged shaft was considered but discounted for a variety of reasons. The system that has now been constructed enables any pipe to be emptied by pumping from one to the other, the redundant section having first been isolated.

Site investigation

The construction of the various sections of the regional drainage scheme has produced detailed ground investigation over a wide area of the city. Information obtained from

181

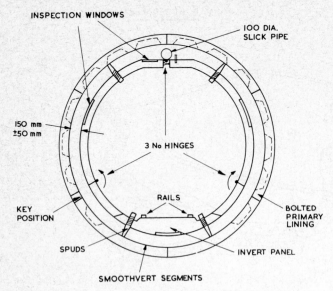

Fig. 4   Typical section of secondary lining shutter in tunnel

previous site investigation contracts in the south of the city was therefore available for analysis at an early stage and assisted in the selection of the preferred route of the interceptor.

The archive mining records retained by the National Coal Board at Cardiff and Radstock provided further useful data regarding evidence of old mine shafts and past mining activity. These workings are recorded to have been carried out at depths between 400 m and 600 m below the proposed tunnel horizon and disturbance to the ground to be excavated would therefore be minimal.

Geological information indicated that the tunnel horizon, for the majority of its length, would be contained within the Keuper Marl and Sandstone of the Triassic Series. A site investigation was undertaken to obtain further information together with laboratory analysis of the rock and soil samples obtained. The total number of boreholes excavated for the main investigation amounted to 17 (Fig. 2), with an average distance between successive drilling of 180 m, a combination of rotary drilling and percussive boring methods being used. The location and depth of each borehole was determined by the engineer and instructions were given to the contractor as the investigation progressed in regard to *in-situ* testing and material sampling. The drilling bit pressures and penetration rates were recorded in all drilled boreholes. Standard and dynamic cone penetration tests were made in granular material and weak rock.

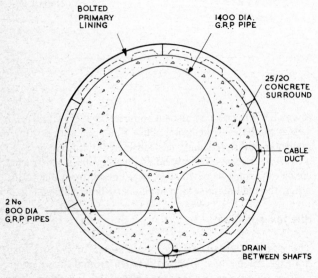

Fig. 5   Typical section of inverted syphon

At selected locations and depths packer permeability tests were made during the course of drilling by use of a single pneumatically inflated packer.

Casagrande-type piezometers, which consisted of ceramic porous pots approximately 250 mm in length at the end of 20-mm internal diameter PVC standpipes, were installed upon completion in selected boreholes.

The investigation confirmed that from manhole 10 to manhole 14, stage 2 (inverted syphon), the tunnel horizon would be within argillaceous sandstone and from manhole 14 to manhole 17 within Keuper Marl. The eastern section from manhole 17 to manhole 18 along the rear of properties on the north side of Bloomfield Road would be through made ground overlying an alluvial cover with Triassic bedrock beneath. Consideration was given to amendment of the line of the tunnel at this location to increase ground cover and provide greater security to adjacent properties. To examine this option in greater detail required an extensive ground investigation programme for the final 330 m of the interceptor. A consultant geologist was appointed to examine the information that was available and appraise the engineer's proposals regarding the nature and extent of a more detailed site investigation of this length. The geologist's recommendations were incorporated within the work specification and three specialist ground investigation contractors were invited to tender. A total of 21 boreholes was sunk at an average spacing of 16 m. Rotary drilling from ground level was employed for seven of the boreholes, the remainder being sunk to their full depth by percussive boring or taken to rock head and then to the required depth by rotary drilling. Standard and dynamic cone penetration tests, field vane tests, pressure meter tests and packer tests were undertaken at site, and laboratory tests included those for classification, strength, consolidation and permeability.

The investigation indicated the presence of a weakly cemented sand stratum from which core recovery was almost impossible even with use of the Trifus triple-tube core barrel. Standard penetration tests at this location met refusal after 50 blows before the 150-mm penetration was achieved, which indicated cemented sand or very weak to weak sandstone.

The investigation of the alternative longer route for the interceptor at Bloomfield Road also revealed the presence of weakly cemented sand at the proposed tunnel horizon. The possible adverse effect of excavating through this material directly beneath properties and the increased cost that would arise from the extra tunnel length confirmed the shorter route within the alluvial material as the preferred option.

Consideration was given to laying pipes in open cut rather than tunnelling with cover of less than 2 m, but the available working space was severely limited by the proximity of industrial units and it was considered that an unacceptable level of disruption to commerce would be caused by major works of this type. Additionally, with modern techniques ground disturbance and dewatering would be controlled to a greater extent by tunnelling than open cut.

Target contract

All tunnelling and similar underground works carry risks that are difficult for contractors to quantify in the preparation of tenders. A detailed site investigation, together with clear and comprehensive contract documents, ensures that the contractor is given the best information available, but uncertainties regarding the actual conditions that will be encountered and their effect on rates of drive and, hence, profitability remain. The Institution of Civil Engineers *Standard conditions of contract* places the responsibility for such decisions on the contractor unless the ground conditions are not reasonably foreseeable (clause 12), and the rates that form the basis of the tender reflect this financial risk.

To share all forms of risk more equitably between the contractor and the client, and thereby reduce the percentage allowance for risks within the tender, most tunnelling in Bristol has successfully employed a form of contract of the target type. A selected list of contractors is invited to submit a tender by completing a standard bill of quantities, the accepted tender then becoming the target figure for the works. The contractor's remuneration is based on two elements – the value of the completed works ascertained by remeasurement and based on the tender rates and the actual cost of all labour, plant and materials wholly employed in the completion of the works. A contract price fluctuation clause in the contract ensures that the remeasurement takes account of inflation. The contractor then receives a payment that is determined by comparison of these elements, the value of any difference being shared equally with the client. In this way the incentive to complete the works economically is maintained, but the effect of unquantifiable factors is reduced.

The type of construction plant is determined by the contractor, but approval must be obtained from the engineer, who will need to be satisfied of its suitability. The payment for such plant is either in the form of an agreed hire rate, if this is likely to be of short duration, or plant is purchased and resold when it is no longer required, the depreciation and running costs forming part of the actual cost of works.

The required amendments to the *Standard conditions of contract* to produce a target type are primarily concerned with all references to cost and payment. Ten clauses have been rewritten and 34 have been modified to ensure compatibility. The remaining contract conditions remain unaltered.

The accounts that are submitted by the contractor every month consist of summaries of labour, plant and material costs incurred in respect of the works for the previous month, together with a statement of the agreed admeasurement for the same period. Within 28 days the engineer, subject to verification, certifies an amount due for payment that comprises the agreed actual cost of works plus a percentage of the remeasured target figure. After the issue of the completion certificate the contractor receives payment of approximately half of the actual cost and half the remeasured target figure.

As an example of the operation of this form of contract consider the situation that normally arises when unforeseen ground conditions are encountered. Under a measure and value contract the contractor incurs additional expense, which he would hope to recover from the client by the submission of a fully documented claim. Unless there is an early agreement to the substance of the claim by the engineer, any additional cost must, initially, be carried by the contractor. With a target contract, however, all costs properly incurred are reimbursed in the following month. The additional cost attributable to the ground conditions and any delay to progress must be quantified for inclusion, when agreed, within the target figure and to give proper consideration to an extension of time for completion.

From the above it should be apparent that a much greater degree of cooperation is required between the resident engineer and project manager and their respective staffs when a target contract is being operated. The resident engineer should become much more involved in the decision-making process, particularly where difficulties are met, and the contractor needs to view this involvement as constructive to the overall objectives of completing the works to the required standard within the time specified and within the approved budget. These objectives can be achieved without either party having to sacrifice his own individual requirements of obtaining a reasonable profit for the contractor and a satisfactory standard of workmanship at reasonable cost for the client.

Construction

Programme
Bovis Civil Engineering, Ltd., were awarded the four-year contract for the construction of stages 2 and 3 in October, 1980. The conditions of contract laid down specific limits on cash payments to the contractor for each financial year of construction. Therefore, particular consideration had to be given during the preparation of the clause 14 programme to the expected rate of expenditure of the various activities and their relationship to the critical path. It was decided that the tunnel from the main compound (manhole 15) to the syphon inlet shaft (manhole 14) be driven first to prove the tunnelling system on a straight 600 linear metre drive through the Keuper Marl before the deeper syphon drive was attempted in the sandstone from the bottom of manhole 10.

Initial works
During the detailed design stage of the tunnelling system and procurement of the necessary equipment work was begun on the construction of a sheetpiled coffer dam 25 m long, 4.5 m wide and 7 m deep at the position of manhole 15 (Fig. 6). This was constructed solely as temporary works to facilitate the installation of tunnelling and mucking arrangements and subsequent *in-situ* secondary lining of the tunnels. Simultaneously, shaft-sinking was begun at the syphon outfall (manhole 10), the 6-m internal diameter excavation being carried out with a Smalley 5 excavator fitted with a Krupp 110C hydraulic impact hammer. Primary concrete linings to shafts were cast *in-situ* by conventional underpinning methods with the use of substantial 900-mm deep timber shutters.

Tunnelling system
Bovis drew extensively on past experience of mechanized tunnelling in the Triassic Series in designing an integrated tunnelling package for the 3 km of 3.05-m outside diameter tunnels. Shield-mounted excavators were investigated, but it was considered that although their use might be possible for the tunnels in the hard clays and mudstones, difficulties would be experienced in breaking out the more competent sandstones on the downgrade section of the syphon. Consequently, the system chosen was based on the Dosco TM1800, but with the following modifications: (*a*) a redesigned chassis to increase clearance for

Fig. 6   Coffer dam with machine being assembled

spoil passing through the machine on the conveyor; (*b*) a 30 m long × 19 mm diameter round link chain conveyor incorporating a reverse curve and powered by twin hydraulic motors: this eliminated the standard strap link and secondary bridge belt conveyors and the inherent problems of spillage at the change point; (*c*) a single substantial tow point between the shield and Dosco, below the conveyor, to improve shield steerage and reduce thrust on the primary lining in the negotiation of bends; (*d*) an increased capacity oil tank to cater for the additional hydraulic requirements of conveyor drive motors and segment erector winches; (*e*) a geometrically designed adjustable guidance cone on the boom of the machine to compensate for wear and to minimize overbreak; and (*f*) a Baldwin and Francis control panel mounted on the Dosco machine and a Wallacetown gate end box on the rear of the sledges to provide sophisticated electrical protection to motors and cables and include a failsafe starting mechanism on the machine.

Other factors that influenced the design are noted below.
(1) The 250-m radius curve on the syphon tunnel limited the height and length of the conveyor.
(2) Because of the necessity to pass trains in the tunnel on the 1600-m drive it was decided to muck one ring with two trains, each comprising one 1.75-t Clayton loco, three 1.5-m^3 skips and two flat bogies for segments and grout.
(3) The preference of keeping laser guidance of the machine on the centre line of the tunnel and on to a target within the shield.
(4) The elimination of damage to invert segments: to reduce this possibility smoothvert segments were adopted by Bovis; this also greatly assisted invert cleaning, especially during the tunnel lining operation.

Fig. 8   Safe access to face along right-hand side of machine

Fig. 7   Dosco TM 1800, shield, guidance cone and segment erector arch during initial installation

(5) An efficient segment handling and erection system: a purpose-made mechanized segment erector arch was incorporated in the shield, the 0.61-m wide segments being rotated anticlockwise by winches during building (Fig. 7).
(6) The necessity to provide safe access to and from the face at all times: the right-hand side was designated to be kept clear of all materials and equipment, the segments being off-loaded on the opposite side beneath the conveyor on to a monorail for manual transportation on trolley chain blocks to the building area (Fig. 8).

(7) The specification requirements to immediately grout each ring as built: a 0.25-m^3 capacity pneumatic grout pan was situated beneath the conveyor and 2:1 ratio PFA/OPC grout containing sodium silicate accelerator was conveyed to the pan on the flat bogies in 25-kg bags.
(8) The necessity for ventilation: dust was extracted from the face by a 375-mm diameter electric fan with silencer mounted on the side of the conveyor and temporarily connected via flexible ducting at the rear to a 450-mm diameter rigid spiral steel duct erected progressively along the side of the tunnel. Two-stage 475-mm diameter contra-rotating axial flow fans were installed at approximately 400-m intervals to maintain suction, the pair nearest the tunnel portal being fitted with a silencer for environmental reasons. A small pneumatic air mover was also mounted near the grout pan to improve air circulation in the vicinity of the grout pan operator.
(9) The services required in the tunnel were a 415-V three-phase 200-kVA electricity supply to the Dosco, pumps and tunnel lighting, a 25-mm diameter water supply for machine cooling and a compressed-air main for air tools and grout pan.

The final layout of the machine is shown in Fig. 9.

Tunnel drive, manhole 15 to manhole 14
The machine was installed in the coffer dam on a bed of segments with a shortened conveyor. After driving forward for approximately 30 linear metres the conveyor was fully extended. Double 600-mm gauge track and a symmetrical turnout were then laid on the coffer dam floor to allow for two-train working. Double-shift working was then commenced, 12-h shifts being worked from Mondays to Thursdays, and 8-h shifts on Fridays. Weekends were thus fully available for maintenance, repairs, extension of the 240-mm^2 aluminium three-core S.W.A. (steel wire armoured) supply cable to the Dosco and any secondary grouting that was required.

The learning curve was relatively short, a production of 90 rings per week being achieved within the first few weeks. Consistent and higher productivity was hindered, however, by frequent conveyor problems and nuisance tripping of the electrics. It was also found to be necessary to lubricate the conveyor on the reverse curve with the cooling water discharged from the Dosco. This, in turn, adversely affected subsequent muck-handling and disposal operations on the surface.

184

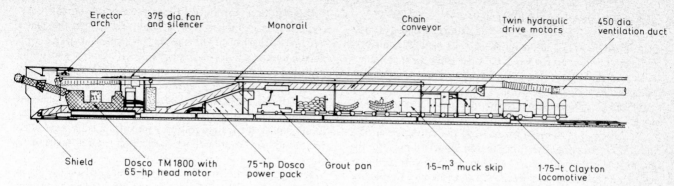

Fig. 9   General arrangement of Dosco tunnelling machine for tunnels, manholes 10 to 17

It was concluded, therefore, that the chain conveyor with its reverse curves was slightly underpowered, so the drive motors were up-rated after the machine was removed at manhole 14. In addition, the Mk. 40 clay cutting head on the Dosco boom was replaced by a Mk. 30, two-start, two-pick align rock cutting head.

Inverted syphon drive

Extensive temporary works were required at the bottom of manhole 10 – a 6-m internal diameter shaft – to service this drive. Sinking the final 4 m of manhole 10 had proved extremely slow, the moderately strong argillaceous sandstone encountered being less weathered and more thickly bedded than had been expected. Blasting was not permitted by the specification. To recoup time lost on the critical shaft-sinking operation a Dosco Mk. 2A roadheader was hired for two weeks to excavate a horseshoe section foreheading 15 m long × 4.5 m wide and a backheading 5 m × 4.5 m from the bottom of the shaft (Fig. 10).

Fig. 10   Dosco Mk. 2A, with boom removed, being lowered down manhole 10

Although the heading required no temporary support during excavation, the crown was subsequently rockbolted and gunited to provide safer and drier working conditions during the tunnelling operations. The TBM was installed in the fore-heading, the conveyor being extended once the machine had advanced 30 linear metres. Double track and symmetrical turnout were installed at pit bottom, the two trains being serviced with the minimum shunting by a 22 RB ICD crane on the surface.

The problems that were encountered on this drive occurred mainly on the initial 1 : 100 downgrade section, manhole 10 to manhole 12, through the sandstones. Briefly, these were (a) cutting head main bearing failures owing to the ingress of fine sand; (b) extensive wear on chain and conveyor pans, although the curved sections had been renewed and reinforced prior to recommencement; (c) conveyor jamming; (d) concentrated water inflows from fissures in the sandstone tending to cause slurry and rapid flooding at the face; (e) slurry and settlement tank problems on the surface, and subsequent difficulties in disposing of slurry off site; and (f) severe congestion of the small, surface working area (this was eased considerably by the adoption of a double-handling procedure for supplies of segments, grout, etc., from the main site and by limiting stockpiles to those sufficient for 24 h of production only).

Good pumping management was essential, inflows of 1500 l/min being experienced just past manhole 11. At this stage 75-mm diameter submersible pumps were required at the face together with two 150-mm diameter pumps and pipelines in the tunnel, one of which had to be kept close to the rear of the machine to be effective. Nevertheless, a major pump break-down occurred that resulted in the complete inundation of the machine and the loss of eight days of production while the machine was dried out. Despite this delay, the drive was com-pleted successfully at an average weekly rate of 54 rings. An analysis of downtime, which amounted to 486 h in total, revealed that 60% of stoppages were attributable to the flooding, slurry or materials-handling problems. Of the remaining 40% that was attributable to the TBM, 6% of stoppages was associated with the electrics, 17% with the conveyor, 10% with the Dosco and 7% miscellaneous.

Fig. 11   Typical face conditions during tunnel drive, manholes 15 to 17

185

Tunnel drive, manhole 15 to manhole 17

Again, use was made of the coffer dam and existing site set-up at the main site. The 1600 linear metre drive was predominantly through the moderately weak to moderately strong Keuper Marl and mudstones (Fig. 11). Occasionally, a thin vein of celestine was encountered, but otherwise there was little variation. Groundwater ingress was minimal and required only nominal pumping.

The length of this drive necessitated the introduction of a third train and modifications to the power supply to the machine to compensate for excessive voltage drop on the aluminium cable. Both were expected and a planned stop of one week at the mid-point of the tunnel drive was incorporated into the programme. This allowed for the installation of a double-track passing bay on ballast and changeover to a 415/3300/415 V system with the stepdown mining transformer sited in a small heading excavated at the side of the tunnel. In addition, the opportunity was taken to overhaul thoroughly the machine and conveyor.

Consistent progress of 100 rings/week (61 linear metres) was maintained throughout this drive, which vindicated the decision to carry out the longest drive last in the programme, the overall system having already been proved and refined on the shorter drives. Machine non-availability as a result of breakdown on this final drive was less than 1%.

Tunnel drive, manhole 17 to manhole 18

The alluvial deposits on this shallow section clearly indicated the use of different techniques to that employed previously. The extensive site investigation data, coupled with the experience gained while excavating manhole 18 through the unstable sandy clayey silts, confirmed that face support would be necessary, the Dosco would only be a hindrance and maintaining a steady rate of advance would be of utmost importance.

Accordingly, Bovis elected to drive the tunnel on double shift in the direction of manhole 17 to manhole 18, while mucking out and servicing the tunnel from the main site of manhole 15. This circumvented the single-shift restriction imposed by the specification on working from the environmentally sensitive site of manhole 18, and effectively halved the total drive time. The decision also allowed the tunnelling system to be installed in the Keuper Marl before rock head rapidly dipped away below invert level some 20 linear metres from manhole 17.

The 3.05-m outside diameter tunnelling shield previously used with the Dosco was modified on site by the addition of a 600-mm long hood extension, three hydraulically operated breasting plates and two 30-t face rams. The shield was installed at manhole 17, a shaft 5 m in internal diameter × 5.5 m deep, and advanced by hand mucking for some 20 linear metres. A modified chain conveyor that required only one curved section over the power pack was then installed, together with all the trailing sledges and ancillary equipment used previously to form a complete system (Fig. 12).

It was found that the sandy-clayey silts and organic peats could be extruded through the partially closed breasting plates well into the body of the shield. Two miners working with pneumatic clay spades on small platforms on either side of the conveyor could easily remove material from the face directly on to the chain conveyor beneath. At shift changeovers and weekends the face was fully boarded, the breasting plates and face rams being used to maintain stability. Fears that line and level would be difficult to control were unfounded, except when rock head rose 600 mm above invert level for a distance of 15 rings.

Briefly, the problems that were encountered on this drive were (a) the tendency of fine-grained sand to wash into the invert building area and through the circumferential joints between the bolted lining, which necessitated extensive caulking and some back grouting; (b) the unforeseen occurrence of a seventeenth century water supply well; and (c) the bursting of two unmapped 150-mm diameter asbestos water mains adjacent to manhole 18, where cover to the tunnel crown was only 1.5 m.

Although strict compliance with the specification to keep grout tight over the last ring built tended to limit production, the drive was completed in ten weeks, progress of 33 linear metres per week being achieved consistently once the conveyor system had been installed.

Secondary lining to tunnels

Concrete containing 360 kg/m³ of sulphate-resisting cement was specified for the 150-mm thick secondary lining. Prior to this operation, however, a variation order was issued to switch from sulphate-resistant mixes to OPC–PFA replacement mixes to capitalize on possible cost savings and improved ultimate strength, surface finish and workability characteristics.

A mix with a total cementitious content of 380 kg/m³ was adopted to maintain class 3 sulphate resistance, 30% being PFA – the proportion recommended by *Building Research Establishment Digest* 250. The percentage fines of the 50-mm slump OPC–PFA mix, used successfully for reinforced-concrete work on the contract, was increased to 43% to produce a high-slump mix suitable for pumping and forming the *in-situ* tunnel lining full circle in one operation.

Bovis elected to form the 2.44-m internal diameter lining in 25-m lengths on a daily cycle by use of a telescopic steel shutter designed and supplied by R. Murer A.G. of Switzerland, one of the few suppliers who were prepared to offer a fully powered telescopic shutter for such a small-diameter tunnel (Fig. 4).

Pre-mixed concrete with an initial slump of 130 mm was supplied to site during the day shift only and transported in 3-m³ Mühlhauser transit cars to a rail-mounted belt conveyor feeding a Sidewinder SW30, 50-hp electric pump. This pumped the concrete via a 45 m long × 100 mm diameter welded slick pipe suspended from chains in the crown of the tunnel and resting on the flat top of the shutter (Fig. 13). As the shutter

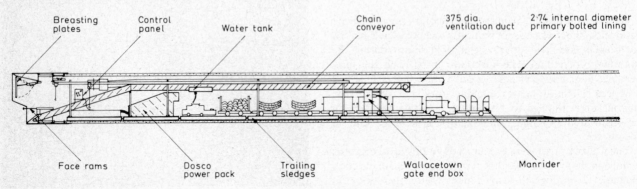

Fig. 12   Modified arrangement of tunnelling equipment for tunnel, manholes 17 to 18

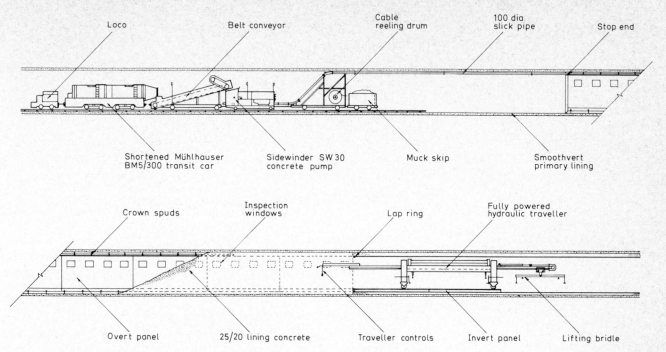

Fig. 13 General arrangement of equipment for tunnel lining operation, manholes 14 to 18

filled progressively from the rear, a slick pipe embedment of 2–3 m in the fresh concrete was generally sufficient to develop enough pressure to thrust the complete pipe and pumping equipment backwards unaided without having to pull with the locomotive.

External clamp-on pneumatic vibrators were used in sequence to finally compact the concrete. A purpose-made stop end and an adjustable lap ring allowed the steel screw spuds of the overt sections of the shutter always to bear directly on the circumferential ribs of the primary bolted lining to resist the considerable uplift forces that were generated during concreting.

During the night shift, and after the invert had been cleaned of debris from the previous pour, the shutter was stripped and re-erected within 5 h by use of an electric powered, hydraulically operated traveller (Fig. 14). A minimum curing period of 12 h was allowed before stripping the first 5-m long panel from the rear of the shutter. Sixteen pours were completed before a daily cycle of concreting was achieved, owing, mainly, to initial teething problems with the equipment, non-acceptance of the production bonus scheme and problems with the concrete mix design that resulted in poor surface finishes being achieved.

The initial pump mix previously described, when stripped after 12 h, resulted in considerable areas of surface pulling away with the shutter. At first the shutter oil was thought to be the problem, but when no great improvements were noted after various trials the mix design was investigated further. Slow early strength gain was considered the major factor, so the total cementitious content of the mix was increased to 440 kg/m^3 while maintaining the PFA replacement at 30% and adjusting the percentage fines to 41%.

Use of this mix resulted in an immediate improvement in surface finish and soon allowed optimum productions of 125 linear metres per five-day week to be achieved.

Acknowledgement

The authors thank A. B. Miller, C.Eng, F.I.C.E., M.I.H.T., M.Inst.W.M., M.B.I.M., City Engineer, Bristol, and R. W. Giles, B.Sc., C.Eng., F.I.C.E., F.C.I.O.B., Managing Director, A. E. Farr, Ltd., formerly Bovis Civil Engineering, Ltd., for permission to publish this paper. They also acknowledge the immense contribution of all their colleagues who were concerned with the design and constructional activities that enabled the project to be concluded successfully six months ahead of schedule.

Appendix 1

Major material supplies
C. V. Buchan (Concrete), Ltd. (bolted lining segments)
Pozament, Ltd. (grout)
Johnston Pipes, Ltd. (G.R.P. pipes)
Mixconcrete, Ltd. (ready-mixed concrete)

Appendix 2

Major equipment supplies
Dosco Overseas Engineering, Ltd. (Dosco machine and chain conveyor)
Grosvenor Tunnelling International, Ltd. (shield and erector)
N.E.I. Mining Equipment, Ltd. (Clayton locomotives)
R. Murer A.G. (telescopic tunnel shutter)
Crow Hamilton (1983), Ltd. (concrete pump)

Fig. 14 View of traveller within lining shutter

187

Automated guidance and profiling systems in tunnel and shaft construction

Peter M. Zollman
ZED Instruments, Ltd., West Molesey, Surrey, England

Synopsis

The number of tunnels that are being driven under automated guidance is increasing steadily. Clients, contractors and machine manufacturers have gained major benefits in terms of safety and accuracy, coupled with significant savings in costs and time. New tunnelling machines have been introduced (and many more are in development) in which instrumental guidance is an essential and integral part of the design. Eight years after the installation of the first automated tunnel guidance system it is appropriate to evaluate the experience that has been gained in a wide variety of applications.

A brief description is given of guidance systems for full-face tunnel-boring machines and shields (straight and curved drives), blind shaft boring (vertical and inclined), pipejacking and micro-tunnelling (straight and curved), roadheaders (with automatic profiling) and circular and arch-shaped shields with fixed booms (with automatic profiling). A selection of accomplished and current projects is presented, economy, reliability and points of operational and surveying interest being emphasized.

General

Instruments and aids of varying precision and sophistication have long been used in tunnelling. In more recent times tunnelling engineers added lasers, electronic distance-measuring devices, levels, TV cameras, off-line computers and programmable calculators to their traditional surveying equipment. Ingenious optical and mechanical devices have been fitted to certain machines to provide further assistance to the engineer or the operator. However useful and valuable these developments may be, they are not automated guidance systems in the true sense.

According to the view presented in this paper, an automated guidance system must satisfy the following definition: (a) all essential details of the tunnel and machine geometry (axis coordinates, profile, etc.) are set and stored within the system; (b) a full survey of the machine is automatically performed either continuously or at sufficiently frequent intervals to provide up to date information on all relevant position coordinates and attitude angles; (c) the survey is immediately converted into guidance information that indicates all deviations from the designed values (it will be seen that this information must include the 'predicted position'); (d) preferably, all information is displayed and transmitted digitally within the system; and (e) the system must be simple to understand and easy to operate, functioning reliably in the tough physical and human environment.

Guidance systems for full-face tunnel-boring machines and shields

Measurement: transducers

As is seen in Fig. 1, the operating principles are very straightforward. A conventional tunnelling laser provides a datum beam – in this case parallel to the designed tunnel axis. A target unit of unique design, mounted on the tunnelling machine, receives the beam and continuously performs three independent measurements – the coordinates of incidence (X, Y) and the angle of incidence (lead) of the beam with respect to the axis of the target unit. Rotations about the horizontal machine axes – look-up and roll – are measured by the inclinometer unit with respect to gravity. An optional distance-measuring unit measures the sixth independent variable – the position of the machine along the tunnel axis – but, often, this is known to sufficient accuracy without additional instrumentation.

Data processing

The measured data are automatically checked for validity and transmitted to a special tunnelling computer housed in the engineer's unit; the engineer can simply dial in the data that relate to the geometry of the tunnel – for example, the position of the laser beam relative to the designed tunnel axis, the position of the target unit relative to the machine axis, the required gradient, etc. From these and the transmitted measurement data are computed the position coordinates and attitude angles of the machine axis. The program automatically compensates all interactions (for example, roll about the machine axis affects the laser spot position as it appears on the target screen).

Outputs

Finally, the computed results are displayed to the operator at the machine controls and to the engineer/surveyor at a convenient position in the tunnel or above ground. The standard display device is a digital monitor unit that shows continuously the deviations of the machine axis from the designed tunnel axis, thereby indicating in clear numerical form the actual corrections that are required. A very useful feature is the 'predictor', which displays on the monitor the deviation of the machine axis from the designed tunnel axis, say, 5 m ahead. The 'predictor' ensures a smooth optimized drive, wasteful overcorrection being avoided. In addition to the digital monitor analogue monitors, remote monitors and printer units are also available on a modular basis.

This system is correct for straight tunnelling and it has adequate facilities for curved drives too by the manual input of conventionally tabulated offset values. Accessories are also available for the rapid and precise repositioning of the target in curves. This is usually a one-man manual operation, but Wirth Maschinenfabrik GmbH (Erkelenz, Federal Republic of

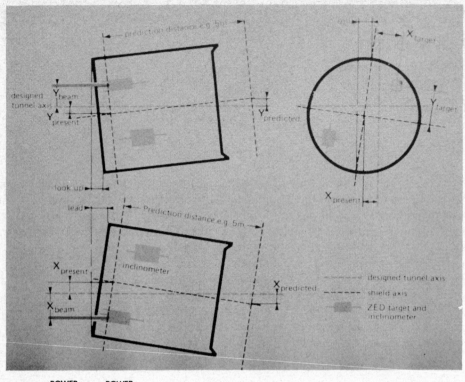

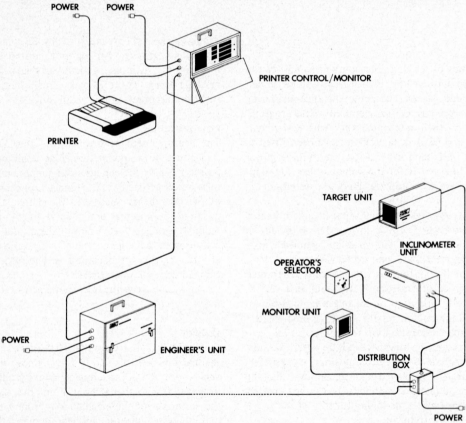

Fig. 1   TG-26 guidance system: definitions and unit schematic

Germany) has motorized this movement on three of their machines for the giant CERN Eurolep tunnel near Geneva, Switzerland.

Two systems are especially suitable for curved axis tunnels. The TG-261 system does not require the manual input of offset values: it utilizes a robust but portable solid-state memory module for the storage of pre-programmed offsets values and other survey information. After being programmed above ground the memory module is taken in the tunnel and plugged into the engineer's unit to provide the offset data without human intervention and without the risk of human error.

The TG-260 system is a powerful modular extension of the basic TG-26. It uses the standard target and inclinometer units and a linear distance-measuring device. In addition, it has an interactive computer above ground, usually in the site office. The global coordinates of the designed tunnel axis (DTA), together with other relevant survey data, are entered and stored in the computer, which is connected to a 'stretched' version of the standard engineer's unit underground. As the machine progresses along the axis its position is measured by the linear distance-measuring device and transmitted to the computer. The corresponding position coordinates and direction angles of

Fig. 2 TG-261 system: memory module and programmer unit

the DTA are calculated and these ideal data are compared with the actual measured values. As in all other TG systems, the present and 'predicted' deviations are continuously updated and displayed on the operator's monitor and at the engineer's unit. Above ground every detail of the operation can be followed on the computer screen and automatically printed out for a permanent record.

Tunnel-boring results

According to available information, automated guidance has been used on at least 32 projects on a wide variety of tunnel-boring machines and shields (the exact number is probably greater because the same equipment will be used on several projects before it is taken out of commission or sent back to the manufacturer for cleaning and a general check).

The installation of an instrumental guidance system has enabled machines to be kept within the required tolerances, which varied, typically, between 25 and 5 mm. Automated guidance systems have proved to be extremely useful on blade shields. In the Antwerp Pre-Metro construction the automated guidance was combined with the pre-existing Stolitzka method. With the use of automated guidance the owners were able to follow the complete data of the axis as the tunnel was built, data being printed day and night after every shove of about 27 cm. Tolerances were maintained throughout with an average deviation of less than 30 mm in the horizontal plane as well as in the vertical. The total length of tunnelling (4 km) was achieved in 21 months.

Blind shaft boring

Some form of automated guidance was essential to steer the vertical blind shaft boring machine shown in Fig. 4 because the operator, in his cabin several metres above the cutting head, has no direct sight of the face. In this case roll cannot be measured by an inclinometer with respect to gravity. On the other hand, inclinometers can be used to establish the attitude angles of the machine. The standard system has been adapted (Fig. 4) to these conditions. Two laser plumbs provided reference for position as well as roll measurement.

Pipe jacking and microtunnelling (straight and curved)

Measurement: transducers

Standard TG-26 systems have been used on numerous pipe-jacking jobs, a fixed laser being mounted at the shaft and the target and inclinometer being attached to the machine. The engineer's unit and the monitor may be at the shaft or on the machine, but always in positions convenient to the engineer and operator, respectively. The maximum distance between shafts is usually limited by the absorption, refraction and dispersion of the laser beam to 200–300 m (this limit may be further reduced when the beam must cross one or more windows or in exceptionally adverse atmospheric conditions). For straight microtunnelling a compact system based on a combined target/inclinometer and an integrated engineer's unit/monitor is usually supplied (Fig. 5).

In curved pipe jacking there is no direct line of sight between the jacking shaft and the machine. Two practical solutions will be described. Fig. 6 illustrates the principle of the TG-260/P system, which is the pipe-jacking derivative of the TG-260 system with the following differences. The laser station (laser, inclinometer and optical goniometer on a common frame) is attached to the tunnel lining and moves along with the drive. An additional unit, the rear station, also attached to the wall, follows some 50 m behind: this contains a special light source directed toward the laser station and an inclinometer.

Data processing

As was stated earlier, the TG-260 system stores, among other data, the global coordinates of the designed tunnel axis (DTA). The laser beam is defined as a point plus the zenith and azimuth angles in the same global coordinate system. The TG-260/P system also stores the actual machine coordinates that represent the measured tunnel axis (MTA). In the first approximation it is assumed that the path of the laser station is the MTA, so its global coordinates are known from 'historical' data. The same does not apply to the zenith and azimuth angles of the beam. We cannot expect the orientation of the laser station to follow that of the machine with sufficient accuracy. The function of the goniometer is to provide a continuous survey of the laser station with reference to the rear station, the position of which is accurately known – again from 'historical' data. The data processed by the computer must also include the inclinometer measurements – for example, for roll correction. The respective distances between the three stations will also vary and must therefore be measured continuously. At first the laser station and, later, the rear station will be stationary at the shaft while the target moves forward. When used, intermediate jacking must also be taken into account.

The accuracy of the TG-260/P system is further enhanced by regular conventional surveys of the tunnel. The coordinates of the surveyed tunnel axis (STA) can be conveniently entered into the computer to replace the MTA points.

Measurement: transducers

Another guidance system suitable for curved pipe jacking in sub-metre diameter tunnels is shown in Fig. 7. The position and the attitude angles of the machine are established by a polygon survey from a known fixed origin at the jacking shaft. The polygon is formed by special survey stations spaced to ensure a safe direct line of sight between neighbours. The length of each chord is recorded when the respective station is inserted. The effect of intermediate jacking stations is measured and accounted for in the computation. Each station consists of two optical transmitter–receiver pairs – one facing forward and the other backward – and a set of inclinometers to provide automatic correction for roll and look-up errors.

Data processing

The stations operate under the supervision of a computer situated above ground or at the shaft. This computer is also responsible for storing the coordinates of the desired tunnel axis, processing the measured values and calculating the present and predictable position of the machine for display on the operator's monitor, remote monitor, printout, etc.

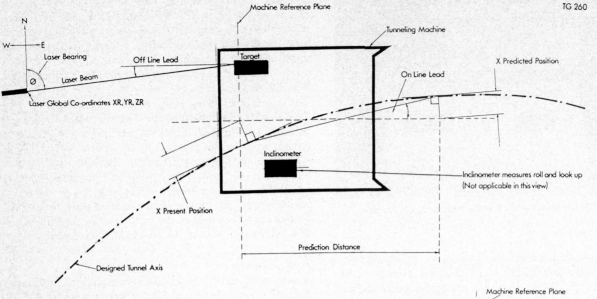

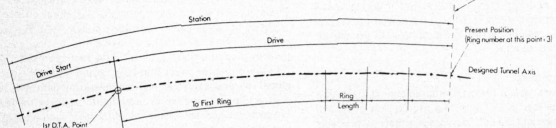

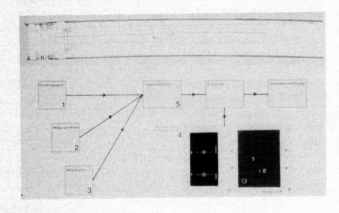

PAGE 1   PROCESSED RESULTS

PRESENT POSITION ----- X = + 17 MM   Y = - 8 MM

PREDICTED POSITION --- X = -125 MM   Y = +183 MM

ROLL ------------------ + 81 MRAD

LEAD ------------------ - 17 MRAD

LOOKUP ---------------- + 8 MRAD

DRIVE ----------------- 1379.65 M

AXIS POINT ----------- X = 10136.519 M   Y = 17532.614 M   Z = 103.592 M

PAGE 4   UNPROCESSED DATA

TARGET POSITION ------   X = 0.000 M Y = 98.876 M

PREDICTION DISTANCE --   -.928 M !

LEAD STEPS -----------   336 DEG !

SPOT POSITION --------   X =   0 MM   Y = 483 MM !

ROLL -----------------   8237.4 MRAD !

LEAD W.R.T. LASER ----   -064.5 MRAD !

LOOKUP W.R.T. VERT. --   -295.4 MRAD !

SHOVE LENGTH ---------   -.769 M

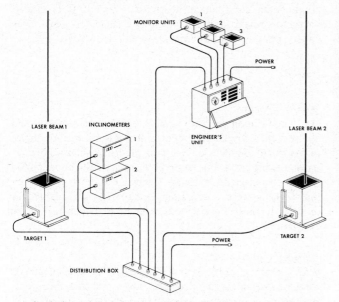

Fig. 3 TG-260 system (*see also previous page*): definitions, system schematic, printout samples and VDU pages

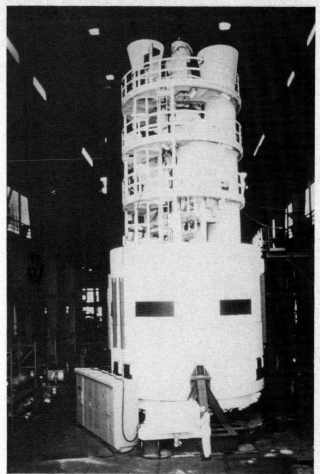

Fig. 4 TG-26/V system: system schematic (*left*) and Robbins vertical blind shaft borer (*above*)

It is obvious that the position of the machine axis, i.e. the last chord, can be determined if all angles and chord lengths of the polygon are known with sufficient accuracy. In long tunnels and tight curvatures the number of stations may become prohibitive. It can be shown, and the Hamburg results[3] support this, that the number of stations can be reduced significantly if use is made of the earlier mentioned 'historical' data.

Pipe-jacking results
At a sewer construction in Berlin Karolinenstrasse in a straight drive through sand the accuracy was within a tolerance of less than 3 cm. A Wirth HBG 701 small-diameter boring machine, equipped with a TG-26/E guidance system, has been tested extensively at the Institute for Building Machinery and Building, Aachen Technical University, and at demonstration

sites in Recklinghausen. Uffmann[2] noted that the deviations of the machine from the designed tunnel axis and its attitude angles are displayed on a monitor outside the tunnel. With this information and the handling characteristics of the machine an overall accuracy of 30 mm is achieved. Steering accuracy was very good, especially as in the latter part of the second demonstration drive the machine had to cross a relatively hard limestone layer at a very acute angle.

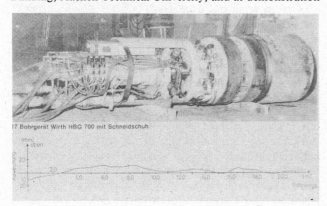

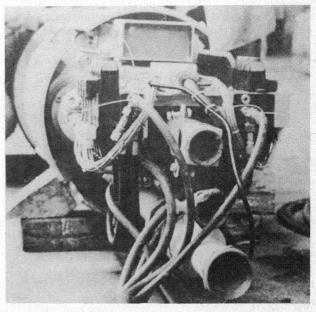

Fig. 5 TG-26/e system for small-bore tunnelling

PAGE 5   LASER AND REAR STATION PARAMETERS

L BEAM CO-ORDINATES X= -1.781 M   Y= 0.000 M!

L STATION AXIS ------ X= -9167.834 M   Y= 58596.064 M   Z= 98978.599 M !

L ROLL ------------- 3436.6 MRAD !   M-L TRAIL -3.882 M !

ZERO BEARING -------   -55.3050 GON !

R SPOT CO-ORDINATES X= 86.395 M   Y= -4.919 M !

R STATION AXIS   X= 79757.606 M Y= -3127.464 M Z= 54622.993 M !

R ROLL ---------   8446.3 MRAD !   L-R TRAIL   62.945 M !

Fig. 6   TG-260/P system

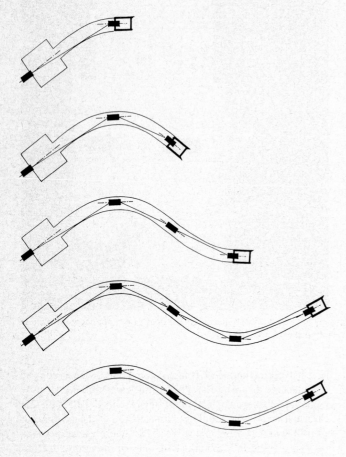

Fig. 7   Pipe jacking by polygon guidance

Müller[3] gave a detailed account of a major curved pipe-jacking project in Hamburg in which surveying and guidance were prominently discussed. He considered as advantages of the system the fact that the survey is continuously updated, the operator uses digital information and the survey results are printed out. Obstacles in front of the machine could be detected at an early stage. In the first use of a system with a movable laser station in pipe jacking after the first 350-m drive with a radius of 900 m the machine arrived at the receiving shaft with a 12-mm accuracy.

Fixed centre-line roadheaders and circular and arch-shaped shields with fixed centre booms

For safe and cost-effective operation these machines need guidance to remain on the designed tunnel axis as well as profile control to ensure correct clearance for the support arches or the shield. The two functions are interdependent.

Measurement: transducers

For profile control the instantaneous position of the cutterhead has to be known with respect to the designed profile. The profile is usually referenced to the designed tunnel axis.

Assuming that the roadheader carriage or the shield is precisely aligned to the tunnel axis, the position and direction of the boom pivots can be found. These, with the boom slew and lift angles and the boom length, define the cutter position. For boom angle measurement suitable electromechanical or electro-optical encoders are used. If the machine or the shield is not perfectly aligned, a guidance system will measure the linear and angular deviations and provide the necessary corrections. Roadheaders are subject to sudden movements and intense vibration. For this application, therefore, a larger size target unit and heavily damped inclinometers are used.

Data processing

Variable data from the transducers of the guidance system (target and inclinometer) and the boom angle encoders, together with preset constant parameters, are processed in an engineer's unit. The constants define the geometry of the given application and include profile dimensions, laser coordinates, boom length and pivot configuration. These data are entered on thumb wheels and can be easily changed to new values underground without any programming knowledge.

Outputs

Monitor display

On standard monitors the engineer and the operator can read all the usual information about the position and attitude angles of the machine or shield, including predicted values. Furthermore, the instantaneous cutter clearance and the boom angles can also be selected for display. Special warning is given when the profile is overcut. A graphic monitor is also available that displays the present cutter position and the current state of the excavation.

Automatic profile cutting

With automatic profile cutting the engineer's unit is interfaced with the hydraulic rams that raise, lower and slew the boom. By a single push-button command the operator can move the boom clockwise or anticlockwise along the desired profile or inside it. Other push buttons will move the boom vertically or horizontally with automatic deceleration and stop when the cutter reaches the profile. The controls may include a graphic monitor, the present boom position and the current state of the excavation being pictorially displayed. The push buttons and display are on a portable console. This enables the operator to steer the boom remotely from the machine and without having to see the face.

Results

At the time of writing two National Coal Board roadheaders, fitted with Zedminer systems, were ready to start operation underground. Three others are soon to be installed for civil engineering tunnelling in Algeria.

Extensive surface trials have demonstrated that roadheader machines can operate more continuously, cutting a more accurate profile and enabling the machine operator to extract a heading with his hands off the controls. Operators find the system easy to use and need not observe closely the cutting head during excavation. The operator can change the cutting sequence and generally utilize his skill and experience more effectively and without fatigue. A Dosco SB 400 fixed-boom shield for the Don Valley intercepting sewer, Sheffield, has been equipped with a monitor system. The operator drives the boom by observing the cutter clearance with respect to the designed profile on a digital monitor. Their system has been in operation since January, 1984, with very good results.

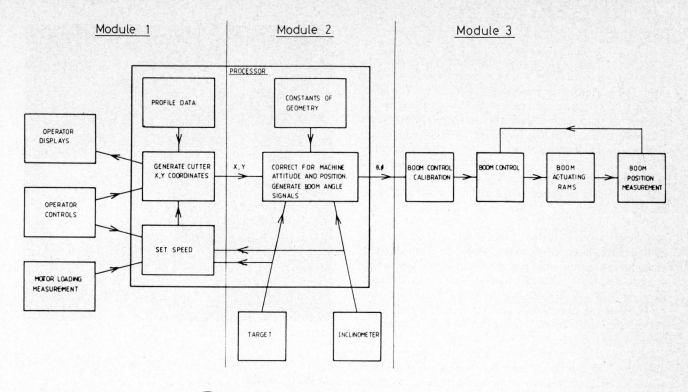

Module 1 | Module 2 | Module 3

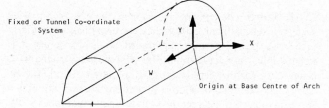

Fixed or Tunnel Co-ordinate System

Origin at Base Centre of Arch

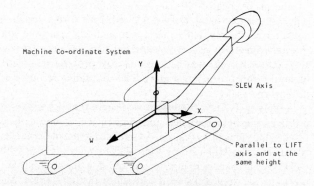

Machine Co-ordinate System

SLEW Axis

Parallel to LIFT axis and at the same height

Fig. 8 Zedminer automatic guidance and profiling system: schematic diagram, operator's console and surface trials.

Conclusions

Automated tunnel guidance and profiling systems have reached a mature stage in their development. The technique is now tried and tested, understood and practised by tunnellers worldwide, but is still capable of further progress. Through its wider use tunnelling becomes faster, safer, more accurate and, therefore, more competitive.

References
1. ARGE *Los 36* (Frankfurt am Main: Hochtief A. G., Philipp Holtzmann A. G. and Wayss & Freytag A. G.), official report.
2. Uffmann H. P. Erste Baustellenerfahrungen. *Hoch Tiefbau*, **36**, Dec. 1983, 19, 22.
3. Müller W. Neue Vortriebs- und Vermessungstechnik auf der Baustelle Nebensammler Kuhmühle II. Ba, Los 2. *Tiefbau-BG*, **96**, Nov. 1984, 680–4.

Discussion

J. N. Shirlaw* said that he was particularly interested in the section of tunnel driven through alluvium (manhole 17 to manhole 18), which Plenty and Law had described. The information that was contained in the paper was somewhat limited and he would appreciate amplification of the following: (1) the groundwater regime before tunnelling, and how the tunnel affected it; (2) a summary of salient soil properties determined in the site investigation, plus a little more on what they had observed during manhole excavation; and (3) any data on heave/settlement measured on the ground surface and in the tunnel.

A. Tanner† asked Plenty and Law for information about the hydraulic roughness coefficients assumed for both the first-phase tunnel, with a single-pass segmental lining, and for the second-phase tunnels, with a cast *in-situ* lining. Any data from the completed tunnels to indicate the actual roughness factors would be useful, as would the authors' view of the minimum thickness of *in-situ* concrete lining that could be placed satisfactorily in tunnels of 2.5- to 3-m diameter.

He would be grateful if Morris could provide progress rates at Cadley Hill or other collieries for roadheaders in rocks of about 100-MPa compressive strength and those for the much harder rocks that were encountered (+200-MPa compressive strength).

He would also like to know the average cost, per cubic metre excavated, of the consumables for the different classes of rock.

T. J. M. Paterson‡ asked if the Bretby or NCB–Eimco tunnelling machines provided a suitable basis for a roadheader-type tunnelling machine that could be fitted with disc cutters for use in harder rocks and picks for use in softer rocks.

Written contributions

M. C. Knights§ Fig. 1 shows a tunnel face of dry, stable Keuper Marl. Did Plenty and Law encounter less favourable geology for tunnelling, and what measures did they take?

B. M. Woods** In view of the decision to adopt a target-type reimbursement basis and the disclosure of the £7 000 000 original award, what was the final project cost to Bristol?

*Formerly Mass Transit Railway Corporation, Kowloon, Hong Kong; now MRT, Singapore.
†Ninham Shand, Inc., Randburg, South Africa.
‡Geostore (South Killingholme), Ltd., South Killingholme, South Humberside, England.
§W. S. Atkins and Partners, Epsom, Surrey, England.
**Amco Consultants, Ltd., Barnsley, England.

Fig. 1

Authors' replies

A. H. Morris In reply to A. Tanner, there is such a wide variety of results from roadheader-type machines, particularly in the rock strength that was mentioned, that a precise answer is not possible. In rock of around 100 MPa the use of medium- to heavy-duty roadheaders is certainly required and characteristics other than that of compressive strength come into play – for example, the degree of homogeneity and, above all, abrasiveness. We have had instances of around 6 m per shift in rocks of this strength, but where abrasivity causes rapid wearing and changing of picks, dust and other problems, considerably lower performances have been returned.

In terms of rock of plus 200-MPa compressive strength the only experience that I know of is with our own tunnelling machine at Cadley Hill: there, although the machine got through some fairly massive rock of this strength, progress was slow and pick usage was high, but at least progress was made without resort to the much more time-consuming recourse of drilling and firing.

In reply to T. J. M. Paterson, we believe that the answer is positive. We have designed and constructed a cutting head fitted with rolling discs that we had intended to use in the harder strata at Cadley Hill if it was impossible to make progress with picks. Owing to the very high torque and slow speed employed, however, the drag picks dealt with all of the hard strata that were encountered. We certainly believe that although we could

Table 1   Results of falling head permeability tests

Borehole no.	Test section, m	Estimated permeability, m/s	Remarks
121A	4.50–5.00	—	Insufficient fall in head, method inapplicable
	8.30–9.30	6.5×10^{-6}	Response zone in sandstone
123	3.00–6.00	3.6×10^{-9}	Response zone in weathered marl from 3.50 to 6.00 m
124	3.00–6.40	1.8×10^{-7}	Response zone in alluvium from 3.00 to 6.00 m; sandstone below 6.00 m
127	3.00–6.00	(i) 8.6×10^{-7}	Results calculated for response zone in sandstone from 4.20 to 6.00 m
		(ii) 12.0×10^{-7}	
128	3.00–4.50	2.1×10^{-7}	Results calculated for response zone in sand from 3.30 to 4.50 m
129	2.00–5.00	11.8×10^{-7}	Results calculated for response zone in sand from 4.25 to 5.00 m
132A	8.25–11.40	7.8×10^{-7}	Response zone in sandstone
134	2.00–4.60	(i) 2.1×10^{-6}	Results calculated for response zone in sand from 3.00 to 4.60 m
		(ii) 4.0×10^{-6}	

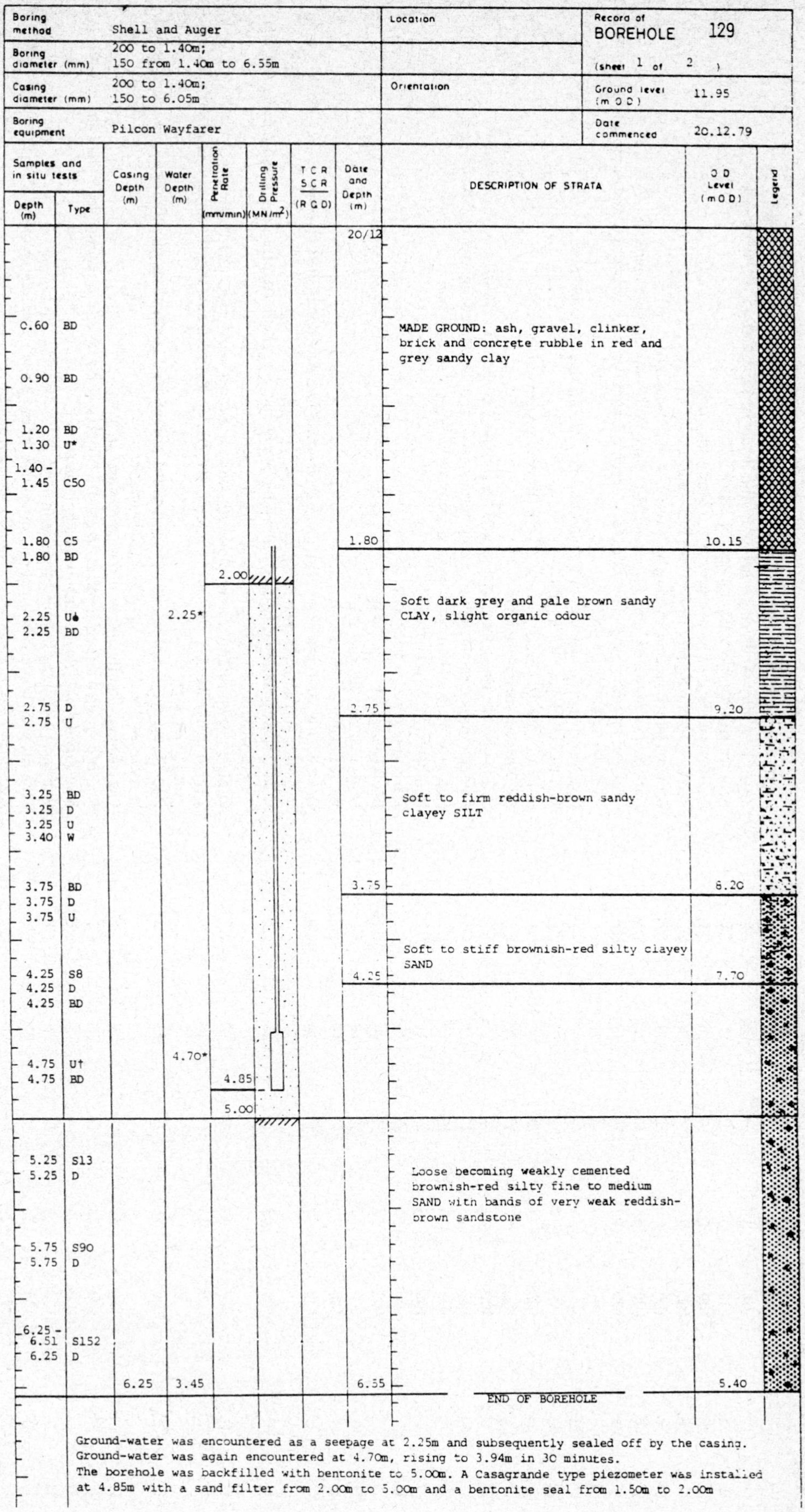

Boring method	Shell and Auger							Location		Record of BOREHOLE 129	
Boring diameter (mm)	200 to 1.40m; 150 from 1.40m to 6.55m									(sheet 1 of 2)	
Casing diameter (mm)	200 to 1.40m; 150 to 6.05m							Orientation		Ground level (m O D) 11.95	
Boring equipment	Pilcon Wayfarer									Date commenced 20.12.79	

Samples and in situ tests		Casing Depth (m)	Water Depth (m)	Penetration Rate (mm/min)	Drilling Pressure (MN/m²)	T C R S C R (R Q D)	Date and Depth (m)	DESCRIPTION OF STRATA	O D Level (m O D)	Legend
Depth (m)	Type									
							20/12			
0.60	BD							MADE GROUND: ash, gravel, clinker, brick and concrete rubble in red and grey sandy clay		
0.90	BD									
1.20	BD									
1.30	U*									
1.40 – 1.45	C50									
1.80	C5						1.80		10.15	
1.80	BD									
				2.00				Soft dark grey and pale brown sandy CLAY, slight organic odour		
2.25	U♦		2.25*							
2.25	BD									
2.75	D						2.75		9.20	
2.75	U									
3.25	BD							Soft to firm reddish-brown sandy clayey SILT		
3.25	D									
3.25	U									
3.40	W									
3.75	BD						3.75		8.20	
3.75	D									
3.75	U							Soft to stiff brownish-red silty clayey SAND		
4.25	S8						4.25		7.70	
4.25	D									
4.25	BD									
4.75	U†		4.70*							
4.75	BD			4.85						
				5.00						
5.25	S13							Loose becoming weakly cemented brownish-red silty fine to medium SAND with bands of very weak reddish-brown sandstone		
5.25	D									
5.75	S90									
5.75	D									
6.25 – 6.51	S152									
6.25	D									
		6.25	3.45				6.55		5.40	
								END OF BOREHOLE		

Ground-water was encountered as a seepage at 2.25m and subsequently sealed off by the casing.
Ground-water was again encountered at 4.70m, rising to 3.94m in 30 minutes.
The borehole was backfilled with bentonite to 5.00m. A Casagrande type piezometer was installed
at 4.85m with a sand filter from 2.00m to 5.00m and a bentonite seal from 1.50m to 2.00m

Fig. 2

not provide the massive thrusts and torques that discs are subjected to when employed on full-face tunnelling machines, there is sufficient on either of the machines mentioned to allow progress – at a slower rate – through quite hard rock.

T. N. Plenty and M. V. M. Law In reply to J. N. Shirlaw, the groundwater levels prior to the commencement of tunnelling from manhole 17 to manhole 18 were approximately 2 m below ground level, and showed a seasonal variation of ±250 mm. At

Table 2 Some liquid and plastic limit determinations and natural moisture contents

Borehole no.	Sample Depth, m	Type	Natural moisture content, %	Passing 425-μm sieve, %	Index properties Liquid limit, %	Plastic limit, %	Plasticity index, %	Classification	Sample description
122	1.30	U	17	98	30	17	13	CL	Red-brown sandy silty clay
123	3.25	U	17	95	33	19	14	CL	Red-brown silty sandy clay with some thin layers of sand and a little medium gravel
	4.25	U	15	98	30	17	13	CL	Red-brown silty clay with pockets of sandy silt
	5.25	U	22	100	28	18	10	CL	Red-brown clayey silt with pockets of sandy silt
124	2.30	U	26	100	22	14	8	CL	Red-brown clayey silty fine to medium sand
	3.30	U	30	100	61	28	33	CH	Brown slightly sandy silty clay with trace of organic matter
	3.80	U	46	100	56	36	20	OH	Dark brown and dark grey clayey silt with sand and some organic matter
	4.30	U	30	100	93	54	39	OH	Grey-brown sandy silty clay with black organic material roots and rootlets and some pockets of red-brown sand
125	5.30	U	21	—	—	—	—	—	Red-brown sandy silty clay with sand and pockets of black organic matter
	2.25	U	23	98	28	18	10	CL	Red-brown clayey silty sand
	3.25	U	24	100	32	17	15	CL	Dark to pale brown silty sandy clay with some pockets of sand
	3.75	U	59	100	57	35	22	OH	Grey-brown sandy silty clay
	4.75	U	33	100	—	—	—	NP	Orange-brown fine to medium sand with silty pockets and occasional organic matter
	5.80	U	64	100	72	47	25	OH	Pale and dark brown slightly clayey silty sand with some organic matter and black peat
126	2.80	D	—	95	30	17	13	CL	Red-brown clayey sandy silt with some gravel
	2.85	D	—	100	38	23	15	CI	Red-brown clayey sandy silt
	3.50	D	—	100	50	21	29	OH	Dark grey clayey sandy silt
	4.15	D	—	100	52	38	14	CI	Black clayey silt with sand
	5.00	D	—	100	37	19	18	CI	Brown clayey silt with sand
	5.50	D	—	100	36	17	19	CI	Brown clayey sandy silt
127	1.80	U	29	100	49	33	16	OI	Grey-brown sandy silty clay with some fine gravel and occasional shell fragments, grey-black organic matter and black-brown silty sand
	2.30	U	23	100	43	20	23	CI	Brown slightly sandy silty clay with some organic matter, small shell fragments and partings of silty sand with occasional fine gravel
128	3.20	U	16	100	23	13	10	CL	Orange-brown slightly clayey sandy silt with occasional small roots and rootlets
	3.70	U	20	100	26	16	10	CL	Grey-brown silty clay with pockets and partings of silty sand and slightly clayey sandy silt with some organic matter
	1.80	U	29	100	48	27	21	CI	Red-brown clayey sandy silt with occasional pockets and laminations of silty sand, some fine gravel, roots and pockets of black organic matter
129	2.30	U	21	100	22	13	9	CL	Grey-brown slightly clayey silty fine to medium sand
	3.25	U	17	100	24	14	10	CL	Red-brown silty fine to medium sand with pockets of clayey silt and some very small shell fragments
	3.75	U	18	100	—	—	—	NP	Red slightly silty clayey fine to medium sand
	2.75	U	20	100	22	14	8	CL	Red-brown clayey silty fine to medium sand
	3.25	U	18	100	35	15	20	CL	Pale brown silty clay with pockets of sandy silt and some roots and rootlets
	3.75	U	22	90	23	13	10	CL	Red-brown slightly silty clayey fine to medium sand
134	1.30	U	18	100	25	14	11	CL	Red-brown clayey silty sand
	1.80	U	23	100	36	19	17	CI	Red-brown clayey sandy silt
	2.30	U	22	100	30	17	13	CI	Red-brown clayey silty sand
	2.80	BD	—	100	33	16	17	CL	Red-brown slightly clayey sandy silt

Table 3 Undrained shear strength test results

Borehole no.	Sample depth, m	Type of test	Rate of strain, %/min	Sample Diameter, mm	Height, mm	Cell pressure, kN/m²	Shear strength, kN/m²	Natural moisture content, %	Natural wet density, mg/m³	Average shear strength, kN/m²	Apparent cohesion, kN/m²	Angle of shearing resistance, deg
117	7.25	U(40)	2	38	76	165	7790	9.8	2.33	8200	—	—
				38	76	305	8930	8.3	2.32			
				38	76	440	7890	4.7	2.32			
	8.10	U(40)	2	37	76	185	6250	8.5	2.39	6700	—	—
				38	76	325	5570	6.5	2.32			
				38	76	465	8300	6.8	2.36			
118	5.90	U(40)	2	38	76	135	4240	9.3	2.35	4780	1060	57
				37	76	205	4760	8.4	2.37			
				38	76	345	5330	8.8	2.38			
	8.27	U(40)	2	38	76	185	1820	11	2.28	2130	—	—
				38	76	325	1970	11	2.31			
				38	76	460	2580	10	2.30			
119	8.67	UM(40)	2	37	76	200	5460	10	2.34	5620	—	—
						335	5780					
123	3.25	U(40)	2	37	75	80	21	27	2.16	23	—	—
				37	75	230	22	26	2.16			
				37	75	370	25	26	2.17			
	5.25	U(40)	2	38	76	115	218	12	2.07	402	—	—
				38	76	275	560	11	2.21			
				38	76	420	428	13	2.13			
124	2.30	U(40)	2	38	76	55	29	20	2.04	34	—	—
				38	76	195	33	20	2.04			
				38	76	330	41	21	2.03			
124	3.80	U(40)	2	38	76	75	26	44	1.80	24	—	—
				38	76	230	26	35	1.88			
				38	76	375	20	47	1.78			
125	3.25	U(40)	2	38	71	75	16	23	2.08	20	—	—
				38	75	210	23	25	2.02			
				38	75	350	21	24	2.04			
	4.75	U(40)	2	38	76	95	84	26	1.89	44	—	—
				38	76	230	13	40	1.77			
				38	76	370	36	32	1.82			
	5.80	U(40)	2	38	76	95	11	71	1.42	12	—	—
				38	76	230	9.9	73	1.66			
				38	76	370	15	48	1.47			
127	1.80	UM(40)	2	107	206	45	38	22	1.92	60	29	7
						180	63					
						320	79					
128	3.20	U(40)	2	38	76	75	43	21	2.08	41	—	—
				38	76	210	34	20	2.09			
				38	76	350	46	20	2.09			
	1.80	U(40)	2	38	76	40	25	29	1.93	25	—	—
				38	76	180	25	32	1.90			
				38	76	315	24	34	1.84			
129	2.75	U(40)	2	38	76	65	23	22	2.10	17	—	—
				38	76	205	18	21	2.09			
				38	76	340	12	21	2.11			

the commencement of tunnelling, water drawdown was quite rapid – largely because of the presence of a sand layer at tunnel invert level. Relatively few boreholes contain piezometers distant from the tunnel centre line, but those which did so demonstrated that the drawdown was quite widespread.

On completion of the primary lining, caulking was carried out and groundwater levels measured to be at tunnel invert level rose by 2 m. The completion of the watertight secondary lining resulted in groundwater levels returning to pre-construction state within a few weeks.

Tables of salient soil properties for this section of tunnel are attached together with the log of a typical borehole (Fig. 2).

Table 4   Laboratory permeability test results

Borehole no.	Sample depth, m	Coefficient of permeability, m/s
123	3.25	6.29×10^{-10}
124	3.80	9.34×10^{-11}
	5.30	7.82×10^{-11}
129	3.25	1.55×10^{-10}

Manhole excavation confirmed the results of the site investigation. At manhole 18 it was necessary to install the shaft lining in sections as the work advanced to prevent ground loss.

A grid of levels was established above the tunnel at distances of 2.5 and 5 m from its centre line. Monitoring was undertaken on a daily basis as the tunnel advanced for those areas likely to be affected, the frequency being reduced in accordance with results obtained.

It was noted that the ground at centre line rose by some 12 mm in advance of the tunnel. This was considered to result from jacking pressures as the shield was advanced into the face.

Subsequent settlements at ground level were of the order of 25 mm, but confined to a width equivalent to the tunnel diameter. This was probably to be expected in view of the shallow tunnel cover (minimum 1.5 m) and the shearing effect of the shield skin.

There was no appreciable heave or settlement of the tunnel invert, which was probably due to the close proximity of rockhead.

In reply to A. Tanner, the hydraulic roughness coefficient value used for all designs of foul sewers in Bristol is that recommended by Wessex Water Authority, for whom the City act as Agents, i.e. 1.50 mm. The design recommendations of the Water Authority are supported by various research projects, including that carried out by the Water Research Centre (Stevenage), where it was found that the growth and weight of slime on foul sewers was independent of pipe material but dependent on the velocity of sewage. Thus, the roughness coefficient for mature foul sewers is recommended, regardless of the construction used.

There are no available data from sewers constructed in Bristol of the actual roughness value.

The recommended thickness of secondary lining depends on three main factors: (a) the expected accuracy with which the tunnel will be constructed to both line and level, (b) the degree of tolerance allowable on the placing of the secondary lining and (c) the minimum thickness of in-situ concrete required for structural stability/durability. Experience has shown that damage can occur during construction to the primary lining, resulting in exposure of reinforcement.

Taking account of the above factor, a 100-mm thickness would be considered the practical minimum for tunnels of 2.5- to 3-m diameter.

In reply to M. C. Knights, the less favourable geology that was encountered has been referred to above. Additional measures to minimize the effect of tunnel excavation within the alluvial material included (1) incorporation of face breasting plates and the construction of a hood extension to the shield before commencement of the drive (the breasting plates were used when the drive was halted for any reason, such as at weekends); (2) hand excavation; (3) 24-h driving; (4) the shield was embedded up to 1.5 m into the face, the spoil then being extruded into the tunnel and loaded on to a belt conveyor; and (5) grouting behind the tunnel lining was carried out immediately after the last ring built had been pushed back from the shield: experience showed that the ground relaxed on to the lining 20–30 min after the shield advanced.

In reply to B. M. Woods, the final account has yet to be concluded, but an indication of out-turn valuation can be given. The original tender figure, which included contingencies of £250 000, was £5 800 000. It is expected that the final account, including inflation, will be approximately £6 400 000.

Session 8 - Machine tunnelling

Co-Chairmen: J. V. Bartlett and T. I. King

Performance of a 7.6-m diameter full-face tunnel-boring machine designed for a Canadian coal mine

J. H. L. Palmer
Geotechnical Section, Division of Building Research, National Research Council of Canada, Ottawa, Ontario, Canada
R. P. Lovat
Lovat Tunnel Equipment Inc., Toronto, Ontario, Canada
J. C. Marsh
Donkin-Morien Development Project, Cape Breton Development Corporation, Sydney, Nova Scotia, Canada

Synopsis
In March, 1982, a contract was placed for the construction of a 7.6-m diameter rock tunnel-boring machine (TBM) to drive haulageways for a new coal mine. Because the coal deposit is situated offshore beneath the Atlantic Ocean, the machine had to be designed to negotiate grades from − 20% to near horizontal and to be readily removed from the tunnel, which would blind-end at the intersection of the coal seam some 3.4 km from shore. The rock along the proposed alignment was expected to vary from 10 to 100 MPa in compressive strength, so a further requirement was that the machine be designed to use disc cutters in the hard rock and rippers in the very soft rock. As a consequence, a design was evolved that is possibly unique.

The tunnelling machine is a full-face, fully shielded design, which can be dismantled within a tunnel cut by itself and reassembled in a similar chamber. Disc cutters or rippers can be employed as dictated by the rock conditions. All cutter and bit changes are effected from within the machine. The tunnel support, with use of steel ribs, thrust beams and wire mesh, is also assembled within the safety of the machine shield.

The machine, which has been certified for use in coal mines, was delivered in August–September, 1983, and tunnelling was begun in October, 1983. Verification and performance tests were completed in March, 1984, and mining of the first decline is under way. In mining on the 20% decline through competent sandstone, rates of 1.8 m/h and overall average progress of 1 m/h have been achieved. Although some overcutting of spoil at the face has occurred because of the steep decline, removal of the cuttings has generally been good and cutter usage has been quite satisfactory. Overall performance is comparable with that reported for TBM tunnelling in other coal mines. The TBM-mined decline was superior in quality, more economical and safer than a conventionally mined adjacent decline.

One of the earliest uses of a full-face tunnel-boring machine (TBM) in a coal mine was reported by Harding[1] to be in about 1971 in Germany. Handewith[2] reported that a TBM was used in a coal mine in the U.S.A. at about the same time. In spite of these early applications, the general acceptance of TBM for use in coal mine development in North America has yet to occur: it was, therefore, a bold step when the Cape Breton Development Corporation (CBDC) decided in June, 1981, to use a Canadian-built TBM to drive access tunnels for a new subsea coal mine near Sydney, Nova Scotia, Canada. This decision was made with the proviso that the manufacturer prove his ability to build a machine capable of boring on the required − 20% grade. At that time the National Research Council of Canada (NRCC) was encouraging Lovat Tunnel Equipment Inc., producers of world-class soft ground TBM, to enter the rock TBM field. The timing was fortuitous.

With strong support from the Canadian Federal Government a contract was issued in July, 1981, to build and test an experimental TBM. For the purpose of the contract a used 4-m diameter soft ground TBM was modified and tested at the site of the proposed mine, but sufficiently remote from the coal deposits that the machine did not have to meet permissible standards. A total length of 173 m of tunnel was bored with the experimental TBM along the alignment of one of the declines for the Donkin–Morien mine near Sydney, Nova Scotia. The trials were quite successful and have been reported by Palmer and co-workers.[3] In March, 1982, an order was placed to construct a 7.6-m diameter full-face shielded TBM. The machine had been delivered to the site by September, 1983, and tunnelling commenced by overcutting the experimental tunnel in October, 1983.

Donkin–Morien mine

The Donkin–Morien mine is located on the northeastern shoreline of Cape Breton Island, about 300 km north of Halifax and 25 km east of Sydney, Nova Scotia. A vast potential coal resource lies beneath the Atlantic Ocean just offshore of Cape Percé, Nova Scotia. The coal seams of current interest outcrop on the sea bottom near shore and dip an average of 11° to the north (i.e. seaward). The western limits of several seams have been mined, but the eastern and northern extent of the deposits are essentially limited by depth and distance from land. Details of the proposed Donkin–Morien mine have been published.[4,5] The first three seams recommended for exploration are estimated to contain a total potential resource of 1400 000 000 t, of which approximately 1000 000 000 t is considered to be recoverable. To intersect the coal seams initial plans call for two declines some 3.4 and 3.8 km long with, ultimately, close to 14.5 km of access tunnels.

Geology

The coal seams of interest are situated within the upper unit of an extensive sedimentary basin. The deposits consist of inter-bedded sandstones, siltstones, mudstones and coal seams of Carboniferous age. They strike approximately east–west and dip northward at 5–15°. A bed of massive grey sandstone that outcrops along the north shore of Cape Percé provides an ideal location for portals. This bed dips north at about 12° and provides good-quality rock for much of the 20% decline, but includes frequent carbonaceous siltstone and mudstone lenses. The sandstone consists of quartz and feldspar, grain sizes ranging from 0.06 to 2.0 mm. Compressive strengths vary from 30 to 100 MPa (mean, ~50 MPa). The sandstone is quite abrasive. Uniaxial compressive strength tests of other rock types, which include mudstone, siltstone and laminated sand-stones, indicate strengths that vary from 10 to 100 MPa.

Machine design features

To provide contract control a verification matrix was established based on the machine specifications. This matrix contained some 140 items. Of these items, only the most pertinent are mentioned here. Major technical specifications are summarized in Table 1.

Table 1   TBM technical data

Bore diameter   7.6 m
Overall length   6.3 m
Overall weight   350 t
Cutters (all cutters backloading)
   39 356-mm Robbins disc
    6 330-mm Robbins disc
   55 Lovat tungsten carbide ripper teeth
Conveyors
   11.5-m primary belt, 122 cm wide
   165-m secondary belt, 122 cm wide
Connected horsepower 2050
Cutterhead
   Fully articulated and retractable
   Clockwise and counterclockwise rotation
   Variable-speed hydraulic drive, 0–4 rev/min
Pentechnicon   5 platforms, 6 m long
Propulsion
   24 hydraulic jacks
   1.7-m stroke
   Cutting head thrust 1088 t @ 13 790 kPa
Steering
   Thrust jacks
   Articulated cutterhead
   Stabilizer rollers (also used for control of counter rotation)
Hydraulic fluid   60/40 water/oil emulsion
Power supply
   Main, 1100 V, three-phase, 60 Hz
   Lighting, 110 V, single-phase, 60 Hz
Equipped with mechanical rib erector, rib expander, diamond drill for probing ahead and provision for shotcreting
Certified intrinsically safe electrics
Certified for use in coal mines

The machine (Fig. 1) was required to be capable of boring a tunnel 7.6 m in diameter on a decline of 22% (the actual decline is 20%) and at other gradients between −22% and horizontal. A penetration rate of 3 m/h in rock of 100 MPa was specified with a minimum advance on a horizontal grade of 105 m per 100-h working week over four consecutive weeks. The machine is capable of cutting softer rocks with carbide-tipped rippers when disc cutters are not appropriate. All cutters are positioned and replaced from within the machine. To minimize ignitions a maximum cutterhead peripheral speed of 92 m/min was also specified (i.e. a maximum of 4 rev/min).

Because each decline dead-ends beneath the sea the machine had to be built in such a manner that it could be readily dismantled into components small enough to be transported through the completed tunnel. The largest component weighs about 27 t. Normally, a large chamber is constructed for this purpose; however, excavation of such a chamber is expensive and time-consuming. In this case there was a further consideration that the chamber would have to be excavated in the weak

Fig. 1 TBM – largest and smallest of the Lovat tunnel-boring machines

rocks close to the coal seam. Welding, of course, would be prohibited. Consideration of these facts led to the design of a machine that can be dismantled within a tunnel only marginally larger than its own diameter – in fact, a tunnel cut by itself. This design implied a means to handle, position and transport the pieces in the tunnel. To accomplish this a new piece of equipment, called an erector transporter, was designed and built.

Since the machine is fully shielded, permanent support in the form of steel ribs with wire mesh protection and steel thrust beams can be erected within the protection of the shield. These are expanded into position when the rock is exposed 6.5 m behind the face. The shield is slightly tapered from front to rear and the head of the TBM is fully articulated.

The machine is designed to be flame- and explosion-proof. It had to be certified by the Canada Centre for Mineral and Energy Technology (CANMET) for use in a methane atmosphere and had to meet Labour Canada standards as well as standards imposed by CBDC. Ventilation, safety, dust control and ease of maintenance were all items of concern for the design.

The TBM is equipped with a diamond drill, which is capable of probing ahead of the face (a significant safety requirement, particularly for a subsea tunnel), and can drill and obtain core samples vertically, horizontally and on several angles through the machine shield, if necessary.

Erector transporter

The design and construction of the erector (ET) were undertaken by Beaver Construction Group Limited, Dorval, Quebec, since such a specialized piece of equipment suitable for use in a gassy atmosphere was not readily available. The desired equipment was required to manoeuvre within a 7.6-m diameter tunnel while lifting and precisely positioning components weighing up to 27 t each. The largest component to be handled was 6 m in diameter and 0.5 m thick.

Fig. 2   Erector transporter lifting 30-t proof load

The ET that was developed (Fig. 2) is, in effect, a highly manoeuvrable telescopic boom mounted on an expandable, self-propelled straddle carrier. It is a diesel-hydraulic unit certified as safe for operation in an underground coal mine. It can negotiate 20% grades while carrying a load of 30 t and can be controlled and manoeuvred with sufficient precision to assemble or dismantle the TBM.

The ET was used to dismantle and reposition within simulated tunnel dimensions all major components of the TBM while the machine was being dismantled and shipped from the manufacturer's plant in Toronto, Ontario, to Sydney, Nova Scotia. The proven versatility of the ET is such that many other uses besides its specified functions underground are possible.

Machine performance

The performance over the first 1.5 km of tunnel is presented with emphasis on the 20% decline portion. There are relatively few other data published on the performance of a TBM on a decline for comparison. As shown in Fig. 3, several vertical curves have been traversed with the objective of remaining within the sandstone formation as much as possible, while still obtaining the desired intersection with the coal seam. Performance of the machine through these curves has been excellent, but is difficult to assess quantitatively because of the other operational requirements, such as installation of conveyor belt transfer stations, construction of a railway siding, changeover from hoist to locomotive operation for material handling, etc.

Penetration rate

Penetration rate is defined as the rate of advance of the TBM while mining. An average penetration rate of 1.48 m/h was achieved on the 20% decline from the commencement of the full-face tunnel at 227.5 m through part of the 20% to 10% transition vertical curve to 846.5 m. The maximum penetration rate was about 1.8 m/h. This rate is about 60% of the specified rate of 3 m/h. It might be argued that the lower rate is attributable to operation on a decline, but the main reason is the limitation of rotational speed to 4 rev/min. Rate of penetration is approximately proportional to rate of rotation, so if a normal rock TBM rotation of about 8 rev/min were permitted, a penetration rate of 3.6 m/h would be possible. The prescribed rate of 3 m/h is not otherwise achievable for this machine in rock of 100-MPa compressive strength.

Rate of advance

For the purpose of verifying the performance of the machine an evaluation was made of the rate of advance over four consecutive weeks on the 20% decline. The specified performance of the machine under normal conditions was 105 m/100-h week. To fairly appraise the performance of the machine the following formula was accepted:

$$\text{Advance per 100-h week} = \frac{A \times 100}{T - (M + D)}$$

where A is actual advance per week, m, T is total hours available per week (i.e. three shifts × eight h × five days = 120 h), M is allocated maintenance time (four h × five days = 20 h) and D is delays beyond the allocated maintenance time that could not be attributable to machine performance (e.g. power failure).

On this basis the four-week average from 13 February to 11 March was 95.2 m/100-h week. It was reasoned that the machine was performing at 10% lower efficiency than it would on a horizontal drivage; accordingly, the specified rate on a horizontal drive of 105 m/100-h week was considered to have been demonstrated.

The fundamental consideration, however, is the overall rate of progress of the tunnel. From Fig. 3 it is evident that the face was advanced from 227.5 to 838.0 m in two months, i.e. the overall progress on the 20% decline was 305 m/month. In fact, because of the normal learning curve, only 120 m was achieved in the first three weeks of January.

Operating and delay time

A further appreciation of the overall operation of driving the decline can be achieved by inspection of an operating and delay time chart. For the week ending 17 March (i.e. the last week of drivage of the 20% decline, including part of the transition) the chart of times is shown in Fig. 4(a). The major times were for mining (43.4%), support assembly (10.8%) and replacement of

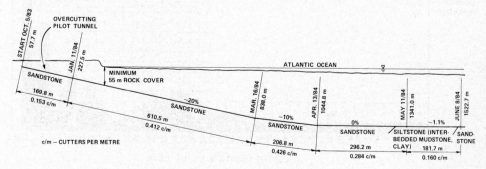

Fig. 3   Profile of tunnel showing progress and cutter use

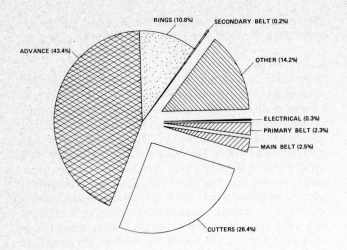

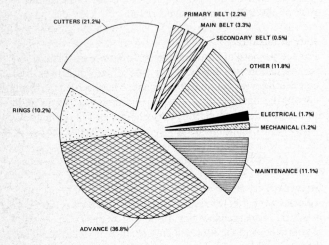

Fig. 4 Operating and time delay charts: (*a*) (*top*) week ending 17 March, 1984, and (*b*) average 9 January to 17 March, 1984

comparison with available time. A typical mining cycle currently is about 45–50 min of mining and 10–15 min for support assembly. The next major time component is that required for cutter changes. Clearly, an objective would be to minimize that time, which amounts to about 30–45 min per cutter change. By 24 June the total time for cutter changes had decreased significantly because of decreased cutter wear. Where the rock is soft enough and methane make low enough that the rippers can be used safely, this time loss could be almost eliminated.

Cutter usage

As was noted above, cutter changes account for a significant part of the overall time. The actual average cutter usage is shown in Fig. 3: cutter usage decreased as the job progressed, except for a small increase when the vertical curves were being negotiated. On the 20% decline an average of 0.412 cutters per metre was consumed, whereas on the horizontal drive only 0.284 cutters per metre were used. The further decrease to 0.160 cutters per metre is a reflection of the change in rock type.

Although the TBM was clearing rock chips from the face quite well on the 20% decline, some overcutting of the pieces was inevitable. Also, it is impossible to prevent some water accumulation at the face, so additional abrasion was caused by a slurry of sand grains. As was mentioned in the section on geology, rock abrasivity tests indicated that the sandstone was very abrasive.

Cutters are being rebuilt and maintained at the mine site. All cutters removed are not necessarily rebuilt immediately but may be reused in a low wear location. Fig. 5 shows the cutter changes from chainage 450.85 m to 690.71 m as a fairly typical pattern on the 20% decline. The greatest wear is experienced on the gauge cutters, as might be expected because of the adverse angle of attack of the cutter. From information such as this it is easier to predict cutter wear and to plan cutter changes.

Ventilation and dust suppression

Full-face tunnel-boring machines greatly enhance dust suppression design, particularly for extraction-type ventilation. Unfortunately, full-face containment is a distinct disadvantage for the achievement of adequate air movement to dilute any methane gas encountered. This problem was recognized during the design of the 7.6-m TBM and a series of full-scale tests was undertaken to ensure that the proposed ventilation system was adequate and to establish, if possible, optimum operating conditions in terms of head speed and rotation direction. This

37 cutters (26.4%). The segment called 'other' (14.2%) is composed mainly of travel (4.8%), luncheon (2.5%), a broken hydraulic hose (1.6%), support repair (1.3%), cold oil (1.2%), an oil leak (1.0%) and survey (1.0%). During this week all maintenance was completed in the time that cutters were being changed, so maintenance time is not shown. A similar chart for the period from 9 January to 17 March is shown in Fig. 4(*b*). Travel (2.4%), support repair (2.2%) and luncheon (2.1%) are the major components of the segment called 'other'.

As in all TBM projects, actual machine utilization is low in

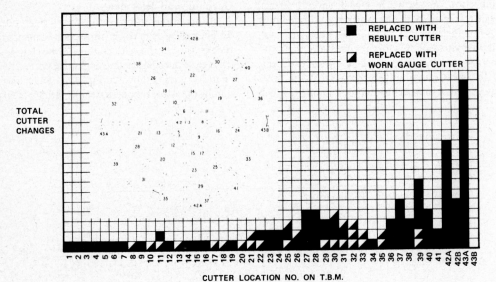

Fig. 5 Cutter position versus changes from chainage 450.85 to 690.71 m

study[6] indicated that full rate forcing and exhaust ventilation effectively cleared tracer gases from the face of the machine.

The two main ventilation ducts are 1.2 m in diameter and are sized to carry 28.3 m^3/s of fresh air, of which 4.72 m^3/s is carried to the cutting head area. Air is forced into the top of the face through two 0.47-m diameter holes in the forward bulkhead. Twenty similar-size holes are located at regular intervals around the backplate so that as the cutterhead rotates the holes align intermittently, providing a minimum of 0.75 m^2 of open hole. Some air can also flow through a 5-cm gap between the backplate and the bulkhead. The head rotation also improves air mixing.

The exhaust ducts carry 7.1 m^3/s of air so that the airflow differential between exhaust and forcing ducts ensures entrapment of dust and methane. Exhaust air is passed through a scrubber unit, which is rated at 7.8 m^3/s at 89-mm static pressure drop with a load of 63.5 kg/h of dust.

Comparison with drill–blast tunnel operation

A 20% decline was driven by conventional drill and blast techniques parallel to that driven by the TBM. This decline was driven to the end of the 20% portion and will be completed by the TBM. The declines cannot be compared exactly because the size and conditions are not identical. For example, since the drill–blast tunnel was completed before the TBM started operation, it was practical to use that tunnel to drain water produced in the TBM drivage. A general comparison indicates, however, that the TBM was progressing about four times faster than the rate that was achieved on the drill–blast decline and the man-hours expended per metre for the TBM drive were of the order of one-third of those for the conventionally driven decline.

Additional advantages of the TBM tunnel are reduced ventilation costs as a result of a more uniform and smooth-walled tunnel, reduced long-term maintenance costs and much improved worker safety. There were three very minor lost-time accidents in the first 1.5 km of tunnelling completed with the TBM. The economic benefits of quicker access to the coal seam and earlier mine production are also quite significant, though very difficult to quantify.

Discussion

The comparison of the performance of one tunnelling machine with another is extremely difficult, even if the machines are working on the same project, because of inevitable variations in geology and other conditions. Commonly, tunnelling projects are rated according to the length of tunnel completed per unit of time. On this basis a comparison can be made between published records for the Selby mine in Great Britain,[7] the Monopol colliery in Germany[1] and the Donkin–Morien mine. Other than the fact that all three mines are coal mines, conditions are different for each. Nevertheless, the average advance at Selby during the first portion of the drive was reported to be about 110 m/week (90 h) or 1.2 m/h. At Monopol colliery the average advance was 280 m/month (360 h) or 0.8 m/h. By comparison, the average rate for the Donkin-Morien mine was about 1 m/h on the 20% decline. On this basis rates for the three projects agree fairly well.

A somewhat different picture emerges if a comparison is made of the actual volume of rock excavated – a criterion applied to all excavation projects except tunnels. The volume of rock removed at Selby is 26.42 m^3/m, that at Monopol is 38.18 m^3/m and that at Donkin-Morien is 45.36 m^3/m. On this basis the average rate of excavation at Donkin-Morien was 45.36 m^3/h (26.5 m^3/h at Monopol and 31.7 m^3/h at Selby).

It is interesting to note that the best month's progress at Monopol was 570 m or 52.5 m^3/h and the best week at Selby was 150 m or 44.0 m^3/h, assuming a 90-h week. This basis of comparison indicates better than average progress at the Donkin–Morien decline, in spite of the −20% grade. The remaining portions of the project include significant time losses for installation of various mine elements, but if these times are discounted, tunnelling progress per hour is about the same. It may be concluded that the Lovat machine has performed as well as the other machines, despite the −20% grade and the fact that this machine is the first rock TBM to be built by the company. Future prospects are certainly encouraging.

Rear-mounted disc cutters were introduced by the Robbins Company for a machine in Spain in 1970.[8] Recently, a machine being built by Mannesmann Demag was reported[9] to include such a feature. Brockway,[10] in an excellent summary of problems associated with incline and decline tunnel boring, pointed out the risks that are associated with going forward of a cutterhead on a decline, but also noted that load-from-behind cutters cause structural and internal accessibility design problems. The Lovat machine has the additional complication that not only the disc cutters but also a full set of rippers are rear-mounted. Design was a problem, but good accessibility has been achieved. The safety aspect alone justifies such a design not only for declines but for any tunnel drivage. In addition, ready access to the cutters for inspection and the speed of making changes are very worthwhile benefits. The full value of the dual-purpose disc cutter and ripper design has not yet been proved on this project. In the softer rock types that are expected to be encountered later, the capability of using rippers in the main portion of the face and disc cutters for the outer cuts and gauge cutting may provide significantly better rates of penetration.

Other potential design problems discussed by Brockway[10] were lubrication, hydraulic and back-up systems: these must be carefully considered in the design. In the case of the current machine the capability had to be provided not only to operate on the 20% (11.3°) decline but also to traverse the short 10% decline and then operate successfully on the near-horizontal grade. All transitions were completed smoothly and did not result in machine delays.

During the initial stages of the design careful consideration was given to the merits and difficulties associated with a fully shielded machine design. In very competent rock a full shield is unnecessary and probably a hindrance. In very weak rock a full shield may prevent the initiation of dangerous and costly rock falls by providing immediate support until the primary lining is expanded into place. The geology of the Donkin–Morien site indicated that even the portal sandstone stratum contained thinly bedded deposits and frequent minor carbonaceous mudstone and siltstone lenses that would intersect the crown at a low angle and cause spalling of the roof. It was decided to minimize the length to diameter ratio (a ratio of 0.83 was achieved) and to provide maximum protection to men and equipment with a full shield. The articulated head of the machine provides extra manoeuvrability and the tapered design of the shield mitigates the likelihood of the machine becoming stuck.

Conclusions

The performance of the TBM driving the first 1.5 km of the Donkin–Morien decline indicates that the decision to use a TBM for this project was well founded. The quality of the completed tunnel (Fig. 6) is superior to that of an adjacent drill-blast decline, the economic benefits justify the initial machine cost and the improvement in worker safety is very gratifying.

The −20% grade did not cause any significant machine

Fig. 6   View of completed tunnel – 20% decline

operational problem, but it did result in higher cutter use in comparison with the performance on the horizontal grade in similar material. The higher use could be attributed to over-cutting of spoil and the inability to remove all water and fines from the face. There was some indication that the advance rate was about 10% less on the – 20% grade.

Acknowledgement

The development of the TBM was jointly supported and funded by the Cape Breton Development Corporation, the Resource Development Fund of the Department of Supply and Services and the PILP program of the National Research Council of Canada. The Ministry of Energy, Mines and Resources through CANMET provided guidance and excellent cooperation in the important task of certification as well as in the ventilation test programme. Numerous other organizations and many indi-viduals contributed to the project. Beaver Underground Structures Limited provided the initiative, enthusiasm and benefit of their extensive tunnelling experience, particularly in the early stages of the project. NEI Mining Equipment co-ordinated the design of the electrical circuits and supplied much of the electrical equipment. Basic Hydraulics coordinated the design of the hydraulic system and supplied some of the hydraulic components.

This paper is a contribution from the Division of Building Research, National Research Council of Canada and is pub-lished with the approval of the Director of the Division.

References
1. Harding P. G. TBM's stay down the mine. *Tunnels Tunnell.*, **13**, June 1981, 67.
2. Handewith H. J. TBM tunnels in the western hemisphere – an overview. *Tunnell. Technol. Newsletter* no. 41, March 1983, 1–8.
3. Palmer J. H. L. Cox W. and Lovat R. Construction and perform-ance of a Canadian rock tunnel boring machine. In *Rock breaking and mechanical excavation: 14th Canadian rock mechanics symposium, Vancouver, May 1982* Baumgartner P. ed. (Montreal: Canadian Institute of Mining and Metallurgy, 1984), 51–3. (*CIM Spec. Vol.* 30)
4. Branch S. N. Devco aims for 95 per cent recovery at Donkin colliery. *Can. Min. J.*, **103**, April 1982, 21–32 (5 p.).
5. Marsh J. C. *et al.* The Donkin–Morien mine: building the mine of the future. Paper presented at the second coal operators conference, Sydney, Nova Scotia, Oct. 1983, 24 p.
6. Stokes A. W. and Stewart D. B. Ventilation trials of a full-face tunnel-boring machine. In *Mine ventilation: third international conference, Harrogate, 1984* Howes M. J. and Jones M. J. eds (London: IMM, 1984), 83–8.
7. Tunnicliffe J. F. Spine roads at Selby. *Tunnels Tunnell.*, **15**, March 1983, 57–9.
8. The Robbins Company. Advertisement in *Tunnels Tunnell.*, **16**, April 1984, 40–1.
9. New German TBM is put to work. *Tunnels Tunnell.*, **13**, May 1981, 7.
10. Brockway J. E. Incline/decline boring with tunnel boring machine. In *Proceedings of the 1983 rapid excavation and tunneling conference, Chicago* Sutcliffe H. and Wilson J. W. eds (New York: Society of Mining Engineers of AIME, 1983), vol. 2, 743–60.

Use of a Bouygues tunnelling machine in the Bassin du Nord et du Pas-de-Calais coalfield, France

A. Blanc
Houillères du Bassin du Nord et du Pas-de-Calais, Douai, France.

Synopsis
For the development of a new level at Arenberg colliery in northern France Houillères du Bassin du Nord et du Pas-de-Calais commissioned the Bouygues Group to drive the mine roadway (5 m in diameter and 6 km in length). The novel machine that is being employed is described.

Work was started in May, 1984, and an average monthly advance of 200 m is necessary to ensure continuity of output.

In 1977 the French Group Bouygues began the drivage of roadways in rock with an original design of tunnel-boring machine. The technique that Bouygues uses involves a system of articulated arms, each boring in a spiral pattern (Fig. 1). To date, five machines have been used underground on excavations that range from 2.90 to 5 m in diameter.

From July, 1976, to December, 1979, two Bouygues TBM (2.90-m diameter; 255 hp) drilled 12 km of drift in Damascus, Syria, with an average monthly advance of 200 m (maximum 500 m) in rock that ranged in uniaxial compressive strength between 200 and 2 MPa.

Fig. 1   Articulated arms

For a hydroelectric scheme in France the Galerie du Brévan, Haute-Savoie, which is 4410 m long and 3 m in diameter, was driven in 21 months with a 650-hp machine; the Galerie du Vieux Pré, Vosges (1400 m long and 2.90 m in diameter), was completed with a daily rate of advance of 13.50 m; and in 1978 two TBM (3 m in diameter; 750 hp) were sold to a Norwegian company for work on 10.5 km of sewage tunnels in the urban area of Oslo, the average rate of advance per shift being 9 m in sedimentary rocks and 4 m in igneous rocks.

General description

Mine layout
Arenberg colliery is situated in the eastern part of the North of France coalfield, near Valenciennes, and the deposit that is being worked is both narrow and dipping. To ensure the continuity of the hoisting in line with planned production a new level has to be constructed by mid-1985. The mine layout of the new level (at −670 m) will comprise two main roadways, which

will meet the deposit from east to west at a distance of 6 km. Panel access will be via north–south crosscuts. The area of the drifts will be 20 m² and the roof support six-arch set pieces (TH 20 kg/m) at intervals of 1 m (Fig. 2). The 670-m level was reached in May, 1983, via a dipping stone drift (400 m long; 13° dip), which was used to initiate the drivage of the mine layout because the deepening of the main shaft was not completed until the end of 1984.

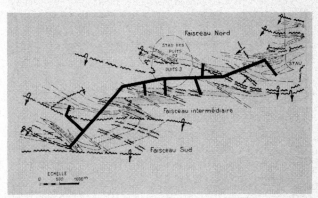

Fig. 2   Roadway project

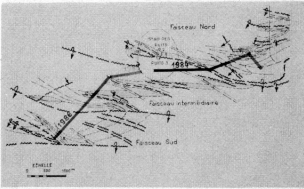

Fig. 3   Driving programme

Planning
To mine in accordance with the prevailing rock pressures it is necessary to use a retreat mining method towards the shaft and to distribute the longwalls in the various areas and veins (Fig. 3). The farthest panels should be reached at the end of 1986 with the use of drill and blast techniques, so the need arose for a monthly rate of advance of 200 m to enable mining to be started in mid-1985. This objective can only be achieved with the use of a TBM.

From 28 October, 1983, to 12 December, 1983, 1054 man-shifts (labourers, technicians, foremen) were required to assemble the machine (transportation from the surface to the stope and installation). During the first four months of 1984 the machine, the method of working and three-shift operation were perfected. The eastern part of the coal field must be reached by mid-1985. After the transportation of the equipment to the western area it is expected that the mine layout will be completed at the end of 1986.

Main aspects of contract

A form of service contract has been agreed between Houillères du Bassin du Nord et du Pas-de-Calais (HBNPC) and the Bouygues Group, the latter providing the machine and its operators. HBNPC excavated the special chamber and transported the tunneller to the stope. During the drivage the owner provides power and roof support and equips the roadway for future use.

A four-month period was allowed to resolve any problems associated with the drivage, the planned monthly rate of advance being 200 m. The benefits of any improved productivity will be shared equally.

Bouygues method

TBM description

The machine (Fig. 4) is 10 m long, weighs 90 t and has a total power of 1200 kW, the cutterhead power being 800 kW. It has a rotary boring head (Fig. 5) with a drilling diameter of 5 m. The head is fitted with four oscillating arms, each of which carries one disc cutter (40-cm diameter). The oscillations are synchronized by a single jack, which is fitted in the axis of the boring unit. Rotational power is 800 kW; initially, rotation frequency was 25 rev/min, but that has been reduced to 15 rev/min.

Fig. 4 Bouygues tunnelling machine

Fig. 6 Overall diagram of TBM

The TBM comprises a non-rotating head (Fig. 6), a three-part shoe, which slides, two tubes that serve as guides (Fig. 7) and a caisson bearing four motors and reducers (Fig. 8).

The slider supports a gripper body linked to levelling jacks that guide the machine. Two thrust cylinders support the grippers and make the machine move, two bottom shoe jacks supporting the body during the advancement of the grippers. Two jacks under the fore slider are used to raise the machine to allow for reversing.

The chain conveyor (Fig. 9) is suspended beneath the non-rotating head; driven in a 30° swinging movement on both sides

Fig. 5 Boring head

Fig. 7 Guides

210

Fig. 8   Four motors and gearboxes

Fig. 9   Chain conveyor

Fig. 10   Equipment for setting up arches

Fig. 11   Bridge unit

of the vertical partition, it scrapes away the excavated cuttings. Four deflectors on the rotating head clear the cuttings towards the conveyor.

The shield, which is in three sections, can be retracted and allows for the backward movement of the tunneller inside the drift, supported by sets. With the specially designed equipment for setting the arches (Fig. 10), this operation is completed in about 20 minutes.

The back-up system (Figs. 11 and 12) consists of a bridge unit, which is drawn by the tunneller, seven belt conveyors for the chain conveyor, electric (1000 V) and hydraulic power, ventilation and driving gear wagons, and 150 m of cable linking the train to a fixed station. With this equipment it is possible to drive curves of 75-m radius.

Method of working

For drilling, the four sweeping articulated arms oscillate in planes passing the axis of the roadway. The sweeping movements are synchronized to a single jack in the axis of the boring unit. On each arm a disc cutter works in an area of the face, boring in a spiral pattern within a spherical domed face. These areas are concentric.

An oil stream activates the thrust cylinders to penetrate the boring head in the rock and to track four concentric cracks. The depth of the track (5–30 mm) is determined by the hardness of the rock, which also determines the speed of the sweeping

211

Fig. 12   Belt conveyors

movement. The cutters follow spiral tracks, the width between the tracks corresponding to the spacing (20–100 mm).

Guidance is by an optical system with a laser beam. At the face, between 142 and 287 m a minimum blowing ventilation of 9 m³/s is used (Fig. 13). Between the face and the shield a drawing ventilation (7 m³/s) is effected by a hole inserted into the shield to prevent any obstruction. After passing through a dry cleaner the air is blown at 297 m of the face.

Fig. 13   Dust cleaner

Fig. 14   Setting up chamber

Heading organization
An overall view is shown in Fig. 14. For three-shift working the complement noted in Table 1 is required.

Table 1

Face crew	10 (×3) shifts	30
Foremen	1 (×3)	3
Loading		5
Equipment transport	1 (×2)	2
Haulage		2
Haulage cleaning	1 (×3)	3
Pipe installation		2
Electrician		4
Total		**51**
Periodic operations		
Every 150 m, installation of haulage point		8
Every 200 m, readvancement of transformers		8

Bouygues TBM – reasons for selection and results

The originality of the technology that is employed lies in the attack of the face with four arms. The small number of disc cutters results in a lower total thrust (10–40 t per disc, i.e. 40–160 t) and, hence, a lower weight and smaller sizes (90 t, 8 m) and a lower compressive stress on the side walls (1.5–2 MPa).

Table 2

	Francs
Special chamber (driving and equipping)	
Cost of labour	572 607.32
Cost of equipment	123 497.60
	696 104.92
Transport down shaft	
Cost of labour	273 439.77
Cost of equipment (crane hire)	302 733.97
	576 173.74
Setting up machine	1 141 495.00
Equipment costs independent of advance/ month (as at 1 September, 1984)	
Roof support	3 726.34
Haulage	748.14
Ventilation	108.72
Various	90.50
Market HBNPC – Bouygues cost	9 148.50
Total	13 822.20

Penetration and spacing can be adjusted to match the machine to the rock conditions at the tunnel face. The machine can be reversed several metres in a short time and access to the face is possible. A boom and hydraulic drill can be fixed on one arm to drill long holes outside the face (for consolidation).

After the four-month 'learning' period 151.5 m was driven in 20 days in May, 1984 – 7.58 m per day (maximum advance, 12.50 m). In June, 1984, only 84.90 m was driven and modifications to reduce the rotational frequency, to change the drawing ventilation, to strengthen the bottom shoe jacks and to build a shield above the machine between the ground and the arch sets were implemented, work being restarted in September, 1984.

A financial summary is presented in Table 2.

Bibliography
1. Larssen L. Tunnel excavation and pregrouting with the Bouygues tunnel boring machine. In *La recherche d'économies dans les Travaux souterrains: journées d'études internationales, Nice, Mai 1981 (Cost cutting in tunnelling)* (Paris: Association Française des Travaux en Souterrain, 1981), 211–5.

Discussion

J. Buchanan* said that he had been privileged to be shown the Lovat machine in the course of fabrication at Rexdale, Toronto, and, having observed the skills and efforts put into its manufacture, was disappointed to read that the maximum penetration rate that had been achieved was only 60% of the specified rate of 3 m/h. Approximate calculations based on the data in the paper showed (1) that the cutting head thrust, 1088 t, over 45 discs, averaged 24 t each, maximum, which was a substantial amount, although not likely to be available on every disc at once; (2) that in achieving 1.8 m/h at 4 rev/min a penetration of about 7.5 mm was being achieved – good for sandstone and in accordance with (1) above; and (3) that the spacing of the kerfs of the cutters was about 95 mm, which was reasonable. Although it might give a slightly high s/p ratio of about 12:1, it probably could not be bettered (unless double or triple discs were used), having regard to the need to provide space for the 55 ripper teeth.

Thus, it appeared that the geometry of the cutterhead was reasonably good and it was not easy to see in what way the performance would fall short. The question was, therefore, with regard to the prescribed rate of 3 m/h, if there had been any research into the cutting properties of the sandstone or if it had been a case of the client 'asking for the moon' and the contractor promising 'the impossible by tomorrow but miracles take a little longer'!

In response to the request for information on the limit of the incentive sparking speed that was being applied to the tunnelling machine at the NCB coalfield at Selby, which had been raised from the original specification (corresponding to that which was being applied at Cape Breton), after similar difficulties had been met, A. Morris† had indicated that there was no fixed value and that an early figure of about 80 m/min for fixed picks had been raised to approximately 93 m/min for roller discs. The MRDE R & D programme had been based on 85% of ground being below 100 MPa – capable of excavation by boomheader at 30 m^3/h (which averaged 20 m^3/h overall).

Overall time spent on changing cutters was a function of the time to change a cutter (which was a matter of machine design) and the frequency of change (which was a matter of ground conditions) and he asked how the estimates compared with the actuality shown in Fig. 4 (p. 206).

J. V. Bartlett‡ noted that one of the prime advantages of the Bouygues machine was the ease with which access was gained to the working face, whereas for the Lovat machine a key feature was the way in which the design made it totally unnecessary to have access to the working face! Since both machines were designed to work in Coal Measures the author's comment on the difference would be appreciated.

D. A. Smith§ asked Palmer and co-workers to supply information on the type and numbers of labour used per shift on the operation of the TBM that they had described. Some indication of the skills required for operation/maintenance would be appreciated – for example, operators, miners, artisans, assistants, etc. Indicative wage rates for the various classes of personnel would be most helpful.

Authors' replies

J. H. L. Palmer, R. P. Lovat and J. C. Marsh In reply to J. Buchanan, an experimental machine 4 m in diameter was tested in the sandstone. A rate of advance of 3 m/h seemed

*Sir Robert McAlpine and Sons, Ltd., London, England.
†NCB, Tunnelling and Transport Branch, MRDE, Stanhope Bretby, Burton-on-Trent, Staffordshire, England.
‡Mott Hay and Anderson, Croydon, Surrey, England.
§Shaft Sinkers (Pty), Ltd., Sandton, South Africa.

achievable for that machine. At the same time a rate of advance of 3 m/h was specified for the Selby machine (5.8-m diameter). Unfortunately, the Selby machine specification of a peripheral speed not to exceed 92 m/min was also applied to the Lovat machine without due consideration of the fact that the Lovat machine was 7.6 m in diameter. All other factors being equal, rate of penetration of a TBM is proportional to rate of rotation. The penetration equivalent to the Selby performance specifications, taking into account the limited rate of rotation because of the increased diameter, is 76% of 3 m/h, or 2.3 m/h. This rate was achieved by the end of the job. The 3 m/h and the 92 m/min peripheral speed specifications were recognized as mutually exclusive and the 3 m/h specification was removed from the contract.

During shop verification tests cutters were changed in 10 min – this was the time that was required when starting with a clean head and a replacement cutter available on the primary conveyor. On site similar times were achieved for that part of the change, but cleaning the bolts and mounts, bringing the cutters to the head, etc., meant that the total time for a change averaged about 30–45 min. There was no 'Class A' type of prediction of cutter usage. The owner has gained considerable experience now and we can predict with confidence that the cutter usage in the second drive will be significantly better than that in the first.

J. V. Bartlett has raised an interesting question. There are a few circumstances in which it is necessary, though highly undesirable, to work at the face. Under those conditions the Bouygues machine does provide good access. The philosophy of the design of the Lovat machine was that work at the face is extremely hazardous and should be minimized or eliminated as much as possible – particularly because of the design requirement that the machine must tunnel down a 22% grade. Few people have the desire to work on an exposed 7.6-m diameter face with a mechanical giant poised upstream of them on a 22% grade. Replacement of all cutters, much of the machine inspection, probing ahead of the face and all face grouting, if required, can be carried out within the safety of the fully shielded machine. The miners are never exposed to unsupported rock because the rings are already fully erected and the thrust beams and wire mesh (if required) are already in place before the rock is exposed. These features were stressed because of the exceptional improvement in worker safety as well as in overall production. Close examination of Fig. 1 (p. 204) will reveal that the face is quite accessible through the Lovat machine. A specification was that a basket-type stretcher should pass through the head and out the tail of the machine without impingement: this was easily accomplished during verification tests, but it is hoped that it will never be required.

In reply to D. A. Smith, the TBM was operated with 12 men per shift. The machine itself was controlled by one man, classified as the TBM operator. The remainder of the shift personnel consisted of four miners, whose primary function was erection of the rings, thrust beams and mesh support, as required, one chute tender, one mechanic, one electrician, two trackmen, a crew leader and a supervisor. A TBM maintenance leader and mechanic were responsible for the maintenance shift. Wage rates are very site- and circumstance-dependent; however, the classification of each person is unambiguous, so appropriate wage rates for any location can be assigned. The only exception is the TBM operator, who is a very important member of the team and is paid accordingly.

A. Blanc In reply to J. V. Bartlett, as the Bouygues tunnelling machine can walk back inside the arches, it is possible to consolidate the strata before the fall of ground is of any real significance, so there is no risk of burying the machine. Moreover, in a very irregular deposit it may be useful to see the ground at the face or behind (metallic arches and screens).

Session 9 – Drill and blast

Co-Chairmen: Dr. I. McFeat-Smith and A. G. Provost

Segment-shaped blasting in Dongjiang hydroelectric power station tunnels, China

Guo Zongyan
Water Resources and Hydropower Construction Administration, Ministry of Water Resources and Electric Power, Beijing, China
Wan Shengpei
Department of Science and Technology, Ministry of Water Resources and Electric Power, Beijing, China

Synopsis
The new technique of 'segment-shaped blasting', first attempted in the Baishan hydroelectric power station, is being employed in the construction of the Dongjiang power project, Hunan Province, China. Total installed generating capacity will be 500 MW and the first unit (125 MW) will be in operation in 1987.

The advantages of the use of the new technique are considered against the background of underground work on the Dongjiang project.

Background

Dongjiang hydroelectric power station is located 11 km from Dongjiang, Hunan Province, on the upper reaches of the Lishui tributary of the Xiangjiang River, and covers a catchment area of 4719 km², which is 39% of the total available catchment area. The total installed generating capacity will be 500 MW (four units) and the annual energy generation 1.32 TWh. The main dam in the river bed is a concrete arch dam 157 m high (base width, 35 m; top width, 7 m). The thickness/height ratio is 0.233. Total reservoir capacity is 8120 000 000 m³ and available capacity is 5670 000 000 m³. The compressive strength of the granite bedrock when saturated is >1500 kg/cm² and its modulus of elasticity is $3–4 \times 10^5$ kg/cm². The station is under construction and it is planned to have the first unit (125 MW) in operation in 1987.

Underground work consists mainly in the diversion tunnel, the timber pass tunnel, the first discharge and spillway tunnel and the second discharge tunnel (Fig. 1).

The diversion tunnel, situated on the right bank, is 494.6 m long × 11 m wide × 13 m high. Its maximum discharge rate is 1210 m³/s. The timber pass tunnel is also situated on the right bank. The excavation dimensions of this tunnel are 1200 m long × 8 m wide × 5.3 m high and 300 000 m³ of timber can be passed through the tunnel per year.

The first discharge and spillway tunnel is situated on the left bank. Its total length is 320 m, and the maximum discharge capacity is 1942 m³/s. The upstream part of this tunnel, being 201 m long, is a pressure section, and its excavation diameter is 12 m with a lined thickness of 1 m. The downstream part of this tunnel (119 m long) is a non-pressure section, and its excavated form is U-shaped 10.5 m wide × 14 m high.

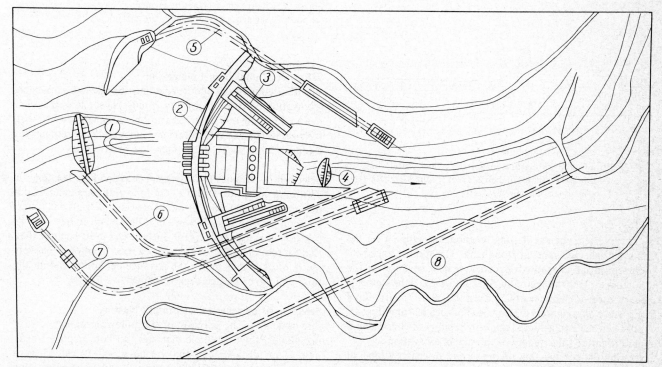

Fig. 1   Plan of construction layout, Dongjiang hydropower station (1, upstream coffer dam; 2, arch dam; 3, spillway; 4, downstream coffer dam; 5, first discharge and spillway tunnel; 6, diversion tunnel; 7, second discharge tunnel; 8, timber pass tunnel)

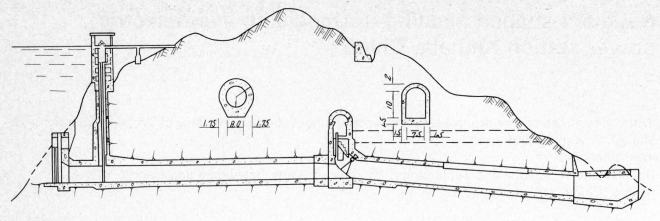

Fig. 2 Profile of second discharge tunnel

The second discharge tunnel is situated on the right bank. Its length is 595 m and the maximum discharge capacity is 1540 m³/s. The upstream part of this tunnel (320 m long) is a pressure section and its excavated form is nearly circular (excavation diameter, 12.5 m; lined thickness, 1 m). The downstream part of this tunnel (275 m long) is a non-pressure section and its excavation form is U-shaped (10.5 m wide × 13.5 m high; lined thickness, 1.5–2 m) (Fig. 2).

Some years ago, to increase the speed of rock excavation at Baishan hydropower station, a 'segment-shaped' blasting method was adopted. This new technique was used in the downstream dyke excavation of the tailrace tunnel and in the rock excavation of the dam base. The construction sequence comprised the excavation of a pilot tunnel before the water outside the dyke was diverted. Then, through the pilot the holes were drilled to increase the excavation to the final size in successive segments. The segments were blasted as soon as the water outside the dyke was diverted (Fig. 3). This construction method gave a good result, increasing the speed of rock excavation.

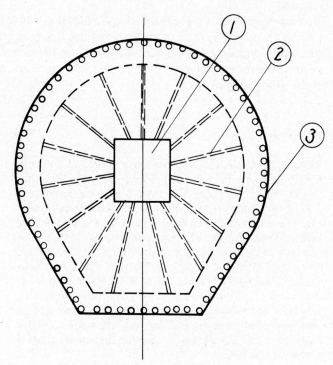

Fig. 4 Cross-section of layout of segment-shaped and presplit holes (1, pilot; 2, segment-shaped hole; 3, presplit hole)

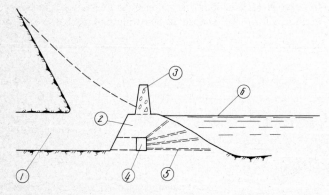

Fig. 3 Profile of dyke blasting in tailrace tunnel portal, Baishan hydropower station (1, tailrace tunnel; 2, dyke; 3, concrete coffer dam; 4, pilot; 5, segment-shaped hole; 6, river)

The 'segment-shaped blasting' method was adopted for the second discharge tunnel at Dongjiang. The specific construction sequence and method involved, first, excavation of the pilot tunnel along the axis of the final tunnel. Then the segment-shaped excavations were drilled from the pilot. Finally, holes for presplit blasting were drilled ahead of rock blasting (Fig. 4).

The new method achieved not only rapidity of construction but also ensured the quality of the tunnel excavation.

During the construction of the second discharge tunnel at Dongjiang the following technical aspects were investigated, tested and resolved.

Selection of pilot tunnel dimension
The dimension of the pilot tunnel must be as small as possible (excavation costs are high), but it must meet the operational needs of drilling and other excavation equipment. In line with the sizes of the YQ-100 drilling machines and other equipment a tunnel 2.8 m wide × 3.2 m high was determined.

Selection of parameters for segment-shaped hole blasting
The results of a site test led to the following parameters: drill-hole diameter, 100 mm; distance between hole ends and tunnel contour, 1 m; distance between hole lines, 2 m. In line with the principle that the charging for the hole end must be more than that for the hole collar, 3.8 m³ of rock must be blasted for every metre of drill-hole. When the advance per round is 4 m, the total volume of blasted rock is 320 m³.

Selection of parameters for presplit blasting
Site tests led to the selection of the following parameters for presplit blasting: drill-hole diameter, 40 mm; depth of drill-hole, 4 m; distance between the holes, 40–50 cm; charged density of explosive, 300–400 g/m; and length of hole stemming plug, 50–70 cm.

Selection of blasting face form

Experience gained during the construction showed that to avoid the blocking of the pilot by debris the blasting face must be kept with the lower part ahead of the upper (Fig. 5).

(5) When presplit blasting is adopted the quality of the tunnel excavation and the stability of the surrounding rock can be ensured.

Following the construction experience at the second dis-

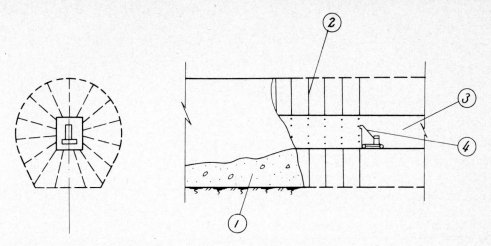

Fig. 5 Profile of blasting face form (1, debris; 2, drill-holes to break segments; 3, pilot tunnel; 4, drilling machine)

Selection of direction of drill-holes

Experience also showed that if the direction of the segment forming drill-holes was made perpendicular to the axis of tunnel, the debris from blasting would be thrown over a long distance. To achieve a good heap shape, concentrated near the excavation face, the angle between the direction of the drill-holes and the axis of tunnel must be kept within 85–87° (Fig. 6).

charge tunnel in the Dongjiang hydropower station we plan to apply the new method in other tunnels. The preliminary intention is to use a tunnel-boring machine (3-m diameter) to drill the pilot, a specially designed drilling machine with a drilling depth of 5–6 m to drill the segment forming holes, and a rubber-tyred drilling jumbo to drill the presplit blasting holes.

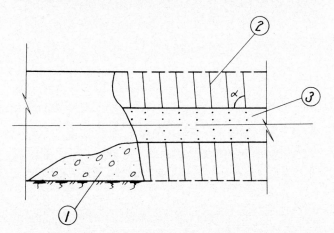

Fig. 6 Angle between direction of drill-hole and axis of tunnel (1, debris; 2, drill-hole; 3, pilot tunnel)

Conclusions

The experience of 'segment-shaped blasting' at the Dongjiang hydropower station has shown that this construction method has the following advantages.

(1) The geological condition of the tunnel can be studied in detail through the pilot tunnel. The pilot can facilitate natural ventilation, especially in a long tunnel.

(2) When the pilot has been completely excavated several drilling machines can be installed and drilling speed is thereby increased.

(3) The parallel operation of drilling holes and loading debris increases the speed of construction of the whole tunnel.

(4) Increased speed of construction is achieved with the use of conventional machines, special machines being unnecessary.

219

Tunnel mechanization at two underground mines in the People's Republic of China

Gao Zidong
Chang Dehe
Hei Shuguang
Changsha Institute of Mining Research, Changsha, Hunan Province, China

Synopsis
In recent years, to improve the rate of tunnelling and production efficiency much work has been undertaken in the development of new equipment. Protracted field testing has provided useful data and the load–haul–dump operation at Xinhuan mercury mine led to a record rate of advance in China of 1056.8 m per month in the construction of a single-head drift of 6.6-m² cross-section. For a hard rock tunnel of 9-m² cross-section at Shizhuyuan mine a combination of CJT700·3 three-boom drilling jumbo, LBZ-1.50 loader and S-8 shuttle car has also yielded excellent results.

Experience on both the projects is described with specific reference to the principal items of equipment used.

In recent years, to improving the rate of tunnelling in hard rock and production efficiency a great deal of effort has been expended on the design and development of new equipment and on investigation of the combination of a complete set of operational equipment. Extended testing has led to successful results being obtained and two examples of tunnel construction are given here.

Xinhuan mercury mine

In March, 1976, a Chinese national record of 1056.8 m/month in excavating a stub heading was set at Xinhuan mercury mine with a combination of newly developed load–haul–dump equipment for mechanized operation. During a period of 31 days a total of 517 cycles was completed. The highest daily advance was 49.8 m, blasting efficiency was 87%, the average consumption of explosives was 19.62 kg/m and average drill-steel consumption was 0.37 kg/m.

Operating conditions
The excavated drift is 1150 m in length with a + 0.3% grade (Fig. 1). The dump distance is 950–2100 m and the ventilation

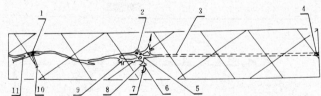

Fig. 1   Drift plan (1, primary dump; 2, secondary dump in worked-out area; 3, excavated drift; 4, ore-intersected prospect hole; 5, maintenance room; 6, underground canteen; 7, powder-packing room; 8, first-aid station; 9, underground store; 10, no. 2 incline; 11, no. 1 incline)

distance in the stub heading is 1200 m. The arrangement in the drift section is shown in Fig. 2.

The drift was excavated through dolomite (stable, $f = 10$–12, ~720 m in length) in E_2 Cambrian no. 5 stratum and siliceous dolomite (most stable, $f = 12$–14) in E_2 Cambrian no. 6 stratum (total length of the two strata, 200 m); limestone and dolomite (fractured, $f = 10$, ~30 m in length) in E_2 Cambrian no. 7 stratum and limestone (crushing zone, unstable, $f = 8$) in E_2 Cambrian no. 8 stratum (~200 m in length). There were in total 81 fissures along the drift and the water inflow was up to 20 m³/h.

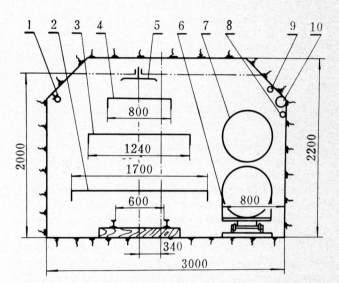

Fig. 2   Arrangement in drift section (1, lighting; 2, loader width; 3, mine car width; 4, belt conveyor width; 5, overhead line; 6, ventilator; 7, ventilation tube; 8, water hose; 9, cable; 10, air duct (dimensions in mm))

The equipment that was used in the excavation, all of Chinese manufacture, is listed in Table 1.

Table 1

Model 7655 drill	6
Model Xin-1 digging and gathering-arm loader	1
Model Xin-1 bottom-dump and belt-conveyor car	18
Model Xin-1 belt-conveyor transfer car (also for power supply)	1
Model Xin-1 unloading bridge	2
7-ton electric locomotive	2
3-ton electric locomotive	1
Mine axial ventilator (11 kW)	3
Laser director	1
Model BK manriding car with 8 seats	1

Excavation techniques
The specially set up engineering department comprised several groups (Table 2). The operation was carried out with four 6-h shifts per day, one drivage team working per shift. There were 48 workers in each team (Table 3).

Table 2

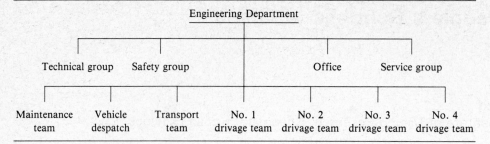

Engineering Department

Technical group   Safety group   Office   Service group

Maintenance team | Vehicle despatch | Transport team | No. 1 drivage team | No. 2 drivage team | No. 3 drivage team | No. 4 drivage team

Table 3

Team leaders	3
Production workers	
Drilling and blasting	15
Roofing	2
Mucking	3
Other	3
Service workers	
Plumbing	4
Track maintenance	2
Tram drivers	2
Dumper/cleaner	4
Repairs	5
Other	5
Total	48

In the interests of speed and safety a total drifting method was adopted in which multi-drills, multi-cycle and multi-process intersecting and parallel operation and partial support were used. Drilling was laser-directed, drifting being both rapid and accurate and drift quality was guaranteed to within 5% overbreak and 0.24% average grade. The excavated section was relatively small with a 10-m³ cubby every 30 m and a 32-m³ cubby every 120 m in order to reduce costs and speed up the advance. Both cubbies were used as a blast shelter, stores for drills and materials, temporary maintenance and canteen. The processes involved are described below.

Drilling and blasting
Six airleg rock drills were employed simultaneously, an average of four or five holes being drilled per shift. Drills, personnel, air and water hoses (including distribution valves) were allocated to specific points with prescribed duties. The blasters

were responsible for the hole pattern with no fewer than 24 holes per round with a slot cut of a 0.1-m overdrilling cut hole and two or three unloaded holes.

To improve drilling and blasting efficiency appropriate modifications were made to the hole pattern, depth, charging, cycle number, etc., to match differing rock characteristics and geology. The drilling pattern for the dolomite in E_2 Cambrian no. 5 stratum is shown in Fig. 3. Although the dolomite is relatively hard, its reaction to blasting is better. A longhole method (2.2–2.4 m) with fewer cycles (five per shift) was used and the cycle time is shown in Table 4. The hole pattern for the

Table 4   Field data for long holes and reduced cycles

Operations	Time (min)	Time Measured (71 min)
Drilling Preparations	3	
Drilling	23	
Hole Cleaning	11	
Charging	5	
Blasting	5	
Ventilation	4	
Mucking Preparations	2	
Mucking	28	
Rail Paving	11	
Pipe Jointing	12	
Cable Installing	17	

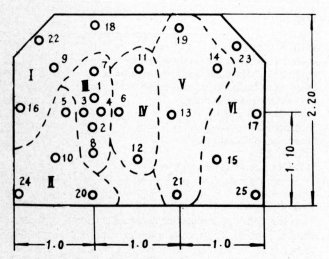

Fig. 3   Hole pattern for dolomite in E_2 Cambrian no. 5 stratum

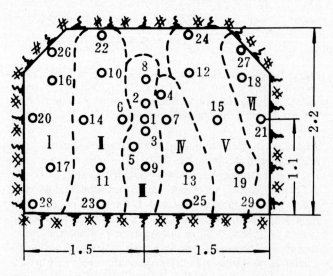

Fig. 4   Hole pattern for siliceous dolomite in E_2 Cambrian no. 6 stratum

siliceous dolomite in E_2 Cambrian no. 6 stratum is shown in Fig. 4: the drillability of this dolomite is better, but its blasting characteristic is very poor. Accordingly, shallow (1.8–2 m) but more holes (20–28) and cycles (six per shift) were adopted. The cycle time is shown in Table 5. Nos. 3 and 4 holes in Fig. 3 and 2 and 3 in Fig. 4 were not charged.

Table 5 Field data for shallow holes, multi-holes and multi-cycles

Operations	Time (min)	Time Measured (58 min)
Drilling Preparations	2	
Drilling	21	
Hole Cleaning	7	
Charging	6	
Blasting	6	
Ventilation	3	
Mucking Preparations	2	
Mucking	18	
Rail Paving	12	
Pipe Jointing	9	
Cable Installing	10	

A home-made dust-collecting hood was used for hole flushing so that the other processes could be carried out simultaneously. With the exception of the bottom holes, the initiators were placed in the bottoms of all holes to prevent the occurrence of cutoff in blasting. Double-initiators were used with 40% nitroglycerine explosive in cut, bottom and water-bearing holes. Only seven misfired holes occurred in the whole month.

Ventilation and dust control
The face ventilation was effected with a combination of a forcing fan and two exhaust fans in parallel. The ventilation time after blasting was within five minutes. The vent opening was 15–20 m from the working face, whereas the air inlet was 6–8 m from the face. A mobile protection hood was installed at the beginning of blasting. With a single-phase protection and two pairs of small rail wheels the fans could exercise control automatically and move on small specially made tracks. The roof and side walls were flushed periodically with water under pressure and sprayed, especially at the mucking stage. The dust content in the drift was maintained at about 2 mg/m^3 and the air velocity was usually kept at more than 0.5 m/s.

Mucking
A load–haul–dump mechanized production line was introduced for the mucking operation – a Model Xin-1 digging and gathering-arm loader, bottom-dump and belt-conveyor cars, a

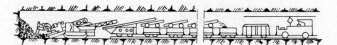

Fig. 5 Model Xin-1 load-haul-dump mechanized production line

belt-conveyor transfer car, an unloading bridge and a 7-ton trolley locomotive (Fig. 5). There was a marked reduction in operating time, the rate of drivage was increased and the labour strength was reduced. The loader that was used (Fig. 6) had the

Fig. 6 Model Xin-1 digging and gathering-arm loader

advantages of both digging and gathering-arm loaders, but eliminated their general shortcomings. The loader used a new type of chain rather than the old flight chain, which was very resistant to running, and featured low power consumption (41 kW), light weight (10 t), high production efficiency (120 m^3/h), greater flexibility and wider scraping range. Even if a partial floor were incompletely blasted, the loader was still able to scrape and load muck. In the drift, with no more than a 3-m width, it could load while moving forward along the centre line of the drift without moving backwards and forwards or left and right repeatedly, thereby making a substantial saving in working time.

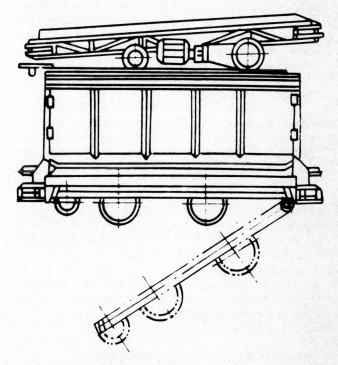

Fig. 7 Model Xin-1 bottom-dump and belt-conveyor car

The model Xin-1 bottom-dump and belt-conveyor car is shown in Fig. 7. Of 1.8-m^3 capacity, one end of its bottom plate was articulated on the box and the other was equipped with unloading rollers to enable movement of the car along the unloading curve rail. The wing rails were welded on both sides of the box so that the car could run along the two rows of pulleys of the unloading bridge while dumping. The rails for the walking mechanism of the belt conveyor were fixed on the upper edges of both sides of the box and at one end of the rails

223

a plate was fixed to connect to the rail of another car. The belt conveyor (2.6 m long, 0.5-m belt width, 3 kW) could run on the rails from one car to another to fill each car.

The belt-conveyor transfer car, 6.6 m long, was located between the loader and belt-conveyor car. When the loader had advanced a short distance the belt-conveyor transfer car and the train of belt-conveyor cars were not required to follow the loader because of the overlapping of the transfer car with the loader tail.

The number of belt-conveyor cars in a train depended on the quantity of muck to be removed – normally, 15 cars per train sufficed. The absence of a belt-conveyor from the last car enabled loading to begin at the end of the car. In general, it took no more than 20 min to load all the muck at the face – about 30–35% of the cycle time.

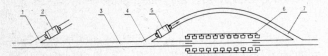

Fig. 8   Dump plan layout (1, no. 1 switch; 2, no. 1 locomotive; 3, main roadway; 4, no. 2 switch; 5, no. 2 locomotive; 6, unloading bridge; 7, bypass)

Two electric locomotives were needed for unloading (Fig. 8). When the train was between no. 1 and no. 2 switches no. 2 locomotive stopped, releasing the hook, and ran with the manriding car through no. 7 bypass to the other end of the unloading bridge; no. 1 locomotive then stopped at no. 1 switch, entered the main roadway and pushed the train into the unloading bridge. When the empty cars were moved away from the other end of the bridge no. 1 locomotive stopped its advance and returned to the starting point, whereas no. 2 locomotive hooked up the empty cars and returned to the heading via the bypass. The belt conveyor and muck cars were flushed with water when they were unloading.

Tracklaying, wiring, etc.
To save time tracklaying and wiring were carried out during drilling and charging. If the work had not been finished in a cycle time, it would be continued in the next cycle. For the same reason the extension of the air ducting and water pipe had also to be done during loading, no interference to drilling being permitted.

Conclusions
For rapid excavation it is necessary to have a well-conceived plan, good preparation, skilled workers and advanced equipment. The technology described is effective for the excavation of a stub heading with a small section, but even in larger drifts the method of continuous loading and mucking is feasible.

To increase production efficiency workers must be trained carefully to enable the number of underground personnel to be reduced correspondingly.

Drifting at Shizhuyuan polymetallic mine

At the newly developed Shizhuyuan mine one drift, 350 m long, was excavated by use of the combination of CJT700·3 drilling jumbo, LBZ-150 digging and gathering-arm loader, S-8 shuttle cars and 8-ton battery locomotive.

The drift is above 490 level, with sections of 8.07 m² (3 m wide) and 11.8 m² (4 m wide), with a three-centred roof arch without support, +0.5% grade and mucking via an adit (Fig. 9). The haul distance is from 490 to 787 m. The strata comprise hard, dense granite ($f = 14–18$) and skarns ($f > 19$) with high specific gravity, strong abrasiveness and poor blasting characteristics.

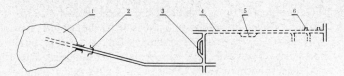

Fig. 9   Drift plan layout (1, dump; 2, drift inlet and outlet; 3, crossover lane; 4, excavated drift; 5, park for drilling jumbo; 6, raise)

During the trial excavation period the operation was undertaken intermittently from August, 1979, to May, 1980, owing to a shortage of electrical power in this district.

The operating system generally comprised one shift per day and 12 men per shift, including two drillers, one blaster, two muckers, two haulers and three service operatives. Later, the labour force was increased to 36 workers with continuous working for eight days, three shifts per day. The measured results are shown in Table 6.

Even though the workers were not familiar with the drilling and loading equipment, performance at the face was three times as high as that with the previous equipment.

Table 6

Average cycle time, min	335
Average drilling time, min	165
Average blasting and ventilation time, min	60
Average mucking time, min	110
Average advance per round, m	1.05
Drill-holes (8.07-m² section)	42–44
Drill-hole depth, m	1.8–2
Average explosive consumption per metre, kg	27.5
Average drill-steel consumption per metre, m	1

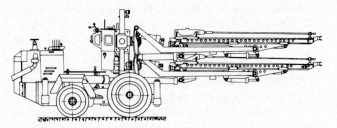

Fig. 10   CJT700·3 drilling jumbo

The CJT700·3 rubber-tyred and self-propelled drilling jumbo (Fig. 10), of 8-ton dead weight, was equipped with three new YGZ-70 drills that could drill 2.5-m holes with a total air consumption of 28 m³/min in the smallest drift. In addition, a newly developed button bit gave a service life of twice that of conventional bits. Drill rod changes were reduced in terms of time and the drilling rate increased.

At the beginning of mucking the drilling jumbo must retreat to the crossover lane (Fig. 9). With drifting up to 120 m a parking area was excavated to reduce the retreat distance. To reduce mucking time two model S-8 shuttle cars were used,

Fig. 11   Model S-8 shuttle car

Fig. 12　Model LBZ-150 digging and gathering-arm loader

mucking in turn (Fig. 11). The LBZ-150 digging and gathering-arm loader (Fig. 12) was an improved version of the Xin-1 loader (the third prototype). It had improved strength and structure and was fitted with an autocontrol device for the digging-arm mechanism; total power was increased by 60 kW and productivity rose to 150 m³/h; the dead weight was 12 ton. The machine could dig and load rocks of differing hardness without the occurrence of blocked chain problems and the temporary track necessary in drifting. Flat bars used instead of sleepers resulted in a better performance.

Conclusions that may be drawn to date indicate a reduction in the overall labour strength and increased productivity. The combination of equipment is suitable for the excavation of drifts more than 4 m wide and those with a small section and more outlets. Tyred or caterpillar equipment can move over the rails without interference with each other in operation.

Discussion

G. C. Burgess* said that in South Africa they had been mining in tunnel sizes of diameters similar to those explained by Gao and co-workers, but did not achieve such good results in blasting cycle times. He would welcome the authors' comments on how they achieved such short charging up times, the length and diameter of the explosives that they used, the hole diameter that they drilled, whether they used any tamping behind the explosives in the drill-hole, whether fuses or electric detonation were used to set off the explosives, if they were allowed to do hole cleaning and charging while they were still drilling, and how they did the mucking of the face.

In the absence of any perimeter holes or any form of smooth wall blasting he asked if they did not get an uneven break and fractured rock on the roof and sides of the tunnel.

Authors' reply

Gao Zidong, Chang Dehe and Hei Shuguang In our drilling and blasting operation the bit diameter is 42 mm, the explosives diameter is 32 mm, and the length 200 mm for each explosive; tamping must be done behind the explosives in the drill-hole, fuses being used to set off the explosives.

The drift at Xinhuan mercury mine was mainly used for production exploration. With the aim of cost-cutting, smooth wall blasting was not adopted in our blasting operation. The roof and sides of the drift after blasting were very satisfactory and had no adverse effect on wiring, pipe laying, mucking out and other work.

Our drill pattern was worked out from the ground condition (jointing and facture development) at Xinhuan mercury mine, and is both economic and effective. Whether it would be suitable in South Africa would depend on local conditions.

*F. Dupré (SA) (Pty), Ltd., Bryanston, South Africa.

Session 10 – Shield tunnelling

Co-Chairmen: G. Margason and M. P. O'Reilly

Construction of a 3.16-m diameter tunnel by extruding shield in Chicago, Illinois, U.S.A.

S. A. Gill
STS Consultants, Ltd., Northbrook, Illinois, U.S.A.

Synopsis
The construction of a tunnel 122 m long and 3.16 m in diameter in downtown Chicago by use of a specially constructed Elgood–Mayo closed-face hand-mine tunnel shield is described. The tunnel invert was located at a depth of about 10–11.5 m below street grade. The subsoils in the area consisted of 3–5.8 m of miscellaneous fill and granular materials followed by very soft clayey silt and soft clay. Groundwater was at a depth of about 3 m. The reasons for the use of the closed-face extruding shield are described, along with its performance, especially in regard to settlement and heaving in the streets. Methods for controlling face instability during the opening in the vertical face of the work shafts are discussed. The performance of the shield for this tunnel is compared with that of larger shields that were utilized in the 1940s for the construction of the subway tunnels in Chicago.

The Tunnel and Reservoir Project of the Sanitary District of Chicago included construction of numerous drop shafts and connecting sewers for conveying excess flow from existing sewers to the deep tunnel through the drop shafts. Structures designated as collecting structures and regulating structures were constructed at various locations on the existing interceptor sewers, where excess sewage flow was diverted to drop chambers for conveyance to the drop shafts through the connecting sewers. The length, size and depth of the connecting sewers varied at the different drop shaft locations. This paper discusses the construction of a connecting sewer 122 m long × 214 mm finished diameter in a tunnel under heavily travelled streets near Drop Shaft 60 in downtown Chicago.

As originally designed, the connecting sewer was to be constructed between three work shafts by the pipe-jacking method. This method was, however, not found to be feasible because of the prevailing soil conditions. The sewer was finally constructed in a tunnel after its invert had been lowered by about 2 m and with the use of a specially constructed Elgood–Mayo closed-face hand-mine tunnel shield.

Tunnel shields with controllable face openings had previously been used in the Chicago area for the construction of the subway in the 1940s. Detailed descriptions of the procedures, instrumentation, and observation of performance of the soils and the shield for these tunnels have been given by Terzaghi[1, 6] and Peck[2] and the data so collected have served as foundations for the design of tunnel linings as well as for that of tunnelling equipment. Limited observations made at this small project have confirmed conclusions arrived at by Terzaghi[6] from his study of shield tunnels in Chicago.

For the control of instability in the front face of sheetpiling in the access and work shafts for the tunnel, prior to contact of the closed face of the shield with the soil, settlement control chambers were constructed outside the coffer dams of the work shafts. These settlement control chambers were designed to reduce overburden pressures in the soil at the face of the tunnel and also to limit the area of settlement in case there is a slide or squeezing of the soils into the opening. Details of the settlement control chambers and their performance are also discussed in this paper.

Site and soil conditions

The locations of the connecting sewer tunnel, the collecting structures, the drop shaft and public utilities within the streets are shown in Fig. 1. The street is full of various utilities and an open-cut method of installing the connecting sewer would have created a nightmare in their handling and keeping them in service during the open-cutting of the trench. Even for the construction of the coffer dams for the work shafts and collecting structures it was necessary to relocate the 61-cm diameter water main located in St. Clair Street near Drop Shaft 60.

The construction of the structures near Drop Shaft 60 had to be done in four phases in three coffer dams – first, for the diversion of the water main; second, for the construction of the starting shaft for the tunnel and that of the collecting and regulating structure; third, for the curved base manhole; and, finally, for another collecting structure, 7F. The alignment of the connecting sewer between the starting shaft and shaft 11D was changed to avoid disturbing the relocated water main. It should further be noted that there existed a freight tunnel within Illinois Street at a depth of 12 m from the street grade, and the top of this tunnel had a controlling influence on the invert of the new connecting sewer or the tunnel in which the sewer was to be installed.

Contract documents for the project included logs of three soil borings extending to a depth of 12.5 m below existing grade. In addition, one deep soil boring had been made near the drop shaft, extending to a depth of 37 m, which included 3 m of coring in bedrock. Three additional borings were performed by the contractor to better define the soil conditions along the profile of the sewer. The locations of all the borings are shown in Fig. 1. Average profile in the area is shown in Fig. 2, which also shows laboratory test data on representative soil samples.

The average profile consisted of about 3 m of fill containing cinders, brick, clay, rubble and miscellaneous materials, underlain by dense fine to medium sand and gravel, which extended to depths of 5–5.8 m. Below the fill and sands, and extending to depths of about 10.5 m, the logs showed very soft clayey silt or silty clay with an unconfined compressive strength of 19–29 kPa. This was followed by soft clayey silt ranging in strength from 38 to 76 kPa to a depth of 11.5–12.5 m. Below 12.5 m the deeper boring encountered silty clay or sandy clay of progressively increasing strength of the order of 100–200 kPa to 20-m depth, at which level very dense glacial tills known locally as hardpan were encountered. Limestone bedrock was encountered at a depth of 34 m.

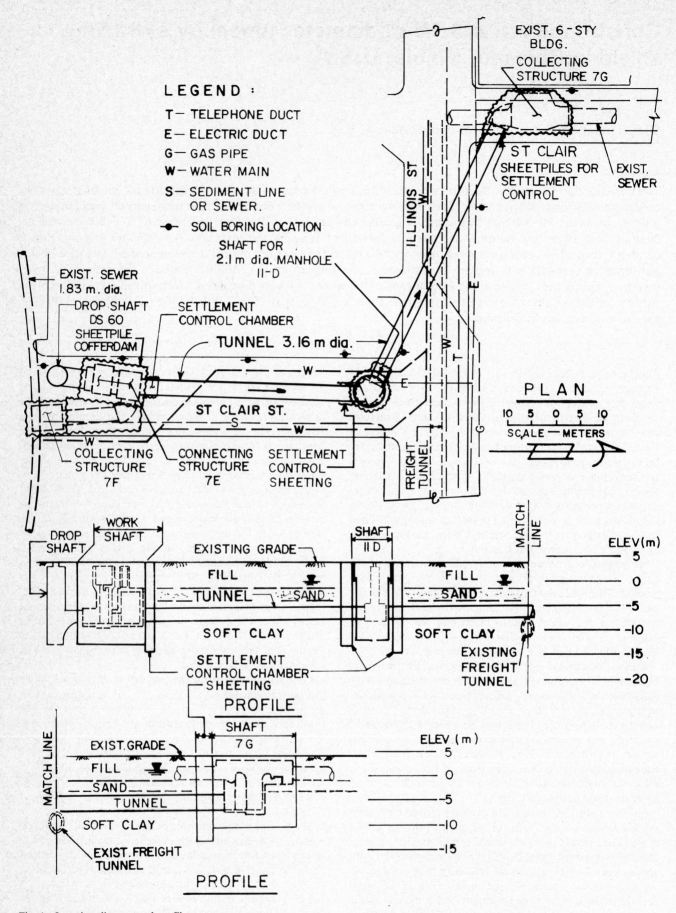

Fig. 1   Location diagram and profile

Construction schemes for connecting sewer

The contract drawings for the project indicated a 214-mm inside diameter sewer to be installed by the pipe-jacking method. The design invert level of the sewer was at depths that ranged from 8.25 to 9.5 m below existing grade. From the soil profile described above it is evident that the proposed sewer was located in the zone of very soft clayey silt or silty clay with strength of the order of 19 to 29 kPa. Above the crown of the

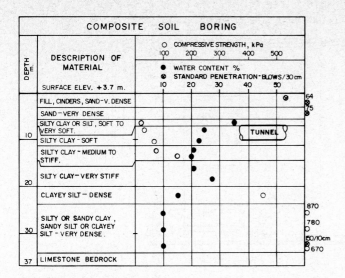

COMPOSITE SOIL BORING

DEPTH	DESCRIPTION OF MATERIAL	O COMPRESSIVE STRENGTH, kPa ● WATER CONTENT % ⊗ STANDARD PENETRATION-BLOWS/30cm	
	SURFACE ELEV. +3.7 m.		
	FILL, CINDERS, SAND-V. DENSE	⊗	64
	SAND - VERY DENSE		75
10	SILTY CLAY OR SILT, SOFT TO VERY SOFT.	O ●	
	SILTY CLAY - SOFT	O ●	TUNNEL
	SILTY CLAY - MEDIUM TO STIFF.	O O ●	
20	SILTY CLAY - VERY STIFF	● ●	
	CLAYEY SILT - DENSE	● O	
	SILTY OR SANDY CLAY, SANDY SILT OR CLAYEY SILT - VERY DENSE.	● O	870
30		● O	780
		●	50/10cm
			670
37	LIMESTONE BEDROCK		

Fig. 2 Average soil conditions

sewer the same materials are indicated in a thickness of 0–61 cm, whereas above that the materials are fine to medium sand and gravel or granular fill materials. It was quite evident that the strength of these soils is insufficient to retain the overburden pressures above the crown of the sewer.

Local pipe-jacking contractors considered conventional pipe-jacking to be impractical because of the likely squeezing in of the soils at the heading and instability at the face of the pipe. The clay cover over the crown of the pipe appeared to be too small to resist the overburden pressures and, combined with probable variations in the depth of granular soils, and possible misalignments during the jacking of the pipe, one could not discount the possibility that water-bearing granular soils might be encountered close to the crown of the pipe. The conventional hand-mining methods during the pipe-jacking operations were therefore not considered feasible. Based on the computed stability number ($\gamma H/C$) of greater than 12, there was a strong indication of basal heave at the invert of the sewer.

The alternative methods of construction of the sewer that were considered are described below.

(1) *Use of compressed air* Theoretically, sufficient air pressure could be provided to balance the water pressures and thus permit installation of the sewer in the tunnel. Air pressure of about 90 kPa had been utilized during the construction of the subway tunnels in Chicago during 1941.[1] These subway tunnels were, however, located at a depth of about 15 m and had more than 4.5 m cover of clay, including a stiff to very stiff crust of about 1.5–2 m in thickness. In the present case, however, clay cover appeared to be very thin. It was thought that it could even be absent over some of the alignment of the connecting sewer. Hence, there was concern that the air could escape not only directly above the sewer but it could find its way into other sewers in the nearby streets and into basements of nearby buildings. This was considered a safety hazard not only to the workers but to the residents and general public in the area.

(2) *Ground freezing* The method of ground freezing would be applicable both for the tunnelling method and for the open-cut method. Although this method may provide sufficient support for the overburden and adjacent soils and prevent face instability as well as basal heave, the disadvantages were the high cost, slow progress and possible heaving that could result from the freezing of the soils. Ground heaving was also thought to cause damage to existing utilities, such as water and gas mains in the streets. Installation of freeze pipes would also disrupt traffic. This was not acceptable to the authorities.

(3) *Grouting of soils* Grouting of the soils for stabilization

was also considered impractical and costly: in fact, grouting of the clayey soils at the face and below the invert was not considered to be of much practical value.

(4) *Open-cut method* The contractor proposed the open-cut method for installation of the sewer, stiff interlocking steel sheetpiles being driven to a depth of about 15 m so that the bottom would be keyed into soils of sufficient strength. The sheeted trench could easily be braced at several levels and prestressed to provide stiff resistance to lateral squeeze. Groundwater leakage through the interlocks of the sheetpiles would be minimal. Theoretical calculations as well as practical experience in the area indicated that with this length of sheetpiles basal heave would be controlled.

The shaft for manhole structure 11D had already been excavated to the design depth by use of sheetpiles of similar length and no basal heave or squeezing in of the soils had been experienced in that shaft construction. The contractor thought that the use of the sheeted trench and open-cut method would permit the expeditious installation of the connecting sewer without settlement in the adjacent ground and damage to nearby utilities. Furthermore, it was thought that the open-cut method would also permit the support of the sewer on piles in case the subgrade soils lacked sufficient strength to sustain overburden loading. Manholes and connecting structures had been redesigned to be supported on piles after examination of the soils in the open shafts had indicated insufficient bearing capacity.

The City authorities as well as the designers of the project rejected the open-cut method because the streets could not be closed, even for short durations of construction in limited areas.

(5) *Construction with a closed-face shield* The above alternatives having been rejected for one reason or other, the only practical alternative that was considered feasible was to use a hand-mining shield. To utilize a tunnel shield for the construction of the sewer the contractor proposed to lower the invert by 1.5–2.0 m, which could be done without affecting the design functions of the connecting sewer. A further lowering of the invert would have brought the tunnel into stiffer soils, but the obstructions from an existing freight tunnel under Illinois Street (see Fig. 1) prevented lowering of the invert by more than about 1.5 m. In any event, with this amount of lowering, the soil borings indicated the existence of a cover of clay of at least 1.5-m thickness, possibly slightly more, above the crown of the tunnel. An especially constructed tunnel shield was available from Elgood–Mayo Corporation of Lancaster, Pennsylvania. Based on experience of constructing tunnels in soft, cohesive soils, it was considered practical and feasible to use this shield to construct the tunnel at this site. This alternative was approved by the authorities.

Tunnel shield

Fig. 3 shows some details of the shield: it consisted of a cylindrical tube with a diameter of 3.163 m and a length of 3.328 m. The skin plate of the shield was 32 mm thick. The cylinder had a hood 0.61 m long at the front covering the upper half of the shield and with tapered ends meeting the invert about 60 cm up from the invert. The shield was stiffened by four horizontal girders (Fig. 3). Ten jacks with a theoretical capacity of 100 ton each were distributed uniformly around the shield just inside the cylindrical wall. Actual hydraulic pressure limited each jack capacity to 60 ton. The jacks were designed to react on steel ribs of the temporary lining already in place behind the shield.

The shield had four ports in the corners, each 35.6 cm wide and 25.4 cm high, and a middle port 55.9 cm wide by 45.7 cm

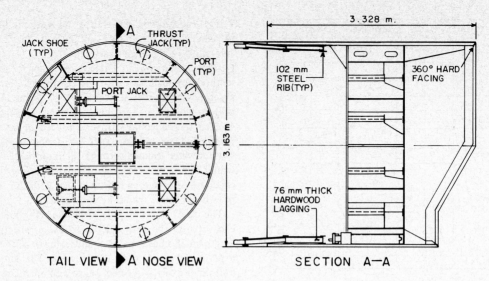

JACK SHOE (TYP) THRUST JACK(TYP) PORT (TYP) PORT JACK

TAIL VIEW ▶A NOSE VIEW

3.328 m.

102 mm STEEL RIB(TYP) 360° HARD FACING

3.163 m

76 mm THICK HARDWOOD LAGGING

SECTION A—A

Fig. 3   Tunnel shield

high. The total area of the ports in the fully open position worked out to about 7.9% of shield area. Each of the openings could be independently controlled with hydraulic jacks and fully closed at any time. Telephone communications were provided between the monitoring station on the surface and the shield operator so that shield advance and port openings could be adjusted as needed to control ground heaving or ground losses.

Primary lining of the tunnel consisted of three-piece 102-mm wide flange steel ribs weighing 19.4 kg/m, spaced 61 cm on centres, with hardwood lagging 7.5 cm thick × 15 cm wide × 61 cm long between the flanges of the ring beams. The ribs were erected in the tail shield as soon as the shield had advanced 61 cm. There was room at the tail of the shield for installation of two ribs at a spacing of 61 cm. Steel ribs for the temporary support of the excavation were erected by manual methods. A hardened cutting shoe had been provided at the front face of the shield and this induced a slight overcut beyond the skin plate of the shield. The 32-mm thickness of the skin plate, along with the slight overcut induced by the cutting shoe, temporarily created a void outside the shield as the last rib was installed within the shield. The ribs had a finished outside diameter of 3.10 m.

As soon as the tail section of the shield had advanced to a point at which the support rib was outside the tail section, the ribs were expanded to make contact with the surrounding soil. Spacers (dutchmen) were inserted between the segment butt plates and made secure. Any voids between the expanded segments or lagging and the mined soil were filled with grout. The grouting operation lagged about two or three rib sets behind the shield to prevent inflow of this grout on to the area of the shield. There was, however, little grout intake above the crown because of squeezing in of the overburden soils. Once mining of the tunnel was started, it was pursued on a 24 h per day, seven days per week basis until the next shaft had been reached.

Mining procedures

Mining by means of the shield involved two alternating procedures – advancing the shield by shoving against the already erected lining and setting the temporary lining when the shield had advanced to a distance equal to the spacing of the temporary lining ribs. In advancing the shield, pressure was applied to all or some of the jacks, reacting on the last erected rib. This reaction was, in turn, transferred to the timber lagging installed between the ribs. Eventually, the reaction was transferred to

either the soil around the ribs or to the jacking thrust block erected on the back wall of the work shaft.

The forward movement of the shield was accompanied by inward squeezing of the clay through each of the five ports, which was then cut off by steel wires or a power knife or it fell directly into the muck car that was located just below the hoppers adjacent to each of the five ports. Tracks were laid in the invert of the tunnel for removal of the extruded soil in 1.5-m³ muck cars, which were pushed by tunnel labourers.

Settlement control chambers

The stability of the face of an opening in a vertical sheeting located in cohesive soils can be investigated by the method described by Broms and Bennermark.[3] According to the criteria given by them, failure will occur when the total overburden pressure at the centre line of the opening exceeds about six to eight times the undrained shear strength of the soil. For the present case, using the average undrained shear strength as indicated by the soil borings, computed overload ratio was of the order of 12. Thus, there was a strong possibility of face instability when an opening would be cut in the vertical sheet-piles prior to the jacking of the front face of the tunnel shield into the soil.

To reduce the overburden pressure, settlement control chambers were constructed adjacent to the face where the tunnelling would begin. These chambers consisted of interlocking steel sheetpiles driven into the stiff clays at a depth of about 14 m. The width of the chamber was about 1 m larger than that of the tunnel shield and its length along the axis of the tunnel was about 2 m, which was sufficient for the full entry of the front part of the tunnel shield into the soil.

The sheetpiles of the settlement control chamber minimized overburden pressure due to adhesion or friction between the soil and the sheetpile surface. By use of an average frictional value of 12 kPa between the soil and the surface of the sheetpiles the total frictional resistance within the settlement control chamber reduced the net overburden pressure at the centre line of the tunnel by more than 65% (with a factor of safety of 2), so the overload factor dropped to about 4.5. At this value face instability is not indicated. Further reduction of overburden pressure could be accomplished by excavating soil within the settlement control chamber to the extent necessary to prevent face instability.

The front edge of the hood of the tunnel shield contacted only a part of the sheetpiles of the coffer dam because of its circular shape. The sheetpiles opposite to the shield were removed one at a time when contact was made by the hood. Simultaneously, the tunnel shield was pushed into the soil so that the full opening into the face of the shaft would not be made at any one time. When the entire shield had been pushed into the settlement control chamber, sheetpiles of the chamber in front of the shield were pulled out. Surface monitoring indicated that no settlement or heave occurred in the overlying street during this time of initiating the tunnelling. No face instability occurred and it was not necessary to dig out soil in the settlement control chamber to further reduce the overburden pressure.

At the entry of the tunnel shield into the next work shaft the settlement control device consisted of two rows of steel sheetpiles in a length of 4–5 m, extending from the face of the coffer dam of the work shaft parallel to the tunnel alignment and located about 0.5 m on each side of the tunnel shield. These sheetpiles, which served as flank walls, reduced the overburden pressure by friction or adhesion and permitted cutting the sheetpiles opposite to the tunnel shield in the next shaft as the shield extended into the shaft. Again, no settlement or any type of difficulty was encountered as the shield advanced into the next shaft.

Shield advance

To obtain reaction for thrust jacks of the tunnel shield a thrust block was constructed in the rear face of the starting work shaft. The thrust block consisted of a reinforced concrete wall 80 cm thick cast against sheetpiling of the coffer dam to a height of 4 m from the base of the shaft and a length of 7 m, which formed the entire width of the rear face of the shaft. Thrust block area was computed for the required capacity of the tunnel jacks and considering passive pressure of the soil based on Coulomb failure theory. According to Broms and Bennermark,[3] the ultimate resistance is equal to about six to eight times the undrained shear strength of the soil plus the overburden pressure. Coulomb passive resistance is, however, only equal to the overburden pressure plus twice the undrained shear strength. Even though, on the former basis, a smaller area of the thrust block could be utilized, a conservative design with use of the Coulomb method was adopted to avoid heaving of the street surface along the shaft.

Resistance to advance of a tunnel shield results from passive pressure of the soil in front of the face of the shield and from friction or adhesion of the clay on the shield surface. The shield thrust jacks must also overcome the friction force of the jacks themselves, which, according to Terzaghi,[1] is roughly 25% of the total jack pressure. Based on tests described by Broms and Bennermark,[3] the passive resistance for pushing a circular disc into a plastic clay is roughly equal to the overburden pressure plus six to eight times the undrained shear strength. Resistance expected for pushing the tunnel shield into the clay at this site is made up of the following components. The resistance is based on an average shear strength of 14.5 kPa.

(1) Frictional resistance = $\pi DL \times C = 48$ ton

(2) Passive resistance = $\dfrac{\pi D^2}{4}(\gamma H + 6C) = 210$ ton

(3) Jacking pressure = $0.25P$

The total resistance, P, therefore is equal to

$$\frac{(48 + 210)}{0.75} = 344 \text{ ton}$$

In this theoretical calculation an unknown factor is the shear strength of the clay, which varied along the alignment of the tunnel. The actual load encountered by the thrust jacks was generally of the order of 350–400 ton. According to the

observations by Terzaghi[6] during the construction of the subway tunnels in the Chicago area, the actual jacking pressure for the tunnel shield was about 80% of the theoretical pressures calculated on the above basis. King's observations on the Holland tunnel in New York agreed with Terzaghi's theoretical calculations. In the present case, also, the actual pressures were of the same order of magnitude and this has confirmed the validity of Terzaghi's method to estimate the force required to shove an extruding-type shield.

Occasionally, the jack pressure had to be increased to the actual capacity of the hydraulic system, which was 41 MPa for a total of 600 ton for the ten jacks. At this pressure ground heaving was observed: to control that, shield advance was reduced. When the jack pressure increased, Shelby tubes were driven through the ports into the clay in front of the tunnel to determine shear strength of the soil. In each instance it was found that there existed a pocket of stiff clay in the upper portions of the shield. To reduce the resistance to the advance of the shield the clay was mined through the two upper ports by use of a 20-cm diameter air-operated auger. Similar mining by auger was conducted through the middle port when stiffer soils were observed in that location.

The rate of shield advance and port opening were controlled such that heaving of the street would not occur. Constant monitoring at the ground surface and communication with the shield operator ensured this control. During the advance of the shield 85% of the soil squeezed out through the middle port, although all five ports were fully open at the time of advance. The small amount of soil that squeezed out of the upper two ports and the lower two ports was removed by spades or cut by a wire knife.

Average advance of the shield was 76 cm per shift with a maximum of 244 cm per shift when very soft clays were encountered.

Settlements and heaving

Fig. 4 contains a plot of maximum street settlement along the tunnel alignment after completion of the tunnelling. In this case heaving was prevented by control of the rate of advance of the shield. Maximum settlements were 75 mm and average settlements were about 65 mm above the tunnel centre line. The total

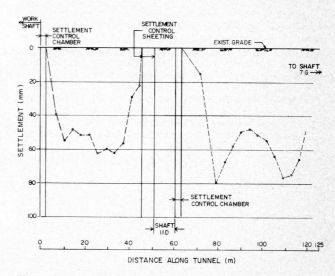

Fig. 4 Surface settlement profile

volume of settlement trough was of the order of 5% of tunnel volume. Settlements and volume loss of greater amounts have been reported by Lo et al.[4] and Peck[5] for several cases of tunnelling in soft clays, with strengths somewhat greater than the soils at this site, even though air pressure was used in a number of those cases to reduce the overload ratio to about 5. In the present case the overload ratio was about 12, but surface settlements were within a similar range. The use of a tunnel shield with a closed face therefore permitted accomplishment of tunnelling at this site with acceptable loss of ground in spite of the existence of very weak soils.

Conclusions

The following conclusions can be drawn from observations during the construction of this tunnel.

(1) An extruding-type shield can be utilized in tunnelling through very weak and soft soils, even in conditions where overload ratios are on the order of 12 or more, in cases where normal tunnelling would not be feasible.

(2) Surface settlements and ground losses cannot be avoided during tunnelling, even with the best control measures and use of a closed-face extruding-type shield. Settlements can, however, be minimized to values commonly encountered in stiff clays with normal tunnelling methods.

(3) The force required to shove an extruding-type shield in cohesive soils can be estimated by use of the method described by Terzaghi.[6]

(4) Face instability during the opening of the vertical face of the work shaft for advancing the tunnel shield can be controlled by use of settlement control chambers or driven interlocking steel sheetpiles, which will reduce the overburden pressure at the face of the tunnel through friction and adhesion of the soil with the sheetpile surface.

Acknowledgement

The tunnel described in this paper was constructed by Walsh Construction Company of Illinois. The writer had many discussions with Joseph Santucci and Kenneth Peterson of the Contractor's staff during the various stages of construction: data provided by them are gratefully acknowledged.

References

1. Terzaghi K. Liner plate tunnels on the Chicago (Illinois) Subway. *Proc. Am. Soc. civ. Engrs*, **69**, no. 8, pt 2, Oct. 1943, 970–1007.
2. Peck R. B. Earth pressure measurements in open cuts, Chicago (Illinois) Subway. *Proc. Am. Soc. civ. Engrs*, **69**, no. 8, pt 2, Oct. 1943, 1008–36.
3. Broms B. B. and Bennermark H. Stability of clay at vertical openings. *J. Soil Mech. Found. Div. ASCE*, **93**, SM1, 1967, 71–94.
4. Lo K. Y. Ng M. C. and Rowe R. K. Predicting settlement due to tunneling in clays. In *Tunneling in soil and rock, GEOTECK '84 conference, Atlanta, Georgia, May 1984*, 46–76.
5. Peck R. B. Deep excavations and tunneling in soft ground. In *Proceedings 7th international conference on soil mechanics and foundation engineering, Mexico, 1969, state of the art volume* (Mexico City: Sociedad Mexicana de Mecánica de Suelos, 1969), 225–90.
6. Terzaghi K. Shield tunnels of the Chicago Subway. *J. Boston Soc. civ. Engrs*, **29**, no. 3, July 1942, 67–121.

Research studies for slurry shield tunnelling

M. Mohkam
Ecole Nationale des Travaux Publics de l'Etat, Vaulx-en-Velin, France
C. Bouyat
Société d'Economie Mixte du Métropolitain de l'agglomération lyonnaise, Lyon, France

Synopsis
One of the tunnel sections of line D of the Lyon, France, subway project is 1200 m long and is to be executed by the slurry shield method. The shield will pass under the Rivers Rhône and Saône with low overburdens and through layers of alluvium deposits that contain large-size gravels with a high permeability coefficient. In preparation for the execution of this work a large research programme has been started, including the study of stabilizing slurry.

A large-scale prototype apparatus, which was developed in collaboration with the Société d'Economie Mixte du Métropolitain de l'agglommération lyonnaise, at the Ecole Nationale des Travaux Publics de l'Etat and intended for slurry filtration tests in conditions as close as possible to those in the ground, is described. Different materials, composed in accordance with the shape of the actual *in-situ* particle size distribution curve, are tested with different slurries and at various concentrations. Filtration tests are performed under identical groundwater and slurry pressure while the excavation process takes place, in a horizontal direction, with a specially adapted tool. Evolution of the mud cake and the pressure gradient is studied visually and by the use of pressure transducers, as well as filtration volume. Slurry is replaced by compressed air to simulate the manual extraction of oversize boulders and obstacles. Thus, the stability of the ground, under either slurry or air pressure, can be examined.

Some results are provided and it is revealed that, contrary to the earlier belief, the pressure gradient within the mud cake is non-linear. It is also seen that a thick layer of slurry membrane and suspended grains, formed on the tunnel face, could create some problems during the evacuation of the slurry and the substitution of compressed air. Accordingly, the necessary countermeasures are given. It is concluded that the apparatus was, to a large extent, able to simulate the *in-situ* characteristics of the ground as well as the state of the tunnelling process under slurry pressure.

The Société de l'Economie Mixte du Métropolitain de l'agglomération lyonnaise (SEMALY), which is responsible for the subway projects in Lyon, France, has decided to use mud shield tunnelling in the construction of one of the sections of line D, which is the fourth underground line of the Lyon subway. Other sections have been constructed by the open-cut method, but this section, 1200 m long with two parallel tunnels 6.5 m in diameter, will be executed by a full-face cutting mud shield method. It will pass under the beds of the Rivers Rhône and Saône with a cover as low as 5 m. The shield will pass through gravel layers of alluvium deposits (Fig. 1) with a coefficient of permeability as high as 10^{-2} m/s. Geological surveys indicate that the gravel layers contain a large quantity of gravel > 10 cm as well as the presence of boulders 50 cm and more in diameter. This implies that it will be the first time in the world that mud shield tunnelling will be used in soft ground with such difficult conditions. Therefore, to ensure a safe and economical execution of this project, a vast programme of research is in progress in connexion with the varied tasks that are to be performed by the tunnelling machine. This programme includes a study of injected concrete reinforced with steel fibres, used for the lining of the tunnel; a study of the hydraulic transportation of the excavated material, containing gravel up to 12 cm in diameter, over a long haulage distance (1.3 km); a study of *in-situ* measurements and calculations; and, in particular, a study of the stabilizing slurry.

This paper deals mainly with the study of the stabilizing liquid (mud). A large-scale unique testing apparatus was designed and constructed in collaboration with SEMALY at the Geotechnical Laboratory of the Ecole Nationale des Travaux Publics de l'Etat (ENTPE) that enables ground conditions (stratification, particle size distribution, permeability, density,

etc.) to be reproduced in the laboratory. Contrary to classical filtration tests[1,2,3] performed in a vertical direction to favour a faster formation of the cake, in this apparatus tests are carried out in a horizontal direction parallel to the layers of the ground and, hence, anisotropy of the ground is taken into consideration. The simulation of the excavation process by use of special equipment allows a better approach to reality where slurry under pressure penetrates continuously a pre-infiltrated but not a virgin ground, as is the case in the classical mould filtration test. Moreover, the evolution of pore pressure at several points is measured by use of pressure transducers for the direct determination of the pressure gradient and the stability of the tunnel face as well as the time of formation and reformation of the mud cake. Also, simulation of the evacuation of slurry and its replacement with compressed air is performed – a process that takes place generally for manual extraction of the boulders more than 50 cm in diameter and/or other obstacles.

Thus, the evolution of the mud cake under slurry pressure as well as compressed air and, consequently, the stability of the tunnel face are examined. Besides the above characteristics of the apparatus, slurry consumption can also be estimated.

The apparatus, testing material and procedure are described, some test results being given and analysed. It is shown that the apparatus that has been developed has advantages over the classical mould filtration apparatus that is normally used for the study of stabilizing slurry and for percolation tests.

Test equipment, materials and procedure

Fig. 2 shows the mechanism of the test equipment: it comprises (1) a parallelepiped caisson with a cross-section of 80 cm × 90

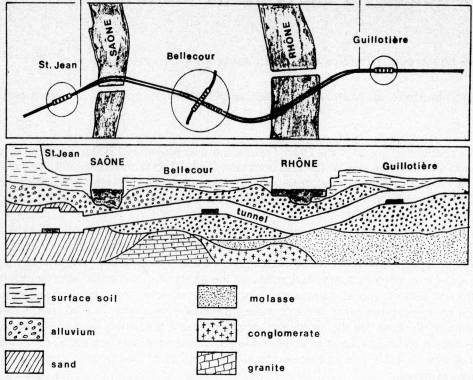

Fig. 1   Geological profile and tunnel route

cm and a length of 230 cm, and normally filled with the ground to be tested; (2) a slurry chamber, 220 cm high with a central cross-section of 80 cm × 90 cm, which receives mud slurry under pressure and simulates the pressure chamber of the slurry shield; (3) a water reservoir, of 600-l capacity, withstanding pressures of up to 600 kPa, which is designed to simulate hydrostatic pressure; and (4) a slurry reservoir, identical to the water reservoir, to feed the pressure chamber with the slurry under pressure.

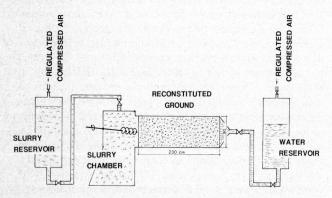

Fig. 2   Mechanism of tunnelling simulation apparatus

The caisson is equipped with four windows on each side (Fig. 3) and can be disconnected from the chamber and erected in the vertical position with the help of a hydraulic jack (Fig. 4). The slurry chamber, which is normally separated by a trap gate from the caisson (Fig. 3), is equipped with a specially adapted tool for the excavation process and treatment of the excavated materials, which drop and accumulate in the lower part of the chamber. This tool is made from a stainless-steel bar 3 cm in diameter × 300 cm long at the tip in which a modified auger 15 cm in diameter is fixed. It can pivot and move freely through a leakproof ball and socket system installed at the rear centre of the slurry chamber. It is rotated slowly by a drilling machine

mounted at the other end of the bar, which is guided to control the depth and the pattern of movement.

The water and slurry reservoirs are equipped with manometers, pressure-rectifying valves and graduated tubes to indicate water and/or slurry levels.

Ground to be tested is composed of four classes (Table 1), mixed in the batch plant according to the desired particle size distribution curve within the envelope of *in-situ* material extracted from boreholes along the tunnel route (Fig. 5). Batches of 500 kg are prepared and placed and compacted in layers of 15 cm in the caisson, which is half filled with water. After closure of the upper part with a cover, the caisson is erected in a vertical position. The trap gate is opened, regulated compressed air is introduced into the water reservoir and under a small hydraulic head the permeability of the ground and its coefficient, K, are determined.

The formation of an artificial cake then proceeds, 3–4 cm of the head layer of ground being replaced by a cement–slurry mortar to prevent sliding of the ground in a horizontal position before the slurry pressure is applied to the face. After the trap gate has been closed the caisson is pivoted to the horizontal position and is coupled to the slurry chamber (Fig. 3). The

Table 1   Different compositions of types of ground tested

Composed ground	Class			
	I 0–5 mm, %	II 5–12 mm, %	III 12–20 mm, %	IV 20–50 mm, %
T 15	14.4	42.2	2.65	16.9
T 20	19.2	39.8	25	16
T 25	24	37.5	23.5	15
T 30	29	35	22	14
T 35	33.5	32.8	20.6	13.1
T 40	38.3	30.4	19.1	12.2
T 45	43.1	28.1	17.6	11.2
T 100	100	0	0	0

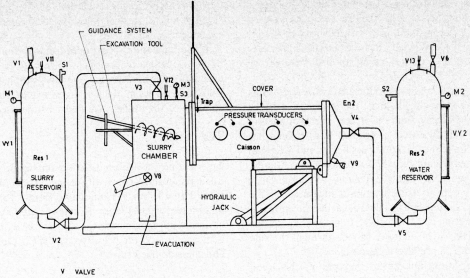

- GUIDANCE SYSTEM
- EXCAVATION TOOL
- COVER
- Trap
- PRESSURE TRANSDUCERS
- Caisson
- HYDRAULIC JACK
- EVACUATION

V1 V11 S1 M1 VY1 Res 1 SLURRY RESERVOIR V2 V3 V12 M3 S3 V8 En2 V4 V9 V13 V6 S2 M2 VY2 Res 2 WATER RESERVOIR V5

V   VALVE
M   MANOMETER
S   PRESSURE-RECTIFYING VALVE
VY   GRADUATED TUBE
En. END CONE

Fig. 3   Apparatus in horizontal position – percolation and excavation

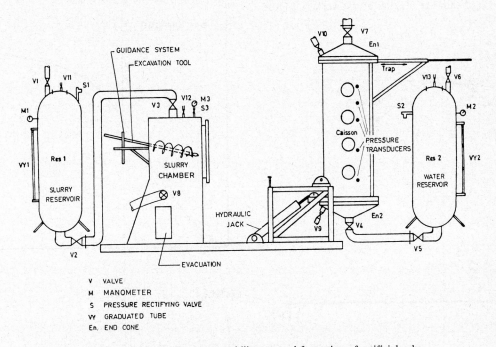

- GUIDANCE SYSTEM
- EXCAVATION TOOL
- V10 V7 En1
- Trap
- Caisson
- PRESSURE TRANSDUCERS
- HYDRAULIC JACK
- EVACUATION

V1 V11 S1 M1 VY1 Res 1 SLURRY RESERVOIR V2 V3 V12 M3 S3 V8 V9 En2 V4 V13 V6 S2 M2 Res 2 WATER RESERVOIR VY2 V5

V   VALVE
M   MANOMETER
S   PRESSURE RECTIFYING VALVE
VY   GRADUATED TUBE
En. END CONE

Fig. 4   Apparatus in vertical position – permeability test and formation of artificial cake

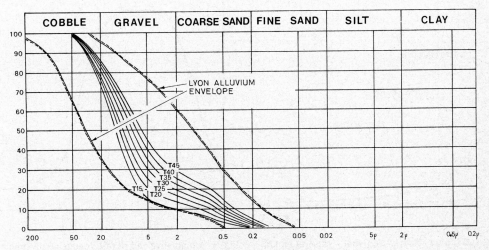

Fig. 5   Grain size distribution curves for recomposed grounds tested with envelope of Lyon aliuvium

slurry chamber is filled (slurry is prepared in 200-l plastic containers), the trap gate is opened, the gate's exit slot is closed and regulated air pressure is supplied to the slurry reservoir. Next, the outflow valve is opened, the necessary back pressure, simulating hydrostatic pressure, being applied through the water reservoir.

The outflow is very small owing to the artificial cake. At this point excavation begins with, at first, the destruction of the artificial cake. The slurry fluid infiltrates the ground and percolation occurs until a cake is formed and leakage has almost stopped. The next excavation pass begins and a vertical layer of impregnated ground 4 cm thick is removed. Eventually, 24 passes are made. The filtrated volume is continuously measured and the pore pressure change is measured by the pressure transducers, which are installed at various positions on the caisson, registering on a recorder. Impregnation of the slurry and the thickness of the cake as seen through the side windows of the caisson are also measured.

In practice, the tunnelling shield engaged in the Lyon subway project can tackle boulders up to 50 cm in size. For oversize boulders and/or other obstacles manual intervention is necessary. The shield is brought to a stop and the slurry is evacuated from the working chamber while compressed air is substituted. The obstacle is then removed manually. At this stage any error could endanger the life of the workers and be costly. Therefore the evolution of the mud cake and the stability of the tunnel face under compressed air must be examined carefully.

To simulate the above procedures in the apparatus at the end of the 25th excavation pass each test is followed by the evacuation of the slurry and the substitution of compressed air. Evolution of the mud cake, pressure gradient and, hence, the stability of the tunnel face under compressed air is studied.

Test results

Tests are performed on different slurries in combination with different ground types with a coefficient of permeability of from 1 to 10^{-5} m/s. Cumulative filtrate volume is measured and plotted against lapse of time for each excavation pass. In addition, pore pressure in the cake as well as in the ground mass is measured and the pressure gradient is plotted for the peak and the stabilized state.

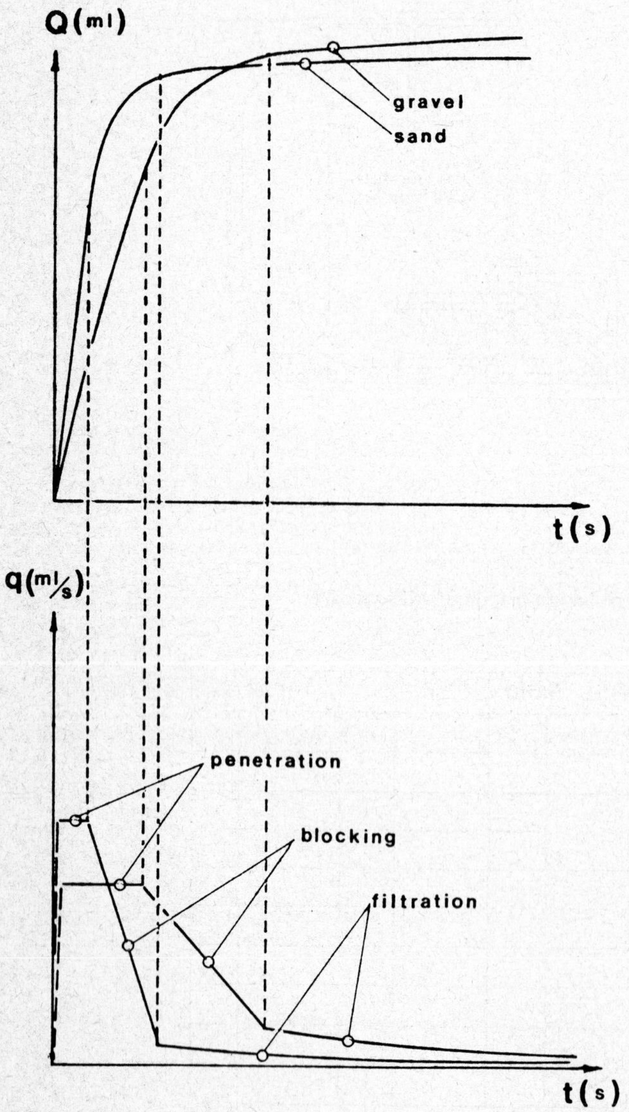

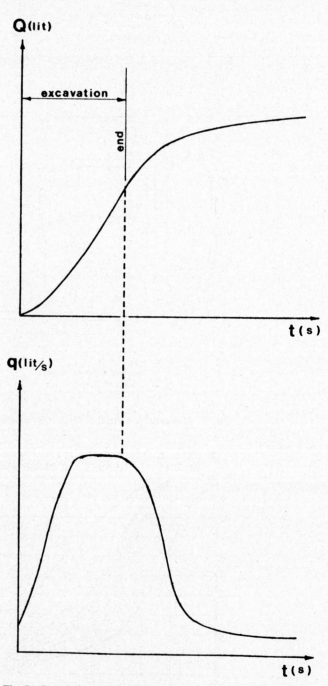

Fig. 6 Cumulative and filtrate volume versus time – classical mould test

Fig. 7 Cumulative and filtrate volume versus time – new simulation apparatus

Cumulative filtrate

In general, from normal mould filtration tests a parabolic curve is obtained for the total volume of filtrate versus elapsed time. The filtrate volume with respect to time is then deduced from this curve and shows the three phases slurry penetration, blocking and filtration (Fig. 6). The first phase corresponds to a peak (generally flat), followed by the second phase as the filtrate volume drops, indicating a blocking effect, and, finally, a third phase when filtration occurs as a mud cake is formed.

Similar curves for the tests with the new apparatus do not distinguish these phases (Fig. 7) because at each moment in time a portion of the ground face is in one of the three phases and/or in transition from one to another. The total filtrate volume across the ground face is then the sum of the filtrate volume across each element of the surface at the different phases.

In the classical mould filtration test slurry is percolated into virgin ground, whereas in reality the ground is pre-impregnated. Fig. 8, for example, shows cumulative filtrate volume curves against the lapse of time for different successive excavation passes in fine ground. It can be seen that the total filtrated volume for each excavation pass decreases considerably until the third or fourth excavation passes and thereafter is the same for the next passes. This phenomenon is explained by the fact that in the first excavation pass an intermediate cake, as defined by Yamazaki and Mackawa,[2] is formed whereby penetration and mud cake formation occur simultaneously. In the next few passes the penetration depth increases, whereas the duration of penetration diminishes. At the same time the finer soil solids suspended in the slurry fill the pores upstream of the ground mass and form a cake under a blocking and/or bridging effect. The differential pressure is then sustained by the viscous drag force and the formed cake.

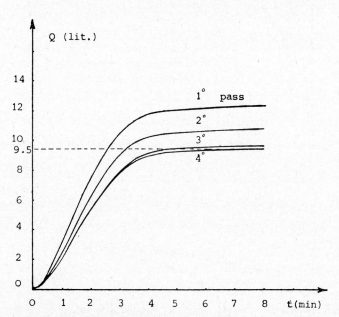

Fig. 8 Cumulative filtrate volume versus elapsed time for different successive passes

This mechanism continues until the penetration reaches a stable length, which stays unchanged throughout the succeeding removals. From this stage on the cumulative filtrate volume corresponds to the volume of pore water contained in the removed mass in each pass. In fact, this can be verified easily from the equation

$$V_w = (n \times S \times D) \qquad (1)$$

where V_w is the volume of pore water, n the porosity of the ground mass, S the cross-sectional area of the apparatus and D the depth of the layer removed. Then, inserting values for the corresponding test,

$$V_w = (35\%)(0.72 \text{ m}^2)(0.04 \text{ m})$$
$$= 0.010 \text{ m}^3$$

or

$$= 10 \text{ l}$$

The calculated volume is in agreement with the cumulative filtrate volume measured for the fourth pass in Fig. 8.

Pressure gradient

The pore pressure is measured with the pressure transducers installed so as to ensure measurements at each instant close to the excavation pass and within, as well as downstream of, the cake. Fig. 9 shows a typical pore pressure evolution, plotted from a transducer, for a complete pass. The observed peak corresponds to the pressure registered when the excavating tool passes at the closest distance to the pressure transducer. The subsequent flat part of the curve indicates stabilized pressure after the end of the pass. Thus, from the measurements from the transducers and for the successive passes of 4-cm depth the pressure gradient can be stabilized.

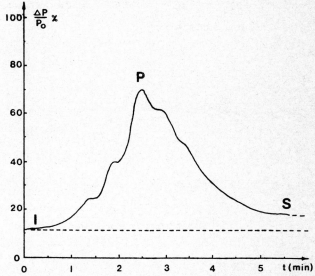

Fig. 9 General form of pore pressure measurements versus time

Studies were made both for the peak and stabilized state and plotted in terms of $\Delta P/P_0$ with respect to the distance from the slurry–ground interface to a point in the cake, where ΔP is the drop in pressure with respect to the slurry pressure and P_0 is the differential pressure applied. In Fig. 10 a typical envelope is shown within which the pressure gradient develops.

In practice, when the slurry shield operates the pressure gradient oscillates between the upper and the lower limit values. When a pick on the shield destroys a cake that has already formed the pressure gradient immediately reaches its upper limit. Then a new cake is gradually formed until the following pick eliminates it. Depending on the time lapse between the passage of two successive picks, the cake could be formed partly or completely. In parallel with the formation of the cake the pressure gradient tends toward its lower limit and could reach it in the case of a complete formation of cake. If the shield comes to a halt, the final gradient is the lower limit of the envelope.

In general, the pressure gradient is assumed to be linear, whereas in reality it is not. Even at the moment when the cake is destroyed and the pressure gradient is at its critical value, it is quite non-linear.

The gradient envelopes for tests with different slurries in combination with a different ground mass are shown in Figs. 11–14. The influence of the ground is shown in Figs. 11, 12 and

239

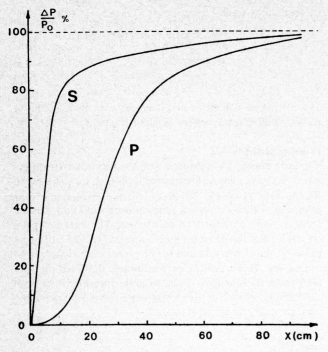

Fig. 10   Pressure gradient envelope

13, different grounds being tested for the same bentonite slurries; the influence of the bentonite slurries is shown in Figs. 13 and 14.

For bentonites *J* and *C* at the same concentration tested in the same ground the effective pressure is very small when the shearing resistance of the slurry is small. For the same bentonite, but with a different slurry concentration, the difference in the gradients is not very significant. Despite the variation of the slurries and the filtrate media at the stabilized value, at least 75% of the effective pressure is reached over the first 10 cm of the length of the cake.

Visual observations

All the tests that were performed showed the formation of an intermediate type of cake – impregnation of the ground plus mud cake at the slurry-ground mass interface. Even in finer soils, such as sand, this observation was made, showing a zone completely impregnated by the slurry upstream of the ground, separated by a mud cake from the slurry. The length of the observed impregnation, however, as well as the thickness of the mud cake varied as a function of the different characteristics of the slurries used and the ground tested. In general, for slurries at low concentrations and small shearing resistance the depth of penetration was greater, and the thickness of the mud cake was smaller. For higher concentrations the opposite was

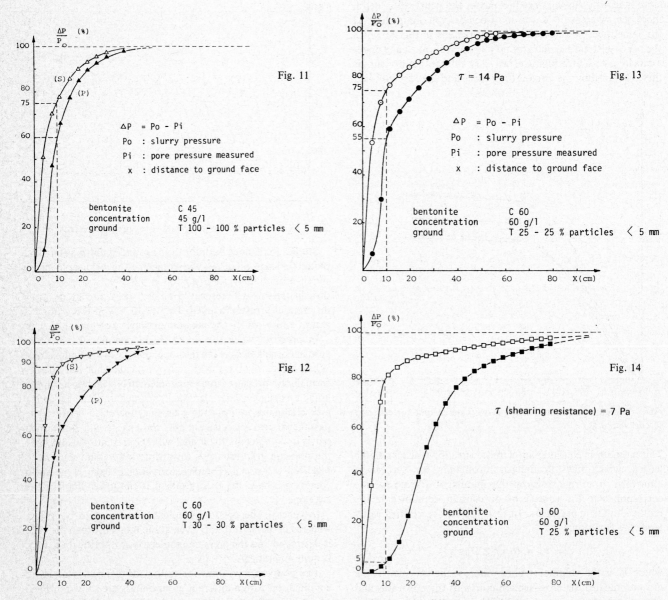

Figs. 11–14   Pressure gradient envelope for tests on different slurries in combination with different ground mass

observed – a thicker mud cake and a shorter depth of impregnation.

In the simulation of manual extraction of obstacles when slurry is replaced progressively by compressed air it was observed that the mud cake tends to detach itself from the ground face under the effect of its weight. Shearing bands appear in the mud cake and some pieces fall off as the slurry level is lowered. Discontinuities thus created within and/or through the mud cake cause a significant air leakage, which increases with time. The slurry that fills the ground pores decreases gradually and the structure of the cake is modified completely.

As was pointed out by Miki and co-workers,[1] in the intermediate mode of cake formation slurry pressure is supported by the mud cake plus the viscous drag force. As was mentioned above, this is the type of cake observed in all the cases studied. Therefore if the mud cake is partly eliminated, the differential pressure should be offset by an increase in the depth of penetration of the slurry, whereas in the absence of the slurry this depth cannot be prolonged and the existing drag force will not be sufficient in itself to resist the air pressure that is applied. Consequently, the slurry in the pores is 'blown away' and a very unstable state results.

To avoid such instabilities, prior to the substitution of air the differential pressure was increased in small steps until the mud cake was pushed for the most part into the ground mass. The differential pressure was then lowered to its initial value and progressive evacuation of the slurry proceeded while compressed air was introduced. This procedure proved to be efficient, no air leakage being observed while the ground face was under compressed air.

Conclusions

This research study is not yet completed and at this stage conclusions can be drawn only on the performance of the new apparatus and the results of the tests to date.

It was found that the new apparatus was properly conceived and served to simulate the *in-situ* condition, a better approach to reality as compared with classical percolation equipment being achieved.

The more interesting features of the simulation model include the percolation test in a horizontal direction under actual hydrostatic and slurry pressure; the successive excavation of vertical layers to allow simulation of the actual tunnelling process in the ground already impregnated by the slurry and not in virgin ground as in the classical mould; the reconstitution of the ground at a 1 to 1 scale; the verticality of the ground face and, hence, the elimination of favourable intervention of gravity; the pore pressure measurements by pressure transducers, leading to the determination of pressure gradient and its evolution with time; and the simulation of the state when obstacles are being extracted manually and/or work stoppages, substitution of slurry by compressed air, etc.

The apparatus, because of the numerous advantageous features described above in regard to the results obtained from the tests, has demonstrated that one type of cake 'intermediate' was formed, despite the variety of grounds and slurries; filtrate volume curves are not sufficient in the determinations of the tunnel face and, in particular, internal stability, and the pressure gradient should be considered; the pressure gradient, contrary to assumptions in stability calculations, proved to be non-linear; if the differences in the pressure gradients at peak values were observed to be important for different slurries, in association with the different grounds tested, they are less

important at the stabilized state; and mud cake, which was observed to stay attached to the ground face, proved to be quite unstable during the substitution of slurry by compressed air. A substantial increase in differential pressure, before evacuation of the slurry and substitution of compressed air, presses the mud cake into the ground face and consolidates the rheological blocking of the pores. Thus, eventual air leakage while the ground face is under compressed air was seen to be halted and a stable state was reached.

In spite of the improvements that have been carried out on the apparatus, there remain some parameters that require further study; the apparatus is able to simulate tunnelling in completely saturated ground where the water head is much more important than the ground pressure. The situation is reversed in semi-saturated ground, ground pressure being the dominant factor. The apparatus is not yet equipped with means for inducing artificial ground pressure. Moreover, the scale effect remains to be verified once the actual execution of the job is well advanced and test results can be compared with the *in-situ* observations and actual measurements.

References
1. Miki G. Saito T. and Yamazaki H. Theory and practice of soft ground tunnelling by the slurry mole method. In *Ground engineering review: highlights of the ninth international conference on soil mechanics and foundation engineering, Tokyo, 1977, Specialty session no. 1 – tunnelling in soft ground* (London: W. M. Braun, 1978), 6–10.
2. Yamazaki H. and Mackawa A. Application and control of mud slurry in shield tunnelling. Tekken Construction Co., Ltd, Tokyo, May 1982.
3. Yamazaki H. Problems of slurry shield method and their counter measures. In *Design and construction of tunnels and shafts: papers presented at the second Australian conference of tunnelling, 1976* (Parkville, Vict.: Australasian Institute of Mining and Metallurgy for Australian Tunnelling Association, 1976), 113–22. *(Aust. Tunnell. Ass. Publ.* no. 4)

Development of mechanized pipe jacking in the United Kingdom

J. Washbourne
Department of Construction, Oxford Polytechnic, Oxford, England

Synopsis

To reduce the cost of larger pipe-jacking operations and to enable the work to be executed more rapidly, mechanization is becoming an accepted practice in this section of the tunnelling industry. Pipe jacking, when carried out with mechanized excavation, is by far the most rapid form of tunnelling, as installation speeds of up to 6 m/h are possible. Pipe-jacked linings are more desirable than any form of segmental lining because they form a less jointed, more robust structure, which is more easily sealed. It is probable that when mechanized pipe jacking is fully developed it will become the universal form of tunnelling, being limited only by the maximum pipe diameter that can be handled. The introduction of mechanization into pipe jacking has enabled longer runs than were practicable by use of hand excavation, but this has necessitated changes of approach to the operation. More substantial jacks and jacking walls are required, slurry lubrication for the sliding pipes has been developed and, except for bentonite machines, belt loaders are necessary to handle the excavated material at the face.

As with other forms of tunnel excavation, the machines that are used in mechanized pipe jacking have to be matched to conditions at the face. At present in the United Kingdom a wide range of tunnelling machines is used for pipe-jacking excavation in the size range 1.75–2.25 m in outside diameter.

Technical developments associated with the various machines that are available are outlined, together with their applications. The successes that have been achieved are recorded, as are some of the problems that have arisen and the ways in which these have been overcome.

From its introduction into the United Kingdom in the 1950s pipe jacking has often been regarded as a system of tunnelling for hand-excavated, short, small-diameter tunnels. Manual excavation is flexible and versatile, but it is also very expensive and very slow in comparison with mechanized excavation.[1] The considerable cost of putting a tunnelling machine into the ground, its maintenance and the risk of its failure to deal satisfactorily with conditions at the face have, however, caused contractors to be very wary of the mechanized approach to pipe jacking. Nevertheless in the past few years several tunnelling machines have appeared in the United Kingdom that have successfully replaced traditional manual excavation for larger pipe-jacking jobs. There is now every indication that mechanized pipe jacking will become a major tunnelling system in the United Kingdom, provided that sufficient work is made available to allow it to flourish.

Fig. 1 Use of pneumatic clay spade to excavate firm clay face for 900-mm internal diameter concrete pipe tunnel

Manual excavation

In the United Kingdom pipe-jacking industry manual excavation has usually been associated with the installation of class H reinforced-concrete pipes with a minimum internal diameter of 900 mm. These pipes usually have a wall thickness of 150 mm, giving the miner a shield with an internal diameter of about 1150 mm in which to work. Fig. 1 shows a miner in such a working space excavating firm clay with a pneumatic spade, which considerably enhances his digging capacity. On that particular job – a 30-m pipe jack near Oxford – the installation rate of the pipes was about 5 m/10-h shift. He completed the job in six shifts, but had the face been very easy digging his rate of progress might possibly have been as high as 10 m per shift and the completion time would then have been three shifts. It is not possible to justify the use of a tunnelling machine for this type of work as the installation, operating and removal time would exceed that for manual working.

For longer runs, however, with about 2-m outer diameter, mechanized excavation can become a much better prospect. For hand excavation at this diameter two miners would be able to work at the face and a rate of progress of between 2.5 and 5 m per shift might be achieved, though with a water-bearing or hard face progress would be considerably slower. A tunnelling operation can be illustrated by an idealized multiple activity chart,[2] which gives the minimum allocation of time for the various components of the operation and their inter-relationship. For a fairly easy 2-m diameter pipe jack (Fig. 2) at 50 m into the drive the miners are totally committed for more than 90% of the pipe installation time, whereas the crane – a very expensive item – is only used for slightly more than 5% of the time (less as the drive progresses). The major benefit of mechanized excavation for pipe jacking is the great speed of the excavating part of the installation process and the consequent improvement in the utilization of equipment.[3]

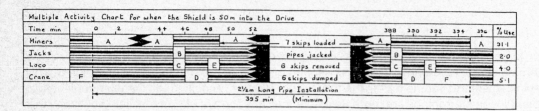

Multiple Activity Chart Data for a 2·0m OD Tunnelling Shield with Single 1×1·5m³ Skip Muck Train			
Item	Operation	Description	Max. Rate of Execn
Miners	A	Two miners hand excavate face and load muck skip	⁵/₁₆m per +5 min
Jacks	B	Jacks push lining forward	⁵/₁₆m per min
Loco	C	Loco pulls full muck train into access shaft	50 m per min
Crane	D	Crane empties muck skip and replaces on tracks	1 skip per 2 min
Loco	E	Loco shunts empty muck train to face	50m per min
Crane	F	Crane lifts pipe and places it on launch pad (services extended)	1 pipe per +min

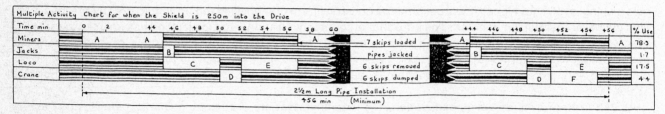

Fig. 2 Idealized multiple activity chart for hand-excavated 2-m outside diameter jacked concrete pipe tunnel in soft earth

Back-acter machines

In August, 1981, the first modern pipe-jacking back-acter machine was introduced into the United Kingdom, the 2.12-m outside diameter Zokor machine owned by Fairclough Civil Engineering[4] having, to 1 September, 1984, driven 4.6 km of tunnel, the longest drive distance being 460 m with a maximum

Fig. 3 2.55-m Grosvenor tunnelling machine used in London Borough of Croydon Mitcham Road surface water drainage scheme. Photograph by courtesy of *New Civil Engineer*

speed of 22 m per shift. The second back-acter machine, introduced in August, 1982, was the 2.55-m Grosvenor machine (Fig. 3). Manufactured in the United Kingdom and owned by Johnston Construction, it has driven 0.8 km of tunnel with a longest drive of 205 m.[5] Both of these machines have electrically powered hydraulics and load single muck skips.

Back-acter machines are normally used for a clay face or granular soil above the water-table, though if they are to be used below it, compressed air presents problems with pipe jacking in that the airlock hampers the soil-removal process. In addition, the airlock is not static if it is installed in the pipe run.

Back-acter machines are particularly useful where boulders may be encountered as access to the face is easy; however, they tend to excavate more slowly than full-face machines. On the other hand, they are considerably cheaper to manufacture. Fig. 4 is an idealized multiple activity chart for a back-acter machine constructing a 2.0-m tunnel with a jacked lining. The chart depicts a much better balance of work than that for the corresponding manually excavated job. The pipe installation cycle requires eight cycles of operation of the soil-removal skips. If the skip size can be increased, the work can be speeded up, especially when there is a long run between the machine and the access shaft.

Full-face tunnel-boring machines

A couple of early attempts were made to build and use full-face soft earth TBM for pipe-jack work. Both machines (a Ross and a Markon) had oscillating boring heads and neither seems to have had a great deal of impact on the tunnelling industry.[6] In November, 1981, the first full-face TBM to be used extensively for mechanized pipe jacking in the United Kingdom was the 2.18-m Lovat machine (Fig. 5), which is owned by A. Streeter and Co.[7] To date, this has driven 4.2 km of tunnel (longest drive distance, 580 m; maximum rate of progress, 42 m per shift). It is important to note that the Lovat machine has been in almost continuous use over the past three years on four separate contracts. The boring head of the Lovat machine consists of a conical drum revolving in an outer shell with an arm along one diameter at the front. On the arm are mounted the cutting teeth, easily changeable and for soft ground conditions of the type usually used for excavator buckets. The drum can be rotated in either direction. There is a facility for fitting overcutting teeth at the end of the arm; otherwise, the arm revolves completely within the diameter of the cutting edge. The circular area immediately behind the cutting arm is divided into four segments, two of which are covered by fixed plates (the other two segments have movable plates that can be rotated individually behind the fixed plates, controlling the size of the opening to the mining face and, hence, the flow of excavated material). These movable plates can be operated while the

Multiple Activity Chart Data for a 2.0m OD Back Acter Tunnelling Machine with Duplicate 1.5 m³ Muck Skips			
Item	Operation	Description	Max. Rate of Execn
BAM	A	BAM excavates face and loads muck skip	5/16 m per min
Jacks	B	Jacks push lining forward	5/8 m per min
Winch	C	Winch pulls full muck skip into jacking pit	50 m per min
Crane	D	Crane lifts full muck skip and empty muck skip is put onto tracks	30 s
Winch	E	Winch pulls empty muck skip to face	50 m per min
Crane	F	Crane empties muck skip	1 skip per min
Crane	G	Crane lifts pipe and positions it on launch pad (services extended)	1 pipe per 4 min

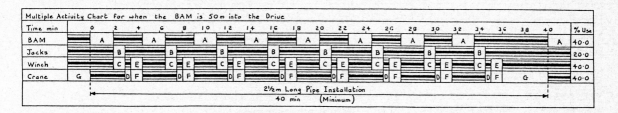

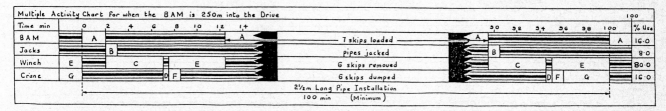

Fig. 4   Idealized multiple activity chart for back-acter machine constructing 2-m jacked concrete pipe tunnel in soft earth

cutterhead is either stationary or rotating and, in the event of a power failure, the hydraulics that close them can be operated by hand. When the movable plates are shut the cutterhead is virtually watertight.

Fig. 5   2.18-m Lovat fast TBM used for installation of jacked concrete pipes

In water-bearing granular soils problems may arise with the sealing arrangements in the telescopic part of a self-thrusting machine owing to contamination by soil particles. Experience has shown that the best way of dealing with this problem is to inundate the zone around the machine with a thick lubricating slurry, which also assists in the formation of a seal.

Fig. 6 – an idealized multiple activity chart for such a full-face TBM (at 2.0-m outside diameter) – gives an idea of the great speed of this machine in favourable ground conditions. The full speed of installation suggested by the chart cannot be sustained for any length of time and an efficiency factor of between one-half and two-thirds normally applies, even in favourable conditions. Between 50 and 60 m per shift has been achieved in the U.S.A. with a Lovat machine.

When pipe jacking is carried out with a Lovat full-face machine it is normal to use duplicate multi-skip muck trains for spoil removal to make good use of the very rapid excavation. To accommodate a full multi-skip muck train at the access shaft a back-shunt is normally provided. This can be a previously completed run of tunnel or pipes placed between the jack frame and the jacking wall. Fig. 7 shows the loading of a multi-skip muck train (the locomotive and driver must fit under the loading belt). Fig. 8 shows the transfer in the access shaft of the full and empty trains.

In January, 1984, the fourth full-face TBM was introduced to the United Kingdom for pipe jacking. Owned by Thrustbore Construction, the 1.2-m Akerman machine (Fig. 9) is a very modest machine probably intended for drives up to only 100 m as the power transmission to the face is by hydraulic pipeline.[8] To date, the machine has completed only 0.15 km of tunnel (longest drive distance, some 40 m; maximum rate of progress, about 15 m/shift). As this machine becomes more sophisticated and the operators gain more experience in its use, its speed may increase to give it the necessary edge over hand excavation and provide some economic justification for its continued use.

Slurry (bentonite) tunnelling machines

The first slurry tunnelling machine was built in the United Kingdom in the late 1960s and was used with mixed success at Warrington on a bolted segment tunnelling project.[9] Since then, no more seem to have been built in the United Kingdom, but hundreds have been built and used in Japan – many for pipe-jacking work.[10]

The first slurry tunnelling machine to be used for mechanized pipe jacking in the United Kingdom was imported from Japan in September, 1983, the 1.8-m Iseki Poly-Tech crunching mole having, to date, driven 0.6 km of tunnel, the longest drive being about 250 m with a maximum rate of progress of about 13 m per shift. This machine, which had to be dug out and repaired on its first job when it was damaged by an obstruction,[11] is slow in comparison with other similar-diameter machines and its speed is limited by the rate of spoil removal and the need to disconnect and reconnect more services with each pipe addition. Fig. 10 shows a slurry machine and an idealized multiple activity chart for a 2.0-m slurry machine is given in Fig. 11.

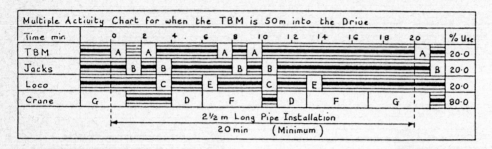

Item	Operation	Description	Max. Rate of Execn
Multiple Activity Chart Data for a 2·0m OD Tunnel Boring Machine with Duplicate 4×1·5m³ Skip Muck Trains			
TBM	A	TBM excavates face and loads muck train	5/8 m per min
Jacks	B	Jacks push lining forward	5/8 m per min
Loco	C	Loco shunts full muck train into back shunt	50 m per min
Crane	D	Crane lowers empty muck train onto tracks	1 skip per 30s
Loco	E	Loco pulls empty muck train to face	50 m per min
Crane	F	Crane empties muck train	1 skip per min
Crane	G	Crane lifts pipe and positions it on launch pad (services extended)	1 pipe per 4 min

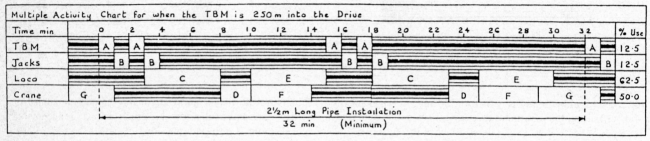

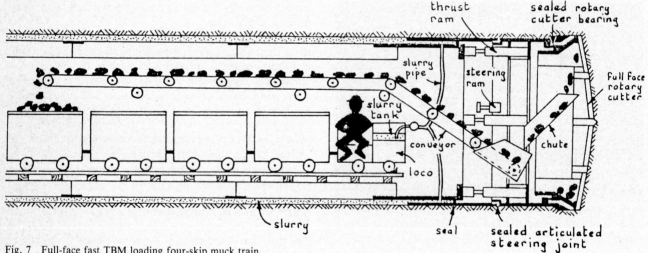

Fig. 6   Idealized multiple activity chart for fast TBM constructing 2-m jacked concrete pipe tunnel in soft earth

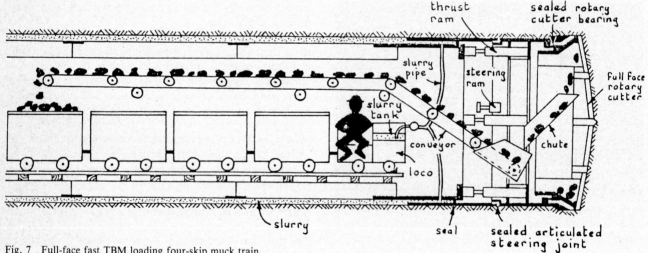

Fig. 7   Full-face fast TBM loading four-skip muck train

About 3 m/h would be a typical maximum rate of progress 50 m into the drive and 2.5 m/h 250 m into the drive. It has been assumed that the introduction of intermediate jacking stations every 100 m adds 5 min per jacking station to the minimum pipe installation time. This loss of progress with distance is modest in comparison with the other two types of soft earth machine. Slurry machines are advantageous in granular soil where there is a high pore water pressure. The balancing of pore water pressure by slurry pressure at the face completely inhibits erosion and the associated settlement. The 'crunching mole' has the additional feature of a crusher mounted on its main shaft, which reduces large stones to a size suitable for pumping. For each cubic metre of spoil removed by use of a slurry machine 3 m³ of slurry is required to carry it and a large separation plant is required adjacent to the access shaft.

Boom cutter rock tunnelling machines

In June, 1983, the first boom cutter rock tunnelling machine (a United Kingdom produced Dosco, Fig. 12) was introduced on to the United Kingdom pipe-jacking scene by Fairclough Civil Engineering. It was used on the River Bolin surface water outfall contract in Manchester, where it set up the present British pipe-jack distance record of 693 m.[12] A sliding resistance of only a small proportion of the 12 000-kN jacking force was observed on this drive without intermediate jacking or slurry lubrication. Maximum progress rates with this machine have been about 15 m per shift. A teething problem for this machine was the chain conveyor, which from time to time became jammed by excavated shale. The belt conveyor that has now been fitted seems to have eliminated this problem.

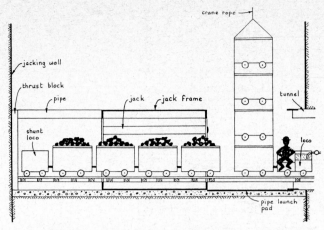

Fig. 8   Use of back shunt in jacking pit allowing empty muck skips to be attached to locomotive before full skips are removed from pit

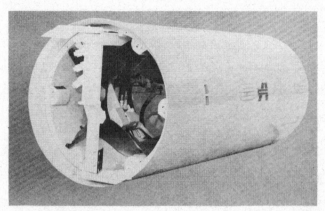

Fig. 9   Akerman full-face TBM (basic models available for concrete pipes of 36-, 42-, 48-, 54- and 60-in internal diameter)

Fig. 10   Iseki Poly-Tech crunching mole slurry TBM (slurry machines developed to install pipes of from 300-mm to 3-m internal diameter)

The prototype machine had the cutter firmly attached to the shield, but the design has now been modified and future models will have a cutter that can be drawn back from the face, and this will make operation much easier. Dosco has more than 2000 boom cutter machines in use and the firm produces 39 different cutting heads for a wide range of rock. The philosophy behind the design of Dosco equipment is power and robustness, which makes their machines seem expensive at first sight, but there is no such thing as a good, cut-price tunnelling machine – the hostility of the environment in which they have to work excludes such a possibility. The philosophy that light, easily removable equipment can be advantageous on a tunnelling job

invariably leads to excessive maintenance and, often, early abandonment in favour of more manually assisted excavation in some form.

Disc cutter rock tunnelling machines

In January, 1984, the first disc cutter machine (a United Kingdom produced Markham, Fig. 13) was introduced by Fairclough Civil Engineering for a contract in Halifax, England, and rates of progress in excess of 15 m per shift have been achieved. A teething problem involved clearance of the bore in front of the machine and maintaining alignment with a variable face.[13] Early in the first drive debris in the invert caused the machine to be deflected upwards. The problem has been largely overcome by modifications to the cutting head edge scrapers, which seem to need to be matched to the material that is being excavated. Disc cutter machines, although very fast and very powerful (and the Markham is 250 kW more powerful than a D8 bulldozer), seem to be sensitive to variation of hardness at the face and can be hampered by bore debris that collects in the invert of the hole that they are boring unless careful consideration is given to its adjustments and use. The first use of this machine included several 500-m radius bends – the first time in the United Kingdom that mechanized pipe jacking has been used to install pipes deliberately around a curve.

Jacking pipes through rock bores

Pipes can usually be jacked very easily through clean straight rock bores, but rock excavation machines are risky in fractured or friable rock, especially if a jacked lining is used. The installation can be gripped in the bore by wedge-shaped particles similar to a prestressing cable in an anchorage. Rock bores should be supported by a very thick slurry injected just behind the tunnelling machine to prevent loose particles from becoming dislodged and wedging the pipes.

Slurry lubrication

On large pipe-jacking contracts slurry is pumped into the overcut just behind the machine and at intervals through the soffit of the pipes. It is piped from the surface for short runs (Fig. 15) and taken in on the locomotive for injection directly into the injection points for longer runs (see Fig. 7). Apart from its ability to reduce sliding resistance the introduction of slurry into the overcut brings other benefits. The loading on the pipes is homogenized because the deformation of the bore from its initial circular shape is not reflected by the deformation of the lining, as occurs with segmental lining. Slurry flows away from the area where the bore shows increased tendency to close. Thus, there is a marked tendency for uniform pressure to prevail around a jacked pipe surrounded by slurry. This is important in that a 2-m class H reinforced-concrete pipe can safely take the full overburden pressure of 150 m of soil if it is a uniform all-round pressure, but it will take only 15 m of overburden soil if the pressure in unidirectional. Slurry is usually pumped into the overcut at pressures up to 10 bar (equivalent to 50 m of overburden soil). This offers the possibility for any tendency for the soil to settle around the pipes to be counteracted.

Experience has shown that to provide effective lubrication for pipe runs, especially in granular soil, the slurry must be very thick, and this implies a high gel strength and high viscosity. The gelling time on site is often measured in hours or days and with these thick slurries there is a need to measure gel strength after long intervals. At Oxford Polytechnic gel strengths can be measured over protracted periods of time (Fig. 16 shows a Fann viscometer for such a test).

Multiple Activity Chart Data for a 2·0m OD Slurry Tunnelling Machine			
Item	Operation	Description	Max. Rate of Execn.
STM	A	STM excavates face	2½ m per 30 min
Jacks	B	Jacks push lining forward Interjacks (every 100m) push lining forward	2½ m per 30 min 5 min per Inter Jack
Pumps	C	Pumps circulate slurry to remove spoil	7·9 m³ per 30 min
Crane	D	Crane lifts pipe and positions it on launch pad (services extended)	1 pipe per 20 min

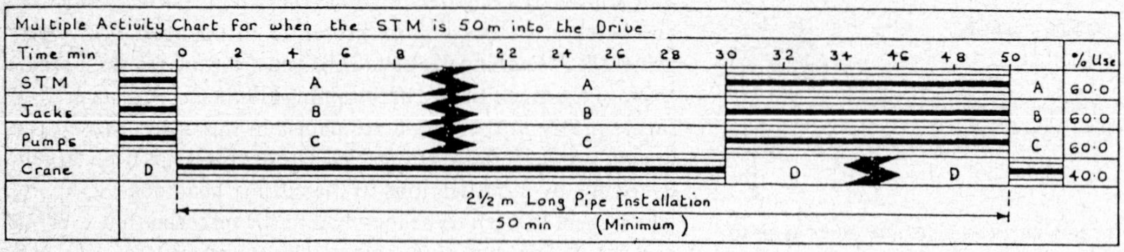

Multiple Activity Chart for when the STM is 50m into the Drive

Time min		% Use
STM	A ... A ... A	60·0
Jacks	B ... B ... B	60·0
Pumps	C ... C ... C	60·0
Crane	D ... D ... D	40·0

2½ m Long Pipe Installation
50 min (Minimum)

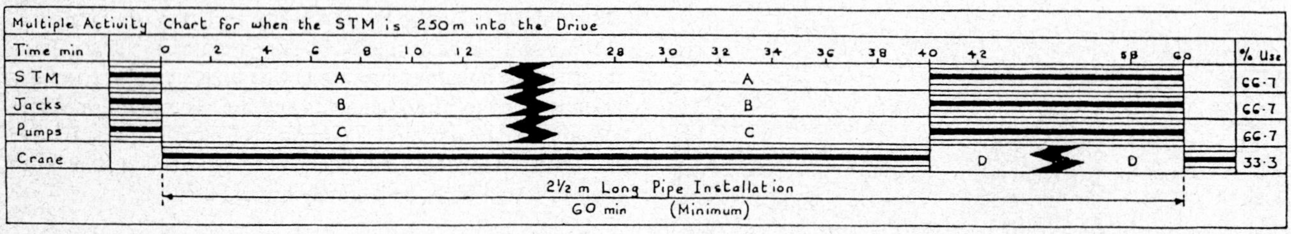

Multiple Activity Chart for when the STM is 250m into the Drive

Time min		% Use
STM	A ... A ... A	66·7
Jacks	B ... B ... B	66·7
Pumps	C ... C ... C	66·7
Crane	D ... D ... D	33·3

2½ m Long Pipe Installation
60 min (Minimum)

Fig. 11   Idealized multiple activity chart for slurry tunnelling machine constructing 2-m jacked concrete pipe tunnel in soft earth

Fig. 12 Dosco boom cutter rock TBM (first machine of its type built specifically for use with jacked lining)

Fig. 14   Jacking pipe daubed with bentonite sludge prior to its entry into ground

Fig. 13   Markham disc cutter rock TBM (first such machine built specifically for use with jacked lining)

Fig. 15   Slurry injection pipework and intermediate injection points in jacked tunnel lining

248

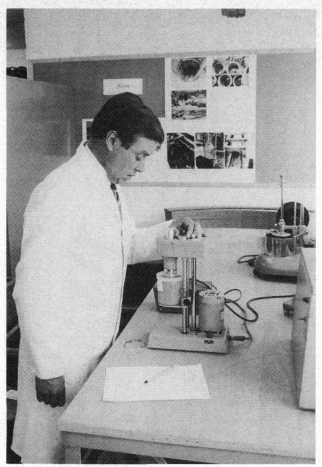
Fig. 16   Fann viscometer

Conclusion

The introduction of mechanized pipe jacking into the United Kingdom has been late but rapid. There can be no doubt that the structural form and joint quality of the end-product of pipe jacking is preferable to any of the segmental alternatives.[18] Mechanized excavation has now been applied to the full range of ground conditions, including rock – sometimes with considerable success. Over the next decade there will be a considerable increase in mechanized pipe-jacking activity, particularly if there is increased expenditure on sewer replacement. This will be achieved by an increasing proportion of jacked lining work and by contractors opting for mechanized excavation in preference to slower hand work. Mechanized pipe jacking will bring considerable benefit to the tunnelling industry, but the process demands a good understanding of the technology, constant rigorous maintenance and eager back-up from equipment manufacturers. Given these needs, it is an industry that should have a prosperous future.

Acknowledgement

The author wishes to thank the following for assistance in the preparation of this paper: Zokor International, Fairclough Civil Engineering, Lovat Tunnelling Equipment, A. Streeter and Co., Hawker Siddeley Dosco, Iseki Poly-Tech, Lilley Group, *Tunnels & Tunnelling*, Markham and Co., Rees Hough, Thrustbore Construction, Johnston Construction, Grosvenor Tunnelling International, Akerman Manufacturing, Inc., Pozament and Gemas Construction.

References
1. Washbourne J. The general philosophy of large scale earth moving. *Civil Engng Technician*, Oct. 1982, 5–9.
2. Pilcher R. *Principles of construction management, 2nd edn* (New York, etc.: McGraw Hill, 1975), 110–3.
3. Washbourne J. Mechanised pipe jacking as a method of sewer construction. In *International conference on the planning, construction, maintenance and operation of sewerage systems, Reading, September 1984* (Cranfield, Bedford: BHRA, 1984), 288–304.
4. Wallis S. West Feltham pipe jackers push into the future. *Tunnels Tunnell.*, **14**, no. 8, Sept. 1982, 41–2.
5. Fullalove S. Hydraulics boosts pipe jacking. *New Civ. Engr*, Nov. 24 1983, 20–1.
6. Craig R. Pipe jacking – a state of the art review. *CIRIA Tech. Note* 112, 1983, 14.
7. Washbourne J. The slurry lubrication of jacked tunnel linings. *Civ. Engng Technol.*, March 1984, 7–9.
8. Dadson J. Mini mechanised pipejack. *New Civ. Engr*, April 12 1984, 32–3.
9. Walsh T. Bentonite bore in Hamburg. *New Civ. Engr Spec. Supplem.*, June 12 1975, 22.
10. Fujita K. and Ueda K. The Japanese experience. *New Civ. Engr Supplem.*, March 1979, 4–6.
11. Damaged slurry digger halts for repairs. *New Civ. Engr*, Feb. 9 1984, 7.
12. Degerlund C. Sewer work under way. *Civ. Engng*, June 1984, 27.
13. Webb C. Fairclough pays the price of innovation. *Construction News*, Nov. 15 1984, 20.
14. Jacking concrete pipes. *Pipe Jacking Association Design Specific. Bull.*, no. 1, Feb. 1975, 11.
15. Washbourne J. Sliding resistance of jacked tunnel lining. *Tunnels Tunnell.*, **14**, no. 10, Nov. 1982, 17–18.
16. Leonard J. Guide to drilling workover and completion fluids. *World Oil*, June 1980, 57–117.
17. Washbourne J. Three-dimensional passive analysis for jacking walls. *Tunnels Tunnell.*, **13**, no. 2, March 1981, 13–17.
18. Washbourne J. The shape and nature of concrete soft earth tunnel lining. *Civ. Engng Technician*, Feb. 1982, 7–10.

Usually, the need to mobilize the gelled slurry in the pipeline after a period of rest is more critical than that of overcoming viscous resistance. Here the pump pressure must shear the material at the boundary layer on the inside of the pipe as well as overcome back pressure from the zone that is being injected. This means that delivery pipe lengths must be short and of adequate diameter.

It may be difficult to organize blending of slurries on site and there is a growing feeling in the industry that, ideally, a slurry-forming material should be pre-blended. Pozament is introducing a material that contains bentonite, a polymer and void-blocking additives to fill the gap in the product range brought about by the superseding of bolted segments by jacked pipes.

Sliding resistance for a pipe run can be increased greatly by small projections, such as plywood joint packing used in conjunction with ogee joints. The newer steel collars give a much smoother joint, but they are relatively expensive because the bevelled edge has to be accurately machined. This type of joint, which gives the pipe run a much greater jacking load capacity, could perhaps be manufactured from strip rolled with a bevelled edge in corrosion-resistant steel when increased demand justifies this. Steel collars with epoxy resin protective coatings are being used by Gemas Construction for a mechanized pipe-jacking contract in Folkestone, England.

The control of sliding resistance is important since the need for intermediate jacking (an expensive addition to pipe-jacking costs) depends upon this. The lower the unit sliding resistance, the further the pipes can be pushed for a given jacking capacity. It is most convenient and economical to supply all of the thrust at the jacking pit closest to the power source, and this has led to an increase in jacking capacity and a more sophisticated method of jacking wall passive earth pressure analysis.[17]

Discussion

Dr. P. H. Phillips* said that the shield that was described by Gill did not appear to be an extrusive shield, as say, that of Hochtief, but rather an earth pressure balanced shield. Because of the importance of international terminology perhaps the author could explain why he had used the term 'extrusive' when it would appear that, for example, 'intrusive' seemed to be more appropriate.

Author's reply

Dr. S. A. Gill   The operation of the shield is not truly like an earth pressure balanced shield because, in this case, excess pressure is required to squeeze the soil into the tunnel. For an earth pressure balanced shield the pressure on the shield is just sufficient to match existing lateral pressure of the soil outside the shield.

I agree that the shield terminology should be intrusive or an intruding shield when one considers the operation from within the tunnel. The word 'extruding' had, however, been used previously by Terzaghi for similar operations. There is a definite need for agreed international terminology for proper communication.

*Phillips and Sons, Cookham, Berkshire, England.

Session 11 – Grouting

Co-Chairmen: Dr. B. Pigorini and S. G. Tough

Grouting of completely weathered granite, with special reference to the construction of the Hong Kong Mass Transit Railway

D. A. Bruce
Colcrete, Ltd., Wetherby, West Yorkshire, England
J. N. Shirlaw
Mass Transit Railway Corporation, Hong Kong

Synopsis
The construction of the tunnels and stations of the three routes of the Hong Kong Mass Transit Railway has been under way since 1975. Difficult ground conditions and the practical limitations that are associated with civil engineering works in congested locales have dictated the use of specialist geotechnical processes as vital adjuncts to progress and safety in the overall construction. In particular, ground treatment, by cement and chemical injections, has been used widely, and data from a variety of sites have proved its effectiveness, especially in the ubiquitous completely decomposed granites.

Judged by the standard criteria of grading curve analyses and permeability, however, such materials should be but marginally, if at all, treatable by such methods, whereas post-grouting mass permeabilities of 1×10^{-7} m/s have been achieved in ground with more than 40% fines. In examining the working method and the observed mechanisms of the successive elements of the ground treatment the apparent paradox is resolved in the light of the peculiar microstructure that is to be expected in weathered rock of this type.

Cut and cover methods were widely adopted during the construction of the first two lines of the Hong Kong Mass Transit Railway (MTR) – the Modified Initial System (MIS) and the Tsuen Wan Extension (TWE) (Fig. 1). These lines, opened in 1980 and 1982, respectively, currently carry 1 200 000 passengers per day. Construction of the Island Line – the third

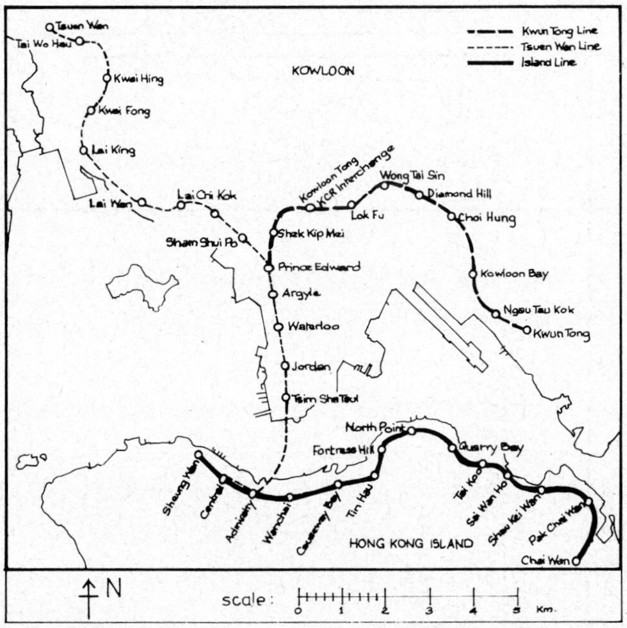

Fig. 1   MTRC routes, Hong Kong

major artery, which will double the traffic when fully operational by 1986 – was commenced in 1981. Its route coincides with the densely populated fringe of the north foreshore of Hong Kong Island itself and so underlies the commercial and trading heart of the Territory. To minimize the disruption of the already congested road traffic system the 10.5 km of new subsurface track is being created in 8-m diameter bored tunnels,

and the ten new underground concourses are being constructed in off-street locations up to 50 m away from the line of the tunnels.

Whereas approximately 6 km of these tunnels is in hard granite bedrock, the balance is in soft or mixed ground – fill, marine deposits, alluvium, colluvium and various grades of decomposed granite. The tunnels are 25–35 m below ground surface and their safe passage through saturated deposits (the water-table is generally within 2 m of the surface) and under structures with old and questionable foundations has demanded meticulous planning and execution. Similar concerns about minimizing construction-related damage to adjacent property have seen the concourses being constructed by top down methods, within tight boxes formed by load-bearing diaphragm walls extending to rock head, to depths of 50 m. Columns to support the intermediate floors and roof are constructed inside hand dug caissons in advance of excavation.

Given very variable ground conditions, and understandably demanding settlement criteria and construction programmes, contractors have exploited a wide range of geotechnical processes to secure and advance their works. Thus, anchoring, shotcreting and grouting have been common adjuncts to the diaphragm walling, piling and tunnelling activities that constitute the larger-scale processes. The grouting methodologies have been particularly interesting, featuring the exploitation of replacement (jet grouting) and flash setting (DDS, LAG) systems, as well as the more conventional, European, approach of permeation grouting by the *tube à manchette* system.

The beneficial effects of *tube à manchette* injection, in completely decomposed granites (cwg), in particular, were established during the construction of the MIS in 1976[1,2,3] and have since become an integral feature of construction. The work is executed to a common specification, which has, *inter alia*, facilitated the synthesis and assessment of performance data from the numerous working locations. These analyses have highlighted that the grouting of the cwg has been repeatedly effective – to the point of challenging the conventional limits of groutability consistent with current theory. This paper

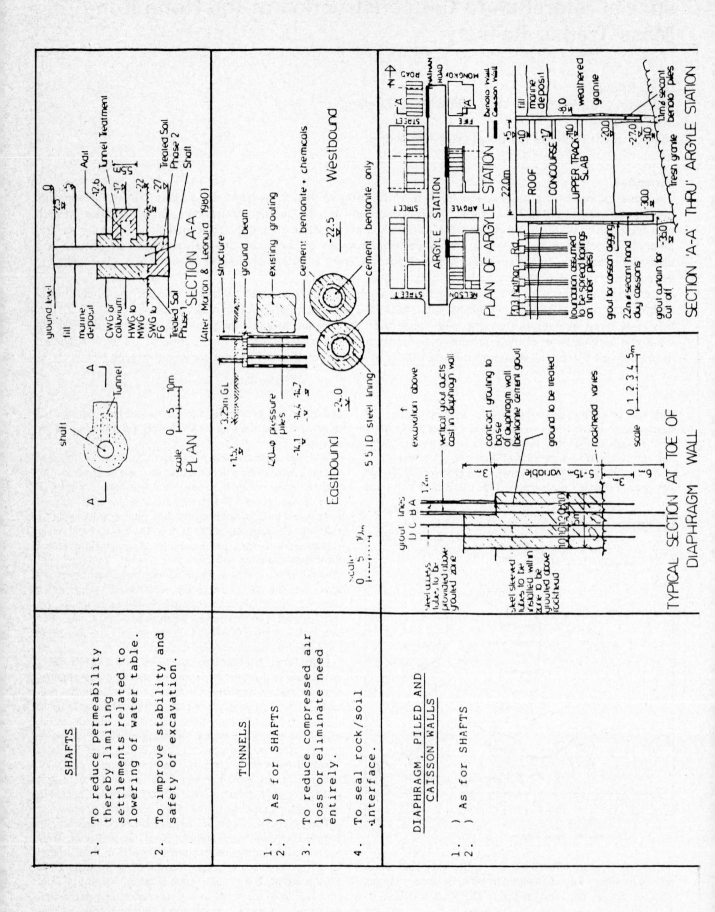

SHAFTS

1. To reduce permeability thereby limiting settlements related to lowering of water table.

2. To improve stability and safety of excavation.

TUNNELS

1.) As for SHAFTS
2.)

3. To reduce compressed air loss or eliminate need entirely.

4. To seal rock/soil interface.

DIAPHRAGM, PILED AND CAISSON WALLS

1.) As for SHAFTS
2.)

PLAN

scale 0 5 10m

SECTION A-A

(After Morton & Leonard 1980)

Eastbound

Westbound

5.5 ID steel lining

TYPICAL SECTION AT TOE OF DIAPHRAGM WALL

scale 0 1 2 3 4 5m

PLAN OF ARGYLE STATION

SECTION 'A-A' THRU 'ARGYLE' STATION

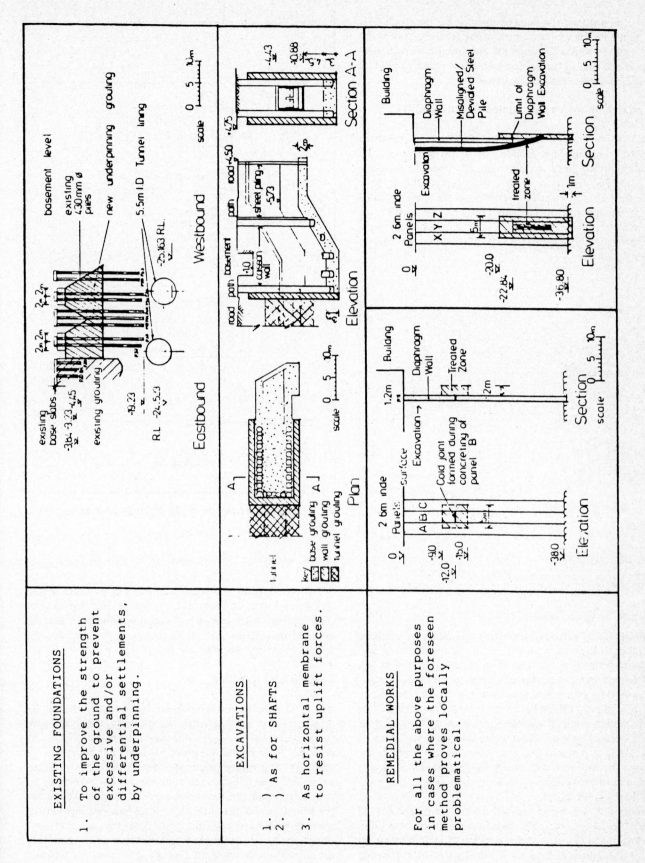

Fig. 2 Summary of major grouting applications

records the advances made and offers conclusions as to the surprisingly low permeabilities that have been achieved.

Applications of grouting in MTR construction

Specific applications of ground treatment are illustrated in Fig. 2. In summary, the prime purpose of the grouting has been to maintain the stability of the ground and groundwater, thereby safeguarding against surface settlements and promoting safety and ease of construction underground.

Characteristics of cwg as related to groutability

The north foreshore of Hong Kong Island and the southern Kowloon peninsula are founded on a Cretaceous granite batholith intruded into volcanic rocks of Middle Jurassic age (Fig. 3).[4] The rigours of a wet, sub-tropical climate have promoted extensive chemical weathering of the rock: feldspars and ferromagnesian micas have reduced, principally, to kaolinite and sericite, respectively. The quartz, which accounts volumetrically for 23–42% of the fresh rock,[5] of course, remains unaltered.

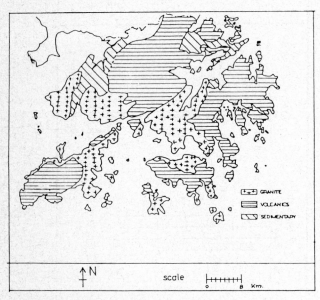

Fig. 3   Geological sketch map of Hong Kong. After Lumb[4]

The results of chemical weathering on granite masses have long been recognized and are well documented.[6,7] A continuously grading profile from fresh jointed granite, through fresh 'corestones' in a weathered matrix, to completely decomposed residual soil can be identified (Fig. 4). In Hong Kong major weathering effects have been recorded more than 50 m below present sea-level, probably enhanced by the different global ocean levels of recent geological history. Zones of particularly deep weathering, such as are found at North Point, appear to be associated with ancient stream channels, and often parallel northeast–southwest-trending dyke swarms that postdate the batholith injection.

Completely weathered masses display permeabilities of 2×10^{-4} to 1×10^{-7} m/s. The specific example that was given by Morton and Leonard[3] shows a strikingly bimodal material with permeabilities of from 1×10^{-5} to 1×10^{-6} m/s. It would seem that this characteristic is consistent with the varying degrees of weathering, and is reflected in the bimodal strength data recorded by Howat.[8] Typical dry density, SPT and drill-ability profiles recorded in west Hong Kong by the same author are shown in Fig. 5.

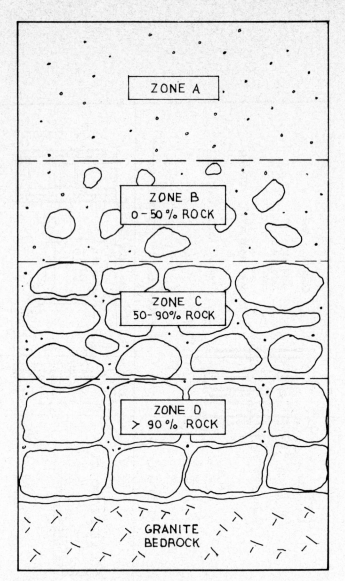

Fig. 4   Idealized weathering profile of Hong Kong granite. After Linney[7]

Envelope grading curves are shown in Fig. 6. Lumb[9] noted that the curves are all skew, with a wider range of fine material than coarse; with increasing decomposition the grading becomes bimodal as the quartz remains unchanged but the feldspar becomes progressively finer.

Execution of grouting

The MTR specification requires the basic method of treating materials other than rock to employ perforated pipes with rubber sleeve valves, and so the *tube à manchette* system, as described by Ischy and Glossop,[10] is commonly used.

Rotary, and rotary percussive, duplex drilling with pneumatic and hydraulic drilling rigs (Fig. 7) has proved to be necessary to penetrate the onerous ground conditions to permit the installation of the tubes. The inter-hole spacings, in the zones to be grouted, are from 1 to 1.5 m (average 1.2 m), but often holes have to be fanned from the surface to accommodate access and service restraints (Fig. 8). The tubes are typically plastic, and approximately 50 mm in diameter, although in certain cases, especially for deep holes under diaphragm walls, steel tubes have been used. Both types have injection sleeves at 0.33-m intervals.

A phase of cement–bentonite grouting is conducted prior to

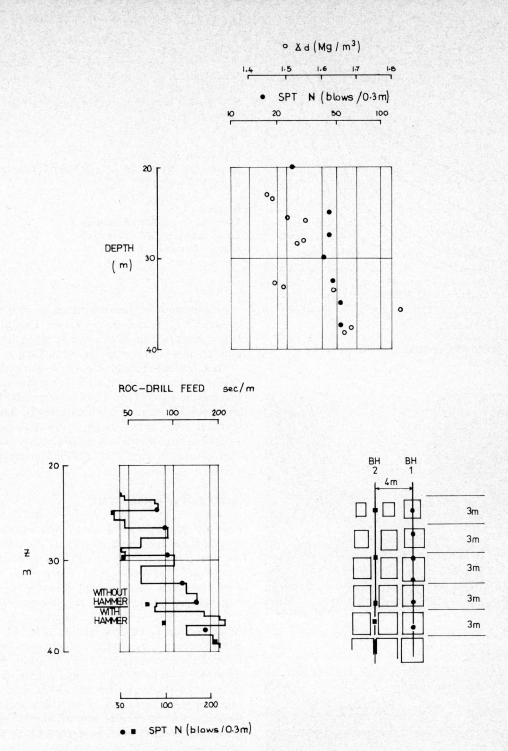

Fig. 5   Dry density, SPT and drillability profile, MTR site, west Hong Kong. After Howat[8]

chemical treatment to 'repair' any damage to the ground caused during the (water-flushed) drilling activities, permeate any coarse, highly permeable zones and fill any major relic fissures in the mass (Flintoff and Cowland[11] referred to sets at 1.5- to 10.0-m spacings).

Injections are typically made at 1-m ascending stages over the entire volume to be treated. The specification calls for a minimum solids content of 350 kg OPC and 35–70 kg bentonite per cubic metre of grout.

At injection rates of up to 8 l/pump/min flow pressures of 5–15 bar are typical of the cwg, although pressures of up to 25 bar (more than twice overburden) have been exercised. Such pressures during tunnel pre-grouting have occasionally resulted in local surface heaves of up to 30 mm, but they have at no time been judged deleterious. Target volumes are preset, based on

notional groutable voids figures, and any groups of sleeves that accept this target volume at below overburden pressure are reinjected. Pressure-volume-time records are maintained for each injection. Back-analyses show typical cement-bentonite takes to be equivalent to 6–10% of the theoretical treated ground volume.

Chemical grouting is afterwards conducted through the same holes and, except in the case of certain shafts and tunnels, at the same horizons: in these cases the chemical treatment is restricted to an annuloid of thickness 2–3.5 m. Flow rates and injection pressures are generally as for the cementitious phase, and reinjection is conducted wherever necessary. Injections are usually made at 0.33-m vertical intervals. Surface heave due to chemical injection is very rarely encountered, and has never exceeded 10 mm.

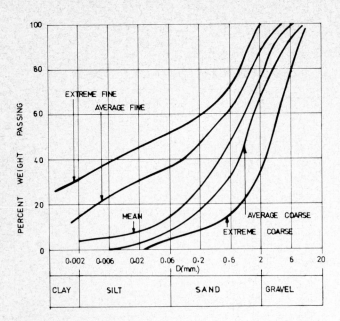

Fig. 6 Limiting and average grading curves of decomposed granite (72 samples). After Lumb[9]

Fig. 7 Diesel hydraulic drilling rig for installation of tubes

Fig. 8 Placing of ducts to avoid damage to near-surface services

The specification calls for the chemical grout to satisfy the following criteria: gelling time, 15–90 min; non-toxic; confer to a standard fine sand a UCS of 0.2–0.3 N/mm² under stipulated test conditions (a stronger gel is required for underpinning – 0.8–1.0 N/mm²); viscosity <5 cP (<8 cP for stronger gel) for as much of the gelling period as possible; to remain effective for at least 30 months.

Table 1

Sodium silicate
Type 35–37° Bé
SiO₂/Na₂O, 3.1 (wt ratio) ⎫ For normal purposes
Sp.gr., 1.31

$$\text{Type 35--37° Bé} \quad \text{SiO}_2/\text{Na}_2\text{O}, 3.1 \text{ (wt ratio)} \quad \text{Sp.gr., 1.31}$$

or

Type 40–42° Bé
SiO₂/Na₂O, 3.0 (wt ratio) ⎫ For underpinning purposes
Sp.gr., 1.37 approx.

Reagent
Rhone Poulenc 600 Series hardener
Long-chain compound diacid ester
Sp.gr., 1.09 approx.

Excellent and long field experience, coupled with economic considerations, has led to the widespread adoption of silicate-based grouts (sodium silicate and an appropriate reagent). A popular choice of material is noted in Table 1.

The effect on the chemical grout of varying the percentages of each component is illustrated, for the case of the 600 Series hardener, in Fig. 9. Typical grouts comprised 33–40% silicate and 3.5–4.5% hardener (both by volume). Back-analyses of chemical grout takes indicate a notional consumption of 25–30% in cwg (approximately 20% in silty marine deposits, 35% in sandy marines and >40% in alluvium and the like).

Aspects of grouting theory

Most grouting applications feature injections into *pre-existing* voids, fissures or pores and, by way of illustration, these may range from bulk infill,[12] through rock grouting[13] to alluvial treatment.[14] The selection of the grouting material and methods reflects the purpose of achieving efficient safe and economic permeation at acceptable injection rates.

Typically, definitive texts on alluvial grouting show the limits of permeation to be expected (e.g. Fig. 10) for standard grouting materials as a function of ground permeability, itself dictated by the natural ground microstructure. Empirical rules do exist,[15] with their bases in filter criteria, that attempt to quantify the limits of groutability. For example, D_{15} (soil) should be greater than $25\,D_{85}$ (grout) for successful permeation. Similarly, for the specific case of silts Littlejohn and co-workers[16] recorded that the predominant pore size is approximately equal to the effective size (D_{10}) of the soil: statistical theory[15] indicates that blockage is highly probable when the pore size is less than three times the D_{90} of the material that is being injected. For silicate-based grouts Baker[17] proposed the limits of Fig. 11, which indicates that permeation is possible in alluvial soils with up to 20% finer than 50 μm, reflecting that even chemical grouts may contain particles up to 20 μm.

The numerous mathematical analyses[18,19,20] that can be cited, however, are based on the assumption that chemical grouts behave as true fluids. These relate the injection hydraulic head, H, required for any given radius of treatment, R, directly to the flow rate, Q, and grout viscosity, μ, and inversely to ground permeability, K:

$$H = \frac{Q}{4\pi K}\left[\mu\left(\frac{1}{r} + \frac{1}{R}\right) + \frac{1}{R}\right] \quad (1)$$

where r is radius of spherical injection source of length L, and diameter D, and $r = \frac{1}{2}\sqrt{L.D}$ approximately.

If the pressure that results from the choice of certain parameters in equation 1 is greater than the 'fracture resistance'

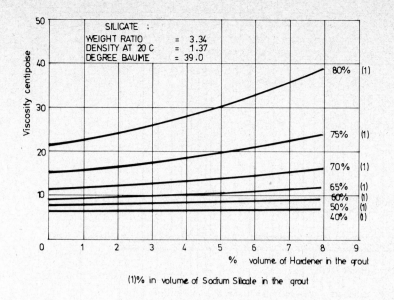

(1)% in volume of Sodium Silicate in the grout

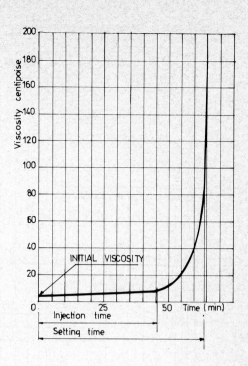

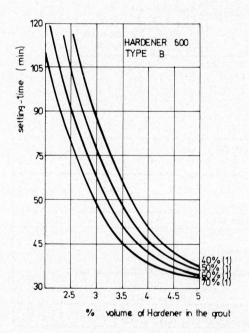

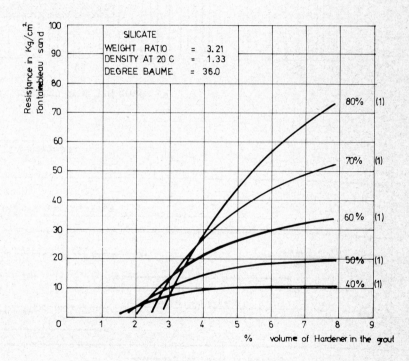

	Type B	Type C	Type D	Type E
Smell	very weak	very weak	very weak	very weak
Colour	dark brown	dark brown	dark brown	dark brown
Melting point	<-30°C	<-30°C	<-30°C	<-30°C
Boiling point	220°C	229°C	232°C	236°C
Flash point	> 93°C	> 93°C	> 93°C	> 93°C
Fire point (Cleveland)	118°C	>118°C	>118°C	>118°C
Density at 20°C	1.09	1.06	1.04	1.03
Viscosity at 20°C	5 cp	5 cp	5 cp	5 cp

Fig. 9   Data on Rhone Poulenc 600 Series – silicate chemical grouts. From technical brochure

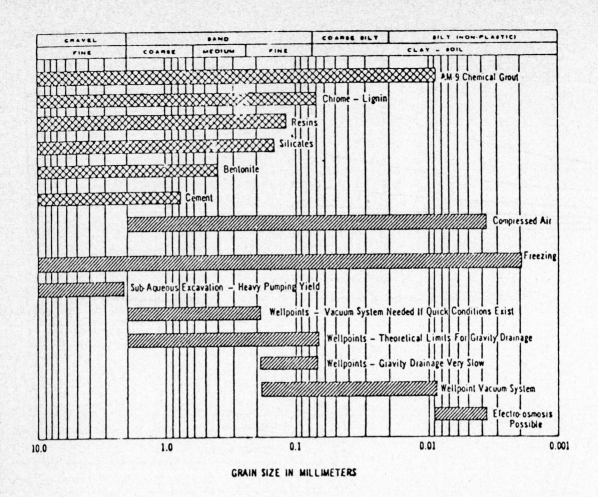

GRAIN SIZE IN MILLIMETERS

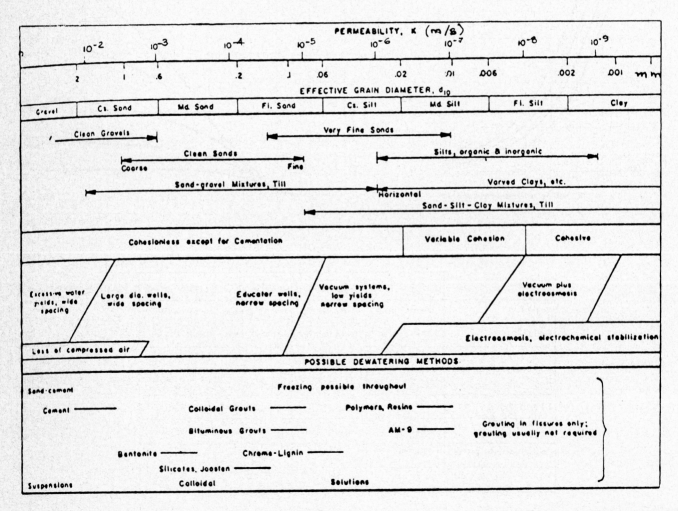

Fig. 10 General theoretical limits of grout permeation. After FHA[15]

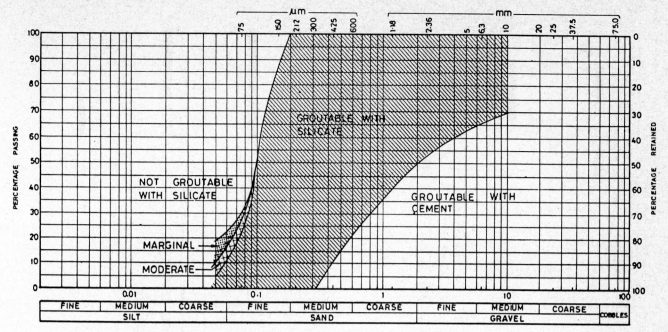

Fig. 11   Limits of silicate permeation in alluvial soils. After Baker[17]

of the ground, the phenomenon of hydrofacture or *claquage*[21] will result. Morgenstern and Vaughan[22] reported that this pressure could be calculated thus:

$$Pf = \frac{(\gamma_h - \gamma_{whw})(1+k)}{2} - \frac{(\gamma_h - \gamma_{whw})(1-k)}{2\sin\phi'}$$

$$+ c' \operatorname{Cot}\phi' + \gamma_{whw} + L \qquad (2)$$

where *Pf* is injection pressure at fracture, γ is bulk density of material above the level under consideration, γ_w is density of water, h is height of material above the level, hw is height of groundwater above the level, k is principal stress ratio, L denotes losses during injection, ϕ' is angle of shearing resistance and c' is cohesion intercept.

Since losses, L, especially through *tube à manchette* systems, are difficult to identify, and ground strength is awkward to assess accurately, equation 2 is not widely used for specific calculations, and prior experience dictates safe grouting pressures to avoid hydrofracture, the results of which may be potentially dangerous, and always difficult to control. Equation 2 does emphasize, however, that fracture pressure, *Pf*, is also related to the 'ground strength' and not merely the overburden pressure.

Performance of grouting

Of the numerous applications outlined above, that which is demonstrated most clearly is grouting for tunnel or shaft stabilization. The results of excavating in untreated cwg were described by Haswell and Umney:[1] seepage occasioned degeneration, loss of cohesion and eventually ground collapse, as was also noted by Peck.[23]

To date, several hundred metres of tunnels up to 8 m in diameter and often under 30 m or more hydraulic head have been driven in treated cwg in free air. Minor seepage, compatible with permeabilities of 1×10^{-6}–1×10^{-7} m/s, is commonly found, but does not lead to significant deterioration of the grouted mass. There is a marked and observable increase in strength: treated ground requires excavation with points, whereas clay spades suffice to remove untreated materials in compressed-air tunnels. Quantification of this strength increase is practically impossible owing to the difficulty of measuring the properties of the virgin mass and the problems of obtaining undisturbed samples from the treated ground.

Exposure of tubes during tunnelling shows good regular geometries, with deviations of up to 1 in 50 over drilled depths of 40 m at most. Cement–bentonite lenses of thickness 5–40 mm, and extending for more than 10 m, have been noted. Laboratory testing of recovered grout samples gives average densities just above 2 Mg/m^3 ($\equiv$ w/c of less than 0.4) compared with mixed grout densities of typically 1.26 Mg/m^3 (w/c almost 2.5). Clearly, an expression of water, into the ground, has occurred during the injection and stiffening phases, thereby leaving a grout of a strength that is considerably higher than the original.

With respect to the performance of the grouting as used to form curtains, Morton and Leonard[3] reported on reductions in permeability of between 300 and 1200 times in three-row curtains to >40-m depth in cwg in Kowloon. In addition, they made extremely valid observations regarding the assessment of the degree of improvement in relation to tests conducted at a nearby shaft grouting location: initial borehole permeability tests gave virgin permeabilities around 5×10^{-5} m/s, apparently reduced after grouting to about 1.6×10^{-6} m/s (i.e. a reduction of 31 times). The actual seepage into the excavation was, however, consistent with an overall ground performance of 3×10^{-7} m/s (i.e. a reduction of 160 times), which was held to be far more meaningful. They strongly urged caution in executing and analysing borehole permeability tests in reasonably impermeable ground, bearing in mind that these results are very sensitive to leakage in the testing apparatus.* Observations that were made during tunnelling have been supplemented by Mazier core samples retrieved from test boreholes. Visual assessment of chemical permeation is facilitated by the technique of spraying fresh samples with phenol phthalene solution. This gives a red reaction from a *PkI* of 9.7. Results from one particular site are shown in Fig. 12. More generally, reaction results from 56 samples obtained from a variety of sites are shown in Table 2.

---

*In constant head testing a post-grouting permeability of 10^{-7} m/s is equivalent to injecting 20 cm^3 water per minute. Hence, accurate results demand losses of less than 0.1 cm^3/s. This is unrealistic regardless of the time and skill taken to form the 'test cell'. Such methods can therefore only be valid to 10^{-6} m/s.

261

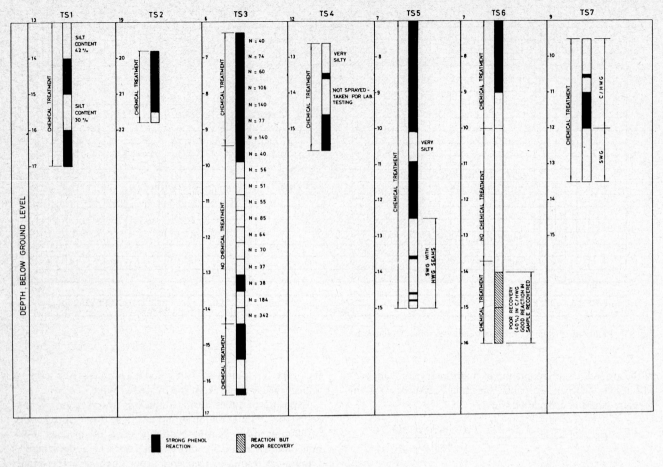

Fig. 12   Results obtained in cwg, east Hong Kong, showing extent of chemical permeation

Table 2   Summary of results obtained on 56 samples of treated cwg

Fines in sample, %	0–10	10–20	20–30	30–40	40–50	50–60
Reaction to test for presence of chemical grout:						
Positive *(total, 43)	2	9	14	15	3	0
Negative *(total, 13)	0	0	5*	2	4	2

*Includes two samples in region not regrouted following initial low-pressure attempt.

It is significant that 32 of the 43 grouted samples had at least 20% fines, whereas none that did not react had less than 20% fines. The averaged fines content of all samples was 31% (cf. the 15% mean of Lumb[9]); 78% of the samples showed positive reaction.

Discussion of observations and test results

Demonstrably good results have been obtained by silicate-based treatment of the decomposed granites in Hong Kong. This success seems to contradict standard theory as related to permeability (virgin permeabilities have often been significantly lower than the conventional 1×10^{-5} m/s limit for successful permeation, and post-grouting permeabilities as low as 1×10^{-7} m/s are frequently recorded) and grading* (most

*It is noted that the fines contents of materials encountered on MTR works have generally been higher than the 'general cwg' figures quoted by Lumb.[9] It is suggested that since all of the MTR samples were taken

samples treated successfully had fines contents far in excess of the 20% limit usually advocated). In formulating a reconciliation it is instructive to assess the contribution of each successive stage of the ground treatment process.

Installation of tubes   It has been established that the decomposed granites retain a relict structure, in a general way increasingly clearly defined with depth. Thus, the insertion of closely spaced plastic tubes, strong in tension, and surrounded by a cementitious annulus of appreciable strength (up to 4 N/mm²) could be held to contribute to the overall mechanical improvement of the ground in a way similar to the *pali radice* principle described by Lizzi.[24] In support of this proposal are the numerous observations of exposed faces where large blocks of ground appear supported by adjacent tubes, especially so in inclined hole locations. In any event, the annulus grouting clearly contributes to the consolidation of the upper permeable fill horizons and so aids the formation of a shallow 'crust' in these regions.

Cement–bentonite grouting   The common observation of lenses of grout of appreciable thicknesses travelling many metres from source has been remarked on, and there would seem little doubt that the three principal aims of this phase, outlined above, are fulfilled. A common suggestion is that the travel of the grout in veins and lenses compresses the enclosed volumes of cwg, therefore reducing their voids ratio, increasing the frictional properties and reducing the permeability. Given the volume reduction commensurate with the increased density of the set grout now measured, however, it would seem that the

from depths well below existing groundwater level little leaching out of (fine) decomposition products has occurred. In contrast, many of the 'general' samples were taken from hillside locations where leaching could well have taken place.

262

actual strain exerted on the ground is small (probably less than 1%). Thus, the resultant degree of improvement in the strength and permeability of the cwg at the injection level would appear to be minimal.

Anomalously, in the fresher granites an improvement in mass permeability can be expected, as the grout will penetrate and seal rock fissures intersected by the tubes, dependent always, of course, on their geometry and cleanliness.

A secondary contribution of this phase, however, is often apparent. No excessive ground heave has been recorded, even when injecting at flow pressures several times overburden. In addition, the presence of injected grout in the very permeable upper horizons has often been revealed during post-grouting coring programmes. (These horizons have also yielded permeability readings consistent with permeation by cement–bentonite grouts.) It is therefore reasonable to assume that upward migration of grout does occur, and that on reaching suitable ground it flows laterally, so forming a horizontal membrane over the ground designated for treatment. This blanket apparently dissuades the subsequent upward migration of the chemical grout, which is therefore constrained to flow laterally into the horizons bearing the injection sleeves. In addition, it is reasoned that such horizontal grout curtains, lying above the face to be tunnelled or the toe to be sealed, act towards locally reducing the hydraulic forces that act on such openings and so contribute to the reduction of seepage. Soft, untreatable pockets occur inevitably: within the time frame of the construction cycle, however, they show little tendency to dislodge owing to seepage forces, although they can easily be disturbed by hand.

Chemical grouting Observations have shown uniform permeation of chemical grout radiating away from injection points and, occasionally, following the lines of cement–bentonite travel. Coupled with the belief that the other steps in the ground treatment process do little to improve the properties of the cwg micro-fabric, it is held that its local reduction in permeability and increase in strength are largely due to the chemical grouting. Thus, silicate permeation is occurring in material of virgin permeability often as low as 1×10^{-6} m/s, and of high fines contents.

By way of explanation, one factor that merits consideration is the method of treatment. Modern reagents give acceptably high strength and stable gels at low concentrations and viscosities, and yield excellent viscosity–time characteristics. In addition, the natural 'strength' of the ground and the inferred presence of horizontal cement-grouted membranes permit relatively high grouting pressures to be exercised and so allow more work to be done on the ground while economic injection rates are maintained. More fundamental, however, would appear to be the rather special nature of the cwg itself, as suggested by the apparent contradiction of permeabilities and particle-size distribution: the average virgin permeability of the cwg (and its degree of groutability) are significantly higher than would seem consistent with the grading analysis. (The possibility of micro-fracturing in the cwg is not considered valid, as it is only in less weathered masses that such structural discontinuities are apparent.)

Baynes and Dearman[6] observed that weathering of feldspars produces a variety of microfabrics, including an extremely open feldspar microfabric consisting of thin struts of feldspar, extremely porous cardhouse clay microfabric and densely tightly packed clay aggregations.

It was also recorded that 'very variable microfabrics were often found in the same specimen indicating a marked variability of weathering environments'. Mitchell and Sitar[25] found that 'cementation of particles into clusters and aggregates by the sesquioxides and the hydrated state of some of the minerals is responsible for high voids ratios (low densities), high strength,

low compressibility and sometimes high permeability, in relation to the plasticity and small particle size that would be anticipated on the basis of the content of clay size particles'.

Hence, the picture emerges of cwg being a material that features, in random distribution, dense agglomerations of clay minerals and very open permeable microstructures in other pores. Grading curve analyses will not differentiate the source of the large fines contents so held and, indeed, Gammon[26] recorded almost identical curves for an apparently clayey residual soil, and an apparently coarse-grained cwg. Such curves, therefore will indicate nothing of the pore size distribution and characteristics, and so the permeability and groutability.[21] Conversely, in the case of the deposits that are usually measured in providing standard curves (e.g. Fig. 10) the fines may be expected to be more evenly distributed throughout the material, and so the link between their size and frequency, and therefore pore size, is more predictable.

Conclusions

Consistently excellent performances have been recorded by silicate-based permeation of cwg in association with the construction of the MTR in Hong Kong. These results are confirmed, despite the facts that virgin permeabilities of 1×10^{-6} m/s, and fines contents of more than 40%, have been measured for the cwg – both parameters consistent with 'ungroutable' ground on the basis of conventional theory. Certain aspects of the execution can be cited as contributory factors, such as the use of modern low-viscosity, stable, high-strength gels, and the facility to apply relatively high pressures without inducing hydrofracture or surface heave. It would seem, however, that it is the microstructure of the cwg itself, and, in particular, the concretionary nature of the fines distribution (and therefore the presence of atypically large pores), which has permitted effective permeation. Thus, although it is now valid to extend the theoretical and practical limits of silicate grouting in residual soils, there is no suggestion that reassessment of grouting theory in deposited materials is warranted, even given recent advances in grouting methodology.

Acknowledgement

The authors have pleasure in thanking the Executive Board of Hong Kong Mass Transit Railway Corporation for permission to present this paper and for assistance in its preparation. The opinions expressed are not necessarily those of the Corporation. The contribution of the staff of Colcrete, Ltd., is also gratefully acknowledged.

References
1. Haswell C. K. and Umney A. R. Trial tunnels for the Hong Kong Mass Transit Railway. *Hong Kong Engr*, **6**, Feb. 1978, 15–23.
2. Haswell C. K. Tunnels for the new Hong Kong Metro. *Tunnels Tunnell.*, **9**, Nov. 1977, 31–5.
3. Morton K. and Leonard M. S. M. Observations on the effectiveness of chemical grouting in residual soils in construction of the modified initial system of the Mass Transit Railway, Hong Kong. Paper presented to sixth South East Asia conference on soil engineering, Taipei, May 1980, 13 p.
4. Lumb P. The residual soils of Hong Kong. *Geotechnique*, **15**, 1965, 180–94.
5. Allen P. M. and Stephens E. A. *Report on the Geological Survey of Hong Kong* (Hong Kong: Government Printing Office, 1971).
6. Baynes F. J. and Dearman W. R. The relationship between the microfabric and the engineering properties of weathered granite. *Bull. Int. Ass. Engng Geol.*, **18**, 1978, 191–7.
7. Linney L. F. A review of the geotechnical aspects of the construction of the first phase of the Mass Transit Railway, Hong Kong. *Q. Jl Engng Geol.*, **16**, 1983, 87–102.
8. Howat M. D. Personal communication, 1984.
9. Lumb P. The properties of decomposed granite. *Geotechnique*, **12**, 1962, 226–43.

10. Ischy E. and Glossop R. An introduction to alluvial grouting. *Proc. Instn civ. Engrs*, **21**, 1962, 449-74.

11. Flintoff W. and Cowland J. Excavation design in residual soil slopes. In *Engineering and construction in tropical and residual soils: proceedings of conference, Honolulu, 1982* (New York: American Society of Civil Engineers, 1982), 539-56.

12. Patey D. R. Grouting old mine workings at Merthyr Tydfil. *Ground Engng*, **10,** no. 8, Nov. 1977, 24-7.

13. Bruce D. A. Aspects of rock grouting practice on British dams. In *Grouting in geotechnical engineering: proceedings of the conference, New Orleans, Louisiana, 1982* Baker W. H. ed. (New York: American Society of Civil Engineers, 1982), 310-6.

14. Bell L. A. A cut off in rock and alluvium at Asprokremmos Dam. Reference 13, 172-86.

15. FHA. *Grouting in soils, volumes 1 and 2* (Duncan, Oklahoma: Halliburton Services, June 1976).

16. Littlejohn G. S. Ingle J. and Dadasbilge K. Improvement in base resistance of large diameter piles founded in silty sand. In *Improvement of ground: proceedings of the eighth European conference on soil mechanics and foundation engineering, Helsinki, 1983* Rathmayer H. G. and Saari K. H. O. eds (Rotterdam: Balkema, 1983), vol. 1, 153-6.

17. Baker W. H. Planning and performing structural chemical grouting. Reference 13, 515-39.

18. Maag E. Ueber die Verfestigung und Dichtung des Baugrundes (Injektionen). Course on soil mechanics of the Zürich Technical School, 1938.

19. Hvorslev J. Time lag and soil permeability in ground water observations. *Bull. Waterways Exper. Station, U.S. Corps of Engineers* no. 36, 1951.

20. Raffle J. F. and Greenwood D. A. The relationship between the rheological characteristics of grouts and their capacity to permeate soil. In *Proceedings of the fifth international conference on soil mechanics and foundation engineering, Paris, 1961* (Paris: Dunot, 1961), vol. 2, 789-93.

21. Cambefort H. The principles and applications of grouting. *Q. Jl Engng Geol.*, **10,** 1977, 57-95.

22. Morgenstern N. and Vaughan P. Some observations on allowable grouting pressures. In *Grouts and drilling muds in engineering practice: proceedings of the Institution of Civil Engineers conference* (London: Butterworths, 1963), 36-42.

23. Peck R. B. The properties of decomposed granite. *Geotechnique*, **12,** 1962, 226-43.

24. Lizzi F. The 'Pali Radice' (root piles). Paper presented to symposium on soil and rock improvement techniques, Bangkok, 1982, pap. D1, 21 p.

25. Mitchell J. K. and Sitar M. Engineering properties of tropical residual soils. Reference 11, 30-57.

26. Gammon J. R. A. Weathering of shoreline rock masses: an introduction. *Bull. geol. Soc. Hong Kong* no. 1, 1984, 35-48.

Soil improvement by jet grouting for the solution of tunnelling problems

R. Tornaghi
A. Perelli Cippo
Ing. Giovanni Rodio & C., Milan, Italy

Synopsis

Jet grouting represents the most recent development in injection techniques. The outstanding feature of this method is the ability to treat a wide range of soils – from coarse granular to fine medium-soft cohesive materials even – by use of a simple cement grout mixed in place with soil particles under a very high nozzle pressure (20–70 MPa).

   Fundamental principles, equipment, design criteria and quality control with specific reference to the Rodinjet® procedures developed by Rodio & C. are considered. Large-scale tests and specific applications in tunnelling practice are outlined in regard to vertical treatment from the surface around the periphery of a planned tunnel or extended to the area to be excavated and sub-horizontal treatment ahead of the excavation face.

Improvement of soils in terms of reduced permeability and increased strength can be achieved by various injection techniques, which may be summarized as *permeation* grouting, in which the grout fills the voids without any essential change to the original soil volume and structure; *displacement* or *compaction* grouting, in which a stiff mix acts as a radial hydraulic jet, creating bulbs or lenses and thus displacing or compressing the surrounding soil; *encapsulation* grouting, in which the ground is fragmented by hydraulic fracturing: the grout coats and compresses but does not permeate the individual fragments; and *jet grouting*, in which the soil is mixed in place with a stabilizing mixture, under a very high nozzle pressure (>20 MPa) (in an alternative procedure soft fine-grained soils can be removed to a great extent by air–water jetting and replaced by the grout).

Permeation grouting is feasible for a wide variety of mixtures (from particulate suspensions to colloidal and pure chemical solutions), but both technical and economical hazards increase with decreasing soil permeability.

   In terms of the coefficient k the normal permeation limits are of the order of 10^{-3} cm/s for silicate-based mixtures and 10^{-4} cm/s for the most expensive resin-based grouts.

Displacement grouting and deliberate hydrofracturing are procedures that should be used carefully in particular cases – mostly as temporary or remedial measures for underpinning, correction of differential settlements of structures or recompression of ground loosened by tunnelling.

The particular advantage of the most recent techniques that are based on jet grouting is the possibility of treating a range of soils from gravel to clay by means of simple cement grouts. Accordingly, an effective soil improvement is obtained that bypasses the problems of penetrability raised by pure permeation criteria as well as the controversy related to the permanence and potential toxicity of chemical grouts.[3-6] On the other hand, the jet grouting principle overcomes the inconvenience and limitations of other modes of injection, such as displacement and hydrofracturing. To sum up, jet grouting techniques offer a valuable alternative to conventional grouting and sometimes to slurry trenching, freezing and other soil-stabilization methods.

Jet grouting procedures

The Rodinjet technique comprises the fracturing and simultaneous mixing of the soil *in situ* with a cement grout; alternatively, the soil can be removed to a certain extent (depending on grain size and consistency) by air–water jetting and simultaneously replaced by grout jetting. Hence, the treatment may imply either the use of a single fluid (the grout) as a fracturing medium and stabilizing agent (Rodinjet-1) or three fluids – air and water as the fracturing and washing media and grout as the stabilizing agent (Rodinjet-3).

The sequence of operations related to the former procedure (Fig. 1) consists, generally, of the following main phases: (*a*) drilling down to the required depth by use of a string of rods fitted at the bottom with a drilling and jetting tool (monitor) (usually, uncased boreholes are drilled by direct circulation of water or bentonite mud) and (*b*) grout jetting through radial nozzles located along the monitor axis while revolving and drawing up the tool.

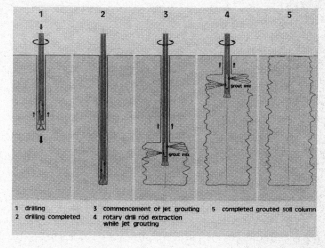

1 drilling
2 drilling completed
3 commencement of jet grouting
4 rotary drill rod extraction while jet grouting
5 completed grouted soil column

Fig. 1   Rodinjet-1 single-fluid system: sequence of operations (uncased borehole)

The size and mechanical properties of treated soil columns depend on the combined effects of the type of soil and composition of the grout, the grout discharge and pressure, related to the number and size of nozzles, and the rotational speed and lifting rate of the monitor.

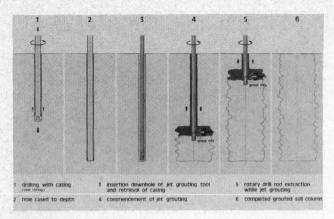

Fig. 2   Rodinjet-3 three-fluid system: sequence of operations (cased borehole)

The diameter of single columns (normally, between 0.4 and 0.9 m) may be increased to 2 m or more by the alternative Rodinjet-3 procedure, which involves air–water jetting through coaxial nozzles placed just above the grout injection nozzles. In this method (Fig. 2) a cased borehole is first drilled with circulation either of water or bentonite mud to the required depth. A string of three-way rods fitted at the bottom with a jetting tool is then lowered into the casing. When the casing has been wholly or partly withdrawn, the injection phase is started by revolving and drawing up the monitor; the procedure comprises fracturing the soil and removing its finest particles by air–water jets just before the injection of cement grout.

Drilling and grouting equipment

A Rodinjet-1 plant[2] comprises, in essence, the drilling rigs provided with a mud circuit, an automatic mixing plant that, starting from water and dry products (bentonite and cement), supplies the drilling mud and the injection grout, and the injection equipment – automatic batchers and high-pressure pumps.

Fig. 3 shows a rig that was specially designed by Rodio for sub-horizontal rotary percussion drilling. A system of hydraulic jacks allows the mast to be rotated to within 180° (acting as a large-scale compass) and inclined up to 15° to the horizontal. By use of this rig all the holes necessary for the treatment of a tunnel section ahead of the excavation face can be drilled to a length of 16 m and with a single rod with no displacement of the equipment.

The selection of a rig that enables operation with a single rod or very long units is advantageous not only to speed up drilling but, more important, to minimize interruptions during the injection phase. Any operation (such as rod-handling, in particular) that causes an interruption of flow under pressure may involve the risk of clogging the nozzles and cutting the column of treated soil.

The Rodinjet method requires a special heavy-duty pump that is capable of delivering water or cement grouts up to a pressure of 60 MPa or more. The grout is prepared in automatic plants that are designed to obtain accurate batching and mixing of the components and to produce adequate quantities for continuous treatment. Each rig may require 5–8 m^3/h of grout.

Generally, in Rodinjet-1 the same string of rods is used for both drilling and grouting, whereas Rodinjet-3 involves the use of two strings of rods consecutively. The drilling and jetting tool for the former procedure is shown in Fig. 4(*a*). A check ball is introduced, at the end of drilling, to change the jet direction from axial to radial. Fig. 4(*b*) shows the Rodinjet-3 jetting tool.

In practice, during the grouting stage the monitor is raised in stages, but rotation speed is kept constant.

Design criteria

Preliminary site investigation and testing
The factors that affect the feasibility of jet grouting and the selection of working parameters can be assessed by the following general and specific experimental steps: detailed soil profiles and hydrogeological information; simple *in-situ* tests,

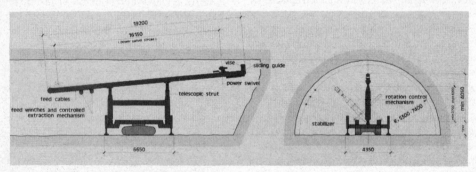

Fig. 3   SR-500 rotary percussion drilling rig

In addition to the above units a Rodinjet-3 plant includes the water and compressed-air circuits. The high-pressure pump is provided in the water circuit, a medium-pressure pump (up to 12 MPa) being sufficient for the cement grout injection. Air is supplied by a compressor (usually delivering 24 m^3/min at 1.2 MPa).

The mode of drilling is selected according to soil conditions, general features of the site and design specifications in regard to length and inclination of holes. Rotary drilling is preferred in medium- to fine-grained soils, fairly small rigs being required. The use of a power swivel with hollow spindle running on a mast 4–5 m long permits the use of a single rod to a depth of about 16 m.

In coarse-grained soils, including cobbles and boulders, rotary percussion may be more suitable in terms of drilling speed, but this technique requires a heavier rig with a mast as long as the longest rod that is to be used.

such as cone penetration or SPT, for estimation of soil consistency or relative density; classification tests on representative soil samples for evaluation of the grain size distribution of cohesionless materials or the water content, bulk density and Atterberg limits of cohesive formations; laboratory tests on trial grouts and soil–grout mixtures, depending on the importance and specific requirements of the site (in any event, the testing programme is simpler than that associated with permeation grouting requirements); and *in-situ* jet grouting tests for checking the operational parameters and, if necessary, for the provision of more detailed information for the final design.

Treatment geometry
The flexibility of the Rodinjet method allows a wide range of problems to be solved by suitable geometrical patterns.[4] These include (1) continuous strip treatment by one or more rows of vertical overlapping elements to form cutoff walls for ground-

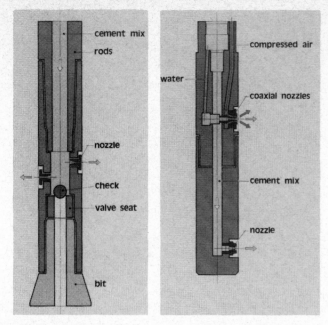

Fig. 4 Jetting tools for Rodinjet-1 (*a*) (*left*) and Rodinjet-3 (*b*) treatments

water control or earth-retaining structures (such barriers may have a circular or elliptical shape when the protection of deep shaft excavations is required); (2) block treatment by vertical staggered columns (secant or not) to increase the bearing capacity of foundations or to improve mechanical properties of soils in tunnelling problems (where conditions permit the treatment is done from the surface around the periphery of a planned tunnel or extended to the entire area to be excavated); and (3) sub-horizontal treatment ahead of the excavation face in deep tunnelling when operations from the surface are impossible or inappropriate.

Selection of grout

The grout mix constituents and composition that are selected to meet the specific requirements of strength and permeability have different and less restrictive criteria than those which apply to conventional permeation grouting.

In regard to the initial rheological properties, viscosity and rigidity should be fairly low to allow an effective treatment to the greatest extent. When strength is the main design criterion a simple cement slurry is used, the cement/water ratio (mostly between 0.5 and 1.0) being selected according to various factors besides that of the required strength, i.e. the type of soil in terms of grain size and permeability in general and water content in cohesive formations and the mean quantity of grout per unit volume of treated soil. In permeable granular formations a considerable amount of water may be drained out both from soil and injected grout, whereas in a cohesive soil of low permeability poor drainage is likely to occur. This is the main reason why the strength (depending primarily on the cement/water ratio) is much lower for a clay than for a sand treated with the same volume of grout.

The amount of cement may be limited by suitable selection of composition and volume of injected grout within ranges defined by previous experience and preliminary specific tests to produce an effective treatment as cheaply as possible. The addition of bentonite may be appropriate to reduce drainage effects in granular soils when permeability control is the main concern and high strength is not required. The use of a cement grout stabilized with bentonite is also suitable in Rodinjet-3 treatments when soft soils can be removed by air–water jet to a great extent.

Selection of jet grouting parameters

The influence of nozzle size, pressure, type and quantity of grout, monitor rotation and withdrawal speeds has been widely investigated for various soils and hydrological conditions. The particularly comprehensive testing programme that was carried out in the experimental site of Varallo Pombia about 60 km northwest of Milan involved calibration tests to define the pressure–discharge relationship as a function of other parameters, several vertical and variously inclined columns with variable jet grouting parameters and full recovery of columns (Fig. 5), permitting a detailed analysis of size, composition and mechanical properties of treated medium to coarse alluvial soils.

Fig. 5 View of a jet-grouted column in experimental site, Varallo Pombia

In addition, the testing programme included the excavation of a small shallow tunnel through coarse cohesionless soil after Rodinjet-1 horizontal treatment around the tunnel section (see later).

Experience to date from several field trials and sites indicates that the main Rodinjet-1 parameters fall within the following ranges: pressure, 20–50 MPa; nozzle diameter, 1.5–5 mm; rod rotation speed, 10–20 rev/min; rod withdrawal speed, 20–70 cm/min in steps of a few centimetres, with a waiting time of 4–20 s; grout discharge, 1–3 l/s; and volume of delivered grout, 150–350 l/m.

In general, the radius of influence is mainly related to the waiting time between the drawing up steps, i.e. to the permanence of the monitor at the same level. An increase in pressure enhances the fracturing effect of the jet, reducing the time necessary to inject a given quantity of grout.

In each case the selection of operational parameters must be based on a reasonable balance of technical and economic factors that require practical experience and may demand site trials.

267

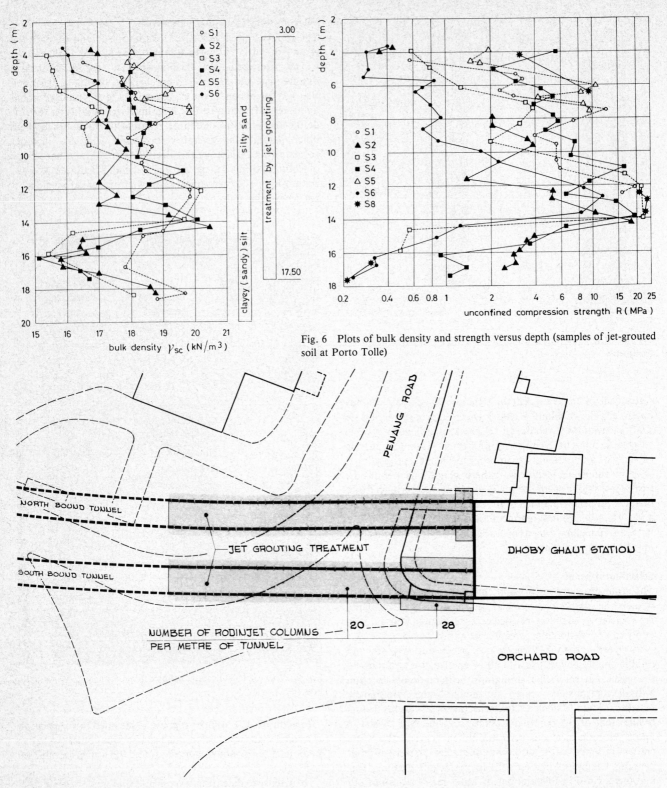

Fig. 6 Plots of bulk density and strength versus depth (samples of jet-grouted soil at Porto Tolle)

Fig. 7 Singapore Mass Transit System: layout of Rodinjet treatment along two tunnel sections from Dhoby Ghaut Station towards Victoria Street

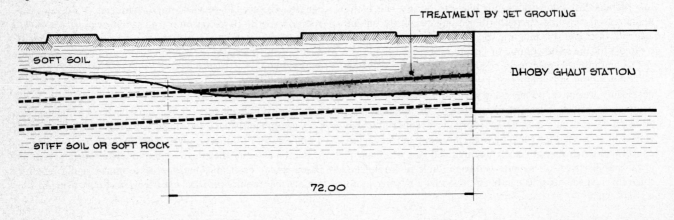

Characteristics of treated soils

The result of a treatment, in terms of uniformity and mechanical properties, depends on a number of interdependent factors concerning the type of soil and the jet grouting parameters. The most extensive studies on samples of soils treated by the Rodinjet-1 procedure have been made in the following cases: medium-coarse alluvial materials in the experimental site at Varallo Pombia, medium-fine to fine-grained soils at Porto Tolle (delta of the Po River) and soft marine and peaty clays in Singapore.

The Porto Tolle site[1-4] represents a typical and well-documented example of continuous strip treatment; a jet-grouted cutoff has been created around the existing outlet station of the ENEL thermal power plant to prevent further seepage and internal erosion through loose medium-fine silty sand.

The cutoff was formed by three rows of overlapping columns 17.5 m deep at 0.4–0.5 m centre to centre and penetrating 3 m in a soft silty-clayey formation. The volume of injected grout (cement/water, 0.6) was 250 l/m. After the work had been completed some 100 samples were recovered from eight boreholes drilled inside the cutoff by rotary core barrels.

An extensive laboratory investigation involved systematic unconfined compression tests and determination of bulk density, the results obtained being given in Fig. 6. Disregarding a few data that are affected by local non-homogeneity or sample disturbance (BH S6, in particular), the compressive strength of grouted silty sand ranges mostly between 2 and 10 MPa, with peaks > 20 MPa and a mean value close to 6 MPa. Beyond 14-m depth there is a variably layered transition zone from silty sand to silty clay in which strength decreases significantly.

A comprehensive statistical interpretation of the experimental data involved the correlation of bulk density to strength to enable the actual composition of treated soils to be estimated. The contents of water, cement and dry soil were calculated on the assumption of a general relationship between overall cement/water ratio and strength on the basis of calibration tests.

The loss of water in the fairly permeable silty sand has involved an increase in cement/water with reference to pure grout (from 0.6 to about 0.8 on average), whereas in silty clay the addition of grout reduced to about 0.3 the final c/w ratio.

A more extensive investigation on jet-grouted clay in Singapore is dealt with below.

Case histories

Vertical treatment

To date, the majority of jet grouting work has involved strip and block treatments by means of vertical or sub-vertical holes for the solution of a wide variety of problems. In the field of tunnelling the first important application of the Rodinjet technique is now in progress on lot 106 of the Singapore Mass Transit System (Phase I project) between Dhoby Ghaut and City Hall Stations.

The geology of the Island of Singapore is complex, several types of soils, such as beach, estuarine and fluvial deposits,

marine clay and sedimentary soft rocks, occurring. In general, beach sand and fill, 3–5 m deep, overlie very soft peaty clay, marine clay and fluvial soils to combined depths in excess of 15 m. The base of this sequence is often marked by a layer of silty, fine sand overlying stiff to hard cohesive soils or weak rocks. Groundwater levels range from about 2 m below surface to less than 1 m in the Dhoby Ghaut Station area. Here a thin covering of fill overlies up to 7 m of peat and peaty clay, which, in turn, overlie up to 7 m of medium dense silty sands and stiff clays and then stiffer soils, grading into weathered sandstone or siltstone.

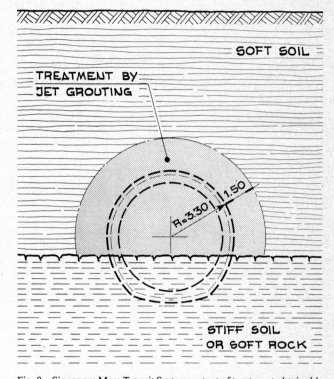

Fig. 8   Singapore Mass Transit System: extent of treatment obtainable by 20 Rodinjet columns per metre of tunnel

The station area has been excavated to about 15-m depth and Rodinjet treatment has been started by means of vertical, staggered holes along the two independent tunnel routes, passing beneath roads and under (or very close to) buildings and public utility services.

Without any soil improvement even shield excavation could be difficult and unsafe, the permissible magnitude of vertical ground movements being restricted to a few centimetres.

Fig. 7 shows the layout of the first section (about 70 m long), starting from Dhoby Ghaut Station, where soil improvement was required at variable depths according to the soil profile; owing to the presence of soft highly plastic formations and to the shallowness of the tunnels, jet grouting from the surface was selected.

Table 1

Samples tested		n	γ	UCS	c/w	Composition, kN/m³			V_g
						c	S	w	
Samples of	Centre of columns	22	15.91	604	0.317	2.04	7.38	6.48	408
jet-grouted	Between columns	12	16.47	477	0.282	1.72	8.65	6.10	344
soil	All samples	34	16.10	559	0.305	1.94	7.81	6.35	388
Samples of ejected soil–grout mixture		30	14.91	641	0.327	2.33	5.46	7.12	466

n, number of tested samples; γ, bulk density, kN/m³; UCS, unconfined compression strength, kPa, after one month; c/w, cement/water ratio = $0.0129 \cdot \sqrt{UCS}$; S, dry soil; V_g, estimated volume of grout, l/m³.

269

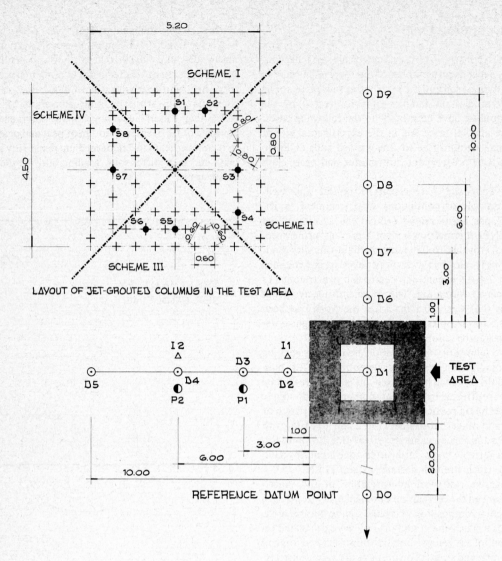

SCHEME	SPAC. (m)	N. OF COLUMNS PER m² OF SOIL (n)	VOLUME OF MIX PER l m OF COLUMN (l/m)	VOLUME OF MIX PER cu m OF SOIL (l/m³)
I	0.6	3.2	187	600
II	0.8	1.8	333	600
III	0.6	3.2	250	800
IV	0.8	1.8	444	800

LEGEND

△ CLINOMETER
◑ PIEZOMETER
○ BOREHOLE
⊙ DATUM POINT

Fig. 9   Singapore Mass Transit System: general layout of Rodinjet test area

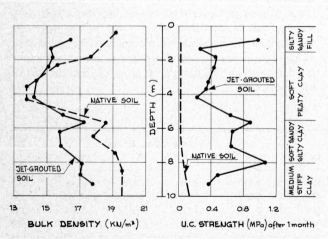

Fig. 10   Plots of bulk density and strength versus depth (mean values recorded in Singapore test area on samples of jet-grouted soil)

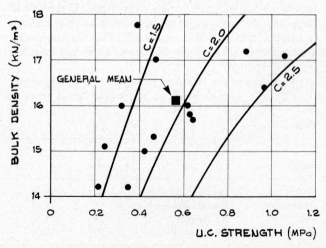

Fig. 11   Estimate of cement content, kN/m³, according to laboratory data recorded in Singapore Rodinjet test area (see Fig. 10)

270

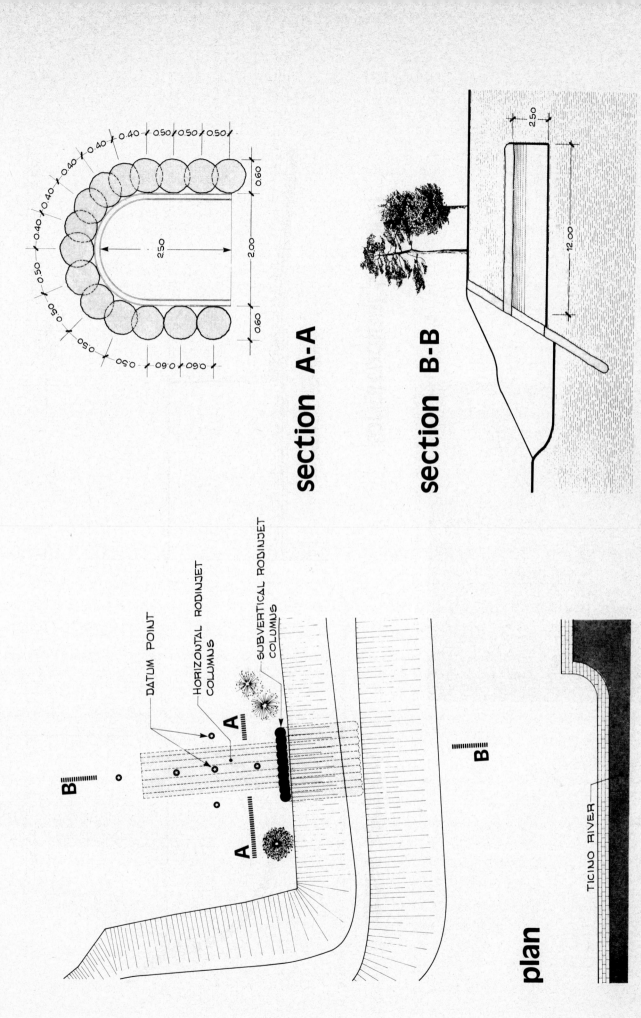

section A-A

section B-B

plan

TICINO RIVER

DATUM POINT

HORIZONTAL RODINJET COLUMNS

SUBVERTICAL RODINJET COLUMNS

0.40 · 0.40 · 0.40 · 0.50 · 0.50 · 0.50

0.60

2.00

0.60

2.50

2.50

12.00

Fig. 12 Varallo Pombia experimental site: layout of Rodinjet treatment for excavation of small shallow tunnel

Fig. 13 Varallo Pombia experimental site: Rodinjet horizontal treatment

longitudinal section

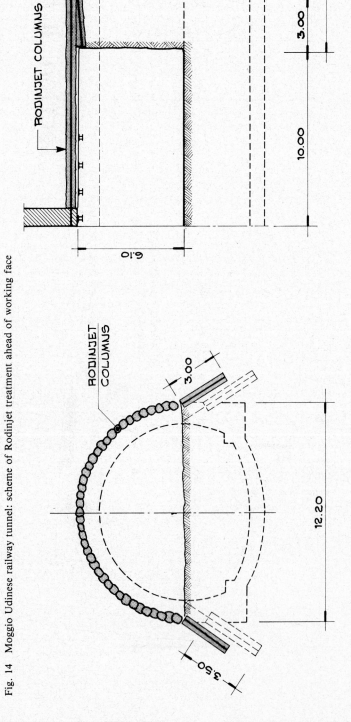

cross section

Fig. 14 Moggio Udinese railway tunnel: scheme of Rodinjet treatment ahead of working face

In line with the design specifications the treatment has to be extended to the full excavation area above soft rock or very stiff clay, and has to create an arch of strengthened soil 1.5–3.0 m thick around the soft soil that is to be excavated (Fig. 8). The thicker treatment was executed close to the station where the shield could not operate (Fig. 7). To check the proposed solution and to set up the working programme a large-scale trial was carried out on site.

As is shown in Fig. 9, two different layouts of jet-grouted columns have been tested – 0.6 and 0.8 m between centres of staggered elements. For each layout two different quantities of grout were injected (600 and 800 l/m^3 of soil). The four schemes that resulted (including a total of 62 columns) have been arranged in order to form the sides of a square area to be excavated subsequently for visual inspection. The following general procedure was applied to each scheme: drilling to 10.5-m depth, treatment from the bottom to 0.5-m depth by the Rodinjet-1 technique, injecting a grout with c/w = 0.6 (5 kN of cement per cubic metre) and a grouting pressure of 40 MPa.

As is shown in Fig. 9, the instrumentation previously installed consisted of two inclinometers to check horizontal soil displacements, two piezometers to record pore pressure build-up and dissipation and nine datum points to check vertical soil displacements with reference to a fixed point 20 m distant from the perimeter of the test area. Inclinometer I-1, located 1 m from the axis of the external row of scheme IV, recorded the maximum horizontal displacement of 23 cm at about 6-m depth; at 6-m distance the displacements were less than 5 cm. The excess pore pressures recorded by piezometric cells 6.5 m deep 3 and 6 m from the perimeter of the treated area were fairly low (20–40 kPa) throughout the injection period. The levelling of eight external datum points has shown fairly similar profiles along the two normal alignments. After completion of the treatment the mean heave values were approximately 30 cm at 1-m distance from the perimeter, 17 cm at 3 m, 5 cm at 6 m and 1 cm at 10 m.

The total volume of injected grout was 190 m^3, which corresponds to 70% of the theoretically involved volume of soil (270 m^3). It is estimated that about 70 m^3 of soil–grout mixture was rejected during injection and that the overall surface upheaval corresponds to about 60 m^3 of upward displaced soil. Since no filling of natural voids can be expected in such a fine-grained soil it may be inferred that the remaining 60 m^3 (almost one-third) of the injected grout has caused mostly radial displacement and compression effects.

Some two weeks after completion of the treatment eight control boreholes were drilled in the test area (Fig. 9) – two for each treatment scheme (I–IV) and, for each pair, one in the centre of a column and one between the centres of two adjacent columns.

Laboratory tests were carried out on 40 representative samples. Plots of mean values of bulk density and unconfined compressive strength versus depth are shown in Fig. 10 for natural and jet-grouted soil.

Assuming a mean relation between one month's unconfined compression strength, R, MPa, and overall cement/water ratio, c/w

$$R = 6.(c/w)^2$$

and full saturation, the actual composition of the treated soil and the cement content can be estimated (Fig. 11). The average content of ~2 kN/m^3 corresponds to 400 l of grout per 600 l of soil, which is close to the theoretical mean proportion of 700 l of grout per cubic metre of soil. The more detailed statistical data that are listed in Table 1 permit comparison of the composition and properties of samples recovered in the centre and between adjacent columns and those of treated soil and of ejected soil–grout mixture. In statistical terms the strength is

Fig. 15   Moggio Udinese railway tunnel: view of Rodinjet treatment (ribs, at 2.5-m spacing, virtually unloaded)

above the specified minimum (300 kPa) even midway between the column centres, the treated soil has a c/w ratio that is half that of pure grout and the ejected soil–grout mixture is somewhat richer in cement and water, which indicates a higher grout/soil proportion.

A test pit was excavated inside the test area 15 days after the end of treatment. There was overlapping between adjacent columns with some discontinuities for scheme II only; a spacing of 0.7 m was selected for the final design.

The results that were obtained are satisfactory in terms of the quality of soil improvement, but the magnitude of surface upheaval necessitated modification of the procedure to increase

Fig. 16   Moggio Udinese railway tunnel: rotary percussion drilling rig (Rodio SR-500) for conical Rodinjet treatment ahead of excavation face

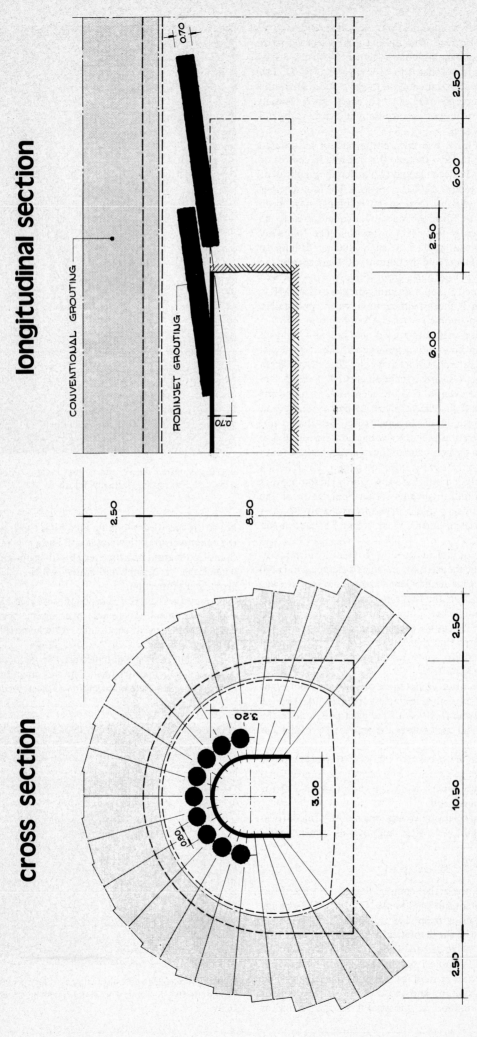

longitudinal section

CONVENTIONAL GROUTING

RODINJET GROUTING

0.70

0.70

2.50

6.00

2.50

6.00

2.50

8.50

cross section

3.20

3.00

0.80

2.50

10.50

2.50

Fig. 17 Milan underground railway, Third line: scheme of soil treatment for drift (sub-horizontal Rodinjet columns) and for main bore (conventional grouting from drift)

the volume of ejected material. Further testing led to a satisfactory solution to the problem by various adjustments of the drilling and jet grouting parameters.

The total volume of soil to be treated is about 9400 m³ along four tunnel sections of a total length of 367 m. More than 1500 jet-grouted columns were undertaken from June to September, 1984, along the two parallel sections that cross Penang Road (Fig. 7). Ground movements, recorded daily by a close network of datum points, were kept within safe limits (2 cm on average), by adjustment of the sequence of jet grouting operations. Systematic control by sampling, laboratory tests and static cone penetration tests are yielding satisfactory results and a good performance is expected when shield tunnelling is carried out.

Sub-horizontal treatment

When operations from the surface are impossible or not appropriate jet grouting can be undertaken by means of sub-horizontal holes ahead of the working face. This procedure was tested initially in the experimental site at Varallo Pombia. As is shown in Fig. 12, the portal was created by means of ten sub-vertical Rodinjet columns set in a row on the edge of a slope. Fifteen horizontal jet-grouted columns 12 m long were then made at variable spacings (between 0.4 and 0.6 m) around the perimeter of a section 2.5 m high and 2 m wide intended for excavation.

The tunnelling operation could be carried out without difficulty under a medium-coarse alluvial covering of only 2–3 m. The treatment (Fig. 13) appeared to be very good and homogeneous along the arch and the right side, where the spacing between centres of elements was 0.4–0.5 m, some small discontinuities being noted only between columns at 0.6 m centre to centre. The recorded heave after jet grouting was, on average, only about 1 cm, despite the thin soil cover above the crown treatment. Subsequent excavation produced settlements of only a few millimetres.

The first major application of the Rodinjet technique ahead of the excavation face was carried out in 1983–84 at Moggio Udinese, northeast Italy. A railway tunnel 12 m in diameter had to be constructed through detrital and mostly cohesionless soil consisting of calcareous rock fragments (up to 10–20 cm in size) in a silty-sandy matrix. Treatment of the first section was effected by a series of 40 overlapping horizontal columns at 0.5 m between centres (Fig. 14). A conventional rotary drilling rig (SR-41) was used in this initial stage. The good results that were obtained by controlled core recovery were confirmed during the excavation, which was started, cautiously, with ribs

at every metre and then continued with a rib spacing of up to 2.5 m (Fig. 15).

For the treatment of subsequent sections the rotary percussion drilling rig (Fig. 3) was specially designed to allow precise and rapid positioning of all holes necessary for a conical treatment (Fig. 16 shows the SR-500 rig during this work). Successive series of 40 overlapping columns 13 m long with a 10% slope to the tunnel axis were formed by holes drilled at an initial spacing of 0.45 m, which permitted excavation stages on 10-m sections alternating with the treatment stages.

The work progressed successfully over a total tunnel length of 150 m at an average overall daily drive rate of 1.50 m. The continuity and mechanical properties of the jet-grouted arch were such that the ribs were virtually unloaded.

A similar type of treatment is being performed in the central area of Milan along the Third line of the underground railway system (lot 3). The alluvial soil of Milan consists of gravel and sand in variable proportions, with fairly thin layers of medium-fine sand and occasional silty-clayey levels.

Drift is driven ahead of the main tunnel bore to allow radial treatment by conventional grouting around the main tunnel section (Fig. 17). Successive series of nine Rodinjet columns 9 m long are formed by holes drilled with an initial spacing of 0.4 m and a 13% slope to the drift axis. This conical treatment has permitted safe excavation in 6-m stages, despite the increasing onward divergence between columns. The geometry of the jet grouting treatment, checked visually during the main tunnel excavation (Fig. 18), proved to be in good agreement with design specifications in regard to both the slope and the expected size (0.7-m diameter on average) of the columns.

References

1. Aschieri F. Jamiolkowski M. and Tornaghi R. Case history of a cut-off wall executed by jet grouting. In *Improvement of ground: proceedings of the eighth European conference on soil mechanics and foundation engineering, Helsinki, 1983* Rathmayer H. G. and Saari K. H. O. eds (Rotterdam: Balkema, 1983), vol. 1, 121–6.
2. De Paoli B. Machines and equipment for jet grouting in Italy. Paper presented at the specialist day on machines and instruments used in special foundation engineering at the 26th international engineering fair, Brno, CSSR, September 14 1984.
3. Hewlett P. C. and Hutchinson M. T. Quantifying chemical grout permanence and potential toxicity. Reference 1, vol. 1, 361–6.
4. Perelli Cippo A. and Tornaghi R. Soil improvement by jet grouting. *Rapid Transportation*, Jan. 1984, 8–13.
5. Tornaghi R. Experimental criteria for design and control of grouting in sandy-gravelly soils. In *Tunnelling '79* Jones M. J. ed. (London: IMM, 1979), 71–8.
6. Tornaghi R. Summary of discussion, specialty session 2. Reference 1, vol. 3, 1099–101.

Fig. 18   Milan underground railway, Third line: view of main tunnel heading crossing Rodinjet columns around drift

Tunnelling and soil stabilization by jet grouting

D. B. Coomber
GKN Keller Foundations, Ryton-on-Dunsmore, Coventry, England

Synopsis
Jet grouting, which permits the controlled *replacement* of unstable ground by a grouted mass, represents a significant advance over conventional injection grouting. The latter technique is dependent on the suitability of the ground to accept treatment by impregnation, the prediction of successful continuity of treatment, cost of the work and risk of heave resulting in considerable uncertainty.

Jet grouting relies on the use of a high-energy erosive jet of water and air to flush out soil in the zone that is to be treated, grout being simultaneously tremmied into position below. From a small-diameter pre-bored hole discrete columns of varying diameter, often as large as 2 m, of grouted ground are built as the grout string is withdrawn and rotated at predetermined hydraulically controlled rates. By careful spacing of columns to ensure interlocking, three-dimensional blocks of a continuous grouted mass can be constructed. Because the soil is removed, its permeability no longer dictates grout acceptance and costs can be predicted accurately.

A much fuller range of soil types can be grouted, including the difficult saturated silts and soft clays.

The technique has been operated commercially in Europe for about eight years – in Britain only since early in 1982. In Japan, with a great breadth of contract experience over 14 years, the most frequent single application has been in the treatment of starting and reception blocks adjacent to shafts for soft ground tunnelling, together with treatment of the shafts themselves.

A general description of the technique and its range of application is given. Thereafter, specific applications in Britain on underpinning and renovation of existing rail and canal tunnel inverts, and on the replacement of unstable ground for tunnelling, are outlined.

The elements of unstable or water-bearing ground replaced by a grouted mass by use of jet grout take three forms – 'wing', 'panel' or 'column' jet grout. Wing jetting utilizes twin erosive jets and a single grout nozzle to form small wedge-shaped grouted masses that seal joints in bored pile walls, connexions between coffer dams and buried installations, etc. Panel jetting allows the formation of a thin grouted slot in the ground, adjacent panels being linked to form a continuous cutoff against underground fluid movement. It is the use of a single rotating erosive jet to form columns, however, that has found the most widespread application in civil engineering temporary works or underpinning applications and that is the subject of this paper.

The procedure for column formation is outlined in Fig. 1. The upper, or excavating jet relies for its power on water under high pressure expelled through a very fine nozzle. The water jet is surrounded by a concentric collar of compressed air, which concentrates the jet, particularly below the water-table, and operates the airlift system for disposal of spoil to the surface. In granular soils all but the coarsest particles are removed, those remaining being dispersed in the solidifying grout as aggregate.

The use of pre-bored guide holes, nominally 150 mm in diameter, encourages the spoil discharge, assists in maintaining verticality and permits a visual check on the continuity of adjacent grouted areas. Technically, the maximum depth of treatment in drift deposits is unlimited. Work has been completed successfully to 43 m in Japan. Frequently, grouting ceases at a defined level below the surface, without disruption of the remaining overlying soils: the monitor is simply withdrawn, restricted grout flow only being maintained to top up the guide hole.

The size of the composite grouted mass to be created is, of course, dictated by the application that is required. The width or diameter of each constituent column is determined at the design stage by reference to the soils that await treatment.

Numerous exposures of completed grout masses have allowed empirical design curves to be derived that relate broad soil categories to the operating parameters of air, water and grout flow and pressure, together with monitor rotation and withdrawal speed. Because these fixed parameters – in particular, monitor withdrawal speed – are under hydraulic control and dictate production rates on site, there is little scope for operator error. As an example, columns of 2-m design diameter are frequently constructed with grout delivered at 180 l/min, water at 70 l/min and 400 bar and a fixed monitor withdrawal speed of 5 cm/min. Reduced flow or increased withdrawal speed produces smaller columns.

The substantial volume of spoil that arises as a slurry retains a significant grout content and gains strength, while losing volume, within 24 h with the result that it can be handled as a firm to stiff clay. At greater age it might often be utilized as a temporary hard standing for construction purposes.

With the two limitations that very low viscosity must be maintained to allow pumping to be carried out and relatively abrasive or coarse fillers, such as sand, must be avoided, the grout mix constituents can be varied to meet the demand for strength or low permeability, or both. If high strength is the principal design criterion, neat cement grouts with or without additive may be employed. The use of cement bentonites is normal if low permeability is the prime criterion and PFA cement based grouts are used for most temporary works applications.

Most tunnelling applications require the formation of three-dimensional grouted blocks formed from interlocking columns, but Fig. 2 illustrates the appearance of a single row of columns for underpinning. The high degree of continuity in column diameter that is attained, at least in soils finer than those of gravel size, is apparent.

Four case histories provide an impression of jet-grout column application to tunnel renovation and new tunnel construction in unstable ground.

COLUMN JET GROUT CONSTRUCTION

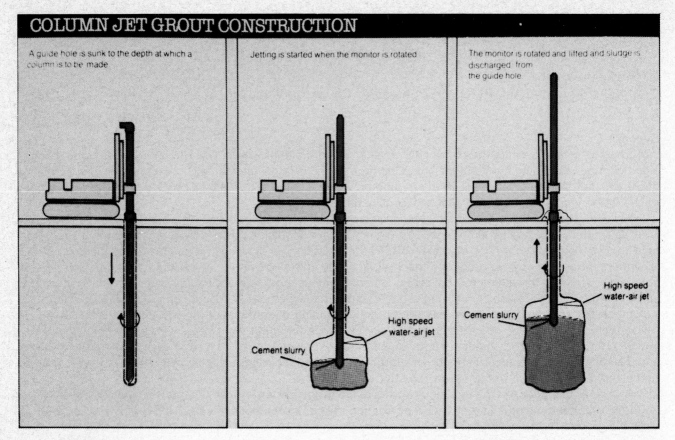

A guide hole is sunk to the depth at which a column is to be made

Jetting is started when the monitor is rotated

The monitor is rotated and lifted and sludge is discharged from the guide hole

High speed water-air jet

Cement slurry

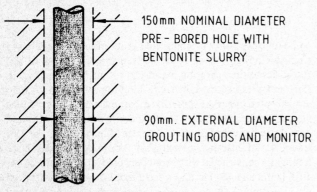

150mm NOMINAL DIAMETER PRE-BORED HOLE WITH BENTONITE SLURRY

90mm. EXTERNAL DIAMETER GROUTING RODS AND MONITOR

Fig. 1   Column jet-grout construction

Fig. 2   Jet-grout columns exposed in underpinning application

British Rail tunnel renovation

British Rail had experienced persistent track maintenance problems with a short length of twin-track tunnel built in about 1885 and now forming a vital link in the Glasgow suburban rail system, which was electrified in 1960. Over most of its length the original tunnel was constructed in rock and continues to function well. Old records indicated, however, that a short section some 100 m from a station portal had been built in cut and cover, where rock head dived well below invert level, and it was in this section that surveys revealed developing problems.

In this difficult area it was believed that the arch was sprung from brick caissons sunk to firm ground, a crude brick-aggregate concrete invert being placed below the running track and bearing directly on the ground. In the late 1970s the invert was improved by installation of a 'hedgehog'-type concrete track that consisted of prestressed concrete sleepers, with extended reinforcement, built into an *in-situ* concrete slab placed directly on the old invert. Cracking and excessive deflection of the slab developed within a few years and increasing movement under traffic load was detected by use of a laser system. Some 22 concrete sleepers had repeatedly debonded from the slab on the side where rock head was deepest. Although some concern arose over limited clearance to overhead lines, problems appeared at this stage to be concentrated in the invert slab.

A site investigation in 1981 confirmed the existence of a buried glacial hollow in bedrock that crossed the tunnel line over a distance of about 25 m. The hollow was filled with a single-sized saturated silt to a maximum depth of 4.5 m below track level, overlying a thin layer of boulder clay before bedrock was again reached.

It was concluded that severe dilatancy with high pore water pressure generation was occurring with the passage of traffic, cyclic pore pressure dissipation causing settlement. Underpinning of the combined tunnel inverts directly to the boulder clay or bedrock at depth would eliminate these effects, but the choice of appropriate techniques was restricted severely by the working conditions within the tunnel and the need to maintain tunnel operation.

The use of two rows of 2-m diameter jet-grouted columns at 2-m centres beneath the centre line of each track was adopted as the only grouting solution that was suited to the soil conditions. The extensive bearing area afforded by these large grouted columns, which connected the underside of the slab directly to either bedrock or boulder clay, avoided the need for total slab reconstruction that is associated with any alternative mini-pile scheme. The small (200-mm diameter) access holes through the slab that were required for column construction could conveniently be located between every third prestressed sleeper. Mixing plant and most ancillary equipment could be located at the surface above the tunnel, grout, water and compressed air being fed into the tunnel via a purpose-drilled access shaft.

Fig. 5 Surface mixing station 30 m from tunnel centre line (includes standby plant)

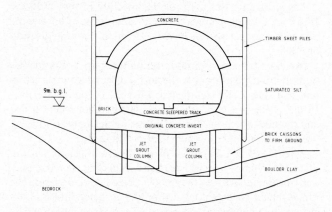

Fig. 3 Cross-section showing tunnel construction and jet-grout treatment

The arrangement of jet-grout columns in relation to tunnel construction is shown in cross-section in Fig. 3, and Figs. 4 and 5 illustrate column construction within the tunnel and the mixing station, respectively.

Jet grouting was carried out during March and April, 1982, eight 29-h weekend track possession and power-isolation periods being used. Specialized jet grouting equipment was erected on a hired rail-mounted drilling rig, which had been built for tunnel working and adapted suitably.

A neat rapid hardening cement grout was utilized to attain the contract requirement that a freshly grouted column should exceed the strength of the surrounding ground that was being treated by the end of the track possession period. It was accepted that the long-term strength requirement of 5 MN/m^2 would be exceeded by several orders of magnitude. During the

grouting operations it became evident that small voids existed in a timber mattress on which the original crude concrete invert must have been laid. This caused excessive lateral grout migration during column formation and some interference between quite widely spaced freshly constructed jet-grout columns. Consequently, jet-grout operations were interrupted to permit low-pressure grout injection filling of these voids. Grout escape at the junction of invert and walls also revealed that, contrary to expectations, a structural connexion had originally existed, but had failed as a result of slab settlement.

Monitoring of tunnel movements and track deflexions under load continued during and after jet grouting operations. These surveys showed that, although on completion of jet grouting, slab movement, unacceptable traffic load deflexion and sleeper debonding effectively ceased, some settlement of the walls and a worsening of overhead clearance continued. Evidence also emerged to suggest that original brick caisson support to walls had been only at a few isolated points rather than at the expected close centres. It became apparent that problems had not been confined to the invert slab, as had originally been thought.

Subsequent contracts to strengthen the arch and drill mini-piles from the surface through the tunnel walls were therefore rapidly implemented and completed by May, 1983. Thereafter, tunnel performance has been satisfactory throughout. British Rail cost estimates showed the various remedial works to have been completed at one-fifth of those of the only alternative course of action – tunnel closure and total reconstruction.

Canal tunnel renovation

Collapse of the invert and damaged brick linings were revealed during a routine inspection of a section of the Trent and Mersey Canal tunnel in Cheshire over a distance of some 12 m between 35 and 47 m in from the west portal. The tunnel was closed pending the repair of this and nearby sections of the canal.

Total invert subsidence of 450 mm with attendant widespread cracking and steps in invert brickwork up to 230 mm were measured during detailed damage survey. A localized zone in which invert brickwork had disappeared completely was also detected and major invert reconstruction was essential. Before this could be carried out it was necessary to stank off and drain the area of the tunnel from the portal for 50 m, to install steel colliery arches to transfer the loads and relieve pressure on the invert and to partially reconcrete the invert.

The preliminary borehole investigation revealed that the tunnel, driven through the flank of a hill above the River Weaver, penetrated the weathered Lower Keuper Marl with the

Fig. 4 Column construction in progress in tunnel (note fluid supply lines from access shaft to surface on far left)

soffit in a thin layer of boulder clay overlain by sand. Within the marl the site investigation boreholes encountered both open and silt- and soft clay-filled voids at levels immediately below the invert and to a considerable depth beneath and downhill from the tunnel. These voids were associated with solution leaching of gypsum veins within the marl.

Detailed investigation of the area of failed invert by use of a MacIntosh probe showed generally between 2 and 2.5 m, but locally more than 6 m, of soft clay-filled void immediately beneath the invert.

No clear conclusion was reached as to whether initial failure of the invert produced extensive softening of the marl followed by solution of the gypsum by the escaping water or whether natural void formation had been the root of the problem. Nevertheless, it was clear that although conventional grout injection would deal with the voids, the remedial works would require the removal of the totally softened marl in the im-

mediate vicinity of the tunnel and partial infilling of the voids elsewhere. A combination of injection and jet grouting was therefore selected.

The proposed grout treatment was carried out in three phases – injection grouting to infill voids beneath and on either side of the tunnel in the marl, jet grouting to follow the first phase with 2.0-m diameter columns to remove and replace the soft clay and silt infilling immediately below the tunnel invert and secondary jet grouting along the centre line to greater depths at selected locations to remove and replace silt and clay filling of critical voids. The extent of work is illustrated in Fig. 6.

Access to the works – along a narrow private track – was extremely limited. The mixer station was set up on the towpath adjacent to the tunnel portal and drilling and jet grouting were carried out from a benched platform formed by excavation in the hillside above the tunnel centre line.

The grout that was used for the injection of the voids was 10:1 PFA:OPC cement with a water/solids ratio of 0.5 and the jet grout mix consisted of PFA:OPC with a water/solids ratio of 1.0.

In the first phase of grout injection three lines of boreholes were sunk 3 m apart – one to the north, one on the tunnel centre line and one to the south and downhill of the centre line. Primary, secondary and, locally, tertiary boreholes were drilled and grouted to refusal. Boreholes sunk on the tunnel centre line were cased through the tunnel soffit and invert.

After the completion of the phase one grouting nominal 2-m diameter columns were constructed at 2-m centres on two lines 1 m north and south of the tunnel centre line to underpin the tunnel invert to depths of up to 10.5 m below invert. Subsequently, a number of secondary jet-grout columns of 1.2-m diameter were constructed along the centre line of the tunnel.

All jet-grout pre-boring and column construction was carried out from the benched platform some 7 m above soffit level and 13 m above tunnel invert. The pre-bored holes were cased to the tunnel soffit and then drilled through the tunnel and its invert, the closely spaced colliery arches and other temporary supports being avoided.

The slurry that was generated in the jet grouting was pumped from within the tunnel via the portal to a permanent storage lagoon that had been provided by the client on the other side of the River Weaver.

Work was undertaken to a tight schedule to allow completion of other repair work and the reopening of the tunnel to traffic in time for the start of the 1984 holiday season.

Stockton on Tees new tunnel construction

A nominated sub-contract used jet-grout column stabilization

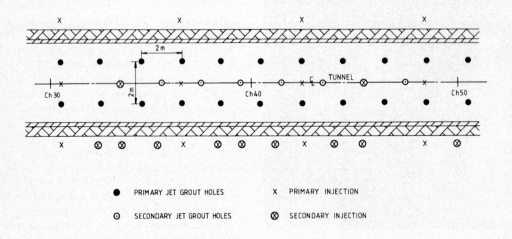

Fig. 6   Typical section through tunnel and layout of grout holes

to assist in the construction of a 9-m deep × 3.5-m diameter segmental concrete manhole and short adjacent section of 2-m diameter segmental sewer in tunnel at Stockton on Tees.

Shaft construction required progressive installation and undercutting of the rings by hand excavation through 3.5 m of cohesive filled ground and 3.5 m of alluvial clays. The deepest three rings of the 13-ring structure, however, would be placed in the underlying unstable ground, which consisted of loose silty-clayey sands with peat traces. The water-table was some 6 m above shaft formation, so treatment was required both to stabilize the sands for ring installation and to plug the shaft base against blowing or piping failure.

The manhole was required to act as reception shaft for a length of tunnel excavated by hand under compressed air with an invert level some 7.5 m below ground level. The potential running sand condition again affected at least the lower half of this face, and the immediately overlying alluvial clays at the soffit were sufficiently weak to cause concern. It was decided to construct a jet-grouted block 4 m square, centred on the tunnel axis and bonded to the outside of the shaft, so that free air conditions could be established and safe working maintained during breakout of the tunnel into the shaft. A minimum length of grouted block of 3 m was chosen, although the extent of treatment would finally be decided on site with the assistance of information from the pre-bored holes used in the process.

The layout of the interlocking jet-grouted columns that were used for these various purposes is shown in plan and section in Fig. 7. A total of 70 linear metres of 1.8-m diameter column was constructed by use of a cement–PFA grout that had been designed to produce a 28-day compressive strength of about 1.5 MN/m^2. Confidence in the continuity and finished properties of the grouted block allowed the shaft base-plug thickness to be designed specifically against piping and heave by use of geotechnical principles.

The work was completed successfully and remeasured, inclusive of materials, within the original tender price, which amounted to £135/m^3 of ground treated. Subsequent excavation of both shaft and tunnel face proceeded without delay, clay spades being used in dry stable conditions throughout.

Gateshead new tunnel construction

Construction of a nominal 1.8-m diameter concrete sewer

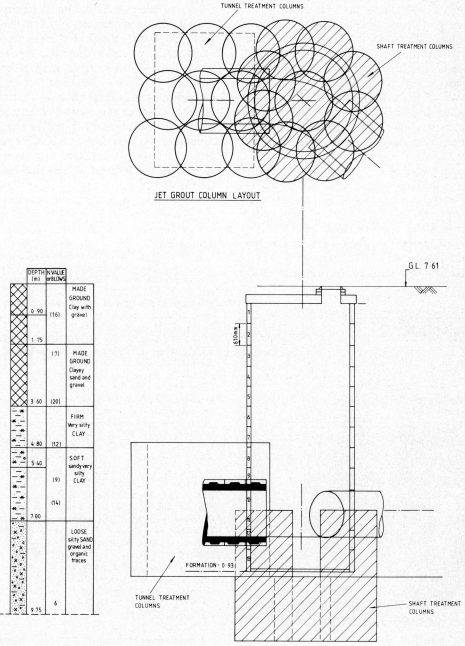

Fig. 7   Jet-grout column layout and section

281

tunnel by use of a full-face bentonite shield tunnelling machine through very variable soil conditions at Gateshead was aided by the formation of four starting, reception and thrust blocks adjacent to shafts. Two legs of tunnel some 280 m and 310 m long were driven – one beneath the River Derwent from a central shaft on the river bank where tunnel axes were typically 12.5 m below ground level.

Soils that were expected in the tunnel face ranged from loose clayey and very silty sands to medium dense silty sands and gravels with occasional, but locally abundant, cobbles. Water-table level was typically 2–4 m below ground level – sometimes tidally affected. After sheetpiled coffer dams had been driven around the shaft locations adjacent blocks of stable ground were required for the establishment or removal of the tunnelling machine at entry or reception shafts with access holes burnt in the sheetpiling. One entry block on the central shaft was also required to serve as a thrust resistance block, sustaining a pressure of 1.0 MN/m^2 during the driving of the opposite tunnel length. These 4 m square blocks were formed by use of arrays of 2-m diameter jet-grout columns at close, interlocking, spacing. Between seven and ten columns were employed for each block, according to its length.

Cement–PFA grout compressive strengths were designed to fall within the range 2–5 MN/m^2 at the quite widely varying ages at which each grout block would be penetrated by the machine. These values conformed with Japanese experience on more than 400 contracts in which bentonite shield tunnelling and jet grouting techniques have been combined. In practice, cube test results average 1.85 MN/m^2 at 14 days, 3.05 MN/m^2 at 28 days and 4.45 MN/m^2 at 56 days. Somewhat higher or lower (perhaps 20%) strengths should be expected *in situ* in working in granular or cohesive soils, respectively, as a result of the incorporation of a proportion of the natural material in the grouted mass. Increased resistance to face excavation was noted as the machine entered the grouted blocks, but the essentially uniform nature of the material ensured satisfactory progress. Rather weaker grouts, possibly cement–bentonites, would be considered for similar applications if substantially greater lengths of tunnel were to be treated.

Fig. 8 illustrates the appearance of a grouted face on an entry block as the sheetpiling is removed progressively before the introduction of the tunnelling machine. Differences in texture

of the grouted mass between sand-dominated areas towards the soffit and gravel–sand mixtures beneath can be seen, and the extent to which grout was moulded to the shape of the sheet-piling during placement is striking. Significant discontinuities in treatment were apparent in one such face in zones dominated by coarse gravel and cobbles, which resulted in less than the desired (though still a substantial) proportion of the total volume being fully solidified. At worst, soil conditions in the defective areas had consisted mainly of cobbles, with very minor fines contents. In this situation the soil particle size is large in relation to the diameter of the erosive jet, particularly if it is encountered close to the nozzle. Consequently, the jet may be deflected and its energy lost before the intended penetration has been achieved. Although the localized use of conventional permeation grouting techniques might have been beneficial, this approach would be ineffective in dealing with the silt- or clay-laden soils that were present in most of the treated zones. A steady groundwater flow entered through these patches at Gateshead, but this was readily handled, the face being pre-pared and the tunnelling machine installed without delay. An alternative design with a larger number of smaller-diameter columns would reduce this risk.

At one reception shaft, during the breaching of the sheet-piling, an entry of groundwater occurred from above the grouted block and immediately behind the sheetpiling, despite good continuity in the block. This later developed to wash in a substantial volume of sand and the shaft was allowed to flood. It is arguable whether, again, more intensive jet-grout treatment would have prevented this occurrence or whether movement of the sheetpiling away from the grouted ground occurred either during excavation, or under thrust from the tunnelling machine within the reception block. With a temporary patch fixed under water, the resultant gap was re-grouted by injection through holes down the outside of the sheetpiling and retrieval of the shield was achieved without further mishap.

The remeasured work was also completed within the tender price, which corresponded to £85/m^3 of treated ground.

Bibliography*
1. Yahiro T. and Yoshida H. Induction grouting method utilizing high speed water jet. In *Proceedings of the eighth international conference on soil mechanics and foundation engineering, Moscow, 1973,* 1973, vol. 4, 402–4.
2. Yahiro T. Yoshida H. and Nishi K. The development and application of a Japanese grouting system. *Water Power Dam Construction,* **27,** Feb. 1975, 56–9, 83.
3. Huck P. J. *et al.* Innovative geotechnical approaches to remedial *in-situ* treatment of hazardous materials disposal sites. In *Proceedings national conference on control of hazardous materials spills, Louisville, Kentucky, 1980* (Washington, D.C.: United States Environmental Protection Agency, 1980), 421–6.
4. Broid I. Z. *et al.* Jet grout method and cut-off walls stability. In *Proceedings of the tenth international conference on soil mechanics and foundation engineering, Stockholm, 1981* (Rotterdam: Balkema, 1981–82), vol. 1, 397–9.
5. Mitchell J. K. Soil improvement – state of the art report. Reference 4, vol. 4, 509–65.
6. Mitchell J. K. and Katti R. K. Soil improvement – general report. Reference 4, vol. 4, 567–75.
7. Shibazaki M. and Ohta S. A unique underpinning of soil solidification utilizing super-high pressure liquid jet. In *Grouting in geotechnical engineering: proceedings of the conference, New Orleans, Louisiana, 1982* Baker W. H. ed. (New York: American Society of Civil Engineers, 1982), 680–93.
8. Yahiro T. Yoshida H. and Nishi K. Soil improvement method utilizing a high speed water and air jet on the development and application of columnar solidified construction method. In *Jet cutting technology: papers presented at the sixth international symposium, University of Surrey, 1982* (Cranfield, Bedford: BHRA Fluid Engineering, 1982), 397–427.

* The references deal with the technique in general and with the wide range of different applications.

Fig. 8 Temporary sheetpiling to shaft being removed to reveal grouted ground prior to tunnelling

9. Aschieri F. Jamiolkowski M. and Tornaghi R. Case history of a cut-off wall executed by jet grouting. In *Improvement of ground: proceedings of the eighth European conference on soil mechanics and foundation engineering, Helsinki, 1983* Rathmayer H. G. and Saari K. H. O. eds (Rotterdam: Balkema, 1983), vol. 1, 121–6.

10. Coomber D. B. and Wright P. W. Jet grouting at Felixstowe Docks. *Ground Engng,* **17,** no. 5, July 1984, 19–24.

11. Baumann V. and Dupeuble P. The jet grouting process and its utilisation in some European countries. In *Preprints* – in-situ *soil and rock reinforcement: international conference, Paris, October 1984* (Paris: Ecole Nationale des Ponts et Chaussées, 1984), vol. 1, 165–72.

12. Miki G. and Nakanashi W. Technical progress of the jet grouting method and its newest type. Reference 11, vol. 1, 195–200.

Grouting and tunnelling in Thames Gravel - a case history

L. H. Swann
Dames and Moore, London, England
C. J. Day
Dames and Moore, London, England
M. A. Lepper
London Borough of Newham, London, England

Synopsis
At a site in east London, England, initial investigations indicated that a 1.5-m diameter sewer tunnel was to be constructed through sandy gravels. There was limited permeability testing during the investigation and from the soil gradation it was assumed that the sandy gravel would be open, requiring treatment with clay-cement grout and a chemical grout. The chemical grout that was selected was a sodium silicate-bicarbonate grout.

During the excavation of the initial shaft a failure occurred. Subsequent investigations demonstrated that the failure was caused by chemical contamination that had not been detected during the site investigation. *In-situ* permeability tests during these further excavations showed that the soil was less permeable than had been expected from the gradings. Consequently, the chemical treatment was stopped and the tunnel was completed in compressed air, chemical treatment being applied as necessary from the face.

The case history is presented and the consequences of the failure of the initial investigation to reflect the actual conditions are discussed. The delays and cost implications are noted, as are the design changes that resulted from the further detailed studies.

This paper describes the construction of a 1.35-m internal diameter tunnel at Sugar House Lane, London Borough of Newham, London, England. A site plan that shows the tunnel route is presented in Fig. 1. The tunnel was constructed with the use of a bolted segmental lining with a tunnel shield, which produced an excavated bore of about 1.9-m diameter prior to lining. Initial site investigations indicated that the tunnel was to be constructed predominantly through Thames Gravel and, accordingly, ground treatment with grouting from the ground surface was specified. Cement-bentonite grout to fill major voids and a sodium silicate-bicarbonate chemical grout were the materials that were selected. The contract was let with the provision that compressed air with a maximum air pressure of 0.5 bar could be used over the main section of the tunnel.

During the excavation of the first shaft (MH2) a failure of ground surrounding the shaft occurred, and detailed investigations were performed to identify the cause of the failure and to determine the best method for driving the tunnel. The results of the investigations, the conditions that were found during tunnelling and the consequences of the investigations are now described.

History prior to shaft failure

Site investigations

Four borings were carried out between 1976 and 1980 at the locations shown in Fig. 1 by three site investigation contractors, and not all were designed for the tunnel scheme that was finally selected. Interpretation of the borings suggested, however, that relatively uniform soil conditions could be expected. The borings indicated that from ground surface to a depth of from 1.2 to 3.0 m soil conditions were 'made ground', consisting of brick rubble, ash, coke, etc., with clay inclusions. This was underlain by 1.3-2.6 m of soft clays, which were organic in parts. In addition, the clays were apparently underlain by predominantly sandy gravels, though in parts the soils were gravelly sands. The relative density varied from loose to very dense. Two permeability tests were performed in the sandy gravels, permeabilities of 2×10^{-1} and 4×10^{-2} cm/s being obtained. The borings showed that the base of the sandy gravels was at least 7.5 m below the ground surface. Over the western portion of the site at 6.5-7.5 m below ground level the sandy gravels were underlain by very stiff clays (London Clay). At the mid-point of the tunnel this clay layer dipped steeply and the borings indicated that the top of the clay was substantially below the proposed tunnel invert. At the eastern portion of the site a layer of organic silty clay was encountered at a depth of about 7 m below ground level.

The groundwater level was recorded in the borings at an approximate depth of 3 m. A simplified subsurface section that indicates the known conditions at the design stage is shown in Fig. 2.

Project description

The tunnel is 280 m long and of 1.35-m internal diameter, and is constructed from bolted segmental precast concrete units. The purpose of the tunnel is to provide a relief sewer to connect a high-level sewer at existing manhole C99 to an existing brick-lined cast iron segment main sewer. The project was designed and supervised by the London Borough of Newham as agents for the Thames Water Authority. Dames and Moore were appointed by the London Borough of Newham in November, 1983, to advise on all geotechnical aspects of ground treatment work and tunnelling.

From manhole C99 to manhole MH1 the tunnel invert is between elevation −0.2 and −0.5 m O.D. At MH1 the invert level drops to approximately −3.5 m O.D., and between MH1 and MH3 the tunnel slopes at about 1 in 230 to an invert level of −4.5 m O.D. at MH3. At MH3 the invert level drops a further 1 m and the lower-level tunnel continues at the same slope until the existing main sewer tunnel is intersected approximately 27 m from MH3.

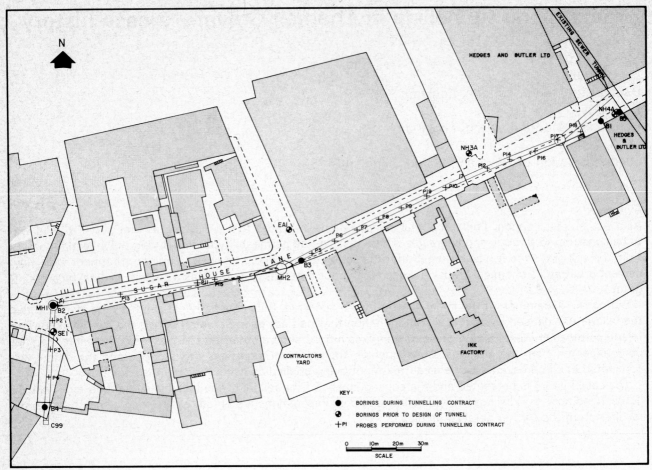

Fig. 1   Site plan

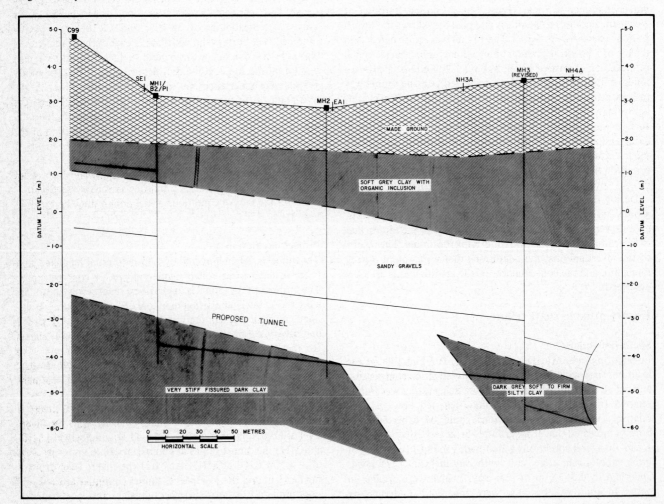

Fig. 2   Initial subsurface conditions as indicated by contract site investigation

The manhole shaft diameters vary from 3.35 to 4.3 m. The depth of MH1 and MH2 is 8 m below existing ground level and that of MH3 is 10 m below existing ground level.

Based on the original ground information, cement–bentonite and then chemical grout with the use of sodium silicate–bicarbonate grout were proposed to treat the ground prior to construction. A treated zone 1.5 m from the outside of the excavation was required.

The cement–bentonite grout was to be injected with lances driven at 1.8-m centres and those for the chemical grout at 0.9-m centres. A constant-volume injection method was selected by the specialist ground treatment sub-contractor. Volumes per stage of 150 l for the cement–bentonite and of 60–80 l for the chemical grout were selected. These volumes were determined on the assumption of an initial porosity of 40%, 15% being filled by the clay–cement grout.

Initial construction

The grouting was started at the beginning of October, 1983, and the grouting of shaft MH2 was completed one month later. Permeability tests by the ground treatment sub-contractor gave initial values of soil permeability that ranged from 9×10^{-3} to 3×10^{-4} cm/s. These values were appreciably lower than those which were obtained during the site investigation. Shaft excavation was started almost immediately afterwards and when the shaft was a few rings from completion there was a major ingress of water, accompanied by a loss of ground. Shortly before this loss of ground it had been noted that the gravels in the shaft were contaminated with hydrocarbon compounds (oils and tars). Following the loss of ground

approximately 2 m of Thanet sand was placed into the shaft to stabilize it and the shaft was allowed to fill with groundwater while investigations into the cause of the failure took place. At this stage chemical grouting was completed over an 18-m length from MH2 towards MH1. The cement–bentonite grouting was continued during these investigations.

Investigations and results

To examine the reasons for the ground failure at the grouted shaft during excavation a series of concurrent investigations – borings, probes, permeability tests, chemical tests and grout trials – was performed. The investigation programme was developed to examine not only the cause of the failure but also the conditions along the whole tunnel length to enable their variability to be evaluated. The investigations included a detailed review of the grouting that had been completed.

Soil conditions

Five borings by shell and auger techniques and nineteen 50-mm diameter driven probes were used to re-evaluate the soil conditions along the tunnel drive at the locations shown in Fig. 1. The borings and probes indicated a number of variations in soil conditions from those which had been established by the initial borings. The conditions were not substantially different, however, investigations demonstrating the variability that is generally expected in alluvial soils. The revised conditions are indicated in Fig. 3 and described below.

The borings and probes indicated that the upper soft clay layer consisted of two strata. The upper stratum consisted of

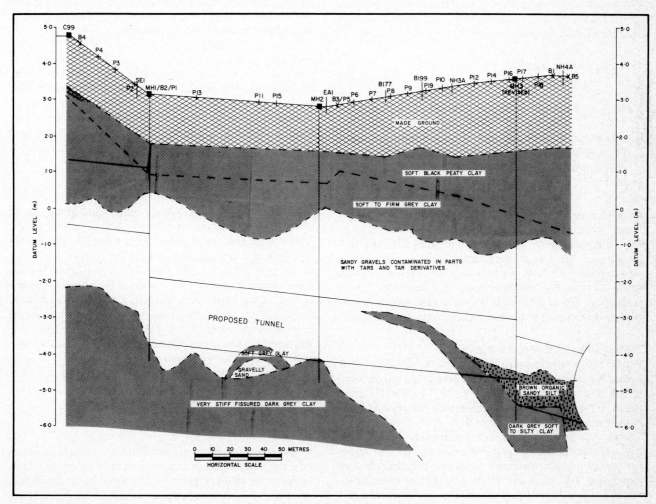

Fig. 3   Revised simplified subsurface section based on borings and probes performed during tunnelling contract

a soft black peaty clay with peat inclusions, and the lower of a soft to firm grey clay with occasional organic inclusions. Between manhole C99 and MH1 this layer appeared to be much thicker and to extend deeper than had been indicated.

The underlying sandy gravels were found to be more variable in grading and permeabilities than had previously been ascertained. In parts the sandy gravels graded to sand and gravels and, occasionally, were found to be slightly silty, though particle size analysis indicated that there was generally less than 5% silt. Occasional clay, silt and peat inclusions were found in the sandy gravels, and occasional very open gravel zones were found with voids filled by the cement–bentonite grout that had already been injected.

For the western portion of the drive the underlying very stiff clay was found to be slightly deeper than the original borings had shown. The probes and borings also indicated that the surface profile of the clay layer was variable and dipped from north to south. In the eastern part of the drive, to the east of MH2, it was thought that the soft to firm organic silty clay inclusions were consistent with the existence of a buried river channel. From a point close to MH3 to the connexion to the existing low-level sewer the silty clay was overlain by a soft black organic sandy silt. This silt was sensitive, becoming a slurry when disturbed.

In all of the borings the standing groundwater-table was recorded at an elevation of about + 1.0 m O.D., a variation of 0.3 m being thought to be due to tidal fluctuation.

Permeability of sandy gravels
Permeability tests were performed by the falling head method[1] in the borings and by the grouting sub-contractor with the grout injection equipment. In addition, four gravel permeability cells were installed in a zone where chemical treatment had been substantially completed and permeabilities were calculated from the chemical grouting records.

Pre-treatment permeabilities
The results of 28 tests in completely untreated soils indicated that within the sandy gravel permeabilities ranged from 5×10^{-2} to 1×10^{-5} cm/s. Of these 28 results, 23 were between 10^{-2} and 10^{-3} cm/s (mean, 2.2×10^{-3} cm/s). This value is lower than that which might be expected for well-graded sandy gravels[2] and below that which is calculated by use of the various predictive equations[3] that are used to relate permeability to grain size.

Permeabilities after clay–cement grouting
All of the results suggested that after cement–bentonite treatment the permeability was generally between 10^{-2} and 10^{-3} cm/s. That the results were similar to the pre-injection permeabilities is indicative of the very low takes in the areas where the grouting had been completed (less than 5% by volume). It was considered that in localized open zones the cement–bentonite injection had reduced soil permeabilities.

Permeabilities after chemical treatment
Permeabilities were measured at 18 locations, including two in boring B2 where chemical treatment was only partially completed. The values ranged from 9×10^{-4} to 2×10^{-5} cm/s (mean, 1.1×10^{-4} cm/s). This represented a reduction from the initial permeability by a factor of 31.

In the four permeability cells the permeability was measured over a ten-day period. Initially, the permeabilities were higher than the average post-treatment values and, subsequently, they diminished. The initial high values were thought to be indicative of a deterioration in the grout and the subsequent reduction was thought to be due to the cells silting up.

Soil contamination
During the grouting and excavation of MH2 it was apparent both visually and from odours that in the zone of treatment the soils were contaminated. At the failure zone the gravels were coated with tars, which were also seen in the borings. During the boring and probing programme the following odours were recognized: diesel (possibly pyridene), methylated spirits, creosote/tar, ammonia and sulphurous compounds. In several of the borings an oily film was noted on the groundwater.

Chemical analysis of two heavily contaminated gravels indicated that the contaminants were derived from coal tars with a phenol content that ranged from 3 to 7 ppm. Simple tests on the samples that were extracted from the probes to determine hydrocarbon and organic contents indicated that the contamination was concentrated at 30 m either side of MH2, but was present to a lesser degree throughout the proposed tunnel drive.

Laboratory tests indicated that where the contamination was tar the silicate–bicarbonate grout did not gel, and for other hydrocarbon contaminants the gel time was significantly increased. The chemical inhibitor was not isolated, but high pH values (up to pH 11) were found. An alkaline environment is known to prolong silicate–bicarbonate gel times.

It was thought that physical as well as chemical factors were affecting the grout and believed that the tars that coated the gravels were preventing the grout from bonding to the gravels and, hence, the expected cohesion was not being allowed to develop. The presence of diesel fuel may have also inhibited the displacement of groundwater by grout. It was considered that the slightly alkaline nature of the groundwater delayed the gel time, and in the open gravels the grout was thus able to flow outside the prescribed zone of treatment. Tests were performed by the grouting sub-contractor on a range of grouts. Samples with normal pH values, but contaminated, were found to have delayed gel times and reduced strengths.

During the investigations unconfined compressive strength tests were performed on uncontaminated and contaminated gravel samples that had been treated with grout. For uncontaminated samples the tests indicated that the strengths were about one-half of the values that are normally quoted for grout-injected sands. In the contaminated samples the strengths were reduced further and shear strengths of 13–22 kN/m² were measured. The strengths of alternative grouts were also reduced by the contamination.

Grout life
In normal circumstances silicate–bicarbonate grout has an effective life of about six months. A consequence of the increased gel time was a reduction in grout life, a minimum grout life of two months being expected. It was believed that the permeability tests in the gravel cells demonstrated that the grout was deteriorating. Examination of the gravels at the base of MH2 about two months after the grouting was completed indicated that there was no cohesion, thereby showing that the grout had deteriorated. A consequence of the reduced grout life was that the grouting sub-contract could not be completed with silicate–bicarbonate grout and kept within the overall contract programme.

Impact of investigation results on tunnelling

It was considered that the lower-level tunnel should be driven by use of compressed air at a pressure of 50 kN/m² (0.5 bar). Initially, the shafts were to be completed by underpinning. After the failure it was decided to complete them with a blister lock, and when the tunnel had advanced sufficiently far a tunnel lock was to be installed. The blister lock was found to be necessary because the remedial grouting that had been attempted during the investigations had proved unsuccessful. Chemical treatment was thought to be necessary because of the nature of the soils, but it was considered that such treatment would produce varied results with some zones of higher permeability. In general, permeabilities of 10^{-4}-10^{-5} cm/s were expected.

During the investigations field trials were performed with an alternative grout with a higher viscosity than the silicate–bicarbonate grout. Although the viscosity was only about twice that of the silicate–bicarbonate, it was found that it could not be injected where the initial permeability was lower than about 5×10^{-4} cm/s. Accordingly a low-viscosity grout was considered essential.

It was decided to complete the pattern of cement–bentonite grouting and also to increase the volume of grout at each injection stage from the previous maximum value of 150 l to 1500 l. It was believed that this increased volume would treat fully any open zones that probing had demonstrated could occur.

The chemical grouting from the ground surface was discontinued and a decision was made to grout from the face on an as-required basis. It was considered that this approach would allow a selective and more cost-effective grout programme. The grout that was selected (a Borden MQ4 resorcinol formaldehyde resin grout) has a low viscosity, a rapid gel time and high strength. Owing to the ground contamination frequent monitoring of the atmosphere in the tunnel was required and contaminated spoil was ordered to be disposed of at controlled tips.

Upper-level tunnel, manhole C99 to MH1
The investigations showed that the upper half of the tunnel face would be predominantly in cohesive soils. High levels of contamination were also noted. Accordingly, it was decided that the upper-level tunnel be completed without grouting, but with limited dewatering where necessary. This was achieved successfully.

Low-level connexion from MH3
This section of tunnel was to be constructed with the lower half of the face in a sensitive silt. It was considered that in free air this silt would be sensitive and that treatment of the face in this zone would prove difficult. Accordingly, it was decided that this section be completed in compressed air rather than free air with use of a shaped hood to the tunnel shield to fit the profile of the existing cast iron segmental sewer. Extensive grouting of the sandy gravels was recommended to eliminate the risk of potential preferential air paths developing adjacent to the existing tunnel. The shield skin would be left in the ground and abandoned.

Review of grouting and tunnelling operations

A subsurface section that shows the conditions that were encountered in the tunnel drive is shown in Fig. 4. The probes failed to predict accurately the changes in soil type, though they did indicate the expected degree of variability.

Cement–bentonite grouting from surface
The cement–bentonite grouting from the surface was completed for the whole of the lower-level tunnel drive. The western

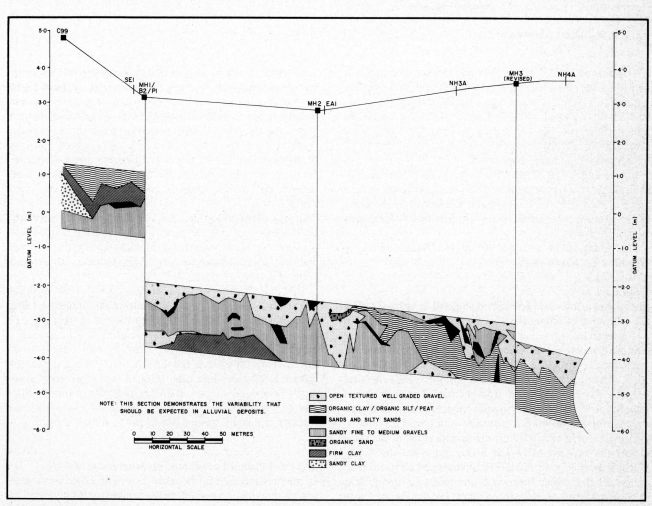

Fig. 4 Subsurface section based on face logs during tunnelling

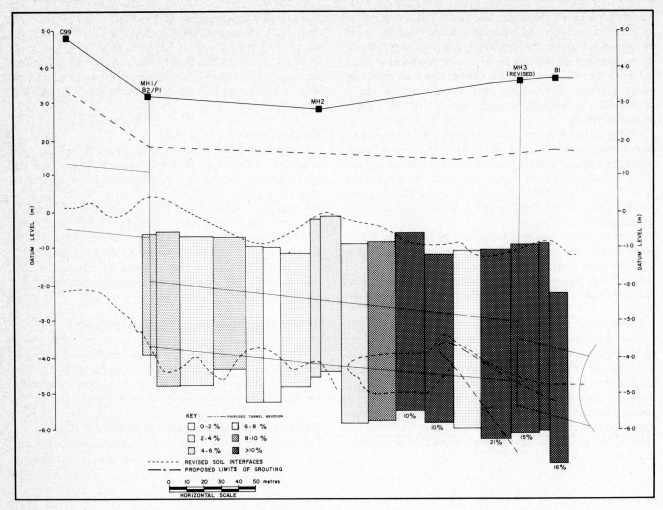

Fig. 5   Clay–cement grout takes

section was completed during the period of the investigations with use of the initial criteria. As a result of the initial tunnelling experience additional grout was injected through an intermediate row of grout holes. The grout takes were low in this intermediate row. For the section between MH1 and MH2 average grout takes by volume were less than 6% and there were no indications of major open zones.

In the eastern part of the drive the grout takes were significantly higher than those in the western part, the take in one zone being as high as 21%. The open zones indicated by the grout takes tended to be isolated with no indication of continuous very open zones.

The grout takes recorded from the surface grouting operation are shown in Fig. 5.

Tunnelling
The tunnel drives were generally completed as intended after the additional investigations were finished. Within the zone in which chemical grouting had been completed no further treatment was required. Once the drive was beyond the pre-treated zone chemical face grouting was done on an as-required basis. Usually, four probes were installed and chemical grouting was done up to 5 m from the face. The probing and grouting generally required between one-half and one shift and were performed on shifts to alternate with tunnel driving.

Between MH2 and MH3 tunnelling proceeded in the same manner as between MH2 and MH1, but when the tunnel reached about 30 m from MH2 the compressed air was turned off during the change from the blister lock to a tunnel lock. While the air was turned off the tunnel became flooded with an ingress of soil.

A review of the MQ4 chemical grouting records indicated that permeabilities in the zone of failure were of the order of 10^{-1} cm/s – higher than had been recorded elsewhere on the project. It was considered that with very high permeabilities the chemical grout would flow from the injection point too rapidly, resulting in a discontinuous grout zone with a limited reduction in permeability. It was also noted that the original cement–bentonite grouting, despite the large volumes injected, had failed to reduce adequately the permeability of the very open zones.

In view of the high grout takes it was believed that other very open zones were likely to exist. It was therefore decided that provision be made for cement–bentonite grouting in open zones with use of an accelerator to permit tunnelling to proceed without delay.

Subsequently, the drive was completed with both chemical and cement–bentonite grouting, grouting and tunnelling being done on alternate shifts. During the drive a number of open zones were encountered, some of which required continuous grouting. No evidence was found of the clay–cement grout injected from the surface. It is thought that although significant quantities of grout had been injected into these open zones from the ground surface, the high hydraulic gradients, high ground permeabilities and low viscosity of the grout had resulted in it being washed out of the treatment zone.

Impact of changed conditions on programme and cost
In the previous sections the changes in tunnelling procedures and grouting that were implemented following the discovery of the contamination and the subsequent investigation have been

outlined. Not only were procedures changed but several modifications to the programme were required.

The initial shaft failure resulted in an approximate six-week delay while remedial grouting was attempted and a blister lock was brought to the site and installed. The main drive took twice as long as had been programmed owing to alternate shifts being required for probing and grouting.

Although a detailed cost analysis has not yet been completed, it is understood that, as a result of the delays, costs have increased significantly. Cost increases also resulted from the contamination and the requirement for air quality monitoring to ensure safe working conditions and also from the need to dispose of spoil at controlled tips.

Conclusions

The pre-contract ground investigations failed to identify sufficiently the variable permeabilities in the soil, though some variability should have been expected because of the depositional characteristics of the soils. With hindsight, however, it is doubtful whether any degree of pre-tender investigation could have revealed economically all the desirable information (apart from the limitations of space imposed by traffic and proximity of buildings). In view of this it would have been preferable to have had a sub-contract that allowed for a greater flexibility in the way in which the grout was applied, i.e. from the tunnel face as well as from the ground surface instead of having to abandon part of the original sub-contract.

The adoption of face grouting rather than surface grouting from lances provided a flexible approach that could be adapted to changing conditions. This flexible approach was effective in limiting the potential delays to the minimum extent.

Acknowledgement

The authors would like to thank A. Tahir, the Resident Engineer, and the resident site staff, who provided much of the information. Thanks are also due to senior engineers of Delta Construction, the tunnelling contractors, who provided valuable input during on-site discussions.

The opinions expressed in this paper represent the views of the authors and do not necessarily reflect the views of the London Borough of Newham.

References
1. Hvorslev J. Time lag and permeability in ground water observations. *Bull. U.S. Waterways Experim. Station, Vicksburg,* no. 36, 1951.
2. Terzaghi K. and Peck R. B. *Soil mechanics in engineering practice* (London, etc.: Wiley, 1967), 729 p.
3. Freeze R. A. and Cherry J.A. *Groundwater* (Englewood Cliffs, N.J.: Prentice-Hall, 1979).

Discussion

Dr. P. H. Phillips* said that Bruce and Shirlaw had indicated that the *tube à manchette* was the main technique in their project in Hong Kong. The *tube à manchette* was invented by Ischy some 50 years ago when he was a young engineer working for Rodio in North Africa. Like all the very best inventions it was simple and efficient and had the added advantage of the ability to regrout or grout selectively without re-drilling and, if used properly, could ensure the required void filling, with a minimum of grout.

Tornaghi and Perelli Cippo and Coomber had described the use of jet grouting. That appeared, however, to be jet soil stabilization or jet soil replacement rather than grouting in the conventional sense.

In tunnelling they were often interested in either increasing soil strength or reducing permeability: perhaps all or any of the authors could confirm that the *tube à manchette* was still the best method for selective void filling in most soil conditions where permeability was the problem.

He would like the authors of the two jetting papers to confirm that no secondary treatment was required, and asked how complicated, costly and delaying in construction operations secondary treatment would be at depth from the surface.

Authors' replies

Dr. D. A. Bruce and J. N. Shirlaw In the paper we do indicate that a very wide variety of grouting techniques has been used during the construction of the railway. Each technique has advantages and disadvantages, depending on the purpose of the treatment and the soil types to be grouted. We do not think that one can talk of a universal 'best' technique. Every grouting site is in some small way unique, and the 'best' method is that which provides technical adequacy at minimum cost.

Nevertheless, it is fair to say that grout delivery by *tube à manchette* has been used for the majority of the ground treatment carried out on the railway. The *tube à manchette* does indeed provide flexibility and selectivity, as mentioned by Dr. P. H. Phillips, but these benefits can only be utilized fully by highly experienced specialists.

Dr. R. Tornaghi and A. Perelli Cippo The merits of the *tube à manchette* method have been widely recognized in regard to the treatment of granular cohesionless soils within the limits of 'permeation' grouting, which is grouting in the conventional sense as intended by Dr. P. H. Phillips. In an earlier paper† the advantages of selective void filling were emphasized and the *tube à manchette* remains the best method so long as conventional grouting is feasible and likely to achieve the required soil improvement. The most recent techniques, based on 'jet grouting', bypass the problem of penetrability raised by pure permeation criteria, permitting the treatment of even silty-clayey soils by means of a simple cement grout; no secondary treatment by chemical grouts (often giving rise to problems of toxicity, pollution or permanence) is necessary since soil–grout mixing in place or soil replacement are the basic principles. Conventional grouting (and therefore the *tube à manchette* method) is still more convenient economically when the required soil improvement can be obtained with acceptable mixes.

The technical advantages of jet grouting increase as one passes from coarse- to fine-grained soils and from simple permeability-reduction to strength-increase problems. Beyond certain limits of natural soil properties and required improvement no comparison is possible since jet grouting is the only applicable injection technique.

In conclusion, it may be stated that conventional injection and jet grouting are complementary rather than alternative procedures, the latter allowing the limitations of the former to be overcome.

D. B. Coomber The view that jet grouting should be thought of as a ground *replacement* technique in most cases is not only endorsed but encouraged. Whether in view of the use of a replacement medium that can only be described as a grout the process is any less of a grouting technique than historical methods is debatable.

The *tube à manchette* method for void filling to reduce permeability remains of comparable reliability only where the naturally occurring voids between soil particles constitute a significant proportion of the volume of ground to be treated and are sufficiently distributed through the mass to allow grout flow from one to the other. In practice this means gravels or coarse granular soils with few if any particles finer than medium sand. Thames Ballast is a good example of such a material, but very few other British geological deposits fall in this category. Tunnelling problems more often deal with fines-contaminated soils in which permeability is moderate but instability, when unconfined in the tunnel face, inevitable. In these conditions jet grouting offers a significant technical advance.

No secondary treatment is normally required and the risk of incomplete treatment is sufficiently remote to permit, in many cases, the offer of an indemnity from the specialist. In the author's experience two examples exist where minor flaws in major grouted blocks required subsequent patching, the problem by then being sufficiently restricted to allow the use of readily mobilized, simple grouting lances that involved a delay to excavation of some two weeks.

---

*Phillips and Sons, Cookham, Berkshire, England.
†Tornaghi R. Experimental criteria for design and control of grouting in sandy-gravelly soils. In *Tunnelling '79* Jones M. J. ed. (London: IMM, 1979), 71–8.

Session 12 – General

Co-Chairmen: R. J. Robbins and G. E. Pearse

Tunnelling hazards and risk-sharing

Sir Alan Muir Wood
C. J. Kirkland
Sir William Halcrow and Partners, London, England

Synopsis
It is now ten years since the hazards of tunnelling were discussed at the Third International Safety Conference. The passing of time has not made the practice of tunnelling less hazardous. It should have made us more perceptive, but has it?

CIRIA published its report on improved contract practices in tunnelling in the hope that it would increase the effectiveness of the *ICE Conditions of Contract* by establishing reference conditions prior to tender and by identifying the presence of risk and apportioning liability.

Some additional hazards, most of them man-made, that now beset tunnelling contracts and of which the authors have had recent experience, are outlined and suggestions are made on where to look for improvements in our present practices.

An account of tunnel hazards only ten years ago[2] was able to concentrate upon the problems that stem largely from the surprises sprung by nature, the unforeseen events that are not necessarily unforeseeable being discussed. In tunnelling, Sir Harold Harding reminded us that the state of perception of the engineer should ensure that although he may be surprised by the turn of events, he should never be astonished. In particular, he should understand the engineering significance of the geological structure and history. All defects of the ground are initially latent, but some are more latent than others.

At the present day, however, too many of the factors contributory to tunnel hazards are man-made. These stem largely from ill-conceived attempts to achieve minimum apparent cost by those who commission engineering projects and, it must be said, by some of those who, in consequence, are persuaded to undertake the work without awareness of their assumed responsibilities. The climate of risk[3] that entails several aspects of scale of enterprise, innovative design and materials now has new factors in the subdivisions and confusion of powers and responsibilities, with corner-cutting in response to insistence on an apparent minimum cost. The results are very expensive.

Today is the day of the accountant, who is concerned with cost but not necessarily with value. Pressures from auditors lead to insistence on price competition, often with several stages of a project separately tendered and possibly accompanied by a nominal recognition of competence. Tunnelling is the most demanding of all civil engineering undertakings in foresight and imagination. These qualities are submerged in the current fashion. The community bears a heavy cost.

As engineers, we need to extol the virtues of quality assurance. For civil engineering in general and for tunnelling in particular, quality assurance is not a question of calculated measures to achieve acceptably low probabilities of hazard. We do not have quantifiable data for this purpose. For tunnelling, quality assurance must entail addressing the appropriate questions as a project unfolds so that the answers, in a useful form, are available to be applied skilfully and imaginatively, when required. We need to recognize the iterative nature of much of our work, when performed to the highest standards, not only between the different aspects of a single project, e.g. the relationship between design and site investigation, but also between one project and another. Otherwise, we will continue to observe the same mistakes perpetuated. 'Those who do not know their history are fated to repeat it' as Santayana wrote.

Yet we continue to see this recipe to disaster:

(1) Initial planning is undertaken by those with no understanding of the relative difficulties of different tunnelling options, with no notion of optimization.

(2) Investigation is put in the hands of those who will have no responsibility for the development of schemes of design and construction. In consequence, the investigation assembles data, which are often irrelevant, not being directed towards answering the most pertinent questions. Geological descriptions concentrate, for example, on mineralogy rather than on the particular weaknesses of rock structure.

(3) Design is undertaken by the lowest bidder, who may believe that sketchy designs may be directly transferred from another scheme, without knowledge of the special features of relevance, with no attempt at optimization and with every intention of sidestepping any responsibility in execution. Alternatively, inappropriate schemes of construction are specified unwittingly.

(4) In the absence of an engineer who is appropriately experienced in tunnel construction, the contractor will not be screened for capability. The result is a lottery – with little prospect that cost and time will approximate to undertakings.

(5) The project may end in the hands of lawyers. Costs are many times those of a properly optimized project, planned and orchestrated by a skilled engineer. The engineering profession is blamed, and the episode appears erroneously to be further evidence to support stronger accountancy control of a fragmented project rather than an informed synthesis of the elements.

Much ingenuity therefore needs to be displayed by the engineer to overcome physical problems in energy mis-spent: had the project been properly conceived, the problems would have been circumvented not confronted.

Contract basis

One relevant development in recent years has been the appearance of the CIRIA report[1] that discussed the main sources of hazard and contractual uncertainty, itself a hazard, that may be eliminated or contained by complying with certain rules of conduct.

There is no panacea in the choice of the form of contract: the first need is for clarity in the assignment of duties and powers; the second is to contain causes for risk and uncertainty, by selection of tunnel route and construction method, associated with relevant investigations; the third is to assign outstanding risks, recognizing that the assignment of risk and the form of contract will together determine the liability for payment for risks that do not eventuate. The nearer to a lump sum contract, the greater are the contingent sums for risk in the tender price.

Three principal requirements were perceived by the CIRIA report as crucial: (*a*) ground reference conditions, adequate in scope and definition, should be established – both to form the basis for tender estimates and to judge when the limits of the foreseeable ground conditions are reached during construction; (*b*) contract documents should be drafted explicitly to identify and describe the presence of unavoidable risks, stating where liability is placed in the event of their occurrence; and (*c*) the engineer should be thoroughly experienced in underground construction and free to act independently so that his knowledge and judgement can be wholly entrusted with the decisions that will regulate the conduct of the contract.

The recommendation of *CIRIA Report 79*[1] that has attracted most attention concerns the use of 'reference conditions'. This concept entails the statement of certain assumptions concerning the ground that have an important bearing on the scheme or cost of tunnelling and go beyond a watertight interpretation of the available facts. It is stressed that this device should only be adopted by an engineer who is fully alive to the consequences: properly and skilfully used, cost and uncertainty are both reduced. The engineer needs to be wise before the event – a facility that is much more demanding than the arbitration lawyer's demonstration of sagacity after the event.

Much confusion has recently arisen from an accountant's inspired view that there is a necessary virtue in a minimum difference between the tender total and the final contract cost. A generation ago the percipient engineer set aside for tunnelling contracts within the tender total specific sums to deal with expected contingencies. This practice is now only rarely authorized, but the engineer should continue to advise his client on the range of uncertainties for which such sums might be required. The greater the onus that is put upon the contractor to cover the cost of uncertainties, particularly those which are related to problems of the ground, the greater is the probability that the worst combination of circumstances will be paid for through the contract. There will remain, in view of the uncertain range of reasonableness of interpretative action of the physical conditions to be expected, a possibility that the contractor may even then have grounds for a claim. There is then the outcome that particular risks that do not eventuate are paid for, whereas certain major risks that do are paid for twice! This is an expensive consequence of accountancy overriding good engineering.

'Claims' are only bad when they derive from poor engineering or unprofessional contracting. Otherwise, payments extra to the tender total are related to proper variations in the work performed and their attempted suppression is expensive.

To the uninitiated a problem in comprehension arises from the fact that there are no standard rates for tunnelling. Where, therefore, a lump-sum contract for favourable ground is shown to be less than a measured contract for difficult ground, only the experienced will appreciate the absence of virtue in this achievement.

There is much loose discussion on the virtues of target contracts, implying that such a form of contract avoids antagonism between the parties, with the expectation of a fair price for a good job. This is to ignore totally the essential features of good engineering necessary to attend tunnelling contracts that are successful in outcome for the several parties involved. A target contract shifts the areas of skill between the parties, but in no way avoids the need for their manifestation and mobilization. Many recent problems in tunnelling emanate from early steps of planning and investigation: by the time the contract phase was reached, an optimized project was no longer possible. Furthermore, major problems arise when changed conditions lead to a revised value of the target. But it is in the area of changed conditions and in determining where the un-

foreseen becomes the unforeseeable that the main problems of hazard and risk arise. A target contract may be the right framework for a tunnel, but never the solution. Often, there is a high price to be paid in bureaucratic control that is no alternative to the continuous thread of good engineering thinking throughout.

It is axiomatic for this discussion that the system include the office of Engineer, who is able to unify the project definition, planning, investigation, design and construction with the requirements for project life and use. The quasi-judicial role of the Engineer in the operation of the contract between employer and contractor entails the constant exercise of an appropriately skilled and expert engineering judgement. The system is given a bad name by those who attempt to operate it without this appreciation. The office of Engineer cannot function properly if it is denied the criteria for optimization of the project, including the continuity across the phases of the project and the acceptance by the Engineer of responsibility for appropriate aspects for success in construction. There are, of course, alternative models, but these entail greater complexity in the transition of responsibility through the evolution of a project, with reduced understanding (following from lack of experience of continuity) of the hazards that arise from inadequacies in the early phases of a project.

One particular recent practice, inequitable and unprofessional, is for massive quantities of undigested geological and geotechnical reports to be provided to tenderers with limited time for them to absorb the data. The ploy, deliberate or naive, attempts to load responsibility on a contractor. The legal proceedings that follow are often expensive for all parties.

Idealized examples

The present climate of pressures from government and elsewhere for the accountant's chimera of pursuit of the least apparent first cost has provided the authors with considerable recent experience of consultations on the problems that are encountered in tunnelling projects, their resolution and the attachment of liability. This is a situation in which the engineer needs deliberately to attempt to see the situation from the viewpoints of the parties involved rather than with an Olympian detachment in the knowledge of the out-turn after the event.

Perhaps the most frequent problem arises directly from the absence of the discipline of the application of reference conditions: this may lead to the failure to appreciate that the information available about the ground, however voluminous, fails to address questions of vital importance to the viability of particular systems of tunnelling. When surprises lead to astonishment, there is clearly either a case for suggesting negligence in the conduct of the ground investigations or for lack of care in its application. Too often, the engineer, pressurized and inexperienced, takes the line that the circumstances that have eventuated were entirely to be expected – in the hope that this view will not be challenged. If he had undergone the discipline of forecasting rather than hindcasting the ground conditions, his powers of prognosis would have been tested.

As a variant, the engineer arms himself with the options of different forms of tunnel construction, but then refuses to admit the need to adopt an alternative that entails greater cost in measured work when the ground so merits. This is a spurious confusion of the Engineer's two roles of technical consultant and administrator of the contract between employer and contractor. If the contractor has good grounds for expecting the Engineer to exercise his technical role with objectivity and understanding, and if the Engineer fails to do so, the Engineer must bear at least partial responsibility for the consequences. It is dishonest to imply in a contract that the method of construction will be varied to suit the ground if the Engineer does not intend objectively and expertly to exercise this option.

A similar phenomenon has been seen to operate in the opposite direction, however, the contractor having taken advantage of inexperienced engineers. In one such example provision had been made for the need for arch supports throughout the length of a tunnel through variable rock, much of it sound and massively jointed, but locally faulted and broken. The contractor insisted that the support would be needed and that supplies for the whole tunnel had to be obtained at the inception of the project to avoid additional cost. This was a tunnel for which arch support was inappropriate in the first place. It was erected and lightly sheeted over in such a way as to provide negligible support but to conceal the state of the roof and walls of the roof and walls of the tunnel, thereby adding to the danger of local falls. The engineer had introduced an inappropriate option on which he was incapable of ruling; the contractor took advantage of this oversight. The result combined additional cost for the project with increased risk to those who were working in the tunnel.

Another series of problems arises when geological investigation and engineering proceed in series rather than in conjunction. A fairly thorough investigation of a pressure tunnel missed a thin, steeply inclined, karstic band of limestone. This zone was encountered in tunnelling, but its significance was partially obscured by alluvial deposits in the voids and no geological explanation was sought. Inadequate grouting and over-rapid pressurizing of the tunnel combined to lift and shift the crown when the tunnel was first commissioned.

The pooling of expertise and experience between engineer and contractor has often contributed to a good job with a satisfactory outcome for all parties. Although contractual responsibilities should be clear, good engineering does not recognize a sharp division between design and construction. There are many examples of timely discussions that have had a successful outcome in avoiding a concealed danger, in mitigating the cost of an unexpected hazard and in modifying a technique to achieve a cost-saving with an improvement in performance. The inexperienced engineer tends to back away from discussions with a contractor who is encountering problems, unaware that by so doing he may be adding to the ultimate bill to be met by his client and possibly even to be contributed by himself if he is proved to have been negligent.

Examples that follow are intended to illustrate particular types of recent problems with a wider application, mostly from the experience of the authors. Project identity has to remain anonymous and situations have been highly idealized. No attempt should be made to attach the personal views that are expressed here to any particular project.

Contract price provision

Fig. 1 indicates the folly of reducing the apparent cost of the project at the tender stage to satisfy the finance provider's penchant for misleading himself.

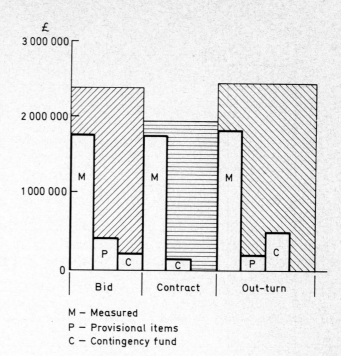

M – Measured
P – Provisional items
C – Contingency fund

Fig. 1   Contract price provision

A contract was devised in which risks were identified and evaluated. A contingency fund and provisional items were included to permit the Engineer to deal with lower-probability risks as appropriate.

The Client ordered the removal of all provisional sums, and most of the contingency fund, to reduce the apparent value, before awarding the tender. The resulting difference between bid and contract values introduced a quite unnecessary lowering of the contractor's confidence, and additional pressure on the Engineer in management of the contract.

In the event, the out-turn cost was very close to the bid, despite additional works being ordered.

Geological constipation

Figs. 2 and 3 indicate a fairly typical misunderstanding of *CIRIA 79*'s ideal of the establishment of reference conditions of tunnelling. A tunnel was proposed to be driven through a complex geological structure that had also been undermined, the water-table being almost at ground level.

A considerable amount of site investigation was carried out and expert geologists spent a great deal of time and money in postulating what the geological section through the tunnel might be like.

When the contract was put out to tender all the site investigation information was heaped on the tenderers, who were allowed only a short tender period in which to reach conclusions about how the rock that they were likely to meet might behave in a tunnel face.

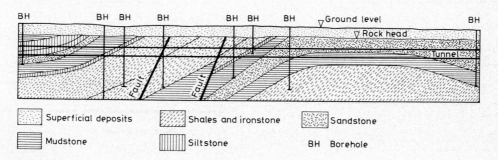

Superficial deposits	Shales and ironstone	Sandstone
Mudstone	Siltstone	BH Borehole

Fig. 2   Typical geological section

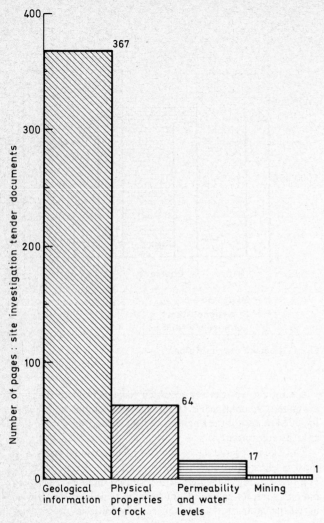

Fig. 3   Usefulness of geological information

The Engineer, who had considerably more time at his disposal, failed to provide any view on how he thought the material might behave, which is prerequisite to the establishment of ground reference conditions.

Method selection
Fig. 4 shows an idealized section through a proposed tunnel in alternating layers of hard and soft material. The inexperienced engineer sought advice of many contractors during the gestation period of the contract and decided that two alternative forms of lining should be included in the contract. A 'rapid' tunnel lining (Fig. 5) was envisaged for use where the ground was self-supporting, standard bolted lining being erected within a shield when difficult conditions were encountered (Fig. 6).

In the event, the Engineer refused to order bolted linings, even when the erection of rapid lining became impossible, and the resulting arguments over the inevitable claim served only to increase the cost of the project.

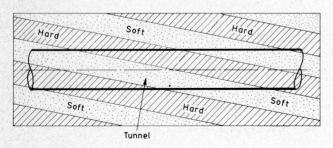

Fig. 4   Method selection – geology

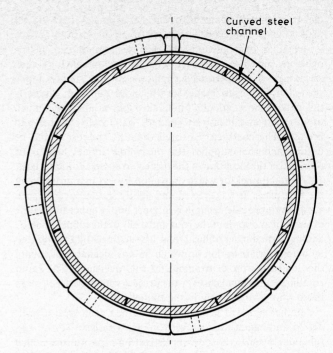

Fig. 5   Rapid tunnel lining

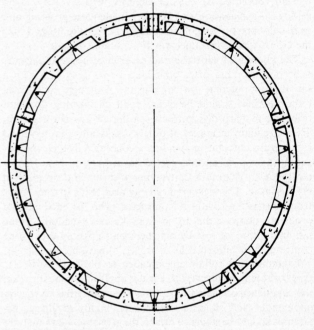

Fig. 6   Standard bolted concrete

Method application
The Engineer prepared a contract for the construction of a main sewer, by cut and cover methods, through sands and gravels generally overlain by a clay stratum. The clay stratum disappeared, however, at one end of the contract (Fig. 7).

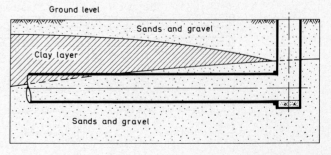

Fig. 7   Method application

The successful tenderer proposed the construction of this part of the sewer in tunnel, with the use of smooth bore linings, and assisted by compressed air to control the groundwater. The Engineer admitted no experience in this field, and his site staff refused to expose themselves to the health hazards of compressed air. The Contractor took advantage of this situation and made extravagant claims for additional compressed-air equipment, etc., when he began to lose pressure in the tunnel as the clay cover disappeared.

The resulting expense of litigation and settlement could have been avoided easily if experienced advice on risks had been sought before embarking on the Contract.

Risk-sharing

Finally, an example of how unforeseen tunnelling problems may be overcome at minimum cost is provided. Fig. 8 depicts two tunnels, in close proximity, which intersected a large sand lens 40 m below surface. The tunnels were being shield-driven and lined with an expanded, boltless lining (Fig. 9).

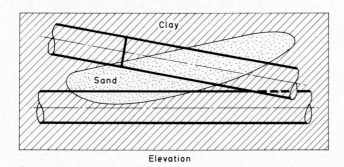

Elevation

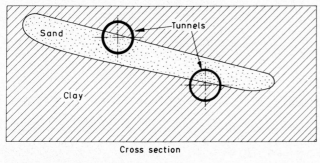

Cross section

Fig. 8   Jubilee line – geology

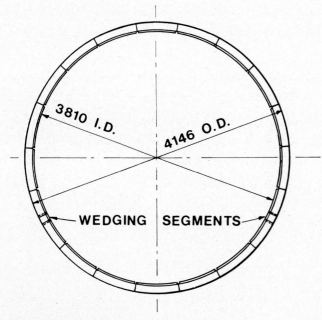

Fig. 9   Jubilee line – 3810-mm internal diameter lining

The upper of the two tunnels met the sand lens first, in the invert of the excavation. To everybody's complete surprise the lens was charged with water under artesian pressure, the shield dropped 150 mm in two 600-mm shoves and a quicksand condition developed in the invert.

The Engineer had complete freedom to decide his course of action, and promptly agreed with the Contractor to drain the lens by gravity by insertion of perforated steel lance tubes, and to continue with the specified form of lining. This section of the tunnel was later brought up to the required internal dimensions by simply raising the crown of the tunnel ring by ring (Fig. 10). The Contractor naturally claimed for the additional costs of these operations and these were agreed without difficulty.

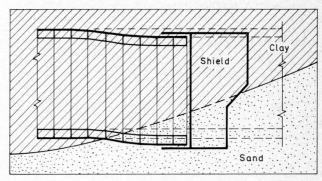

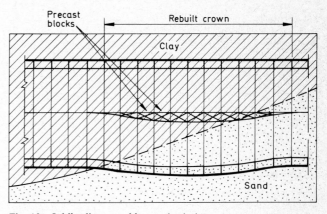

Fig. 10   Jubilee line – problem and solution

Conclusion

A besetting present-day problem in civil engineering worldwide stems from the attempt to maximize competition on cost without an appreciation of the problems in defining and ensuring appropriate quality. This attitude has many manifestations, including concentration on management to the detriment of engineering, the lack of appreciation of the nature of expertise in unfamiliar branches of engineering and the emphasis on certainty of ultimate cost. Politicians, national and local, believe that there is no important lobby for quality, whereas apparent increases in cost disturb the *dolce vita*. The unprincipled are ever ready to exploit a situation in which 'audit' does not include 'technical audit'. The lawyers are then the main beneficiaries and the sufferers are the good engineers who know how to achieve real and often highly significant savings in cost, combined with high standards in achievement and benefit to the community. Despite the developments in tunnelling techniques, the increasing understanding of the relationship between characteristics of the ground, design and construction, and the availability of clues to good and bad practice from recent examples, poor value for money continues to be obtained on account of lack of observance of the fundamental features of quality and how it is achieved. The situation can be restored. It must be restored if value for money is to be achieved.

The message that the authors would wish to convey to the promoters of tunnel works is threefold: (1) establish the continuous thread of sound engineering throughout the project and you will save precious resources; (2) placing all the risks on one party to the contract without definition will lead to payment for risks that do not eventuate; and (3) refusal to recognize changed conditions is expensive and damages the public perception of the Engineer in society.

References
1. Construction Industry Research and Information Association. Tunnelling – improved contract practices. *CIRIA Rep.* 79, 1978, 70 p.
2. Muir Wood A. M. Tunnel hazards: UK experience. In *Hazards in tunnelling and on falsework* (London: Institution of Civil Engineers, 1975), 47–59.
3. Pugsley A. *The safety of structures* (London: Arnold, 1966).

Preliminary studies for tunnel projects in Hong Kong

Ian McFeat-Smith
Charles K. Haswell
Charles Haswell & Partners (Far East), Hong Kong

Synopsis
The planning, environmental, alignment and geotechnical studies that have been carried out for tunnels in Hong Kong are discussed. Experience is drawn from a number of major tunnelling projects: these require the construction of extensive underground works for roads and aqueducts in hilly terrain, and for subway railways under one of the world's most densely populated urban areas. The works include the excavation of shafts, tunnels and caverns in soft ground conditions or in massive igneous rocks. Many tunnels are, however, being driven close below a highly variable rockhead, where zones of completely weathered rock are encountered together with washout channels of marine and alluvial sediments.

Emphasis is given to geotechnical aspects of these projects and to the measures that have been adopted in Hong Kong to drive tunnels in arduous conditions.

Introduction

An outline is made in this section of some of the environmental, social and economic factors that are involved in the development of Hong Kong and how these have led to the extensive use of tunnels. Tunnel projects have, in effect, played a vital role in fulfilling a unique – almost frantic – demand for major improvements in Hong Kong's infrastructure.

In the following sections planning, environmental control, land and social issues, which pertain to conditions within the territory, are discussed in addition to alignment studies, site investigations and geotechnical considerations. Decisions reached in these preliminary studies are often irreversible owing to the pace of development: hence, considerable emphasis is placed on reaching the most practical engineering solutions within the initial period of study.

An attempt is made to provide details of all major tunnel projects initiated within the last six to eight years, many of which are currently at the tender, design or construction stages.

Land use and population
Hong Kong has a total surface area of about 1000 km^2, although only some 40 km^2 is suitable for development. The main urban area is located along the harbour on reclaimed land, where most of the territory's population is housed in high-rise buildings (Fig. 1). This is one of the densest population concentrations in the world, averaging around 100 000 people/km^2.

The population has increased mainly by immigration from China from an estimated 600 000 after the second world war to 5 300 000 today. Coupled with this population increase there has been a remarkable 8.5% real increase in gross national product per year over the same period. These rapid growths have imposed vast demands on housing, services and transportation systems.[1] About 75% of the population uses public transport and this alone currently provides 60 000 000 passenger trips per week.

Geology and climate
Hong Kong is formed primarily from volcanic and granitic rocks (Fig. 1). A small proportion of sedimentary rocks outcrop near to the border with China to the north, the granites being concentrated around the harbour area. The terrain is deeply weathered in many areas by the combined effects of periodically intense rainfall and the removal of the natural vegetation. In 1982 3200 mm of rainfall was experienced with peak falls of 400 mm in one day and 110 mm in 1 h. This caused extensive flooding and a total of 1500 landslips, of which one-third were examined by the Hong Kong Geotechnical Control Office.[2]

Rapid denudation of the hills has resulted in the widespread distribution of colluvial deposits containing boulders up to 5 m in diameter. This ill-sorted landslip material, described by Huntley and Randall,[3] is normally 5–20 m thick and overlies rock weathered to depths of up to 40 m. Rockhead is notoriously difficult to define owing to a high proportion of large weathered core boulders above rockhead and weathered zones below rockhead.[4,5]

The colluvium is covered by alluvial deposits in most low-lying areas, such as the wide, flat valleys of the New Territories, and these are again overlain by shallow marine deposits along the coastline areas. As is illustrated in Fig. 1, extensive reclamation has taken place along the harbour, often with the use of coarse uncompacted fill materials.

Tunnel projects in Hong Kong
The advantages of the use of tunnels are directly attributable to Hong Kong's difficult terrain and the resultant high land costs. This situation is well illustrated by the diagrammatic section in Fig. 1 that shows the distribution of various types of tunnel projects throughout the territory.

Tunnels have been instrumental in providing essential links between the heavily populated harbour areas, new town developments and the rural areas. These connexions include the network of aqueduct tunnel projects (A–G) and the road tunnel projects (G–L) (Fig. 1). The construction of the Beacon Hill twin-line tunnel (project Q) in 1981 was part of a modernization programme for the Kowloon–Canton (Guangzhou) Railway, which provides an important link with mainland China.[6]

Table 1 gives details of all major driven tunnel projects initiated in the last six years, summarizing the various parties involved, the quantity and type of tunnelling carried out and the status of the project as known in November, 1984.

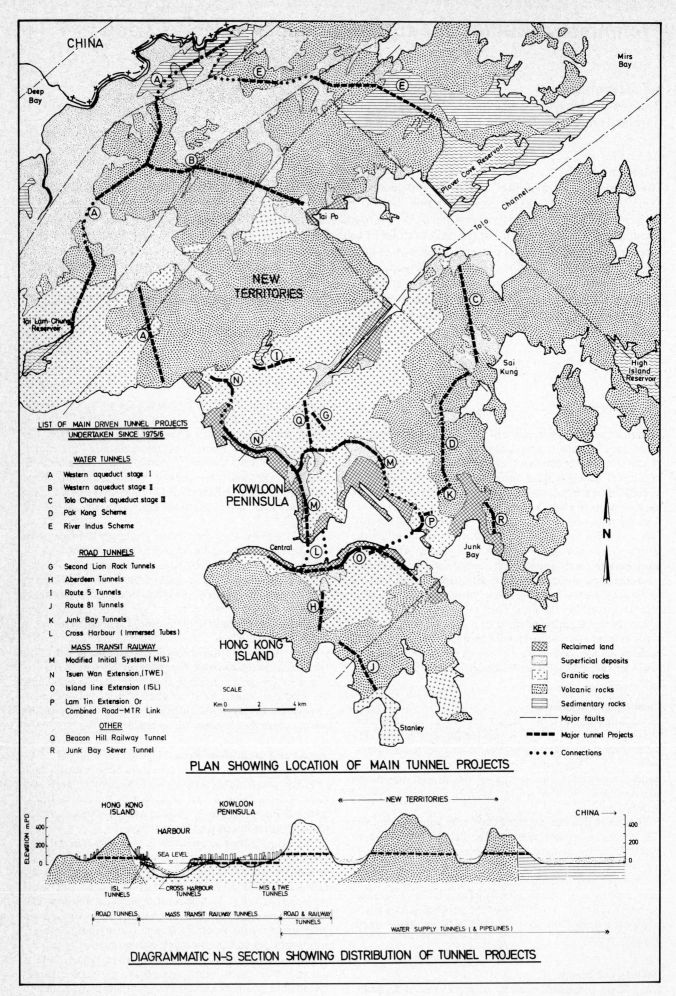

LIST OF MAIN DRIVEN TUNNEL PROJECTS
UNDERTAKEN SINCE 1975/6

WATER TUNNELS

A Western aqueduct stage I
B Western aqueduct stage II
C Tolo Channel aqueduct stage III
D Pak Kong Scheme
E River Indus Scheme

ROAD TUNNELS

G Second Lion Rock Tunnels
H Aberdeen Tunnels
I Route 5 Tunnels
J Route 81 Tunnels
K Junk Bay Tunnels
L Cross Harbour (Immersed Tubes)

MASS TRANSIT RAILWAY

M Modified Initial System (MIS)
N Tsuen Wan Extension (TWE)
O Island line Extension (ISL)
P Lam Tin Extension Or
    Combined Road—MTR Link

OTHER

Q Beacon Hill Railway Tunnel
R Junk Bay Sewer Tunnel

SCALE

Km 0   2   4 km

KEY

Reclaimed land
Superficial deposits
Granitic rocks
Volcanic rocks
Sedimentary rocks
Major faults
Major tunnel Projects
Connections

PLAN SHOWING LOCATION OF MAIN TUNNEL PROJECTS

DIAGRAMMATIC N–S SECTION SHOWING DISTRIBUTION OF TUNNEL PROJECTS

Fig. 1   Geological plan and section, Hong Kong

302

Planning studies

In the 1960s a series of studies was commissioned – from which was developed a transport policy that outlined[7] the need for the following: (1) restraints on less efficient users of road space, (2) improvement of the roads and (3) the extension, particularly off-road, and improvement of public transport.

Road tunnels

It was recognized at the outset that the expansion of the existing road system alone would be insufficient owing to narrowness of the principal transportation corridors and the proximity of existing structures. Nevertheless, its development was critical and has played an essential role, albeit minor, in alleviating the situation. This has included the construction of a four-lane cross-harbour connexion by immersed tube in 1971 together with the various road tunnel projects outlined previously. An urgent need for a further harbour tunnel is self-evident and has recently been outlined in the local press.

Mass Transit Railway tunnels

In 1967 consulting engineers submitted a report that recommended the construction of a Mass Transit Railway (MTR) to run under the most populated parts of the urban zones. The core of the underground system was to run along the corridor from Central district on Hong Kong Island, across the harbour (by immersed tube) and along Kowloon Peninsula.[8] This core and its various branches are generally located below major highways within the narrow coastal strips between the harbour and the steep hills. Unusual features of the selected system were recognized as being that (1) the system was planned to be financially viable, (2) it was designed with exceptionally high passenger handling capabilities, which, after completion of the Island Line in late 1985, is expected to be of the order of 2 400 000 passenger trips per day, and (3) it was to be constructed under one of the world's most intensely developed areas with minimum disruption to the populace.

To meet the demands of the first two criteria stations 300 m long were planned at 1-km centres. Platforms were to be located at shallow depths, where practical; all access connexions were designed to prevent congestion; air conditioning was to be provided throughout; and a 2-min interval between trains was planned.

To limit disruption to the city and to permit easier financial planning a phased implementation of discrete sections was planned. This commenced in 1973 with the Modified Initial System[9, 10] and was soon followed by the Tsuen Wan Extension and later by the Island Line, which is currently under construction. In total, the MTR has involved the construction of 50 km of driven tunnel.

A notable trend has developed during this period in that the large cut and cover station boxes used on the initial section were discarded in favour of driven tunnel station platforms and off-line concourses. Most stations on the Island Line employ this new arrangement.

Water supply tunnels

In the mid-1970s Hong Kong's main water supply was stored in a number of reservoirs, including the Plover Cove, High Island, Tai Lam Chung and Shing Mun reservoirs (see Fig. 1). From these raw water was distributed from a network of 80 km of raw water tunnels.[11] Each reservoir's limited catchwaters area is supplemented by a series of catchwaters.

With Hong Kong's rapid development over the past decade critical water shortages have been predicted and experienced. As a result agreement has been reached between the Hong Kong Government and the Guangdong Provincial Authority of the People's Republic of China for the water supply to Hong Kong to be increased by approximately equal annual increments from 182 000 000 m^3 per annum in 1982 to 620 000 000 m^3 in 1994.

The Water Supplies Department (WSD) has carried out a planning study and identified the additional aqueducts and other installations that are required to handle this substantial increase. These include the construction of the series of tunnels as shown in Fig. 1 and described in Table 1. The tunnels normally vary from 2.5 to 3.0 m in external diameter. Preliminary studies for the 18.3-km tunnelling works for projects A to B have already been described.[12] These tunnels are currently being constructed through the full range of strata present in Hong Kong. The raw water tunnels are generally unlined in rock, have short lengths of *in-situ* concrete lining in the soft ground sections and have steel lining at the portals.

Environmental control, land and social issues

A notably low level of control has been applied during the rapid development of Hong Kong's commercial activities in the last decade. The steps involved in the drawing up of legislation for Environmental Impact Assessments (EIA) have been outlined.[13] The issues involved in the construction of transport systems, such as the MTR, have been well illustrated, as have the advantages of employing tunnels in preference to open-cut works.

The WSD and Highways Office have also been quick to respond to the new legislation and consulting engineers have been required to consider the impact of portal formation, working sites, access roads, pipeline routes and spoil disposal sites. The objectives of EIA studies for several aqueduct projects have been summarized by Sloan.[14]

As is illustrated in Fig. 2, greater consideration is required on the hillslopes for landscaping and the maintaining of traditional values.

Landscaping of portal areas merits consideration as the desirability to screen portal works in small valleys often conflicts with the geotechnical (and hence cost) advantages of constructing portals in spurs. Conspicuous portal slopes are normally protected temporarily with chunam, a mixture of cement–lime and completely weathered granite or volcanic soil. These areas are later graded and reinstated.

Spoil disposal is normally the contractor's responsibility in Hong Kong. This acceptable fill material can be useful for the large-scale reclamation work that is currently in progress in many parts of the territory. Nevertheless, irregularities in excavation rates, grading and transportation problems can hamper the supply of fill, thereby limiting its acceptability.

Alignment studies

Aqueduct tunnels

Alignments for aqueduct projects are selected to ensure that schemes incur minimum impact and avoid the lengthy and expensive procedures required for the resumption of Private Land. Thus, rock tunnelling is preferred as the construction of unlined tunnels is more economical than pipeline construction. The overall alignment is therefore selected to achieve maximum overburden cover to the tunnels. A minimum cover of about 70 m is generally sought to avoid zones of highly weathered rock.

Some latitude to align individual tunnels to avoid adverse geological features is possible, as is indicated by the alignment of projects A, B and D in Fig. 1. The cost of the additional lengths of rock tunnel is easily offset against the lower quantity of tunnelling in soft ground. The cost ratio between unlined

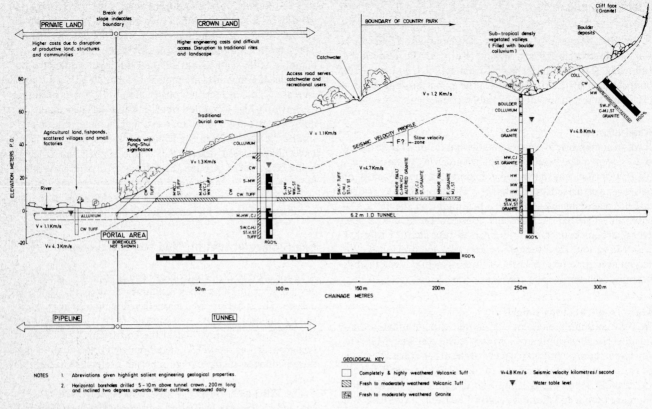

Fig. 2 Site investigation for typical portal in rural area

Table 1 Summary of data from main driven tunnel projects undertaken in Hong Kong since 1978

Key	Project	Client	Tunnel consultant	Stage	Bored tunnel content	Contract
A	Future increase of water supply from China	Water Supplies Department	Charles Haswell & Partners (feasibility, S.I.) Charles Haswell & Partners in association with Kampsax-Kruger (design, construction)	I Western aqueduct	A Four tunnels, 13.3 km long, 2.5–3 m in diameter, for raw water B One tunnel, 5 km long, 2.5 m in diameter, for raw water	Excavation completed by CCEC (China Engineers), Nov. 1984 Completed by Paul Y, late 1984
B			Charles Haswell & Partners (feasibility S.I.) Water Supplies Department (design)	II Western aqueduct	One tunnel, 6 km long, 2.8 m in diameter, for raw water	Tender late 1984
C			Binnie & Partners	II Tolo Channel aqueduct	One tunnel, 5.2 km long, 3 m in diameter, for raw water	Tender late 1984
D	Pak Kong		Charles Haswell & Partners in association with Watson Hawksley	—	Two tunnels, 6 km long, 3 m in diameter, double-lined, for potable water	Tender early 1985
E	Additional water supply from China	Water Supplies Department		River Indus to Lam Chung	Three tunnels, 8 km long, 2.5–3 m in diameter, for raw water	Completed by Mitsui in 1982
F			Binnie & Partners	Tai Po Tau	Uprating of 2.3-km tunnels for raw water	Completed by Maeda in 1983
H	Aberdeen Road tunnel	Highways Office	Maunsell Consultants Asia		3.8 km long, 10 m in diameter mainly rock tunnels	Completed by Aberdeen Tunnel Joint Venture in 1981
I	Route 5 road tunnels		Halcrow Intl. (feasibility, S.I.) Mott Hay & Anderson		5.0 km long, 10 m in diameter rock tunnels	Tender mid-1985

Table 1—*Continued*

Key	Project	Client	Tunnel consultant	Bored tunnel content	Contract
J	Route 81 road tunnel	Highways Office	Charles Haswell & Partners in association with Freeman Fox & Partners and LG Mouchel & Partners (preliminary design)	5.1 km long, 10 m in diameter rock tunnels	Planning
K	Junk Bay road tunnels		Maunsell Consultants Asia	1.4 km long, 10 m in diameter rock tunnels	Tender mid-1985
M	Modified Initial System	Mass Transit Railway Corporation	Charles Haswell & Partners in association with Freeman Fox & Partners MTR Corporation (construction)	17.3 km long, 4.9–11.6 m in diameter tunnels with 8.2 km in rock or mixed face. Includes 7 X-over tunnels and two sets of station tunnels. Many shafts constructed	Completed in 1978–79 by Gammon/Kier/ Lilley JV; Nishimatsu; Aoki; Metro JV; Maeda; Kumagai Gumi; Paul Y
N	Tsuen Wan extension		Charles Haswell & Partners (feasibility, design) MTR Corporation (construction)	10.5 km long, 5.1–11.6 m in diameter tunnels with 5.3 km in rock or mixed face. Includes one X-over tunnel and one set of station tunnels	Completed in 1982 by Nishimatsu; Kumagai Gumi; Maeda; Aoki/ Tobishima JV
O	Island Line Extension		Charles Haswell & Partners (feasibility, design) MTR Corporation (construction)	22.5 km long mainly 3.8–6.9 m in diameter running tunnels or access tunnels with 15 km in rock or mixed face. Includes 2.4 km of station tunnels 7.6–8.9 m in diameter, four X-over tunnels to 12 m in diameter, and one 24 m span 250 m long station cavern. Many shafts constructed	Under construction by Nishimatsu; Aoki/ Tobishima JV; Maeda; Kumagai Gumi; Paul Y; Dragages/Coignet; Okumura
P	Lam Tin Extension		—	Approximately 200 m running tunnel and one 250 m long station cavern	Planning
Q	Beacon Hill railway tunnel	PWD Hong Kong Government	Charles Haswell & Partners (feasibility, S.I.) Railway Divn. PWD (design, construction)	Two tunnels, 2.7 km long, 10 and 7 m in diameter tunnels for twin and single track	Completed by Aoki 1981/82
R	Junk Bay sewer tunnel	Junk Bay Development Office	Mott Hay & Anderson in association with John Taylor International	One, 2 km long, 2.5 m in diameter sewer tunnel	Tender late 1984

rock tunnels and soft ground tunnels is of the order of 1 : 3, although, in a final analysis, this can be more like 1 : 6.

To programme and determine the economics of various alignments geological conditions are estimated from initial site investigations. The volcanic tuffs and granites are easily classified into five rock groups, largely by their weathering and joint spacing characteristics. The proportions of these classes are used to predict the quantities and types of support likely to be required for each alignment, to programme the works and, hence, to cost the various alternatives.

Road tunnels

A similar approach is adopted by the writers for the selection of alignments for road tunnels, although less flexibility exists to avoid adverse geological features. The Route 5 road tunnels (project *I*), for example, have been aligned around and below the Shing Mun Reservoir, where they will intersect a fault zone 30–40 m wide that trends directly through the reservoir. In addition, the eastern sections of these large-diameter tunnels will intersect a series of slit-vein wolfram mines known to be flooded to about 70 m above tunnel level. The extent of the workings is, however, unknown as they were mined during the second world war by the Japanese, who removed both the pre-existing mine plans and their own records.

Mass Transit Railway

The principal transportation corridors and preferred locations for stations having been identified, the next logical step in the designing of a feasible alignment for the Hong Kong MTR was the negotiation of numerous obstacles. In most cases the ultimate solution was a compromise that offered the most favourable economics and construction programme. In many cases, however, the detailed alignment and station positions were not finalized until after the contracts were awarded owing to the impetus and pace of the project.

The station and running tunnels were aligned along the main east–west corridor of the Island harbour area under many sections of reclaimed land. A significant part of the eastern section of the route follows the old coastline, so the tunnels are being excavated close to the former cliff-edged sea front, where the rock tunnels locally intercept boulder zones and washout channels (Figs. 3 and 4). In the western section a high proportion of mixed face and soft ground tunnelling with compressed air is required. Here the tunnel alignments were at times threaded past and occasionally through a multiplicity of building foundations, including many timber pile structures (Fig. 4). In several cases piles were intercepted by the tunnels and underpinning became necessary – at considerable cost. Old granite-block sea walls were also intercepted on this route.

A conflict arises between the need to position the tunnels at as low a level as possible to ensure maximum excavation in rock and, hence, minimum cost and that to locate the station platform tunnels close to the surface to minimize the travelling distance to platforms. A maximum depth of 30 m below road level was generally preferred to avoid the need for unduly high compressed-air pressures where the rock tunnels emerge into major soft ground sections.

Site investigations

Site investigations that are carried out for tunnels in Hong Kong are generally orientated towards the identification of soil strata and the location of rock head. It is common practice to present only borehole logs and test data to tenderers and to avoid the use of interpretative reports. This has, for example, been the case with all sections of the MTR works, where the investigations consist largely of closely spaced boreholes and associated testing. For the Island Line some 1300 boreholes were drilled, located at intervals of 10–20 m where difficult ground, such as mixed face conditions, was expected.

This conservative approach to site investigation work is, however, changing owing to the increasing use of more sophisticated methods of tunnelling; to the appearance of international contracting organizations in Hong Kong that have become increasingly willing to take disputes over unexpected geological conditions to arbitration; and to an increasing awareness that tunnelling conditions in the local volcanic and granitic rocks are not always favourable.

In 1980 the WSD commissioned consulting engineers to carry out a geotechnical feasibility study for projects A and B. A comprehensive and integrated site investigation by geological mapping, seismic refraction surveying, horizontal, inclined and vertical drilling and associated testing was carried out and an interpretative report was made available to the tenderers.[12]

More recently, the advantages of drilling long horizontal boreholes up to 220 m in length have been demonstrated.[15] As is illustrated in Fig. 2, when used in addition to conventional investigation techniques the drilling of long horizontal boreholes at portals permits accurate prediction of expected geological conditions, which is invaluable as a high proportion of tunnelling difficulties occur in this area. It can be argued that drilling beyond the weathered zone is unnecessarily expensive, particularly in the local igneous rocks, but the geological sample obtained in the fresh rock beyond the portal provides important details of the incidence of jointing, weathered zones and minor faulting that can be expected in the remainder of the tunnels, together with an estimate of the lateral variability of the materials expected. A further advantage of this approach is the ease of monitoring water flows from the borehole, which provides an assessment of the inflows that are likely to be experienced in the tunnel. The maximum flow measured to date from 12 such boreholes is 1066 m³/day

The boreholes are located as shown in Fig. 2 to ensure that they are not drilled into the proposed tunnel excavation zone. Borehole deviation is minimized by ensuring that the rig has sufficient power; that it is set up on a stable platform; that the initial drilling direction is on-line; and that the thrust is applied slowly. This is assisted, from the engineer's point of view, by the requirement to realign or redrill the borehole at the drilling contractor's expense where deviations exceed 5° in azimuth or dip. In practice, this has not been necessary as deviations of only 2° have normally been achieved at 200-m depth, irrespective of the geological conditions encountered. Drilling rates of 5–6 m/day are common in the extremely strong volcanic rocks and costs have varied between two and four times those for vertical boreholes.

Fig. 2 shows typical geological conditions encountered at portals in rural areas. An interesting feature is illustrated here: whereas seismic refraction surveying may not detect the presence of highly to completely weathered rock underlying layers of closely spaced boulders (as at chainages 60–100 m), the technique can indicate the presence and extent of unexpected faulting, such as that at chainage 170 m. In one case, for example, the location and extent of a 200-m zone of completely to moderately weathered rock encountered by a tunnel for project A at 150 m below surface level was predicted with notable precision.

As for projects A and B,[12] it is considered essential that an interpretative geotechnical report be issued as part of the tender documents for all tunnel projects. The concept of using the rock classification system (or Ground Reference Conditions) described in the previous section for payment purposes has been advocated by the authors for a number of projects, and may be introduced into the territory in the near future.

Geotechnical considerations

Slope stability
The formation and protection of portal slopes in the local soils can give rise to difficult geotechnical problems. The colluvial materials, in particular, have low cohesion and angle of friction and the interface between this and the residual soils has to be investigated carefully in view of the periodic intense rainfall described previously. The southern portals for the Aberdeen road tunnels (project H) were excavated through a zone of weathered quartz monzonite overlain by colluvium. The presence of this unfavourable interface, a high water-table and the characteristics of the completely weathered monzonite gave particularly adverse slope stability and tunnelling conditions. Extensive ground treatment was required.[16]

Rock excavation
Methods of excavation in rock tunnels have, to date, been entirely by drill and blast techniques. Nevertheless, considerable scope exists for the use of tunnel-boring machines with disc cutters. The aqueduct tunnels, in particular, are often of the order of 5 km in length and are not easily accessible other than at the portals.

Preliminary studies[12] indicated that the local rocks are suitable for excavation by TBM. Rates of advance have been predicted[20] to be of the order of 0.8–3.0 m/h with the use of appropriate hard rock machines. The compressive strength of the granites when fresh is 70–150 MPa, and the massive volcanic tuffs are commonly 120–220 MPa. The contact zones between the materials are often smooth and the rock materials are reasonably consistent, except for the occurrence of occasional zones of intercalations of sedimentary rocks within the volcanic sequence. The joint spacing of both materials outwith the influence of major faults is typically 0.2–0.5 m. Even at a 0.2-m spacing, however, the rocks are largely self-supporting owing to the cohesiveness of the jointing.

Ground control and settlement monitoring
Prior to the construction of the MTR little was known in Hong Kong about tunnelling conditions in the local soils. A series of trial tunnels was constructed in 1973 to examine the behaviour of the soils under different methods of construction and various geotechnical processes for the prevention of water ingress.[17] It was found that the completely weathered granites, in particular, became an ideal tunnelling medium under compressed air.[18] Also a two-stage treatment process (cement/bentonite followed by chemical grouting with silicates) produced similarly effective results. The cost of the latter has,

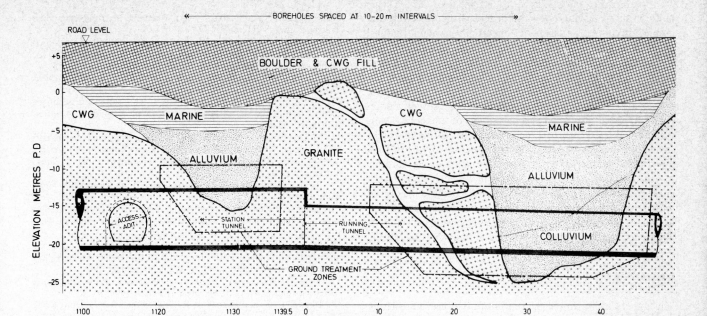

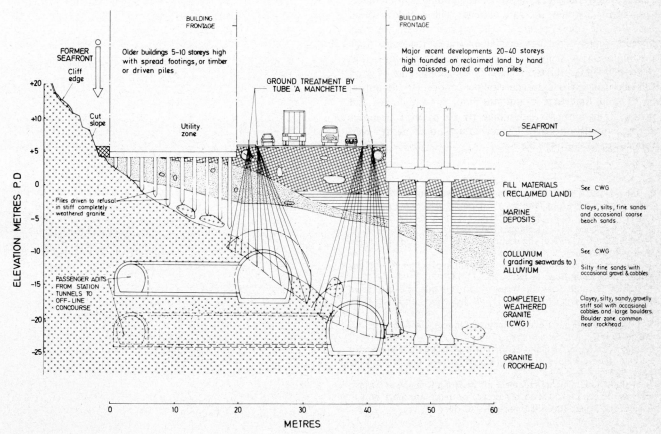

Fig. 3   Longitudinal section showing geological conditions encountered in washout channels and boulder zones

however, limited its use to much shorter lengths of tunnel, such as the localized conditions illustrated in Figs. 3 and 4. Silicate grouts have proved to be generally ineffective in soils that contain more than 15% of materials less than 0.05 mm in size, i.e. silt size or finer, although some success has been claimed in treating clayey silts at very high pressures.

These processes have proved to be successful, allowing rapid soft ground excavation to be carried out in some very critical situations. Support of the tunnel roof is normally achieved by open poling, forepoling or shield. In the completely weathered

granite steel arches and lagging or, more recently, steel fibre-reinforced shotcrete have proved to be effective. Indeed, there have been only a relatively few cases of the occurrence of unduly high settlements or collapses owing to tunnelling. These are attributable to (1) unexpected anisotropy or poor workmanship limiting the effectiveness of ground treatment works, (2) blasting immediately adjacent to rock head resulting in the collapse of the tunnel roof and (3) high water inflows in rock tunnels resulting in dewatering of the overlying soils.

A comprehensive outlook is taken by the MTR Corporation

Fig. 4   Cross-section showing treatment of soft ground sections of rock tunnels

and consulting engineers to the problems of predicting and monitoring tunnel settlements. A geotechnical and structural survey is made of all buildings within 70 m of the railway prior to construction.[19] Monitoring procedures are substantial and for the Island Line concourses and tunnels this included the installation of 7 km of inclinometer tubes plus piezometers, extensometers and an extensive settlement point survey. Settlements recorded, expressed as a percentage of tunnel face loss, commonly vary from 1 to 3, occasionally increasing to 5% on removal of the compressed air. In extreme cases a figure of 10% has been found owing to the rapid removal of air pressures or to poor support arrangements. Even, however, in cases where angular distortions on buildings have exceeded the maximum local 1:300 criterion, structural damage has rarely occurred as a result of the rigidity of the local buildings, which act as box-like structures rather than as a series of individual members.

Conclusions

This paper has illustrated the conditions that prevail in Hong Kong and the necessary approach to preliminary studies for tunnel projects. In view of the high cost of tunnels it is essential that due attention be given at the preliminary stage to planning studies, environmental and social issues, selection of alignments, site investigations and geotechnical considerations. If these initial steps are carried out in a proficient manner, it is likely that the subsequent stages will follow accordingly.

The need for rapid construction of tunnels in Hong Kong has created major challenges to both consulting engineers and contractors. These have been met with a high degree of success. Project development and construction programmes, which would be considered impractical in many countries, have been adhered to. The development of the Hong Kong Mass Transit Railway is a prime example of such a successful project, each phase being completed within programme and budget.

Emphasis has been placed on the importance of the site investigation and geotechnical considerations. If the correct approach is adopted, the data obtained will provide a sound basis for the tunnel contract. The engineer must, however, interpret geotechnical data and demonstrate at the tender stage the limitations of such information. It therefore follows that the issue of interpretative reports is an integral part of good tunnel practice. The logical development of this is the definition of Ground Reference Conditions both for estimating and programming purposes and, ultimately, for payment purposes at the construction stage. The advantages to all parties concerned can be considerable.

References

1. Jones D. J. C. Transport problems in a crowded environment – the Hong Kong problem. In *Transport into the 80s: papers presented at a conference, Hong Kong, February 1982*, organized by the Institution of Civil Engineers *et al.* (London: Thomas Tellford, 1982), 3–11.
2. Brand E. Geotechnical engineering in Hong Kong. *Ground Engng*, **16**, no. 4, May 1983, 2, 5–6.
3. Huntley S. L. and Randall M. A. Recognition of colluvium in Hong Kong. *Hong Kong Engr*, **9**, Dec. 1981, 13–18.
4. Ruxton B. and Berry L. Weathering of granite and associated erosional features in Hong Kong. *Bull. geol. Soc. Am.*, **68**, 1957, 1263–99.
5. Lumb P. The properties of decomposed granite. *Geotechnique*, **12**, 1962, 226–43.
6. Lloyd R. H. and Williams H. B. The modernisation and electrification of the Kowloon–Canton Railway (British section). *Hong Kong Engr*, **9**, May 1981, 9–22.
7. Wilkins A. H. The development of the Hong Kong Mass Transit Railway. Paper presented to conference on mass transportation in Asia, Hong Kong, May 1980, paper B1/01–14.
8. Edwards J. T. and Pearce R. A. C. Planning the Hong Kong Mass Transit Railway. Reference 1, 263–8.
9. Haswell C. K. *et al.* Hong Kong Mass Transit Railway modified initial system: design and construction of the driven tunnels and the immersed tube. *Proc. Instn civ. Engrs: pt 1*, Nov. 1980, 627–55.
10. Haswell C. K. Tunnels for the new Hong Kong Metro. *Tunnels Tunnell.*, **9**, Nov. 1977, 31–5.
11. Vail A. J. Lee G. C. and Robertson I. R. S. Some aspects of the construction of the High Island Scheme. *Hong Kong Engr*, **4**, no. 4, Aug. 1976, 53–63.
12. McFeat-Smith I. Geotechnical feasibility study and site investigation for the Western Aqueduct tunnels, Hong Kong. In *Proceedings seventh Southeast Asian geotechnical conference, Hong Kong, November 1982*, 171–87.
13. Reed S. B. Environmental protection – Hong Kong 1982. *Hong Kong Engr*, **10**, April 1982, 11–19.
14. Sloan R. Future increase of water supply from China – western aqueducts: environmental considerations. *Hong Kong Engr*, **11**, Oct. 1983, 5–11.
15. McFeat-Smith I. The drilling of long horizontal boreholes for site investigation purposes. Paper presented to conference on geological aspects of site investigation, Hong Kong, December 1984.
16. Twist D. W. L. and Tonge W. A. Planning and design of the Aberdeen tunnel. *Hong Kong Engr*, **7**, March 1979, 13–30.
17. Haswell C. K. and Umney A. R. Trial tunnels for the Hong Kong Mass Transit Railway. *Hong Kong Engr*, **6**, Feb. 1978, 15–23.
18. Haswell C. K. and Campbell J. G. Compressed air tunnelling with special reference to the Hong Kong Mass Transit Railway. In *Eurotunnel '83 conference, Basle, Switzerland, June 1983* (Marlow, Bucks, England: Access Conferences, Ltd., 1983), 173–83.
19. Budge-Reid A. J. Cater R. W. and Storey F. G. Geotechnical and constructional aspects of the Hong Kong Mass Transit Railway system. Paper presented to conference on mass transportation in Asia, June 1984.
20. McFeat-Smith I. and Tarkoy P. J. Assessment of tunnel boring machine performance. *Tunnels Tunnell.*, **11**, Dec. 1979, 33–7.

Discussion

N. S. M. Berry* said that he found himself in broad agreement with virtually everything that Muir Wood and Kirkland had said. It was of great concern that so many tunnel contracts ended up with at least threatened arbitration – if not actually in the courts. A common thread in many of those contracts had been the apparent reluctance of the 'Engineer' to make decisions – either because of inexperience or because his dual role as Engineer under the contract and the responsibility for keeping within agreed budgets put him in a very difficult position.

Tunnel contracts by their very nature were difficult to administer, underground excavation tending to be a continually changing process owing to the variability of rock conditions and the administration of such contracts required an experienced and independently minded Engineer. The combination of an inexperienced Engineer and a not too scrupulous Contractor could cause heavy additional cost to the Client. Although by no means always the case, the number of tunnel contracts that ran into difficulties, both in the United Kingdom and overseas, clearly indicated that all was not well and he strongly supported the authors' plea for tunnelling to be directed by engineers appropriately experienced in tunnel construction. That might give rise to apparent additional costs owing to the appointment of additional experienced staff or even an experienced consultant, but such costs were dwarfed by the cost of arbitration as the result of incorrect decisions arising from lack of appropriate experience.

Reference had been made to the use of ground reference conditions as proposed in *CIRIA Rep.* 79, and it was good to see Sir Alan involved in the updating of that very useful document. Most reference conditions to date had tended to identify the expected geology and then to make provision for adjusting the contract value should the rock conditions vary from those which had been predicted. A problem in his experience had been the situation in which the geology, by any reasonable assessment, was as predicted, but some lengths proved very easy to excavate and support and other lengths presented great difficulty. That was particularly the case with machine excavation in shales or mudstone, where very minor and difficult to identify changes in rock characteristics could have a major effect.

He would be interested to know if the authors had had similar experience and whether they considered that the ground reference conditions should be based entirely on identifiable geological parameters or if they believed that it was possible or practical to include a predicted rate of progress that, if it was not attainable owing to conditions outwith the contractor's control, although not necessarily easily identifiable geological conditions, would allow for the adjustment of the contract value.

F. Rowbottom† said that tunnelling projects in some overseas countries had to comply with legislation applicable to mining. In some cases the Inspectorate required standards that had not been foreseen or provided for by the consulting engineers for the project. The authors' comment would be welcomed on the role of the Engineer in such circumstance, particularly where the Contractor might be given direct instructions from the Inspectorate that he had to comply with or be in breach of the law. On the Kariba North Bank project the contractor was not paid for work that he had been legally directed to do. He asked if the authors had any advice for contractors who might be required to work under similar conditions to those which prevailed on the Kariba project to ensure both the safe completion of the project and payment for additional work justifiably carried out.

The authors had mentioned the need, in some cases, for an independent engineer's assessment and he wondered if they considered that the Inspectorate could fill that role and, if so, how the Inspectorate might be involved.

D. F. Fawcett* said that technical papers presented over the past ten years indicated that within the tunnelling industry the expertise existed to investigate, predict and deal with almost any form of ground conditions. Despite that ability, there were still far too many tunnelling contracts, both in the United Kingdom and overseas, that were financial disasters. Tunnels were completed late, the client being asked to bear costs that were in some cases several times the original tender. That situation did the industry tremendous harm and exacerbated the problems caused by the current low workload by leading clients to choose other methods, wherever possible.

The implication of the papers in *Tunnelling '85*, and of that by Muir Wood and Kirkland in particular, was that many of those problems were caused by either the Engineer or the Contractor not having sufficient experience of the particular work being undertaken. Over the past decade tunnelling had become very specialized with the introduction of machines that would deal with nearly all types of ground conditions, and considerable mechanization behind the face. An industry that, only one generation ago, involved mainly muscle and explosives was now extremely complex. That situation was further aggravated by the need to match the modern excavation techniques very carefully with the ground conditions, which, in turn, put more strain on the site investigation and its interpretation.

The expertise to carry out the work successfully was obviously available, but all too often was not used. Many professional engineers were not aware of what they did not know when it came to tunnelling. As a result they did not call in the necessary tunnellers at the right time – with often disastrous consequences for their clients.

The situation that had arisen needed to be dealt with. Other specializations of professions both inside and outside civil engineering did not allow an individual to practise that specialization unless it was recognized that he was competent to do so. The time had come to extend that practice to the tunnelling industry by only allowing *Registered Tunnel Engineers* to be responsible for the design, supervision or construction of underground works. By that action the problems outlined above, so often encountered, should be largely eliminated, with a resultant benefit to the industry.

J. Buchanan† said that the words 'quality assurance' were used in the context of achieving good design and construction. It appeared that the views expressed were not encompassed by any existing British Standards for Quality Assurance. He asked if the authors had any particular Standards in mind or whether they were making a move towards the establishment of a Standard for the control of the 'Owner'.

Authors' reply

Sir Alan Muir Wood and C. J. Kirkland We are grateful for N. S. M. Berry's support in the cause of the appointment of appropriately qualified engineers.

With regard to reference conditions for tunnelling, we

*Babtie Shaw and Morton, Glasgow, Scotland.
†Department of Minerals and Energy, Port Moresby, Papua New Guinea.

*Babti Shaw and Morton, Glasgow, Scotland.
†Sir Robert McAlpine and Sons, Ltd., London, England.

cannot see any way by which reference conditions could be related to the progress of a tunnelling machine short of the Engineer having full control of the design and operation of the machine, and this is obviously unrealistic. Furthermore, most engineers would be reluctant to specify construction method since we would then either lose any advantage available from utilization of a tenderer's existing plant or offer an unfair advantage to a particular tenderer.

Since the point at issue generally concerns the need for support of the ground, this is surely the criterion. Items must be devised to cover varying degrees of support provision, which also cover machine delays, but not to such an extent that the overall incentive for rapid progress is removed. Particular care must be taken in weak rocks that the tunnelling method itself does not bring about a need for additional support – for example, by the use of inadequate gripper pads.

We suspect that F. Rowbottom's question may take us back to our plea for a continuous thread of engineering expertise throughout the project from inception to commissioning. It is surely part of the Engineer's duty to ensure that he understands the relationship of his project to any statutory requirements of other agencies. If the operation of such an agency is well understood and rational, it may be sufficient to ensure that the proposed operational practices are mutually understood to permit the tenderer to price the cost of compliance. To this end we would endeavour to ensure that all tenderers were made fully aware of any local regulations, and would arrange for a 'question and answer' session between interested authorities and tenderers before tenders are submitted.

A further meeting between the successful tenderer and the authorities should be arranged before the award to ensure that the tenderer appreciates the likely costs that could arise from rulings on local legal requirements and that there is adequate means for reimbursement within the contract.

If, however, the agency is considered liable to act in an unreasonable or unpredictable manner, it may be more appropriate to specify some reasonable set of requirements in relation to matters under the jurisdiction of the agency so that payments are only made in respect of any extra requirements, thus avoiding unnecessarily high provisions for possible unreasonable demands.

We do not believe that the inspectorate of any such agency as Rowbottom's would fit the role of referee or independent engineer, since safety is so paramount to their brief that they could not be expected to exercise the Engineer's judgement, which is set by the criterion of reasonableness.

We find ourselves in agreement with D. F. Fawcett's diagnosis, but not with his suggested cure. Tunnelling is far too subtle an occupation, particularly in today's highly specialist atmosphere, for the compilation of a simple register of engineers competent to tackle all types of tunnelling. Even if such a register existed, it would provide no guarantee that promoters of tunnel projects would find themselves obliged to call on a registered engineer.

We believe that the right approach is to take whatever steps we can to ensure that, in all our activities, Chartered Engineers and others that they may influence are aware of the need for quality assurance. If, at the very inception of a project, this need is acknowledged, this should ensure that the promoter is asking questions about potential risks of all types. It is at the very outset that the mistake is first made when it is believed that savings will arise, or underemployed staff be utilized, by avoiding the appointment of an appropriately knowledgeable engineer. We do not doubt that the minds of public servants would be better concentrated in this respect if the District Auditor were qualified to undertake a Technical Audit, which might conclude that professional oversight of this nature is just as blameworthy as direct misuse of funds.

In reply to J. Buchanan, we use the expression 'quality assurance' in respect of tunnelling in the sense that we believe that it requires a set of procedures to ensure that acceptable standards of risk are established.

Our response to Fawcett will perhaps help to explain our approach, which is a move towards education rather than control of the Owner. The problem is that, for tunnelling, we rapidly escape from quantifiable risks (which lend themselves to specification) to qualitative risks, which depend on professional judgement for their definition and treatment.

Session 13 – General

Chairman: Dr. P. H. Phillips

Tunnel simulation computer model

D. R. Grant
H. D. S. Miller
Department of Mining and Mineral Process Engineering, University of British Columbia, Vancouver, British Columbia, Canada

Synopsis
Recent technological advances in tunnel excavation methods and high variability in ground conditions have rendered the task of cost estimation increasingly more complex, largely as a result of the uncertainties that are involved in predicting geological conditions along the proposed tunnel line and in determining the optimal combination of mining equipment. These uncertainties must be accommodated in the tunnel cost analysis. The cost estimation of a tunnelling project becomes very intricate when all variables are considered. This evaluation process becomes lengthy when a sensitivity study is performed to determine the optimal construction method and tunnel line. One method that is used to account for these uncertainties is the 'Monte Carlo' simulation technique.

The Monte Carlo method is a simulation technique based on a numerical sampling of random numbers. A random process is first parameterized by a suitable probability distribution, which models such random variables as drilling time, blast time, etc. The gamma distribution is suitable because it is skewed to the right, which tends to parallel mining activity-time distributions. After a probability distribution has been selected it can be integrated to obtain the cumulative distribution. Subsequently, a pseudo-random is generated to test against the integrated probability distribution. A random number having been generated, linear interpolation is applied to the cumulative distribution to obtain the corresponding random variable for each activity (drilling time, blast time, etc.).

A computer program has been developed by use of the Monte Carlo technique to estimate operational times of a drill–blast–muck–support tunnelling system. The program consists of two basic components – the operational model and the cost model. The operational model includes a geology module to allow activity times to change for different geologic strata. When the operational data have been generated they are used as input for the cost model. The cost model utilizes spreadsheet and database manipulation to systematically analyse tunnelling costs. Quantities and unit prices of cost items change throughout the bid preparation process. These changes can be quickly incorporated by re-entering the data at the appropriate level in the cost model.

This flexibility in the model allows for the development of a 'What if' scenario. For example, what would happen if the indirect costs became inflated just before the bid is tendered?

By varying the input data, sensitivity analyses can be performed very efficiently. Computer modelling is therefore becoming more attractive as a cost-effective method for estimation of the costs and scheduling of tunnelling projects.

Tunnelling projects are becoming increasingly prominent worldwide, and construction costs are accelerating. An optimal design is difficult to achieve because of the numerous possible combinations of engineering design and construction methods and equipment. Even with present-day tunnelling technology excavation rates have not increased appreciably in the past 30 years. The estimation of cost and time to completion for a particular tunnelling project is difficult to predict owing to the large number of variables that influence the project. If the effect of these variables is examined during the project evaluation stage, the degree of project risk is reduced.

A sensitivity analysis that compares various construction scenarios and tunnel alignments should be considered to enable an effective project evaluation to be made. This analysis incorporates a relatively inexpensive computer modelling method to analyse large amounts of data and produce reliable answers. A method is being developed to handle the problems of such an analysis by integrating the techniques of probability, simulation and spreadsheet manipulation into a computer program. The program generates random variables of operational times by use of the Monte Carlo simulation technique. The operational output is then used as input for the spreadsheet cost analysis.

Monte Carlo simulation technique

The Monte Carlo method is a simulation technique that consists in the application of a numerical process on random numbers. A random process is first parameterized by a suitable probability distribution, which models the random variable. The application of the Monte Carlo method is best described in a four-part procedure (Fig. 1).

Choosing a probability distribution

Probability distributions are chosen to match each of the random variables (drilling time, blast time, etc.). The gamma distribution has been chosen to model the data because it is skewed to the right, which fits observed data. The gamma distribution is also attractive because of its versatility. It is easily changed to model different activities. The gamma distribution is defined by two parameters, p and k. The shape parameter, k, changes the shape of the curve, and the scale parameter, p, displaces the curve along the x axis. The following formula defines the gamma distribution (Fig. 2):

$$f(x) = [p^k/(k-1)!] X^{k-1} e^{-px}$$

By this method a specific distribution curve can be chosen for

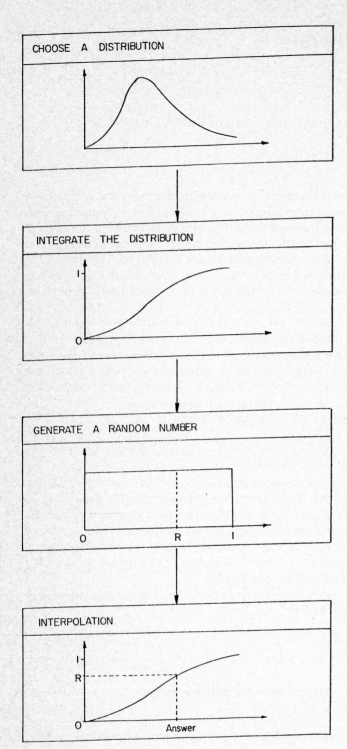

Fig. 1   Monte Carlo sampling technique

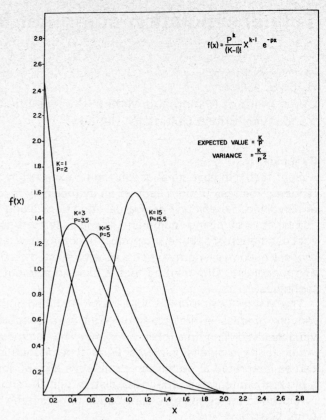

$$f(x) = \frac{P^k}{(K-1)!} x^{k-1} e^{-px}$$

$$\text{EXPECTED VALUE} = \frac{K}{P}$$
$$\text{VARIANCE} = \frac{K}{P^2}$$

Fig. 2   Gamma distribution

each variable. Other suitable probability distributions are currently under investigation.

Integration of the probability distribution

The probability distribution can be integrated to obtain a cumulative distribution. The limits of integration (A and B) are determined by consideration of field-observed operations of the modelled activity. Judgement must be used when the integration limits are selected: for example, A obviously cannot equal zero for most activity times; likewise, B equals infinity cannot be measured (Fig. 3).

Generate a random number

A pseudo-random number is generated to test against the integrated probability distribution. 'Pseudo-random' means that there is a finite number of random numbers generated

before repetition occurs. The method used in this computer model is called the 'mixed congruential method', which uses the formula

$$X'_{n+1} = (aX_n + C) \bmod M$$

and is adjusted to the interval (LL, UL) by the formula

$$r = X'_{n+1} = \left(\frac{X_{n+1}}{m}\right)(UL - LL) + LL$$

where a, C and m are constants, UL is the upper limit, LL is the lower limit, r is the generated random number and X_n is the seed number ($0 < \text{seed} < m$). This formula generates a uniform distribution of random numbers between a lower limit (LL) and an upper limit (UL).

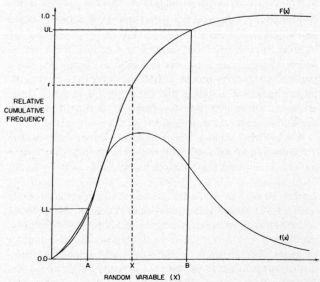

Fig. 3   Integration procedure used in program

Linear interpolation

A random number, r, having been generated, linear interpolation is applied to the cumulative distribution to obtain the random variable X, which is associated with r. The following formula describes the inverse transformation (interpolation) technique:

$$X = X_{i-1} + \frac{X_i - X_{i-1}}{Y_i - Y_{i-1}} (r - Y_{i-1})$$

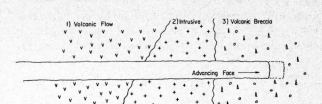

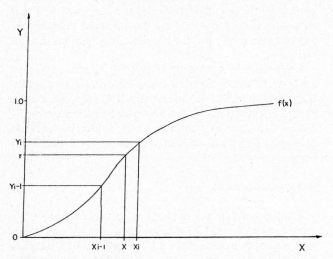

Fig. 4 Linear interpolation

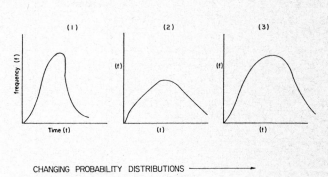

Fig. 5 Random variables as a function of geology

Fig. 4 shows graphically how the interpolation process produces random variables.

Operational model

The tunnel simulation model that is being developed simulates the construction of a tunnel by use of the conventional drill–blast–muck–support cycle of operations. Given the activity-time distributions, the model can be adapted to simulate any tunnel construction method. A geology module is also incorporated into the program to compensate for rock variations, their effect on the drilling, blasting, mucking and supporting cycles being included. Changes in construction method can be allowed for in a similar manner.

As was described above, the Monte Carlo method of simulating activity times allows for uncertainties in the various operations. For example, the time that is taken to drill a round can be dependent on several factors, but it can be expressed as a probability distribution. The distribution may either be estimated or obtained from actual observations. The time to drill a round is then obtained by random selection from this distribution.

The operational model forms the structural base that simulates activity times. A geology module is used to interact with the drilling, blasting, mucking and supporting modules to produce random variables.

The geology module is a vital part of the operational model. As geological conditions change, so will the random variables (drill time, blasting time, etc.). The predicted geology (derived from exploration) that lies on the tunnel line is entered into the model for each intersected stratum that is to be encountered. When a different stratum is encountered the probability distribution that models that specific activity and condition changes (Fig. 5).

The drill–blast–muck–support modules simulate operational times for each round excavated. These can be divided into two groups – times that are determined by use of the Monte Carlo technique (variable times) and times that are usually constant

throughout the simulation (constant times). The number of variables that are used in the simulation depend on the extent of the data and the degree of complexity that is desired in the project evaluation.

Operational model input
The input data for the operational model consist of (1) the tunnel geometry, (2) numbers of men and equipment, (3) probability distribution parameters, (4) constant times, (5) material characteristics and specifications and (6) hours of work.

Operational model output
The operational times are divided into total cycle time, drill, blast, muck and support, and delay time for each round. The total drill–blast–muck–support times per week are printed at the end of each simulated week. The last items that are displayed in the weekly report are the weekly advance and the number of rounds excavated during the simulated week. The total project times are summarized in preparation for input into the cost model.

Variables that influence project completion time
The following variables can be incorporated into the program: (1) geological condition – (a) lithology, (b) structural, (c) water inflow and (d) gas; (2) construction method – (a) equipment combinations, (b) blasting method, (c) support systems and (d) design geometry; (3) learning curve – (a) newly designed equipment and (b) experience of crew; (4) labour conditions – (a) union relations and (b) local political environment; and (5) geography of site – (a) location, (b) weather and (c) terrain.

Cost model

The cost model was developed to decrease the time that is required to prepare bids for tunnelling projects and to compare various construction scenarios. The cost model can be used by contractors and/or owners at various stages in the bid and feasibility development. The cost model is used in tandem with the operational model. The cost model utilizes database and spreadsheet manipulation routines to systematically analyse tunnelling costs. Typically, quantities and unit prices of cost items change throughout the bid preparation process and the actual work. These changes and updates can be performed quickly by re-entering data at the appropriate level in the cost model. This allows for a 'What if' scenario in which a quantity or unit price may suddenly change just before the bid is tendered.

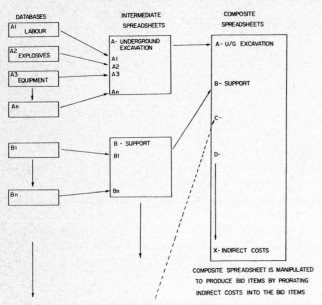

Fig. 6 Cost model flowsheet

The structural flow of the cost model is indicated in Fig. 6. The model consists of a large number of databases and spreadsheets that merge into a single composite spreadsheet. The cost model is comprised of three levels – the database, the intermediate spreadsheet and the composite spreadsheet. Information is transferred from the database to the intermediate spreadsheet and then to the composite spreadsheet.

At the database level only the unit prices and corresponding units of each item are entered. The unit prices are then transferred to the intermediate spreadsheets and quantities are assigned to each item. The total cost for each item is then determined. Costs that are in a similar category are summed into minor cost centres and subsequently grouped into major cost centres. The minor and major cost centres are transferred to the composite spreadsheet. Indirect costs are included at this level of the model. The percentage of the total project cost that is represented by the indirect costs is then determined. By use of this percentage as a weighting factor the indirect costs are then pro-rated into the bid unit prices. In the current model a uniform rate is applied to each bid unit price, but a variable rate can be used as easily.

Cost model input and output
The input data that are required for the cost model are obtained from two sources – the operational model and the unit price and quantities data. The cost model output is presented on the composite spreadsheet as specified by the user.

Conclusions

The task of tunnel project evaluation is becoming increasingly more complex as new tunnel technologies become available. The method of analysis and determination of the optimal solution for tunnel construction are also presenting additional problems. Computer modelling and simulation techniques are becoming much more attractive as a cost-efficient method for project evaluation. Modelling can also be used as a method of estimating the consequences of specific occurrences and their repercussions on the project's progress.

The computer program that is being developed models the full-face drill and blast tunnelling method by use of FORTRAN computer language and a spreadsheet software package. It has the ability to provide assistance on project costs and operating times. By use of the program to perform sensitivity analyses the following aspects can be improved: (1) finding the most favourable alignment, given the geological conditions, and relating these conditions to construction costs and operating times; (2) optimizing the operational policies and construction specifications; and (3) determining the optimum number and combination of (a) drilling and mucking machines and (b) manpower.

The program has the ability to perform the above sensitivity analyses and can be modified to a specific project by changing the previously mentioned parameters. The operational model and the cost model can be used in combination or independently. The computer model is currently at the verification stage. An analysis of data obtained from an actual tunnel project is now being completed.

Acknowledgement

The authors would like to thank R. Guloglu for the initial research work on this continuing tunnel simulation project. They also wish to thank the U.B.C. Department of Mining and Mineral Process Engineering for help in the preparation of the paper. Special thanks are due to the Science Council of British Columbia for its support.

References
1. Einstein H. H. and Vick S. G. Geologic model for a tunnel cost model. In *Proceedings 2nd rapid excavation and tunneling conference, San Francisco, 1974* Pattison H. C. and D'Appolonia E. eds (New York: AIME, 1974), vol. 2, 1701–20.
2. Guloglu R. A tunnel simulation model based on Monte Carlo techniques for analysing tunnelling operations and costs. M.Sc. thesis, University of Newcastle upon Tyne, 1979.
3. Moavenzadeh F. *et al.* Tunnel cost model. Reference 1, 1721–39.
4. Vick S. G. A probabilistic approach to hard rock tunnelling. M.S. thesis, Massachusetts Institute of Technology, 1973.

Tunnelling machine performance in the Oxford Clay

J. Temporal
G. J. L. Lawrence
Transport and Road Research Laboratory, Crowthorne, England

Synopsis
The performance of a full-face tunnelling machine used to construct 3.4 km of 2.54-m diameter tunnel as part of the Oxford Trunk Outfall Sewer system is described: the sewer was constructed entirely in the stiff fissured Oxford Clay. Each of the activities associated with tunnel construction has been analysed in detail from the shift records by use of a minicomputer program: these activities fall into two main categories – the excavation cycle and operations that represent non-productive time or delays.

The overall progress rate of the machine was 1.19 m/h, with a best shift performance of 3.01 m/h: machine utilization was comparatively high at 64%. Although such progress rates are quite respectable, there appears to be considerable potential to improve them. The effects of each of the activities associated with construction on the overall performance of the system are discussed in detail, and recommendations are made that should lead to increased progress rates and, hence, reduced costs. Two possible ways in which this might be achieved are to improve excavation performance by designing a system that allows concurrent (rather than sequential) cutting and lining operations, and to reduce delays by careful consideration of the logistics of all the operations involved in construction.

The original trunk outfall sewer for Oxford was constructed in 1872 together with a number of connecting sewers. This system operated without problems until 1945, when peak flows became too high for the sewer and surcharging occurred. The problem then steadily worsened until, by 1975, sewage regularly flowed out of property air vents and lifted manhole covers in three separate areas of the city. At this stage a feasibility study was started to look at a range of possible solutions.

The solution that was finally chosen was for a bored tunnel of 2.54-m diameter to be constructed entirely within the Oxford Clay that lies under most of the city. The sewer was somewhat larger in diameter than that needed to cope with peak flows, but it was foreseen that this overcapacity would provide sufficient storage of high flows, resulting from a coincidence of heavy storms, peak dry weather flows and high infiltration, without the need to increase the capacity of the Littlemore Pumping Station above its existing level.

The scheme was designed by Oxford City Council as agent authority for the Thames Water Authority, and the main contractor for the works was Edmund Nuttall, Ltd. A detailed description of the project has been given by Watts and co-workers.[1]

A full-face tunnelling machine was used to construct the 3.4 km of 2.54-m diameter main sewer: in addition, some 280 m of 1.2-m diameter tunnel, a shaft of 10.7-m diameter, one of 7.6-m diameter and ten of 4.6-m diameter were also built together with 1850 m of connecting sewers, which were laid in trench. The tender value was just under £2 900 000 in 1979 for a two-year construction period: this compares with a cost of £12 500 for the original system built in the 1870s.

A substantial portion of the costs of tunnel construction is time-dependent. This paper describes an analysis of the performance of the tunnelling machine that was used on the main sewer drive. The total time spent on constructing the tunnel has been broken down into 12 activities, which fall into two main categories – time spent on the excavation cycle and time spent

on non-productive activities. These non-productive activities include travel and transport, breakdowns, meal breaks, surveying and other events that stop excavation. Although some of these activities are essential to tunnel progress, they have been collectively termed delays for convenience. Each of the 12 activities is discussed in detail and methods of reducing the time spent on them are suggested. These recommendations could lead to increased progress rates and, hence, reduced construction costs.

Construction

Ground conditions

The route of the main outfall tunnel is shown in Fig. 1, superimposed on a geological drift map of the area: the shafts are denoted by the letters $A–K$. The borehole site investigation showed that the ground consisted of about 6 m of water-bearing gravels or very soft sandy clay overlying the stiff fissured heavy Oxford Clay. The average depth to the crown of the tunnel was about 14 m, thus ensuring that the tunnel was constructed entirely in the Oxford Clay. Near shaft C at Iffley the maximum overburden height rose to about 19 m and there were some thin beds of calcareous sandstone (the Corallian Beds) overlying the Oxford Clay.

During the course of construction measurements of the strength of the clay were made at a number of locations and the data are shown in Fig. 2. At least four samples were taken at each location by use of standard U38 tubes and tested immediately in a hand-operated compression machine. The data show that the clay is very stiff, with unconfined compressive strengths in the range 100–550 kPa and an average value of about 300 kPa. The large range of strengths reflects the fissured nature of the clay rather than its variability. Moisture contents, measured at the same locations, lay between 15 and 24% (average value, ~20%). The majority of samples fell within the CH subdivision of the Casagrande Classification System, a few points falling in the CI subdivision.

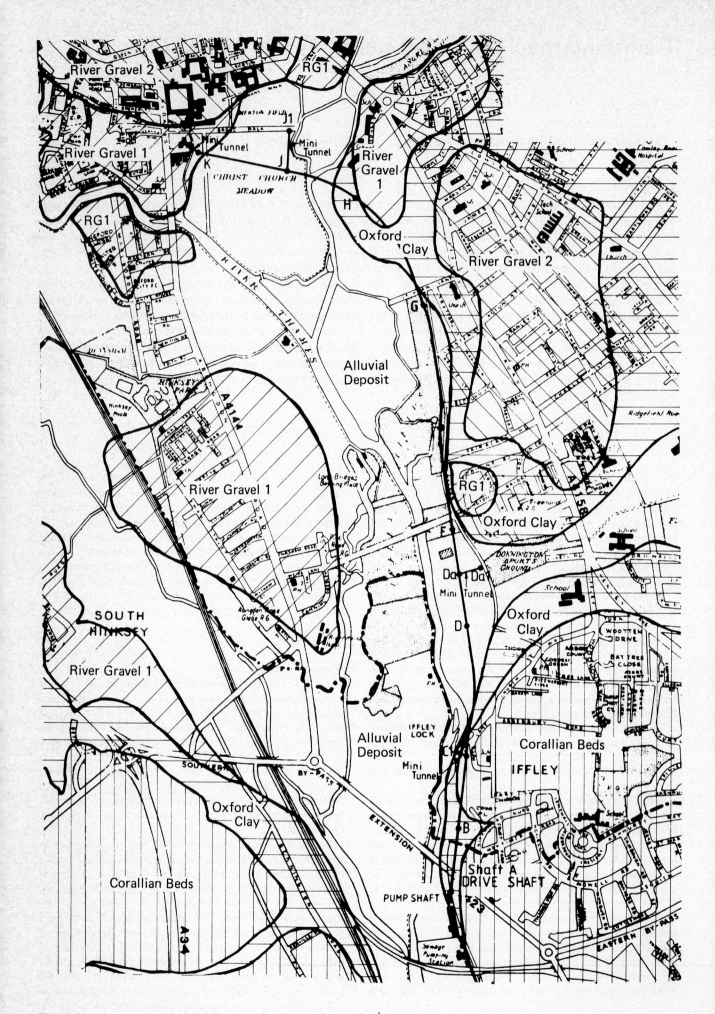

Fig. 1   Tunnel route and geological drift map. After Watts and co-workers[1]

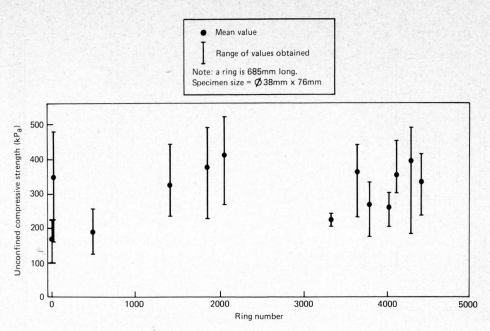

Fig. 2   Variation of unconfined compressive strength along tunnel

Tunnel linings

For the main outfall tunnel the contractor chose to use a full-face tunnelling machine with an external diameter of 2.82 m, and an expanded wedge block concrete lining with an internal diameter of 2.54 m. This type of lining was originally developed by the Metropolitan Water Board and was first used in 1952.[2] Each ring of lining consists of 11 segments and a wedge-shaped key. Nine segments are identical, two tapered segments being used – one either side of the crown; the key is then pushed into the crown, thus expanding the ring against the clay and inducing hoop compression into the lining. There are no bolts or dowels in any of the radial or longitudinal joints. A detailed description of the lining was given by Watts and co-workers.[1]

Wedge block lining can only be used in cohesive ground with a reasonable stand-up time and through which an accurately profiled tunnel can be driven.[3] It has the advantage, however, that it is cheap to construct, can be easily built by hand by use of building bars and rams on the back of the tunnelling shield, and is easy to cast. Manufacture of the segments at Oxford was performed on site by unskilled local labour. Segments were packed into complete rings on pallets for transport down the construction shaft to the tunnelling machine by electric locomotive.

A large number of shafts were required to connect the existing sewer system to the new outfall tunnel. The original contract called for conventional bolted rings and *in-situ* concrete lining to be used at the shaft locations. This would, however, have involved driving through the shaft locations with wedge block lining and building the shaft bottoms later or delaying the tunnel until all the shaft eyes had been completed. The solution finally adopted was to line the shaft locations with a smooth-bore bolted lining (commonly known as 'one-pass') of slightly larger diameter than the wedge block. After the shaft bottom had broken into the tunnel the connexion was made good with a small amount of mass concrete. This alternative solution resulted in some delays to the tunnelling process, but these were less than would have been caused by the original proposal.

Tunnelling machine

The tunnelling machine that was used on the main drive was a conventional full-facer, commonly known as a 'hundred inch' machine because of the finished diameter of the tunnel con-

structed. It was built by Robert L. Priestley, Ltd., a subsidiary of the main contractor, in 1968 and had already constructed more than 18 km of tunnel with peak progress rates of up to 46 rings (31.5 m) in a 10-h shift.

The main elements of the machine are shown in Fig. 3. A cruciform cutting head carrying the cutting picks rotated within the shield. The debris produced was removed by scraper blades to a conveyor, which could be retracted during lining erection. From there the debris was removed by transfer conveyors over the top of the back-up sledges, containing power packs and transformers, to a train of muck wagons hauled by an electric locomotive. This transported the muck to the bottom of the construction shaft (shaft A, Fig. 1), from which it was removed by crane. Lining segments and other supplies were carried into the tunnel with the returning empty muck wagons. Passing places were provided along the tunnel to allow in-bound and out-bound trains to pass each other.

The tunnelling machine was thrust forward by a series of eleven rams on the back of the shield, which reacted against the previously built tunnel lining. These rams could be operated in any pattern to allow the shield to be steered in the required direction. At the end of a stroke the rams were retracted and the next ring of lining was built at the back of the shield. The segments were temporarily supported by building bars on the back of the shield until the key segment was driven home by a small hydraulic ram on the shield at the crown. The ring then became self-supporting and the cycle of sequential excavation and lining continued.

To allow steerage of the machine a bead is normally located on the front edge of the shield to give a slightly larger cut diameter than the shield diameter. These beads normally range from about 4 to 10 mm in thickness: at Oxford the bead thickness chosen prior to the start of the drive was 6 mm. The bead also allows some radial intrusion of the ground into the tunnel, as elastic deformations occur in the clay due to the relief of *in-situ* stresses. A range of lining key sizes are also used to compensate for slight differences between the cut diameter and the external lining diameter. The cutting bead arrangement for a normal clay is shown in Fig. 4(*a*).

At the start of the main tunnel drive the shield was jacked forward from a thrust ring attached to the concrete lining of the eye in shaft A. As the tunnel advanced for the first ring of lining to be erected it was noted that the radial deformation of the ground was about 25 mm at each of the shoulders. This was

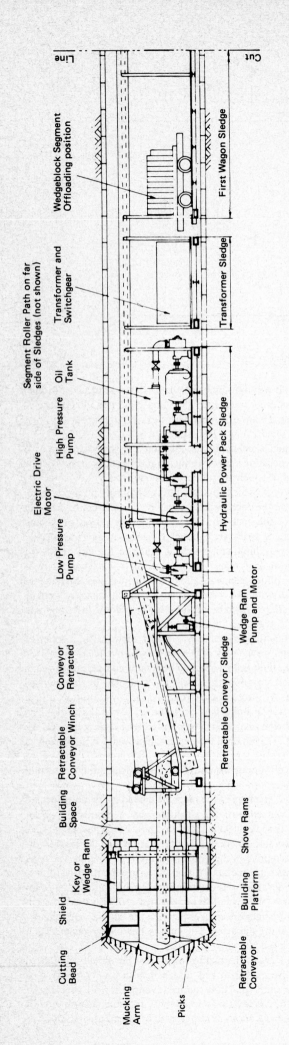

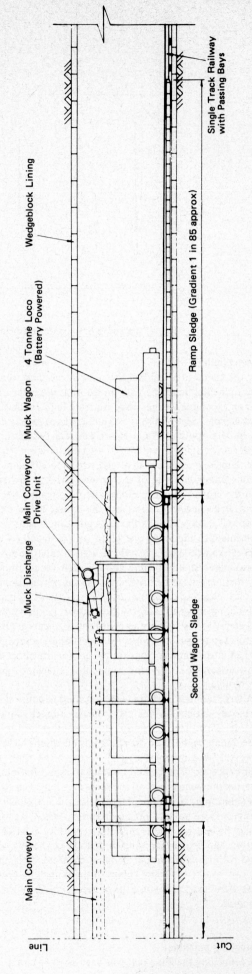

Fig. 3   2.82-m full-face tunnelling machine. After Watts and co-workers[1]

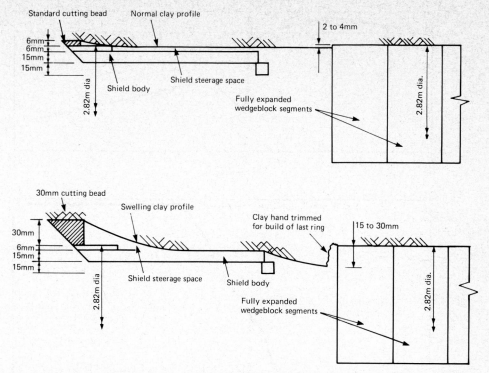

Fig. 4   Cutting bead detail for (*a*) (*top*) normal and (*b*) squeezing clay. After Watts and co-workers[1]

considerably greater than the deformations of 2–4 mm normally encountered in stiff clays. Once the initial deformation had occurred, no significant increase in deformation was observed.

The 25-mm elastic deformation was considerably larger than could be accommodated by use of a short key in the wedge block lining and the tunnel profile had to be trimmed by hand. Various trimming devices were fitted to the tail of the shield until, at ring 90, where the deformations had become slightly less, it proved practical to fit a 30-mm bead to the cutting shield (Fig. 4(*b*)). Some hand trimming was still required but, eventually, this was overcome by fitting a trimming device to the tail of the shield. The squeezing ground lasted for the first 450 rings (310 m), but thereafter the clay behaved in the normal manner. The squeezing ground problem and its effect on the performance of the tunnelling system are discussed later.

Line and level

Even though the outfall sewer was designed as a gravity system, the tunnel gradients were very shallow, ranging from 1 in 1500 to 1 in 400. Tolerances of ±75 mm on line and ±25 mm on level were specified in the contract. These tolerances were only exceeded on two occasions – once by an inexperienced operator who used the wrong thrust rams and once by an error in aligning the beam deflector for the laser when driving round a curve.

Ground settlements

Before the commencement of the tunnel drive estimates of likely ground settlements were made from the depth of the tunnel and the available soils data: these suggested that the maximum settlement would be about 4 mm. In the squeezing ground, however, settlements as large as 8 mm were recorded as a result of the increase in effective face loss associated with the excavation of additional material.

Later in the drive, settlement measurements were made by the Transport and Road Research Laboratory (TRRL) in Christchurch Meadow at ring 4335 (chainage 3006 m). Measurements were made on two series of stations – one along the tunnel centre line and one perpendicular to it, precise levelling techniques[4] being used. At the settlement section the

tunnel axis was 11.7 m below the ground surface. Fig. 5 shows the variation of centre-line settlement and tunnelling machine progress over a period of four months before and after the tunnel had passed the section. The centre-line settlements were about 2 mm and occurred almost instantaneously as the face passed beneath the measuring stations. Fig. 6 shows the settlement trough obtained from the transverse section of stations 59 days after the tunnel had passed the section. This shows that the point of inflexion in the profile is about 5 m from the tunnel centre line, and the half-width of the trough is about 15 m. These results are in good agreement with data obtained from similar tunnelling sites.[5]

Tunnel progress

The main drive was started on 23 July, 1980, and finished on 19 March, 1981 – a period of 28 working weeks. During this time 4877 rings (3340 m) were built, giving an average progress rate of 174 rings per week (119 m/week). Progress peaked at 44 rings in a 10-h shift, but problems with the squeezing ground for the first 450 rings (310 m), curves in the tunnel line, which required extra surveying, and the large number of shaft connexions all reduced the overall progress rate.

From the start of driving on 23 July until 21 September, 1980, one 10-h shift was worked each weekday. Over this period the average progress rate was 19 rings per week (13 m/week). Working was then increased to two 10-h shifts, five days a week, for the remainder of the drive, and the average progress rate increased to 248 rings per week (170 m/week). The shift times were varied from time to time when necessary.

A typical shift crew consisted of one shift boss, one leading miner, three miners, one fitter, one electrician, one to six locomotive drivers (the number increasing with the length of the drive), one pit bottom man, two banksmen and a crane driver. For each shift worked a report of progress and delays was completed: these have been analysed to give a detailed breakdown of the performance of the tunnelling system.

Analysis of shift records

The detailed analysis of these records has been performed for

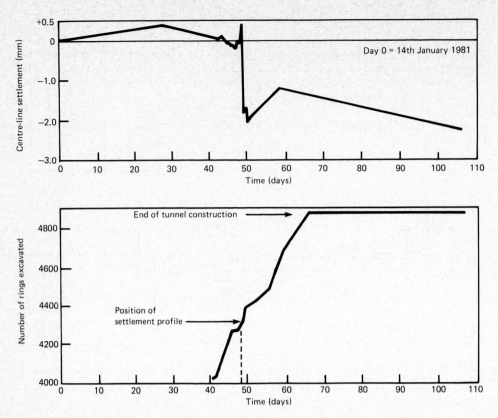

Fig. 5   Centre-line settlement for ring 4335 (3006 m) and tunnel progress versus time, days

rings 10 to 4869, a total of 4860 of the 4877 rings constructed. The first nine rings and the last eight rings of the drive have been excluded as they were built as the starting eye for the machine and as a dismantling chamber at the end of the drive. Although records exist for these lengths, they are not sufficiently detailed to bear analysis: however, the total time to build the first nine rings was three shifts and the last eight rings took less than one shift.

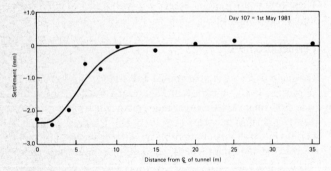

Fig. 6   Settlement profile on day 107 for ring 4335 (3006 m)

Each of the reports were input into a computer program based on a PET computer so that a record of the times spent on each operation during the construction sequence could be made. These operations fall into two main categories.

The *excavation cycle* is subdivided into the three activities necessary to advance the tunnel face: (*a*) cutting time is the time taken for the machine to advance by the full stroke of the thrust rams (which is slightly longer than the length of a ring of lining) so that the next ring can be built; (*b*) lining time is the time taken to build a ring of lining, including any hand trimming of the clay, and replacing segments damaged during erection; and (*c*) reset time is the time taken from the end of cutting to the start of lining, and the end of lining to the start of cutting, to insert and withdraw the conveyor from the cutting head and to set and reset the thrust rams.

Delays is a general term intended to cover time lost to non-

productive operations (i.e. those which are not part of the excavation cycle), although some of the operations are necessary for tunnel construction. The delays have been divided into nine categories.

(*a*) Travel time is the time taken to transport the miners to and from the face at the beginning and end of each shift.

(*b*) Mechanical delays comprise mechanical breakdown and repair of the tunnelling machine and its ancilliary equipment.

(*c*) Electrical and mining delays comprise electrical breakdown and repair of the tunnelling machine and supply system and delays to cutting caused by debris blocking the machine head and conveyors.

(*d*) Transport delays are the time lost as a result of the late arrival of trains at the tunnelling machine and delivery of incorrect supplies. This category includes derailments, flat batteries, problems in removing clay from the muck skips and hold-ups due to the restricted number of passing places for trains in the tunnel.

(*e*) Meal breaks constitute delays caused by taking breaks during shifts.

(*f*) Cutting beads represents the time taken to adjust the cut diameter of the tunnel by fitting, adjusting and removing cutting beads.

(*g*) Grouting is the time spent in preparing and grouting the one-pass lining and areas of wedge block lining where the tunnel had been trimmed oversize.

(*h*) Laser and surveying is the time lost to allow the engineers to check line and level, set up beam deflectors and adjust and repair the laser.

(*i*) Other delays is a category that includes the time taken to fit all the back-up equipment at the start of the drive, that spent in dismantling the machine at the end of the drive, extending services behind the machine, putting in train passing places, clearing up after repairs and in preparation for shutdowns before holidays. The category also includes the delay caused in shoving through the bottom of one of the shafts that had been completed before the machine reached the shaft location. All other shafts were completed after the machine had passed by breaking through the one-pass lining installed in the tunnel at shaft bottom locations.

Of the above categories, (b), (c) and (d) represent true delays, whereas the other categories are non-productive time. When two or more causes of delay occurred at the same time, only the cause that occurred first was counted as a delay unless the second cause outlasted the first. If it did, the latter portion of the total delay was ascribed to the second cause. Breakdowns or other problems during the excavation cycle, but which did not interrupt these processes, were not counted as delays.

Results

The times taken for each of the activities in the excavation cycle and delay categories are summarized in Table 1. Activity times have been summed for sections of 100 rings (68.5 m): all the times listed are in decimal hours. In addition, the total times spent on the excavation cycle and delays have been calculated, as have the progress rates in rings per hour and metres per hour.

Overall averages for the 4860 rings analysed have also been included.

Four periods in excess of 10 h have been allocated to the 'other delay' category; the details of these are (1) between rings 10 and 109 a total of 69.28 h was allocated to fitting back-up equipment at the start of the drive; (2) between rings 710 and 809 a total of 57.75 h was allocated to driving through the one shaft bottom completed before the machine passed; (3) between rings 2210 and 2309 a total of 15.23 h was allocated to clearing up immediately prior to the Christmas 1980 holiday shutdown; and (4) between rings 4810 and 4869 a total of 23 h was allocated to dismantling the machine at the end of the drive.

These four delays account for about 85% of the total time allocated to 'other delays'.

Several sections of one-pass lining were built during the course of the drive to allow subsequent shaft connexions to be made. During the analysis it became apparent that these resulted in increased times taken for the excavation cycle. The

Table 1 Summary of activity times

	Excavation cycle, h			Delays, h									Total excavation cycle, h	Total delays, h	Total, h	No. of rings per hour	Progress rate, m/h
Ring nos.	Cutting	Lining	Reset	Travel	Mechanical	Electrical and mining	Transport	Meals	Cutting beads	Grouting	Laser and surveying	Others					
10–109	30.18	100.89	43.54	5.40	37.29	0.90	0	6.88	40.00	0	0.92	69.28	174.61	160.67	335.28	0.30	0.20
110–209	16.43	39.18	22.52	4.71	8.02	0	1.75	15.94	20.00	0	0	3.75	78.13	54.17	132.30	0.76	0.52
210–309	17.74	12.44	11.10	0.66	22.73	0	5.95	3.08	0	0	0	0	41.28	32.42	73.70	1.36	0.93
310–409	36.05	45.82	14.08	3.14	1.23	0	2.72	7.42	0	39.16	5.25	0	95.95	58.92	154.87	0.65	0.44
410–509	20.82	11.73	11.49	0.96	2.00	0	0.98	3.23	10.63	0	0	4.25	44.04	22.05	66.09	1.51	1.04
510–609	16.86	15.16	9.26	1.36	4.22	0	2.59	3.59	0	0	1.85	0	41.28	13.61	54.89	1.82	1.25
610–709	14.82	13.76	6.05	1.53	1.51	1.85	7.95	2.54	0	0	2.25	0	34.63	17.63	52.26	1.91	1.31
710–809	12.55	14.76	5.22	0.97	0.86	0	3.45	3.91	0	0	0.95	61.00	32.53	71.14	103.67	0.96	0.66
810–909	11.01	10.23	7.22	0.80	0	0	1.07	1.66	0	0	2.32	0	28.46	5.85	34.31	2.91	2.00
910–1009	12.91	12.19	7.12	1.32	4.17	0	1.06	3.06	0	0	2.98	0	32.22	12.59	44.81	2.23	1.53
1010–1109	12.63	11.37	4.83	1.19	0	6.13	1.11	1.40	0	0	0.40	0	28.83	10.23	39.06	2.56	1.75
1110–1209	11.90	13.03	4.80	1.30	0.70	0.32	4.68	2.73	14.38	0	0	0	29.73	24.11	53.84	1.86	1.27
1210–1309	10.41	11.05	4.02	0.80	0.15	1.16	4.50	1.75	0	0	0.83	0	25.48	9.19	34.67	2.88	1.98
1310–1409	10.07	11.38	3.90	0.69	0.15	0	5.39	4.62	0	0	0	0	25.35	10.85	36.20	2.76	1.89
1410–1509	16.49	19.18	5.63	2.22	7.03	0	6.50	1.67	0	4.13	0	0	41.30	21.55	62.85	1.59	1.09
1510–1609	20.71	25.58	6.14	1.84	0	0	1.77	4.03	10.66	7.87	0	0	52.43	26.17	78.60	1.27	0.87
1610–1709	10.48	14.15	4.13	1.26	0	0	0.29	2.33	0	0	0	0	28.76	3.88	32.64	3.06	2.10
1710–1809	25.66	29.09	6.72	3.28	2.78	0.46	2.37	3.13	0	14.50	0.45	0	61.47	26.97	88.44	1.13	0.77
1810–1909	9.86	13.17	7.56	1.02	10.00	0	4.32	0	13.33	0	0	0	30.59	28.67	59.26	1.69	1.16
1910–2009	19.94	24.71	7.01	1.48	1.64	0	1.89	1.41	0	8.08	0	0	51.66	14.50	66.16	1.51	1.04
2010–2109	9.65	11.81	4.08	0.11	0	0	4.02	1.20	0	0	0	0	25.54	5.33	30.87	3.24	2.22
2110–2209	9.55	14.29	4.62	1.62	0	2.21	7.35	1.55	0	3.67	0	0	28.46	16.40	44.86	2.23	1.53
2210–2309	13.29	15.19	4.54	1.52	0.23	1.88	4.76	2.84	0	3.17	2.90	15.23	33.02	32.53	65.55	1.53	1.05
2310–2409	9.18	10.72	3.75	0.48	0.87	0	1.04	1.34	0	0	1.08	0	23.65	4.81	28.46	3.51	2.41
2410–2509	10.14	10.49	4.55	0.22	1.04	0	4.43	1.31	0	0	3.37	0	25.18	10.37	35.55	2.81	1.93
2510–2609	23.76	26.17	8.18	2.49	2.25	0	4.14	1.84	0	8.35	4.88	0	58.11	23.95	82.06	1.22	0.83
2610–2709	9.99	11.24	7.24	1.32	0	0	4.05	1.82	0	0	3.95	0	28.47	11.14	39.61	2.52	1.73
2710–2809	11.06	11.73	4.00	0.70	1.54	0	2.15	1.51	0	0	0.93	0	26.79	6.83	33.62	2.97	2.04
2810–2909	10.11	9.49	3.54	0.76	0	0	0.29	1.23	0	0	0.42	0	23.14	2.70	25.84	3.87	2.65
2910–3009	11.60	10.74	4.35	0.69	0	0	3.83	1.87	0	0	3.85	8.00	26.69	18.24	44.93	2.23	1.52
3010–3109	9.83	8.83	3.46	0.91	0	0	2.67	0.92	0	0	3.82	0	22.12	8.32	30.44	3.29	2.25
3110–3209	20.99	25.97	7.01	3.17	0	0	2.65	3.40	0	8.91	1.56	0	53.97	19.69	73.66	1.36	0.93
3210–3309	10.02	9.20	4.56	1.56	0.12	0	6.14	1.41	0	0	0.12	0	23.78	9.35	33.13	3.02	2.07
3310–3409	9.55	8.10	3.73	0.54	0.25	0	1.18	1.63	0	0	0	0	21.38	3.60	24.98	4.00	2.74
3410–3509	9.49	8.33	3.05	0.55	0.82	0	3.04	0.62	0	0	2.95	0	20.87	7.98	28.85	3.47	2.37
3510–3609	13.26	13.29	5.76	1.45	0.58	0	1.40	1.69	0	2.00	1.45	0	32.31	8.57	40.88	2.45	1.68
3610–3709	8.90	8.79	3.56	0.62	0.06	0	3.52	1.25	0	0	1.37	1.37	21.25	8.19	29.44	3.40	2.33
3710–3809	11.42	12.73	5.02	2.14	1.45	0	3.23	0.45	0	5.32	4.14	0	29.17	16.73	45.90	2.18	1.49
3810–3909	9.91	9.19	3.41	0.66	0.88	0	5.93	1.78	0	0	1.19	0	22.51	10.44	32.95	3.03	2.08
3910–4009	9.50	9.11	4.91	0.62	1.34	0	1.72	1.72	0	0	1.05	0	23.52	6.45	29.97	3.34	2.29
4010–4109	21.90	21.74	5.59	1.94	0	0	2.30	2.61	0	9.67	1.35	6.50	49.23	24.37	73.60	1.36	0.93
4110–4209	10.73	9.33	5.77	1.64	0	0.27	3.03	1.36	0	0	0.40	0	25.83	6.70	32.53	3.07	2.11
4210–4309	10.23	9.69	3.87	1.49	0	0	12.90	1.31	0	0	1.71	0	23.79	17.41	41.20	2.43	1.66
4310–4409	20.77	21.57	5.01	3.00	1.38	0	3.95	3.30	0	5.75	0	1.00	47.35	18.38	65.73	1.52	1.04
4410–4509	12.06	11.86	4.65	1.77	0	0	12.87	1.67	0	1.50	0	0.58	28.57	18.39	46.96	2.13	1.46
4510–4609	8.69	8.38	3.78	1.41	0.78	0	6.66	0.75	0	0	0	0	20.85	9.60	30.45	3.28	2.25
4610–4709	9.21	8.24	3.69	1.42	3.58	0	7.36	1.02	0	0	0	0	21.14	13.38	34.52	2.90	1.98
4710–4809	9.89	8.72	3.39	1.24	0	0	4.66	2.26	0	0	0.42	0	22.00	8.58	30.58	3.27	2.24
4810–4869	5.59	5.17	2.53	0.69	2.70	0	1.50	1.27	0	0	0	23.00	13.29	29.16	42.45	2.36	1.61
Total time, h	677.79	798.98	323.94	72.66	124.35	15.18	183.11	121.31	109.00	122.08	61.11	193.96	1800.71	1002.76	2803.47	1.73	1.19
Time per ring, h	0.139	0.164	0.067	0.015	0.026	0.003	0.038	0.025	0.022	0.025	0.013	0.040	0.371	0.206	0.577		
Percentage of total time	24.18	28.50	11.55	2.59	4.44	0.54	6.53	4.33	3.89	4.35	2.18	6.92	64.23	35.77	100		

Table 2 Lining times for one-pass rings

Ring no. Start	Finish	No. of rings	Total lining time, h	No. of hours per ring
337	356	20	40.16	2.01
1504	1522	19	21.34	1.12
1741	1757	17	16.30	0.96
1974	1990	17	14.37	0.85
2264	2269	6	6.81	1.14
2541	2557	17	15.77	0.93
3186	3202	17	16.86	0.99
3535	3539	5	4.53	0.91
3757	3761	5	4.59	0.92
4017	4033	17	13.36	0.79
4395	4411	17	15.97	0.94
Totals				
One-pass		157	170.06	1.08
Wedge block		4703	628.92	0.13
Both types		4860	798.98	0.16

most noticeable effect was an increase in the time taken to install the lining, but there were also increases in the cutting time. This was due to the fact that the nearest standard size of one-pass lining available was slightly larger than the excavated diameter and so some hand trimming had to be carried out. The times for machine excavation and hand trimming were not always distinguished on the shift reports and so could not be separated in the analysis. The lining times for the one-pass rings were noted, however, and the details are summarized in Table 2. This shows that for the 157 rings of one-pass the average time to build a ring was 1.08 h, in comparison with 0.13 h for the wedge block. The difference in erection times is a reflection of the mismatch between the one-pass lining and an erection

system designed for wedge block. The normal role of one-pass is as an alternative to bolted lining with either *in-situ* lining or secondary lining inserts.

The 4860 rings of lining analysed in detail took a total of 2803.47 h, giving an overall progress rate of 1.73 ring/h (1.19 m/h). The breakdown of activity times between the various categories is shown in Fig. 7. The excavation cycle took 64.2% of the total time available, delays taking 35.8%: of the 64.2% spent on excavation, 24.2% was for cutting, 28.5% for lining and 11.6% for resetting. None of the nine delay categories accounted for more than 7% of the total time available.

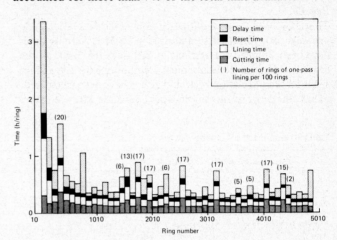

Fig. 8 Variation of activity times with ring number

Fig. 8 shows the variation of cutting, lining, resetting and delay times with ring number and Fig. 9 shows the variation of progress rate. Several interesting features emerge. (1) The time taken per ring advanced generally decreases with increasing chainage. This is due, in part, to a learning effect at the start of the tunnel: after a few weeks the crews adopt a routine for working and are more familiar with the tunnelling system, their production rate increasing accordingly. The second reason is that the squeezing ground conditions at the start of the drive caused considerable delays over the first 450 rings of the tunnel. (2) After this initial period, the time taken per ring is generally less than 0.5 h. In the 49 sections of 100 rings analysed, 29 had total activity times of less than 0.5 h per ring. Of the remaining 20, ten were caused by sections of one-pass lining being built, eight occurred at the start of the drive (including one section delayed by using one-pass and one delayed by driving through an existing shaft bottom) and the other three were caused by mechanical breakdown, removing cutting head beads and dismantling the machine. As the sections of one-pass lining clearly have a major effect on the rate of progress, the number of rings of one-pass in each 100-ring section has been included

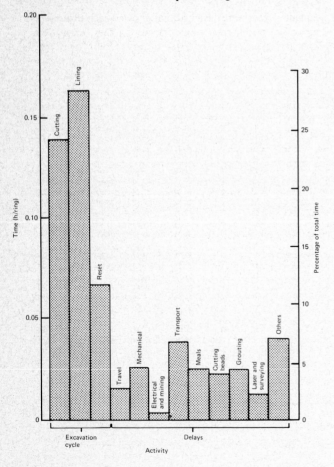

Fig. 7 Activity times for rings 10–4869 (total construction time, 2803.47 h)

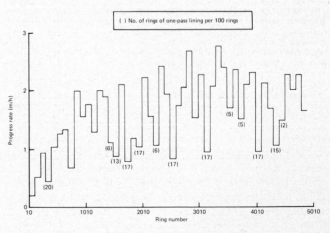

Fig. 9 Variation of progress rate with ring number

in Figs. 8 and 9. (3) As has already been mentioned, the cutting and lining times both increase in sections of one-pass lining. An increase in delay time can also be seen in Fig. 8: this is due to the extra time taken to grout the one-pass lining into the excavated profile – a process not normally required with wedge block lining where the expansion of the lining is usually sufficient to close any gaps.

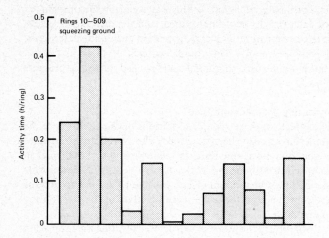

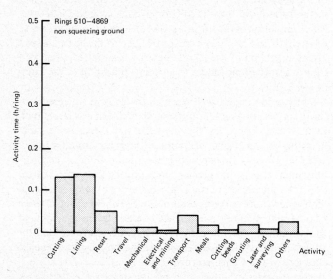

Fig. 10 Activity times for squeezing and non-squeezing ground conditions

Although there are two different causes for the slow progress rate at the start of the drive, a comparison has been made between the performance over the first 500 rings and the rest of the tunnel drive. These first 500 rings cover the 450 rings during which the squeezing ground conditions occurred. Fig. 10 shows that for almost all the excavation and delay categories the activity times were greater at the start of the drive than over the rest of the drive. Two categories remained roughly the same throughout the drive – electrical and mining delays and laser and surveying delays – whereas transport delays generally increased with increasing length of tunnel. The overall rate of advance for rings 10–509 was 0.45 m/h, compared to 1.46 m/h for rings 510–4869; for the whole drive the overall value was 1.19 m/h. The slow progress at the start of the drive resulted in low morale among the tunnelling crew and the squeezing ground conditions meant that the long straight at the start of the drive could not be used to learn how the machine steered before entering the bends later in the drive. Unfortunately, it is impossible to say how much of the slow progress at the start of the drive can be attributed to learning effects and how much to the squeezing ground conditions.

Discussion

About 60% of the costs that are incurred in tunnel construction are time-dependent: considerable savings can therefore be made by quite modest improvements in progress rates. There are two ways in which such improvements might be made – by increasing excavation performance and by reducing non-productive time.

Increasing excavation performance

The data in Table 2 show that the best time recorded for cutting over a 100-ring section was 5.2 min per ring (average over the whole tunnel, 8.4 min). These values correspond to cutting rates of 7.9 and 4.9 m/h, respectively.

The best and average times taken to erect a ring of lining were 4.9 and 9.9 min, respectively: corresponding times per ring for machine resetting were 1.8 and 4.0 min.

Although the best times recorded for each of the three activities in the excavation cycle did not occur in the same 100-ring sections, a measure of the potential excavation rate can be obtained by combining them. This gives an excavation cycle time of 11.9 min per ring or a progress rate of 3.45 m/h, which is only slightly higher than the best shift performance of 44 rings in 10 h or 3.01 m/h. The average excavation cycle time over the whole tunnel was 22.2 min per ring or 1.85 m/h.

The tunnelling system therefore already has the potential to excavate much more rapidly than the overall rate achieved without modification to the mechanics of the system. The major scope for improvement would appear to be in ensuring that the potential rates are achieved through reducing or subsuming non-productive activities.

One possible modification to the excavation system might, however, increase performance. At present the cutting and lining operations are sequential, the tunnelling machine using the lining as a reaction system to gain forward thrust. If a segment erector were designed that allowed each thrust ram to be reset as each segment was placed, it might be possible to eliminate both lining and reset times, thereby reducing the excavation cycle to one of continuous cutting. From the best times discussed above, this would reduce the excavation cycle time to 5.2 min or a progress rate of 7.9 m/h. Alternatively, forward thrust might be provided by a reaction ring that expanded to grip the tunnel walls.[6] In this case the excavation cycle time would be reduced to that for cutting and resetting alone: this gives a best time of 7.0 min per ring or a progress rate of 5.8 m/h. In practice the potential performance of either of these possible modifications might be slightly worse because of the increased complexity of the lining and resetting sequence and the increased difficulty of steering the machine.

Reducing non-productive time

Although none of the nine categories of delay accounts for more than 7% of the total construction time, together they add up to more than 35%. If the total delay time on this drive had been reduced such that the machine utilization increased from just below 65% to 75%, the total construction time per ring would have decreased from 34.6 to 29.6 min, corresponding to an increase in progress rate from 1.19 to 1.39 m/h or 17%.

There would appear to be some scope for reducing the times in a number of the delay categories.

Although *travel time* accounts for only 2.6% of the total, it could be eliminated by changing crews on the tunnelling machine – a practice common in the mining industry. Indeed, Berry[7] has suggested that when three 8-h shifts are used with changeover of crews on the tunnelling machine, there is a dramatic change in progress in comparison with the use of two 11-h shifts far in excess of the change expected from merely working 2 h per day more. Examination of the shift records at

Oxford shows that the times taken to excavate and build a ring of lining did not change significantly during the shift, which suggests that fatigue was not a problem. Such factors as pay rates, bonus schemes and taxation rates, however, which all affect nett earnings, are likely to exert some influence on progress rates.

Increasing the length of the working week can have a significant effect on total construction time. If the working week were extended to three 8-h shifts on a seven day a week basis, for the same rate of advance of 1.19 m/h achieved at Oxford the total time to construct the tunnel would have been reduced from 28 to 17 weeks. Although this may not be an important consideration in all cases, it could be crucial in a development, such as gaining access to new mineral resources, where time to pay back is a prime consideration.

The categories *mechanical, electrical and mining delays* together account for about 5% of the total construction time. Although there appears to be little possibility of reducing electrical and mining delays below the very low level already achieved, there is some scope for reducing mechanical delays by improved detail design and maintenance. No particular cause of mechanical delays stands out, and it is likely that improvements will only take place as better components become available.

Transport delays occur mainly as a result of the confined working space in the tunnel behind the tunnelling machine. Although such events as delivery of the wrong supplies, derailments and flat batteries on the locomotives could be substantially reduced, one of the major problems is the late arrival of trains caused by traffic jams in the tunnel. In a tunnel of 2.54-m diameter the provision of passing places for the trains is difficult, but delays could be reduced if passing places were put in at more frequent intervals.

Advantage is normally taken of other delays to the tunnelling process to minimize the delay termed *meal breaks*. It may, however, be possible to reduce this delay even more by slight reorganization of events in the tunnel.

Delays that arose from fitting, adjusting and removing the *cutting beads* were caused by the squeezing ground conditions at the start of the drive. This was an unusual problem, and during the course of most jobs the cutting beads would probably not be changed at all.

Almost all the *grouting* work related to the use of one-pass linings at shaft bottom sites. Because the machine thrust forward from the lining, it was a contractual requirement that the one-pass lining was grouted as soon as it was erected. If it had been possible to grout up some time after the machine had passed, the delays would have been reduced considerably.

In regard to *laser and surveying delays*, again it should be possible to do most of this work without delaying the tunnelling system. One major problem at Oxford was that there were several curves in the tunnel route (see Fig. 1), which increased the amount of surveying and setting up of the beam deflectors for the laser.

As has already been described, the majority of the time allocated to the category *other delays* covered setting up and dismantling procedures, clearing-up time and driving through the shaft bottom completed before the machine passed. With the exception of the last, the other delays were largely unavoidable.

Although the time lost to delays at Oxford was considerably less than that on many other sites,[8] it is, nevertheless, clear that reducing delays is an important consideration in trying to improve progress rates. It is, however, rather difficult to devise specific measures to minimize delays. Equipment reliability is, of course, a factor, but probably the most important aspect is to give careful consideration to the logistics of all the processes involved in the construction sequence.

Activity loggers are commonly used to perform time studies on various operations and, hence, to enable their efficiency to be assessed.[9] Alternatively, data recorded on site inspectors' reports could be entered into an on-site microcomputer system on a daily basis. This latter process could be expedited by simple modifications to the format of the shift reports.

Either of these two methods of recording activity times would allow direct analysis of operations on-site within a short time of their completion. In this way trends in the times taken for each activity could be studied, and the effects of changes in site organization or working methods would be determined quickly and easily. This rapid feedback of cause and effect could then be used to minimize delays and maximize progress rates.

Squeezing ground conditions

The effects of these ground conditions on the progress of the tunnel have already been described. The overall rate of advance of the tunnel was one-third as fast over the first 500 rings in comparison with the rest of the drive, although it is impossible to say how much of this effect was due to ground conditions and how much to the usual learning effect at the start of any tunnel drive.

A solution to the problem was devised by using a combination of cutting beads and trimming devices,[1] but one major concern, so far unresolved, is the prediction of such ground conditions. Re-examination of the site investigation records, measurements of strength and moisture content of the clay in the tunnel and visual inspection of the *in-situ* material have failed, even with the advantage of hindsight, to give any indication of the cause of the effect.

Observation of the way in which the ground squeezed into the tunnel showed that the horizontal intrusion was larger than in the vertical direction. This suggested that the squeezing may be caused by an elastic relaxation of high horizontal stresses. The Oxford Clay is heavily overconsolidated and, hence, the horizontal stresses are greater than those in the vertical direction. The squeezing ground could therefore be an area of even higher horizontal stresses than occur elsewhere in the Oxford Clay. The fact that this area is still overlain by the remnants of the Corallian Beds (see Fig. 1) may be relevant, but the squeezing effect disappeared before the tunnel drive reached the edge of the Corallian formation.

To determine whether high *in-situ* stresses are the cause, TRRL have installed a number of push-in spade pressure cells of the type described by Tedd and Charles.[10] These cells take some time to come to equilibrium after installation: this is typically of the order of three months in the London Clay, but is likely to be even longer in the much stiffer Oxford Clay. The results of these tests, and measurements of loads on the tunnel lining, which are being performed in both the squeezing and non-squeezing sections of the tunnel by TRRL, will be the subject of a later report.

Measurements of *in-situ* stress state are complex and expensive, however, and it is unlikely that they would be performed as part of a normal site investigation in the foreseeable future. Such squeezing ground conditions are therefore likely to remain an unforeseen condition.

Conclusions

Although the best rate of advance obtained over a 10-h shift was 3.01 m/h, the overall rate of advance for the whole tunnel drive was only 1.19 m/h. Machine utilization was comparatively high at 64%. Such progress rates are quite respectable, but there appears to be considerable potential to significantly improve them. Two possible ways in which this might be achieved are (1) to improve excavation performance by designing a system that allows concurrent cutting and lining, whenever ground conditions permit, rather than the sequential operations currently adopted, and (2) to reduce delays by careful consideration of the logistics of all the processes involved in tunnel construction. This may be helped by on-site computer analysis of construction records.

Acknowledgement

The work described in this paper forms part of the programme of the Transport and Road Research Laboratory and the paper is published by permission of the Director.

TRRL wishes to thank the Thames Water Authority, Oxford City Council and Edmund Nuttall, Ltd., for their help and cooperation in this study. The authors are especially grateful for the helpfulness and assistance of the City Engineer and Director of Recreation, D. A. Butler, and D. Court and J. B. Northfield of Edmund Nuttall, Ltd. The authors would also like to thank the TRRL research team, which consisted of G. H. Alderman, D. A. Barratt, P. D. Hopes, P. E. Johnson and M. P. O'Reilly.

Any views expressed in this paper are not necessarily those of the Department of Transport. Extracts from the text may be reproduced, except for commercial purposes, provided that the source is acknowledged.

References
1. Watts I. L. Northfield J. B. and Palfrey L. F. Wedge-block tunnel for Oxford's main sewer. In *Tunnelling '82* Jones M. J. ed. (London: IMM, 1982), 291–301.
2. Scott P. A. A 75-inch-diameter water main in tunnel: a new method of tunnelling in London Clay. *Proc. Instn civ. Engrs*, **1**, 1952, 302–17.
3. Tattersall F. Wakeling T. R. M. and Ward W. H. Investigations into the design of pressure tunnels in London Clay. *Proc. Instn civ. Engrs*, **4**, no. 4 1955, 400–55.
4. Barratt D. A. and Tyler R. G. Measurements of ground movement and lining behaviour on the London Underground at Regents Park. *Transport Road Res. Lab. Rep.* LR 684, 1975, 53 p.
5. O'Reilly M. P. and New B. M. Settlements above tunnels in the United Kingdom – their magnitude and prediction. Reference 1, 173–81.
6. Hignett H. J. Snowdon R. A. and Temporal J. Tunnelling trials in chalk: rock cutting experiments. *Transport Road Res. Lab. Rep.* LR 796, 1977, 56 p.
7. Berry N. S. M. Tunnelling by full-face machines in Carboniferous strata. *Trans. Instn Min. Metall. (Sect. A: Min. industry)*, **89**, 1980, A144–57.
8. Athorn M. L. Geotechnical factors affecting the selection of tunnelling systems. M.Sc. thesis, Department of Geotechnical Engineering, University of Newcastle upon Tyne, 1982.
9. Parsons A. W. The efficiency of operation of earthmoving plant on road construction sites. *Transport Road Res. Lab. Supplem. Rep.* SR 351, 1977.
10. Tedd P. and Charles J. A. In-situ measurement of horizontal stress in over consolidated clay using push-in spade-shaped pressure cells. *Geotechnique*, **31**, no. 4 1981, 554–8.

Discussion

Sir Alan Muir Wood* said that, recalling the many years of attempts to apply computer methods to the prediction of tunnel costs, he would still encourage Grant and Miller to persevere. They needed to assemble a great amount of good data, with contributory factors clearly identified. Initially, it would only be possible to make reasonable predictions for a project only differing in a few definable respects, in geology and tunnel scheme, from those for which good data were available. Credibility would only be accorded when out-turn for real projects was compared against prediction.

In a small tunnel to combine advance of shield with erection of lining was usually difficult. A better solution was usually to minimize the period of erection – in that instance by adopting expedients to permit the continued use of expanded linings, as had been achieved many times in the thirty plus years since their development. A study of the pattern of overstress around the tunnel could have provided useful insight into its provenance. If it was really squeezing ground, a reaction ring was not a good idea. Apart from high local stress, it greatly increased the area of exposed and unsupported ground for each cycle of advance.

J. Washbourne† said that the failure of the tunnel bore in the vicinity of an access shaft could be explained by superimposing the excess horizontal hoop stresses induced by the access shaft on the horizontal hoop stresses induced by the tunnel bore at the extremities of the vertical diameter of the tunnel bore. The factor of safety, F, against failure on the unsupported tunnel bore vertical diameter could be estimated by use of the Kirsch elastic theory equations as followed:

$$F = \frac{\text{Unconfined compressive strength}}{\text{Excess hoop stress caused by shaft} + \text{Hoop stress caused by tunnel}}$$

i.e.

$$F = \frac{2c_u \tan(45° + \phi_u/2)}{K_0 p_0 \times \dfrac{a_s^2}{r_s^2} + p_0(3K_0 - 1)}$$

where c_u was undrained apparent cohesion of clay, ϕ_u was the undrained angle of shearing resistance of clay, K_0 was the coefficient of earth pressure at rest, p_0 was overburden pressure, r_s was radial distance from the centre of the shaft and a_s was the radius of the shaft.

That analysis ignored the fact that the shaft lining would reduce the hoop stresses to some extent. All other things being equal, F would increase as r_s increased. The excess hoop stress induced by the shaft excavation was the excess over the ambient earth pressure at rest, the ambient earth pressure at rest being included in the expression for the hoop stresses induced by the tunnel bore at the extremities of the vertical diameter.

Authors' replies

D. R. Grant and Dr. H. D. S. Miller The use of a computer model to simulate the construction of a tunnel produces an estimate – not an exact solution. This is partially because of the large number of variables and the interaction between these variables. The uncertainties involved in accurately predicting geological conditions along the line of the tunnel will also affect the estimated time to completion and the project cost. If a sufficient number of simulations are performed, distributions of project cost and time to completion can be produced. With the large amount of information required to be analysed, computer modelling becomes a cost-effective tool to evaluate tunnelling projects. The computer should be regarded as an aid for manipulating large amounts of data. These simulated results should then be evaluated by an experienced project feasibility engineer.

The time allotted to prepare bids for tunnelling projects is generally short. Therefore, by utilizing computer modelling the owner and/or the contractor can evaluate different construction scenarios and perform sensitivity analyses.

With a large and accurate database of activity–time distributions, the uncertainties associated with project feasibility studies can be minimized by computer modelling.

Dr. J. Temporal and G. J. L. Lawrence Sir Alan Muir Wood suggests that minimizing lining erection times is a better solution to increasing advance rates rather than allowing concurrent excavation and lining. Erection times for wedge block lining are already quite small (of the order of 8 min) and there would not seem to be much potential for reducing them below about 5 min. Since the paper was written, however, it has been drawn to our attention that both Miller Buckley Civil Engineering and Thyssen (GB), Ltd., have used vacuum pad erection systems that allow the lining to be placed while excavation is in progress. The projects involved were the North London Flood Relief Scheme and the Three Valleys Water Tunnel: in both cases a 100-in machine was used.

The cause of the squeezing ground is still being investigated by TRRL and may well be due to *in-situ* stresses. In these conditions a system of concurrent excavation and lining may not be wise, but such conditions are extremely rare. The authors still believe that, under normal conditions, the use of concurrent excavation and lining would be advantageous.

J. Washbourne suggests that the squeezing ground conditions could be due to the effects of a stress redistribution around the shafts. In the 450 rings (330 m) of squeezing ground there were two shafts – one of 10.67-m diameter and one of 4.57-m diameter: these were 245 m apart and the magnitude of the squeeze was reasonably constant along this entire length. For the shafts to have caused the squeezing ground conditions over this length their influence would have to be substantial at distances of more than 30 shaft radii. This would appear to be unlikely and it is more probable that the effect is due to *in-situ* stresses.

*Sir William Halcrow and Partners, London, England.
†Oxford Polytechnic, Oxford, England.

Session 14 – Technical summary

Chairman: Dr. P. H. Phillips

Technical summary

M. P. O'Reilly* I am afraid that I am the last of the pressed men and can only hope that I close the innings in something like the good order that Professor Brown opened it.

I am fully aware that it is quite impossible to do justice to the collection of papers presented at this conference and, as is customary on these occasions, I apologize in advance to those who feel that I have been less than fair to them.

In the past five days we have listened to 34 papers and the Nineteenth Sir Julius Wernher Memorial Lecture. During these presentations we have seen the odd Mickey Mouse cartoon (and as an avid fan of Tom and Jerry I am not averse to that), a fair modicum of advertising, which descended very occasionally to the Persil washes whiter level, a fleeting reference to bureaucratic obstacles and a glimpse of a Don Quixote taking a few swipes at today's windmills. We have also had the first paper on a cut and cover tunnel ever presented at this tunnelling series of conferences. Perhaps there will be something on immersed tube tunnels at 'Tunnelling '88' – it might even come from the A55 North Wales Coast Road.

First, let us take a general look at the distribution of papers that were drawn from 16 countries – that is, if one counts Hong Kong as a separate entity. The United Kingdom, with 11 papers, was most strongly represented, Canada produced three and China, France, Germany, Hong Kong, India and Norway each had two. Twenty papers dealt with hard rock tunnels, ten were about soft ground tunnelling and four considered both: 21 papers could be described as being predominantly case histories, and seven dealt with research and analysis. Tunnelling machines were an important element of nine papers.

Apart from the last mentioned, the mixture was remarkably similar to that of 'Tunnelling '82', as can be seen in Table 1. One is indeed tempted to speculate that the reduced emphasis on tunnelling machines may well reflect a reversion to more traditional tunnelling methods following the disappointments of the 1970s and described at this conference in the paper by de Mello Mendes and da Silva Amado; it may also reflect the improvement in drill and blast tunnelling methods and machinery in recent years.

Table 1 Distribution of papers

Year	1982	1985
Total no. of papers	36	34
No. of countries	12	16
No. of papers from United Kingdom	8	11
Hard rock	24	20
Soft ground	9	10
Both	3	4
Case histories (predominantly)	21	21
Research + analysis	8	7
Tunnelling machines	16	9
Mining	4	6
Civil engineering	26	28
Other	6	—

The six papers on mining represent an improvement on 'Tunnelling '82', but indicate that the dichotomy between the civil and mining engineer still persists. Some glimmerings of integration may be emerging in the coal industry, as evidenced by the papers by Bloor and Pink, by Morris, by Palmer, Lovat and Marsh and by Blanc. It is clear, however, that these two

*Transport and Road Research Laboratory, Department of Transport, Crowthorne, Berkshire, England.

engineering disciplines, with so much common ground, often do not speak the same language: hanging-walls and footwalls are something that the civil engineer has to think about.

Of all the various permutations and combinations tried, perhaps the most significant was to classify the tunnels into those concerning energy and infrastructure. On this basis 13 papers related to the mining of coal, the storage of hydrocarbons and the generation of electricity from water and nuclear power. Some 16 papers related to infrastructure tunnels for water supply, sewerage and transportation. A further four papers had elements of both, that by Hendry, Kimball and Shtenko being a particularly good example of a railway line the *raison d'être* of which was the transport of coal to port for onward shipment overseas. The odd paper out was that on metalliferous mining in China. It is perhaps noteworthy that all energy tunnels were in rock, whereas all soft ground tunnels were for infrastructure.

In the United Kingdom energy and inland surface transportation represent 10 and 20%, respectively, of the gross domestic product. One can probably say then that a quarter or so of GDP is a reasonable estimate of the annual expenditure on energy and the use of infrastructure, given that there is some double counting in the two categories mentioned above, only water distribution and sewage disposal being omitted. It is thus clear that tunnelling plays a considerable, often vital, part in a modern industrialized community and we must never lose sight of this as engineers if we are to justify its importance to society.

But enough of these generalities and let us now look at the interesting technicalities that have been thrown up by this conference. And where better to start than the opening *tour de force* by Professor Ted Brown: here is a state of the art paper on the application of elastic and inelastic theories in underground engineering and medieval cathedrals as well. The piece that caught my imagination was the design of the roof for Poatina power station in Tasmania, where stress-relief slots derived from a photoelastic analysis were used in the roof to limit 'the boundary compressive stresses to predetermined acceptable values'. Of particular importance here was the fact that the 'high stress concentrations induced at the top of the slot were of no cause for concern because there was no free boundary available into which the displacement could occur' and so any failure of the rock was contained – a good example of 'if it is not moving, it does not matter'.

In continuing, I must say how much I am indebted to Geoff Pearse, who, as well as dealing with the papers from beginning to end, organized the conference sessions in a very logical manner and by so doing has made my task that much simpler.

In the opening session the theme was underground storage of hydrocarbons, and if ever there was a case both on safety and environmental grounds for storage of such substances underground, then this was it. Johansson, on the one hand, showed us what happens when an above ground tank farm goes on fire (Fig. 1) and then dramatically produced the result of a similar incident below ground. Significantly, in the latter case there was no loss of or danger to life and the storage cavern after minor repairs could be returned to service (Fig. 2). Johnsson's candid admission that the reasons for this explosion were not known is a very succinct and compelling reason for putting such facilities below ground, where they can do no harm. And given that in suitable geology there is no cost penalty but rather a saving I for one fail to see why planning and safety authorities do not insist more often on the placing of oil and perhaps chemical storage facilities below ground.

The last session on Monday was notable for the catalogue of problems on the S. Domingos–Morgavel tunnel in Portugal and the construction on time of the Tumbler Ridge branch railway line in the magnificent scenery of the Rockies. The problems of hydrogen sulphide gas in this latter tunnel and the fleeting

Fig. 1 Oil tank farm on fire (1985). Photograph reproduced by courtesy of S. Johansson

reference in the paper on the Loktak tunnel to a methane gas explosion in 1975 where 16 workers died[1] provided reminders, in the year following Abbeystead, where some 16 people, mainly members of the public, were killed and 28 were injured in an explosion caused by the accumulation of methane in the valve house,[2] that gases emanating from the ground are a continual threat to the tunneller. As in all good engineering, the remedy is continual vigilance and effective supervision by contractors, engineers and owners. Despite all modern innovation, there is still no substitute – and in my view never will be – for good supervision, yet it is something on which engineers are continually being asked to skimp: the legacy of poor or inept supervision is, as a minimum, increased expenditure on maintenance.

The above episode does, I think, make the telling point that conferences such as this play a very important part in ensuring that experience and technology transfer take place as quickly as possible.

And then we come to what Dr. Ian Farmer described as the 'clever session', where the finite-element approach had been used with greater or lesser appreciation to a range of tunnelling problems. There is no doubt that these analytical tools are here to stay, but they must not be treated as infallible and the questioner who prematurely enquired of Potts and Knights as to whether their predictions had been fulfilled in practice was certainly on the correct path. I had a feeling that there might have been a conspiracy too between Professor Brown and Dr. Potts to show us how bright they are at Imperial College! The description of the tunnelling in Tokyo as NATM when the major support was provided by forepoles driven over steel arches puzzled me somewhat: after all, what is new or Austrian about forepoles? I thought too that the two-dimensional finite-element analysis was something of an oversimplification when all the action is so close to the tunnel face. Figs. 3 and 4, taken from papers 4, 5 that described work carried out for TRRL on the centrifuge at Cambridge University, show that the process is clearly three-dimensional; the following paper by Baudendistel also recognized this.

It is now germane to reiterate the caution in Professor Brown's lecture on the dangers of believing the formula and to reinforce it with a quotation from the great mathematician philosopher A. N. Whitehead: 'There is no more common error than to assume that, because prolonged and accurate mathematical calculations have been made, the application of the results to some fact of nature is absolutely certain'.

I am afraid that catalogues of achievements, however extensive and impressive, rarely turn me on and the papers on the

Fig. 2 Oil storage cavern after fire (1985). Photograph reproduced by courtesy of S. Johansson

We come now to the reinvention of the wheel, as retailed in the paper by Bloor and Pink. Until now I had understood that the ideas of multiple jointed unbolted concrete linings had first seen the light of day in this country about 1950. Now I learn that the Belgians did it in the 1930s in the Campine coalfield with rings of between 46 and 90 tapered plain 'concrete blocks up to 500 mm thick and up to 450 mm wide' with crushable chipboard packings 20–40 mm thick; about 500 km of roadway was constructed in this fashion at depths of 600–1000 m. This design reminds me of the 22-element pressed concrete linings used in the 1970s on the Heathrow Extension of the Piccadilly Line.[3]

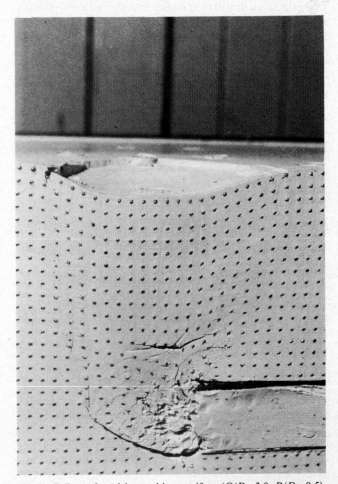

Fig. 3 Failure of model tunnel in centrifuge ($C/D = 3.0$; $P/D = 0.5$). From O'Reilly and co-workers[5]

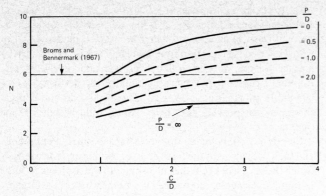

Fig. 4 Influence of heading geometry on stability ratio at failure. After Kimura and Mair[4] (Broms B. B. and Bennermark H. Stability of clay at vertical openings. *Proc. ASCE*, **93**, SMI, 1967, 71–94.)

Fig. 5 Spine-roadway driven by full-face tunnelling machine at Selby coalfield. Photograph reproduced by courtesy of National Coal Board

Fig. 6 Spine-roadway driven by boomheader machine at Selby coalfield. Photograph reproduced by courtesy of National Coal Board

Himalayan hydroelectric schemes and the construction of the new Hannover–Würzburg and Mannheim–Stuttgart sections of the German Federal Railway were no exception: but then it would be an odd world if we all reacted similarly and colleagues at the ensuing tea-break agreed that the paper by Distelmeier and Semprich was the best they had heard until then!

The Scandinavian interlude that followed produced the first comprehensive paper in English that I have seen on the Norwegian method of lake tapping and certainly gave valuable insights into it. The submarine tunnels for the world's first nuclear waste repository show that the politicians in one country at least have at last grasped the nettle: whether the correct decision or not has been made is another question and the sting may come later. The paper on tunnel lining for roads was a welcome interlude from ground engineering: many tunnels need considerable kitting out to make them suitable for their purpose and this quite important aspect of tunnelling tends to be overlooked.

Wednesday was the day of the tunnelling machine, two papers being devoted to particular machines and a third dealing with an extensive programme of R and D to improve the performance of boomheader machines that is being carried out by the National Coal Board in the United Kingdom partly in cooperation with the U.S. Department of Energy and Bureau of Mines. A particular feature here was the development of high-pressure water jets to assist pick cutters. This has now reached a stage at which it has been shown that production prototype light- to medium-weight roadheaders can excavate bands of rock with compressive strengths as high as 160 MPa. Fig. 6 (p. 208) in the paper by Palmer, Lovat and Marsh showed the excellent tunnel profile produced by the 7.6-m diameter Lovat machine. Unfortunately, a view of the parallel drill and blast drive was not shown for comparative purposes and I hope that Figs. 5 and 6 of the parallel spine-roadways on the Selby coalfield development in the United Kingdom will partially fill this gap: there can be no doubt whatsoever that the smooth circular tunnel produced by a TBM is much more stable than its horseshoe-shaped counterpart whether that is produced by drill and blast or a boomheader.

The two papers from China were both interesting and thought-provoking. Certainly, the country that contains one-sixth of the world's human resources is on the move. The segment-shaped presplit blasting techniques that were used on the Dongjiang hydroelectric scheme are novel and when combined, as suggested, with a TBM to drive the central pilot tunnel may well give a hybrid that combines the best of machine and drill and blast techniques. The tunnelling in the two metal-liferous mines was also most efficient and cycle times of 58 and 71 min for pulls of 1.8–2 m and 2–2.5 m, respectively, compare more than favourably with similar tunnelling elsewhere.

The session on soft ground tunnelling was notable on three counts. Gill found that Terzaghi had got it correct in Chicago and that cannot be bad, although his shield was much less sophisticated than the smaller versions used in this country[6] or the slatted type of face control provided on shields in Mexico City.[7] Mohkam and Bouyat showed us some pioneering research work that is being carried out in Lyon for slurry tunnelling and their photographs during the face-stabilization process would have satisfied the most sceptical doubting Thomas. Washbourne then took us through jacking in the United Kingdom for the first time at these conferences. It is clear that pipe jacking must now be accepted as an important tunnelling technique.

The session on grouting was most informative and there is no doubt that jet grouting is an extremely useful technique: with a performance guarantee I am sure that Coomber's telephone will hardly stop ringing from now on! I was interested too in Dr. Bruno Pigorini's comment that the jet-grouting umbrella method is going to replace conventional forepoling in Italy. And if they were to call it the New Italian Tunnelling Method at my instigation, can I have a modest royalty? C. J. Day's suggestion of risk-management rather than risk-sharing gave a new slant to this topic and is certainly worth thinking about. It was clear too that criteria concerning the groutability of ground were not all that they might be, but at least the problem has now been recognized and I am sure that such organizations as the Hong Kong Mass Transit Authority will be giving us the benefits of their endeavours in due course.

The paper by Muir Wood and Kirkland could become a very valuable reference for those of us in the public sector who are called upon to inject some sensible idea of the real world of engineering into accountants and administrators. Here too we should remember that some of the inefficiency of our financial arrangements and controls, particularly in the public sector, are part of the price that we must pay for democracy. No doubt things could work better for a time at least if we had the right dictator – me, for example – and the dramatic achievements in autobahn construction in Germany in the 1930s are clear proof of this. My view, however, is that engineers must struggle on within the institutional framework that we have and with a succession of nudges here and there slowly evolve to something better.

McFeat-Smith identified portals as a problem area where ground information was vitally important and extolled the virtues of horizontal boreholes in these areas. Such problems were also encountered on the Tumbler Ridge tunnel and in another guise in the early sections of the Oxford sewer. Problems in the early stage of a tunnel are doubly disruptive in that they occur at the beginning of the learning curve and immediately put the project behind schedule, but Murphy's law indicates that this is where they will occur. D. R. Grant is obviously a good modeller and I would hope that in due course he can introduce elements of systematic cussedness into his programs to allow for this.

Now, having briefly reviewed the highlights of the wide-ranging and diverse set of excellent papers to this conference, are there any overall messages for us to take away? For me there are four.

The first is the importance of track record both of the ground and the tunneller. As regards the former, it must be extremely comforting to an engineer on a fairly limited site, such as Porvoo in Finland, when he comes to build the twenty-third cavern there. Granted there may still be some surprises, and he must not be complacent, but he must surely be in a better position than the man starting out for the first time with only some borehole information to guide him. That situation was revealed to us by the S. Domingos–Morgavel tunnel in Portugal, where the true behaviour of the ground was only obtained by bitter experience.

It is, I think, a well-known cliché that the best geologist is the one who has seen the most rock – I think that if you look hard, you can conclude from these papers that the best tunnellers are those who have driven the most tunnels. I am particularly reminded here of the comments from the floor by Siegmund Babendererde on the use of compressed air in tunnelling below the water-table.

The second stems from the first and is the importance of site investigation and ground information in its broadest sense. It has always seemed anomalous to me that although clients are often prepared to skimp on such investigations, they rarely bat an eyelid when it comes to expending many times the cost of a site investigation on designs based on inadequate, even erroneous, information; and when there is good site investigation it needs to be interpreted by experienced engineers.

The third point is the importance of flexibility – a recurring theme throughout the conference. One might even say that it has been repeated *ad nauseam*, but I hope to good effect. But then, if we lock ourselves into rigidities of thinking, design, construction or bureaucracy making, there is a price to be paid in the long term.

And, lastly, there are the environmental and sometimes the safety benefits of tunnels. Engineers are nowadays often cast in the role of despoilers of nature when the real culprit is society itself which, through its representatives, invariably wants a Rolls Royce for the price of a Ford and then complains when it does not get it. Engineers collectively must try to dispel such naivety and it was encouraging to see that in Bristol, at least, they have succeeded.

In conclusion, I should like to thank the authors of the papers and you the delegates for making this conference such a successful occasion. Special mention must be made of those who delivered their presentation in a language other than their mother tongue. It was said on the occasion of the recent Rankine Lecture that we in this country are perfectly even-handed in this matter – we speak English abroad and expect foreigners to speak English here – what could be fairer than that!

Mention must be made now of Michael Jones, Penny Gill and their colleagues at the Institution of Mining and Metallurgy for all the hard work that they have put into the conference, and I should thank again, on your behalf, the members of the Organizing Committee – other than myself – and their Chairman for their considerable, often time-consuming, efforts to maintain and improve this tunnelling series of conferences: I hope you feel that they have succeeded.

It is right at this stage to add a disclaimer that the views and prejudices expressed here are my own and not necessarily those of the Transport and Road Research Laboratory or the Department of Transport. *Bon voyage* to you all and good tunnelling until 'Tunnelling '88'.

References
1. Madan M. M. India's efforts rewarded on Loktak hydro project. *Tunnels Tunnell.*, **16**, Nov. 1984, 27–30.
2. Health and Safety Executive. *The Abbeystead explosion: a report of the investigation into the explosion on 23 May 1984* (London: HMSO, 1985), 22 p.
3. Jobling D. G. and Lyons A. C. Extension of the Piccadilly Line from Hounslow West to Heathrow Central. *Proc. Instn civ. Engrs*, **60**, May 1976, 191–218.
4. Kimura T. and Mair R. J. Centrifugal testing of model tunnels in soft clay. In *Proceedings of the tenth international conference on soil mechanics and foundation engineering, Stockholm, June 1981* (Rotterdam: Balkema, 1981), vol. 1, 319–22.
5. O'Reilly M. P. Murray R. T. and Symons I. F. Centrifuge modelling in the TRRL research programme on ground engineering. In *Application of centrifuge modelling to geotechnical design,* Craig W. H. ed. (Rotterdam: Balkema, 1985), 423–40.
6. McCaul C. West G. and Manlow T. V. Driving with a full-face diaphragm. *Tunnels Tunnell.*, **10**, no. 6, July/Aug. 1978, 23–5.
7. Craviota J. M. and Villarreal A. Recent experience in the construction of tunnels and shafts in the city of Mexico. Constructora Estrella SA.

Name index

Agrawal C. K.   134
Akada M.   102
Akai K.   44, 102
Alderman G. H.   327
Allen P. M.   263
Aschieri F.   275, 283
Athorn M. L.   327
Auld F. A.   63, 64, 71, 72, 79
Axhausen K.   108

Babendererde S.   147, 334
Baker W. H.   258, 261, 264, 282
Barratt D. A.   327
Barroso M.   38, 44
Bartlett J. V.   201, 213
Barton N.   119, 125, 127, 131, 134
Bathe K.   108
Baudendistel M.   103, 108, 109, 332
Baumann V.   283
Baumgartner P.   208
Baynes F. J.   263
Bell L. A.   264
Bell M. J.   63, 71
Bennermark H.   232, 233, 234, 333
Berdal B.   159, 170
Bergman M.   25, 26, 33
Bergman S. G. A.   17, 25
Berry L.   308
Berry N. S. M.   78, 309, 325, 327
Bevan O. M.   147
Bieniawski Z. T.   119, 125, 127
Bjurström S.   17
Blanc A.   209, 213, 331
Blind W.   144
Bloor A. S.   63, 72, 331, 332
Blütling H.-H.   144
Bouyat C.   235, 333
Braat K. B.   27, 33
Branch S. N.   208
Brand E.   308
Brock E.   26
Brockway J. E.   207, 208
Broid I. Z.   282
Broms B. B.   232, 233, 234, 333
Brown E. T.   25, 72, 125, 331, 332
Bruce D. A.   253, 264, 292
Buchanan J.   57, 78, 79, 170, 213, 309, 310
Budge-Reid A. J.   308
Buen B.   159, 170
Burgess G. C.   57, 145, 226
Burland J. B.   85, 86, 92
Burman I.   125
Butler D. A.   327

Cambefort H.   264
Campbell J. G.   308
Carlsson A.   149, 157, 170
Carr T. L.   71, 177
Cater R. W.   308
Chang Dehe   221, 226
Charles J. A.   326, 327
Chauhan R. L.   127, 145
Chauhan R. S.   127, 145
Cherry J. A.   291
Christiansson R.   155, 157

Collares Werneck I.   125
Coomber D. B.   277, 283, 292, 333
Court D.   327
Cowland J.   257, 264
Cox W.   208
Craig R.   249
Craig R. N.   71
Craig W. H.   334
Craviota J. M.   334

Dadasbilge K.   264
Dadson J.   249
D'Appolonia E.   316
da Silva Amado F. R. *see* Silva Amado F. R. da
Day C. J.   285, 333
Dearman W. R.   263
Deere D. U.   119, 125
Degerlund C.   249
de Haan J. F. *see* Haan J. F. de
Delin P.   155, 157
de Mello Mendes F. *see* Mello Mendes F. de
De Paoli B.   275
Distelmeier H.   135, 145, 333
Dupeuble P.   283
Duyse H. van   72

Edwards J. T.   308
Einstein H. H.   316
Ellison R. D.   33
Engels W.   144
Eriksson K.   155, 157

Fagerholm G.   15, 25
Farmer I. W.   71, 81, 332
Fawcett D. F.   309, 310
Flintoff W.   257, 264
Freeze R. A.   291
Fudger G.   109
Fujimori T.   93, 109
Fujita K.   249
Fukuoka M.   102
Fullalove S.   249

Gais W. H.   144
Gammon J. R. A.   263, 264
Gao Zidong   221, 226
Garfield L. A.   125
Giles R. W.   187
Gill P.   334
Gill S. A.   229, 250, 333
Glossop R.   256, 264
Golser J.   109
Gomes Teixeira J. A.   44
Grant D. R.   313, 328, 334
Greenwood D. A.   264
Greschik G.   61
Gudehus G.   125
Guloglu R.   316
Guo Zongyan   217
Gupta J. P.   134
Gustafsson R.   25
Gysel M.   109, 145

Haan J. F. de   27, 33
Halberg N.   32
Handewith H. J.   203, 208

Harding *Sir* Harold   295
Harding P. G.   203, 208
Harpf R.   144
Haswell C. K.   261, 263, 301, 308
Hayashi M.   44, 95, 102
Hayes A.   109
Helfrich H. K.   25
Hendry R. D.   45, 57, 58, 331
Hei Shuguang   221, 226
Hewlett P. C.   275
Hibino S.   95, 102
Hignett H. J.   327
Hoek E.   25, 125
Holopainen P.   25
Hopes P. D.   327
Horn M.   44
Horta da Silva J. A.   44
Howat M. D.   257, 263
Howes M. J.   208
Huck P. J.   282
Hudson J. A.   72
Huntley S. L.   301, 308
Hutchinson M. T.   275
Hvorslev J.   264, 291

Ignatius Y.   15, 25
Ingle J.   264
Ischy E.   256, 264, 292

Jain K. P.   134
Jamiolkowski M.   275, 283
Jobling D. G.   334
Johansen J.   159, 170
Johansson S.   13, 15, 23, 25, 33, 331, 332
John M.   144
Johnson P. E.   327
Jones D. J. C.   308
Jones M. J.   25, 208, 275, 292, 327, 334
Jones R. T.   72

Kähönen Y.   16, 25
Kalla J.   25
Katti R. K.   282
Kihlström B.   25
Kilpinen M.   15, 25
Kimball F. E.   45, 58, 331
Kimura T.   332, 334
King T. I.   68, 71, 72, 171, 201
Kirkland C. J.   295, 333
Knights M. C.   33, 83, 109, 145, 146, 196, 200
Koch O. G.   113
Koivisto H.   23, 25
Kramer J.   108
Krokeborg J.   165, 169
Kunimi H.   93, 109
Kusumoto F.   102

Lahtinen R.   25
Lane K. S.   125
Langefors U.   25
Larssen L.   212
Larsson B.   26
Larsson W.   149, 157
Lauffer H.   103, 108
Law M. V. M.   179, 197